SAS Storage Architecture

MINDSHARE, INC.

Mike Jackson

MINDSHARE PRESS

Visit MindShare, Inc. on the web: www.mindshare.com

Library of Congress Control Number: 2005931901

MindShare Press
Attn: Robin Winkles
4285 Slash Pine Dr.
Colorado Springs, CO 80908
Fax: 719-487-1434

Set in 10-point Palatino by MindShare, Inc.

ISBN 0977087808

First Printing September 2005

Acknowledgements:

Special thanks must be extended to several people for their assistance and contributions to this effort. Rob Elliott, editor of the SAS standard, contributed a good deal of time and expertise and provided both guidance and materials. The many helpful people at the SCSI Trade Association (the STA) also contributed time, technical and marketing help as well as encouragement to pursue publishing this book. Hewlett Packard has graciously given permission to use several illustrations in the book, and several people there helped answer questions and clarify technical issues, including Steve Fairchild and Greg Larson. Bill Tillman also contributed his experience in the field by providing feedback on several chapters. And, finally, thanks to the many folks who have participated in our SAS classes up to now and have prodded me to develop better illustrations or explanations as a result of their questions during our time together. To all of you, thanks for your help and patience. I hope this book will represent a good return on your effort.

Note:

This book is derived from the Serial Attached SCSI standard which, at the time of this writing, was at revision 1.1 version 9c. Newer versions of the standard are likely to be approved, possibly even before publication of this book, so the student of SAS will need to refer to the latest official version. The standard is owned by the International Committee for Information Technology Standards (INCITS), whose home page is http://www.incits.org. To obtain the latest approved version of the standard go to their site and click on Purchase Standards and then search for SAS. The SAS standard, like many others, is available to download as a PDF for a nominal fee. At the time of this writing the URL for purchasing a copy of the SAS standard was -
http://www.techstreet.com/cgi-bin/detail?product_id=1141805

Illustrations:

Several illustrations were donated for use in the book by Rob Elliott through the generosity of Hewlett-Packard. Several more were donated by the SCSI Trade Association, and the following is a list of those illustrations:
Chapter 1: Figure 1-1, 1-6, 1-8
Chapter 2: Figure 2-1, 2-12
Chapter 5: Figure 5-3
Chapter 6: Figure 6-1, 6-3, 6-4, 6-5, 6-6
Chapter 8: Figure 8-1, 8-7
Chapter 10: Figure 10-2
Chapter 11: Figure 11-5, 11-7, 11-8

Chapter 12: Figure 12-6, 12-7
Chapter 13: Figure 13-6
Chapter 16: Figure 16-15, 16-16, 16-17
Chapter 17: Figure 17-1, 17-12, 17-13, 17-14
Chapter 18: Figure 18-1, 18-2, 18-7, 18-14
Chapter 19: Figure 19-8
Chapter 20: Figure 20-1, 20-3, 20-4, 20-5

To Lisa, my best friend and my inspiration.

Contents

About This Book

Chapter 1: Part 1: Introduction

Chapter 2: The Motivation for SAS

Chapter 3: Origins of SAS and Background

Contents

Chapter 4: SAS Overview

Chapter 5: Device Types and Topologies

Chapter 6: The Layered Device Architecture

Contents

Chapter 7: Part 2: Initialization and Discovery

Chapter 8: SAS Initialization

Contents

Chapter 13: Port Layer

Chapter 14: Link Layer Overview

Chapter 19: Phy Layer

Contents

Chapter 24: SATA Initialization

Appendices

Appendix A: Expander Devices

Contents

Figures

Figures

Figures

Figures

Figures

Figures

Tables

Tables

Tables

About This Book

Scope

The SAS Storage Architecture book is intended as a tutorial and to serve as classroom materials for the training MindShare delivers on this subject. It should be considered a companion to the SAS standard, helping to clarify and explain the concepts and provide the motivation for decisions that were made in the creation of the standard and decisions that will need to be made by adopters of it. While the author was given permission by the SCSI Trade Association to use illustrations from the materials that went into the standard, this book does not attempt to recreate material from it that should rightly be considered reference material.

The MindShare Architecture Series

The MindShare System Architecture book series includes the publications shown in Table 1.

Table 1: PC Architecture Book Series

Category	Title	Edition	ISBN
Processor Architecture	80486 System Architecture	3rd	0-201-40994-1
	Pentium® Processor System Architecture	2nd	0-201-40992-5
	Pentium® Pro and Pentium® II System Architecture	2nd	0-201-30973-4
	PowerPC System Architecture	1st	0-201-40990-9
	The Unabridged Pentium® 4	1st	0-321-24656-X

Table 1: PC Architecture Book Series (Continued)

Category	Title	Edition	ISBN
Bus Architecture	PCI System Architecture	4th	0-201-30974-2
	EISA System Architecture	Out-of-print	0-201-40995-X
	Firewire System Architecture: IEEE 1394	2nd	0-201-48535-4
	ISA System Architecture	3rd	0-201-40996-8
	Universal Serial Bus System Architecture	2nd	0-201-30975-0
	PCI-X System Architecture	1st	0-201-72682-3
	PCI Express System Architecture	2nd	0-321-15630-7
Network Architecture	InfiniBand Network Architecture	1st	0-321-11765-4
Other Architectures	PCMCIA System Architecture: 16-Bit PC Cards	2nd	0-201-40991-7
	CardBus System Architecture	1st	0-201-40997-6
	Plug and Play System Architecture	1st	0-201-41013-3
	Protected Mode Software Architecture	1st	0-201-55447-X
	AGP System Architecture	1st	0-201-37964-3
Storage Architecture	SAS Storage Architecture	1st	0-977-08780-8
	SATA Storage Architecture	Available 2006	

Cautionary Note

The reader should keep in mind that MindShare's book series often deals with rapidly evolving technologies. This being the case, it should be recognized that the book is a "snapshot" of the state of the targeted technology at the time that the book was completed. We attempt to update each book on a timely basis to reflect changes in the targeted technology, but, due to various factors (waiting for the next version of the standard to be approved, the time necessary to make the changes, and the time to produce the books and get them out to the distribution channels), there will always be a delay.

The Standard Is the Final Word

As with all of our books, this book represents the author's interpretation of the standard - in this case the SAS revision 1.1 version 9c. When in doubt, the INCITS SAS standard is the final word.

Note that at the time of this writing the 1.0 version was approved, while the 1.1 version of the standard was in development, so it may contain changes from the version used to develop this book when it is officially approved by the T10 group. This material is intended to serve as a supplement to aid in understanding SAS, and in any cases where it conflicts with the approved SAS standard, the standard should clearly prevail.

Documentation Conventions

The conventions used in this book for numeric values are defined in the sections that follow.

Hexadecimal Notation

This section defines the typographical convention used throughout this book. All hex numbers are followed by an "h." Examples:

```
9A4Eh
0100h
```

Binary Notation

All binary numbers are followed by a "b." Examples:

```
0001 0101b
01b
```

Decimal Notation

Numbers without any suffix are decimal. When required for clarity, decimal numbers are followed by a "d." The following examples each represent a decimal number:

```
16
255
256d
128d
```

Bits Versus Bytes Notation

All abbreviations for "bits" use lower case. For example:

- 2.5Gb/s = 2.5 Gigabits per second.
- 2Mb = 2 Megabits.

All references to "bytes" are specified in upper case. For example:

- 10MB/s = 10 Megabytes per second.
- 2KB = 2 Kilobytes.

Other designations:

- "lsb" refers to the least-significant bit.
- "LSB" refers to the least-significant byte.
- "msb" refers to the most-significant bit.
- "MSB" refers to the most-significant byte.

Bit Fields (Logical Groups of Bits or Signals)

In many cases, bit fields are documented as [15:8], with this example referring to bits 8 through 15.

Visit Our Web Site

In addition to listing all of our courses and books, our web site contains:

- Forums for posting questions to our staff.
- Errata for a number of the books.
- Information on the courses that we teach at your site as well as live over the web to your site(s).
- Short courses available for viewing.
- Technical papers.

www.mindshare.com

We Want Your Feedback

MindShare values your comments and suggestions. You can contact us via mail, phone, fax or Internet email.

Phone: (719) 487-1417 and in the U.S. (800) 633-1440.
Fax: (719) 487-1434.
Technical seminars: E-mail nancy.shanley@mindshare.com.
Technical questions: E-mail mike@mindshare.com.

Mailing Address:

MindShare, Inc.
4285 Slash Pine Drive
Colorado Springs, CO 80908

Part 1: Introduction

1 The Motivation for SAS

This Chapter

This chapter introduces the SAS (Serial Attached SCSI) solution, describes the motivation for SAS as a replacement for parallel SCSI, and compares SAS to other competing technologies. The advantages of SAS are highlighted, and its expected positioning in the market is explored, especially with reference to SATA.

The Next Chapter

The next chapter discusses the SCSI, Fibre Channel and SATA background from which SAS was developed. While maintaining compatibility with its SCSI software base, SAS borrows from serial transports like Fibre Channel and SATA to develop a next-generation enterprise storage architecture.

Introduction

As is true of many interface architectures, the SAS (Serial Attached SCSI) standard describes the behavior of compliant devices but intentionally contains few specifics about how to implement a design. Minimizing design guidelines allows designers the freedom to add value by implementing designs that are optimized for their applications. Similarly, a body of background knowledge is assumed by the standard-writing committee and little time is spent explaining the motivation for design choices. The intended goals of this book are to fill in some of these gaps with examples and to provide the background for the choices made in the standard.

Serial SCSI

General

The SCSI (small computer system interface) interface has been a high-performance standard in hard disk storage for many years. The performance, reliability, sophisticated software control and error reporting it offered made it a natural fit for server storage applications where such attributes are a must and the cost was not a driving factor. Unfortunately, like all parallel bus designs, SCSI has reached the practical limits of its bandwidth and needs to be replaced with another transport model. As it happens, the set of SCSI interface standards already includes some serial versions. Figure 1-1 gives the full set of SCSI standards, showing the interface options on the bottom rows. This leads to a logical question: Why couldn't one of those other existing serial interface definitions replace parallel SCSI rather than develop SAS as a new one? The answer is that none of them had the proper mix of characteristics that would let them serve that role. Any replacement for SCSI would need to have broad industry acceptance, high performance, the ability to connect a fairly large number of storage devices into one simple network, and relatively low cost. Each of the earlier serial buses had a drawback of some kind in this regard that made them unattractive.

Figure 1-1: SCSI Architecture Roadmap

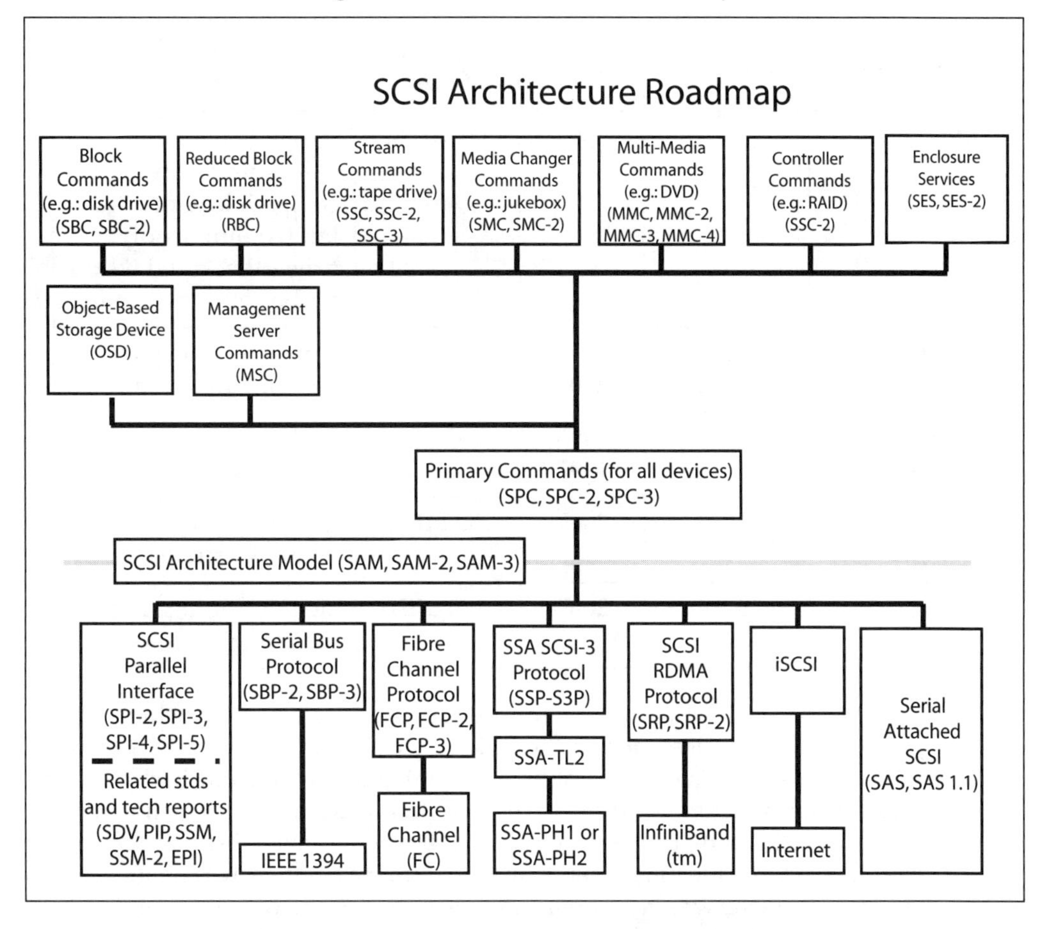

Earlier Serial Buses Supported SCSI

Those earlier buses are summarized in Table 1-1. They work well in the environment for which they were intended, and they are able to support SCSI commands, but they don't fill the role of a general-purpose storage interface the way SCSI does. Let's look at each one of them and consider the tradeoffs they involve.

I

Table 1-1: SAS Predecessor Architectures

Interconnect	Standard	Year	Typical Speed	Drawbacks as SCSI replacement
IEEE 1394	SBP-2	1998	50 MB/s	Earlier versions were slow, software wasn't compatible with ATA, limited number of drives that could be connected
Fibre Channel	FCP FCP-2	1995 2002	200 MB/s	Expensive, complex network architecture
Serial Storage Architecture	SSA	1996 1997	20 MB/s 40MB/s	IBM Only
InfiniBand	SRP	2002	250 MB/s	Expensive, complex network architecture
Ethernet	iSCSI	2003	~100 MB/s	Slow for storage interface, long latencies

The IEEE 1394 serial interface is simple but doesn't scale well to include a large array of storage devices, and at the time was considered costly and slow as a storage interface. This is also a cable solution that doesn't include backplanes or connector form factors for disk drives, and that made it less attractive for the server market. Another drawback was that the entire fabric ends up seeing the same data at the same time. Even with repeaters the network was treated as one big wire, so there was no opportunity for concurrent operation and drives would end up competing for access.

Fibre Channel works well in storage networks, but its drawback is that it was designed as a network interface to support large, complex networks with millions of devices. As a result, it was considered too expensive and too complex to replace a simple storage interface like SCSI.

SSA (Serial Storage Architecture) was never really in the running because this architecture did not achieve wide industry acceptance. Designed by IBM, it was originally a proprietary design and is currently only used by IBM. SSA is a loop architecture, meaning that each drive is daisy-chained to the next. A problem with it is that a failure in one drive can take out the whole loop. Even dual loops designed to mitigate this problem don't help if the failed drive begins to spew data in both directions.

InfiniBand showed early promise but failed to win broad industry acceptance. The main reason was that, like Fibre Channel, its complexity and cost were considered excessive for the kind of simple storage networks for which SCSI worked best.

The iSCSI interface provides SCSI protocol to storage connections over ethernet connections. It allows for complex network topologies, but incurs longer latencies that result in slower performance. In the end, its performance wasn't considered sufficient to replace the SCSI interface.

SAS Design Goals

The previous discussion reveals sufficient motivation for the decision to define a new replacement for the SCSI Parallel Interface (SPI) standard. The resulting SAS standard is a simple, backward-compatible transport with headroom for future bandwidth requirements. The SAS standard was developed with several design goals in mind:

1. **Improved Performance:** The primary motivation for SAS was that SCSI needed higher bandwidth and the existing standard could not be fixed to obtain it. Toward this end, SAS provides a performance roadmap that shows the bandwidth quadrupling within 7 years. SAS also maintains the SCSI concept of a connection, in which one device gains control of the bus to communicate with the target device. The difference with SAS is that one device can now have access to several buses and thereby have several connections in progress at the same time. That increases the effective bandwidth for such a device regardless of the bit rate of transmission.
2. **Low cost:** A serial architecture has an inherent cost advantage because the cables and connectors can be smaller and cheaper than the versions required by parallel bus architectures. Small connectors also support smaller disk drives, facilitating their use in high-performance systems and providing for future drive form factors. SAS networks are economical in part due to the inexpensive expander devices used to create the networks. Smaller SAS connectors and small form factor disk drives enable more efficient packaging and higher I/O density systems as well.
3. **Software Compatibility:** Anytime a new standard is defined to replace an existing one, a primary goal must be to minimize barriers to transition while still meeting the needs. One potential barrier to the acceptance of SAS

is software compatibility. While this could not be completely achieved, the design goal was to minimize changes to the existing SCSI software stack.

4. **Fail-over capability:** This is a common requirement for the highly-reliable, highly-available systems typical in the enterprise market where SCSI has been dominant and was therefore targeted by SAS. Dual-ported drives are a necessity to meet this goal and SAS drives will implement them.

The SAS Solution

The SAS interface is intentionally very similar to other existing serial designs (Fibre Channel in particular) so as to minimize the learning curve and design effort. Some characteristics in common include:

- **Point-to-point connections:** Unlike parallel buses in which several devices share the bus and arbitrate for access, a serial bus is a point-to-point connection between two devices. This is necessary because the high frequencies used by serial interfaces require careful termination and impedance matching, and do not tolerate varying loads or stubs on the transmission path. One link can only connect between two devices, although one device may implement several links, allowing the system to scale.
- **Dual-simplex operation:** The link is often described as a full-duplex connection and, from the perspective of the link as a whole, that's correct. Technically, though, the link is actually dual-simplex because it has a transmit side that can only send and a receive side that can only receive, rather than doing both on the same wire at the same time. The first-generation transfer rate is 3.0 Gbits/s for SAS while the second generation, proposed as 6.0 Gbits/s, is currently under consideration by the electrical working group for the standard.
- **Frame-based transaction protocol:** A serial connection only allows one bit to be presented at a time over the wire, so the protocol must impose a recognizable structure on the sequence of the bits that are to convey the needed information. For SAS this is accomplished by grouping the bits into 4-byte dwords that are used to construct Frames. As shown in Figure 1-2, frames can travel in both directions at the same time between devices. As an example, an initiator could be sending a SCSI command while the target is returning data associated with a previous read command.

Figure 1-2: SAS Link Example

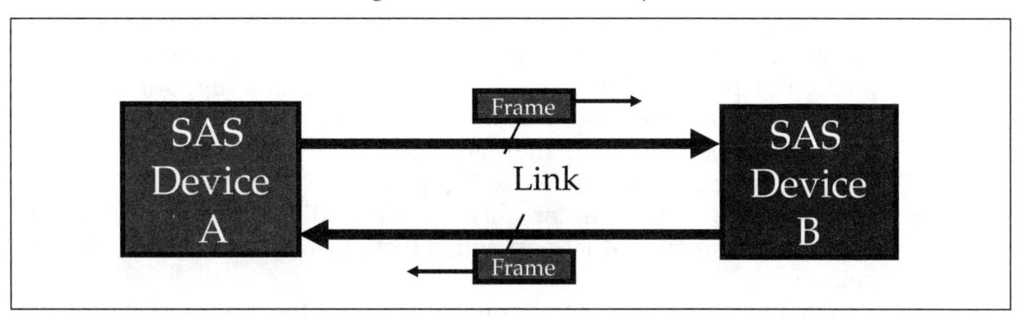

Bandwidth

The current generation of SAS achieves a maximum bandwidth of 300 MB/s using a bit rate of 3.0 Gbits/s. The reason for the difference is that, like other serial interfaces, SAS uses a 10-bit-per-byte encoding scheme to ensure the bit stream will have the properties needed for reliable transmission (see "8b/10b Encoding and Decoding" on page 370). This encoding scheme ensures a sufficient "transition density" in the bit stream to make it approximate a clock and allow the receiver's Phase-Locked Loop (PLL) to lock onto it and recover the clock. The cost for encoding is an extra 2 bits that must be sent for each 8 bits of actual data, resulting in a 25% overhead from the transmitter's point of view (2 bits must be added to every 8 outgoing bits), or 20% overhead from the receiver's perspective because the 10 incoming bits decode to only 8 useful bits. The advantages provided by encoding are considered worth the performance cost, and 8b/10b encoding is commonly used in many serial designs.

Advantages

A bandwidth for SAS of 300 MB/s would not seem to compare favorably to the current parallel SCSI bandwidth of 320 MB/s. However, there are still several advantages:

- SAS operates at full-duplex while SCSI is half-duplex. As a result, it may be said that the aggregate bandwidth available could be as high as 600 MB/s, using 300 MB/s in each direction. The aggregate bandwidth will be significantly higher than a parallel SCSI system could achieve with the same number of parallel SCSI disk drives.

- Improved bandwidth is achieved by permitting a device to have wide ports (more than one link connecting two devices), which allow more than one traffic stream between devices at the same time. Although it doesn't spread one transaction across several serial paths at once the way some transports like PCI Express do, this does allow a device to have several different communication paths operating at the same time. Each link supports 300 MB/s so, if the sustained transfer rate for a 15K rpm drive is 75 MB/s, then the overall available bandwidth translates easily into the number of such drives that can be supported as shown in Figure 1-3.
- Smaller cables and connectors facilitate the addition of a second port to hard drives, proving a dual-port option that can act as a redundant port for failover.
- Among the most important advantages of SAS is the headroom it provides for future speed improvements. Future generations will achieve multiples of the first generation rate. By comparison, SCSI cannot readily be extended beyond its current bandwidth limits.
- SAS also provides scalability by means of devices called expanders that act somewhat like simple network switches to allow one port to be able to see many addresses in the system. The use of expanders and the ability to cascade them allows SAS to scale readily to large disk arrays of over 16,000 devices.

Figure 1-3: Bandwidth Comparison

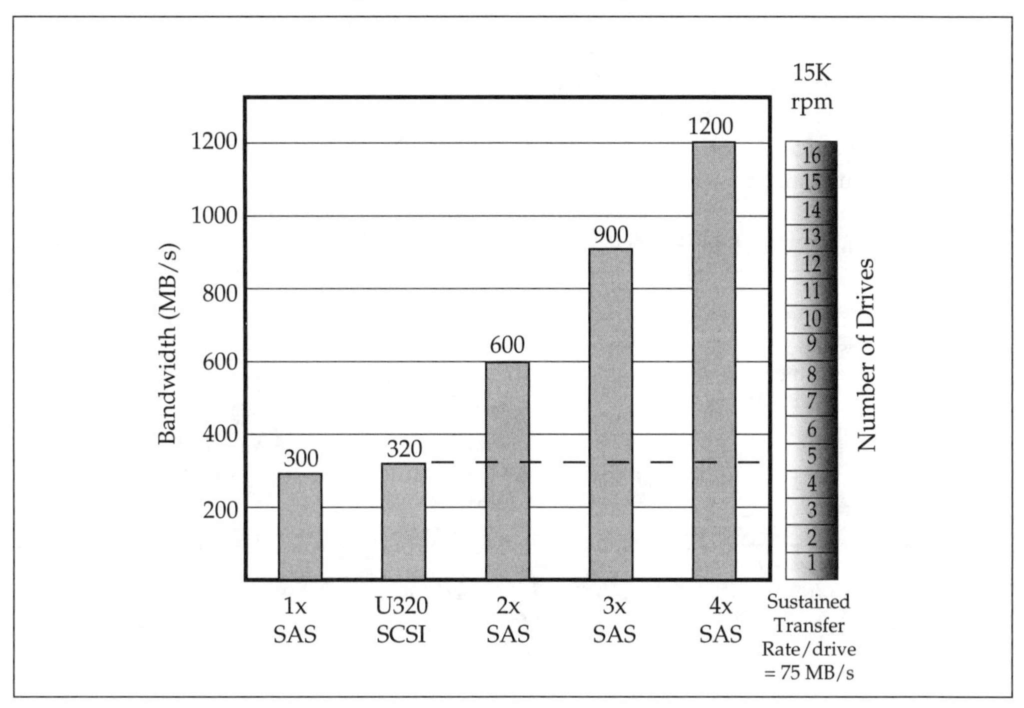

Positioning SAS

Parallel SCSI is still the dominant server storage transport today and the plan is that SAS will gradually take its place, but there are other factors coming into play that will change the balance of the market. For example, there is a desire to take advantage of the low cost offered by SATA drives in the enterprise market, and some adaptations have been made to the SATA transport to improve its suitability for that purpose. At the other end of the spectrum there is an effort to migrate Fibre Channel from the very high end into the larger market as well, perhaps by adding SATA tunneled compatibility. As a result, the question arises as to how these bus technologies will share the market.

To answer that question we need to look at the usage model for the transport itself and then for the drives that will use it. Figure 1-4 illustrates the expectation that, although SAS targets the mainstream server storage market, it may find a use in high-end workstations or sophisticated storage arrays as well because the cost of a SAS infrastructure is expected to be similar to that for SATA. There may be some premium for a SAS HBA (Host Bus Adapter) compared to a SATA HBA, but this difference is expected to be small compared to the combined cost of all the parts in a storage system. In smaller servers, embedded SAS chipsets or HBA cards can be used to connect to internal drives or JBODs (Just a Bunch Of Disks). For large enterprise systems, a SAS RAID (Redundant Array of Inexpensive Drives) card could provide storage options in support of SAN (Storage Area Network) and NAS (Network Attached Storage) implementations.

Figure 1-4: SAS Expands Storage Options

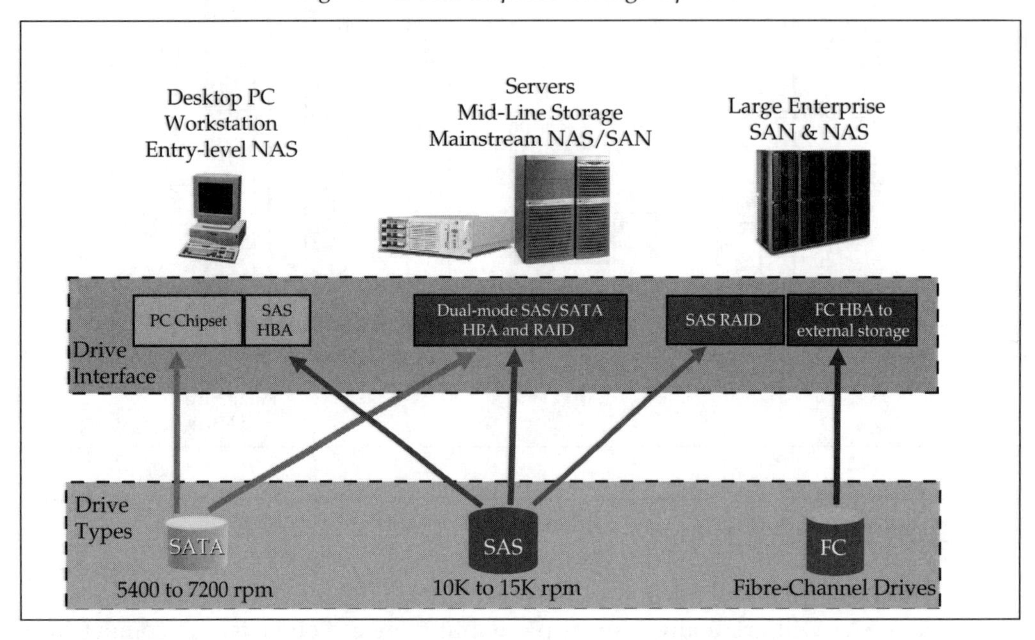

If the infrastructure cost of SAS and SATA is similar, there would be little motivation to include a SATA-only infrastructure in a server because a SAS infrastructure would handle both types.

When discussing large systems, another aspect of both SAS and SATA is that they reside "behind the network". This is shown in Figure 1-5, where the boundaries of the network and SAS domains are easier to see. SAS and SATA are designed for storage rather than networking, which means they do not provide network connectivity for LANs or SANs. The purpose of such a limitation, of course, is to make the storage interface simple, low cost, and low latency.

Figure 1-5: SAS and SATA Reside Behind the Network

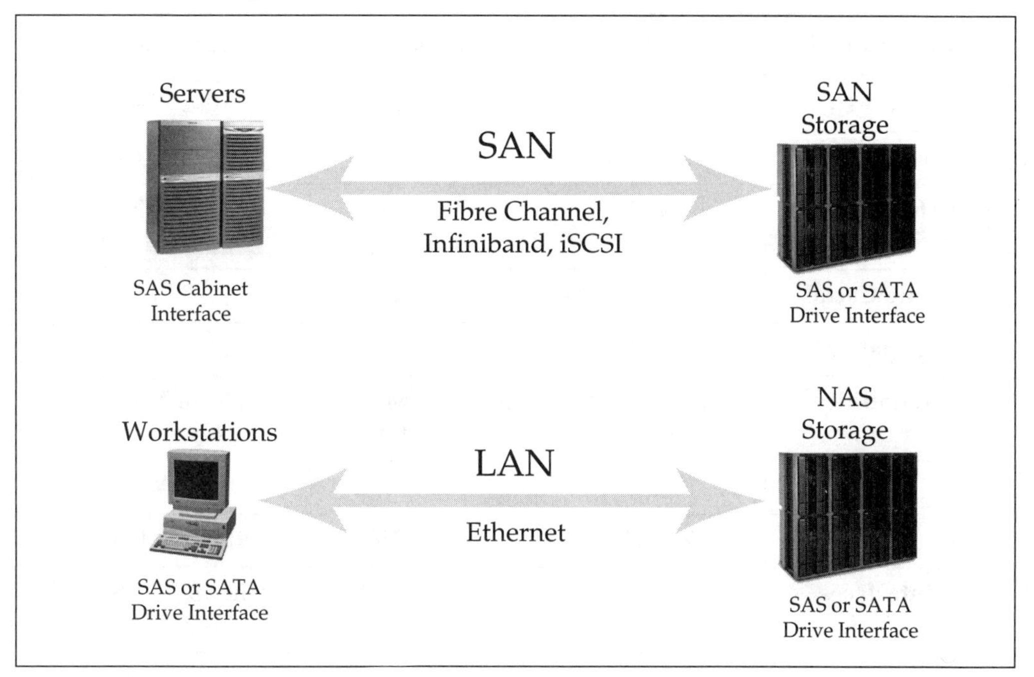

Disk Drive Comparison

The choice of drives will depend on the system requirements. SAS will use high-performance drives optimized for the random accesses that servers typically experience, but will support SATA for low-cost bulk storage and SAS for performance and reliability. Different drive types are designed with certain characteristics, depending on their target market, as shown in Table 1-2. Of course, any of the drive types could be coupled with any of the available storage interfaces, but system requirements have dictated the use of SCSI or Fibre Channel interfaces on the high performance drives and ATA or SATA on the lower ones. As SATA migrates toward the server market this strategy may change, but the premium prices vendors can charge for the faster drives in the server market motivate them to differentiate a high-end group of drives with higher-performance interfaces.

Table 1-2: Comparison of Drive Types

Characteristic	Mobile	Desktop	Enterprise
RPM	3600, 4200, 5400	5400, 7200	10K, 15K
Seek Time	12 - 14 ms	8.9 - 9.5 ms	3.2 - 7.4 ms
Performance as a file server*	N/A	79 - 136	146 - 372
Write Cache	2 MB	2 - 8 MB	2 - 8 MB
Capacity	10 - 500 GB	40 - 250 GB	18 - 300 GB
Reliability	300 K hr MTBF, 8 hr/day	500 K hr MTBF, 8 hr/day	1.4 M hr MTBF, 24 hr/day
Power	2.5 W	10 W	15 W
Cost	$73 - $160	$75 - $240	$160 - $1400
Interfaces	ATA-66, ATA-100	SATA-150/300	Ultra 320 SCSI, SAS, FC

** NOTE: File server performance is taken from StorageReview.com's Drive Performance Resource Center (http://storagereview.com/php/benchmark/bench_sort.php) benchmark "SR File Server DriveMark 2002" and presented here with permission. The site describes the units for the test measured as "The average I/O rate achieved when replaying a synthetic mix of highly random activity weighted mostly towards reads. Such a pattern simulates typical File Server activity."*

As shown in Figure 1-6, disk drive performance usually has a simple relationship to storage capacity:

- Higher capacity drives, such as the 7200 RPM version shown, have a larger media, which increases capacity but limits rotational frequency and performance. The lower RPMs help moderate power consumption and improve rotational stability.
- The 10K RPM drives achieve better performance because they have smaller media, which allows the use of smaller actuators, which in turn reduces seek time and lowers mechanical inertia. The smaller media also reduces seek distance while maintaining rotational stability.

- The 15K RPM drives have even smaller media, further reducing seek distance, and they have space for larger magnets on the actuator to further improve seek time.

Figure 1-6: Drive Performance vs. Capacity

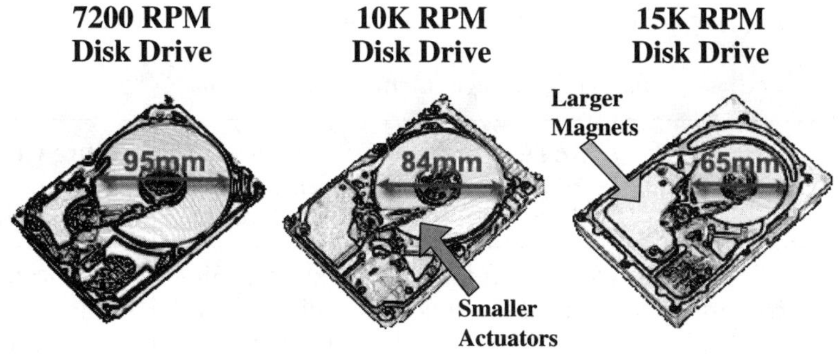

The market is changing all the time, of course, and new innovations will continue to affect the trade-offs associated with drive types. As one example, a new class of 7200 rpm SATA drives has recently become available that is optimized for enterprise near-line solutions.

Interface Comparison

Having looked at the types of drives associated with both the high-end and low-end, it now makes sense to compare the interfaces as well. Refer to Table 1-3 and the following discussion.

- At the low end, the SATA interface is the simplest and least expensive because it was designed for single-user computers that typically have only one drive. Seek times are less important in single-user applications, and accesses tend to be more linear than random, so inexpensive drives provide acceptable performance. Reliability and availability are also less important than cost, so fail-over mechanisms such as dual ported drives are not included.
- To migrate SATA into the enterprise market, a port selector was defined, which is a device that allows two different host devices to access the same target device. This allows a SATA drive to implement a dual-ported interface, though it is limited in that only one host connection is active and switching to the other host is a non-trivial event. Similarly, a port multiplier

was developed, which is a device that allows one host device to talk to several drives by using a new field in the header to select among them. This provides some scalability but it is limited because the port multipliers can only access 15 devices and cannot be cascaded. The expectation is that this drawback, coupled with the ease of constructing useful SATA storage topologies within a SAS topology has caused port multipliers to fall out of favor. Still, these additions allow SATA drives to share some of the higher-level drive characteristics but still maintain their cost advantage.

Table 1-3: Storage Interface Comparison

	SATA	SAS	Fibre Channel
Cost	Low	Low-Medium	High
Complexity	Lowest; port multipliers permit limited expansion, no cascading	Medium; 16K devices with Expanders	Highest; both fabrics and loops, up to 16M devices
	no peer-to-peer	peer-to-peer	peer-to-peer
	single host	multi-initiator	multi-initiator
Cable Length	~1m	~6m	~10Km
Performance	1.5 - 3.0 Gb/s, Half duplex	3.0 - 6.0 Gb/s, Full duplex	2.0 - 4.0 Gb/s, Full duplex
Reliability, Availability	Low	High	High
Dual-Port HDDs	With Port Selector (passive)	Yes (active)	Yes (active)
Drive Capacity	Highest	Medium	Lowest
Other	Stricter consumer product EMI standard requires use of SCC (Spread Spectrum Clocking)	SCC supported only for SATA compatibility	No SSC requirement

- In the middle of this spectrum is the SAS interface. Designed as a direct replacement for SCSI, it supports server designs and includes high-end features like multi-ported initiators, expanders, and dual-ported drives. Expanders enable SAS to implement more complex topologies and support up to 2^{14} (16K) devices. Finally, full-duplex operation provides better bandwidth in systems that can benefit from bidirectional traffic.

- At the high end is Fibre Channel, which was designed to support network-level functionality. Sophisticated switches make possible systems with a 24-bit network address space, supporting fabrics with up to 2^{24} (16 M) devices. The very long cable distances also allow the fabric to extend between floors or buildings. Switches are very expensive devices, but arbitrated loop designs are also allowed, offering reduced cost in exchange for some loss of reliability. Some systems require the level of sophistication that Fibre Channel offers. Network attached storage (NAS) systems, for example, are almost defined by their use of Fibre Channel.

Example Topology

Consider a SAS topology that brings together everything discussed so far. Combining both SAS and SATA drives, a typical high-availability SAS configuration might look like the one shown in Figure 1-7. This configuration is designed to eliminate any single points of failure and has redundant power supplies, RAID controllers, expanders, as well as dual-ported drives. Each of the dual-ported SAS drives is accessible by both expanders. The SATA drives have only a single port, but implementing a Port Selector allows them to be accessed by both expanders as well. The RAID controllers protect against individual drive failures, and having more than one RAID controller protects against a failure at that level, since the other one can take over the workload. Finally, the expanders are attached to each other through their subtractive ports, providing a path for the two RAID controllers to communicate with each other so as to facilitate recovery in case of a failure.

Figure 1-7: Example SAS Configuration

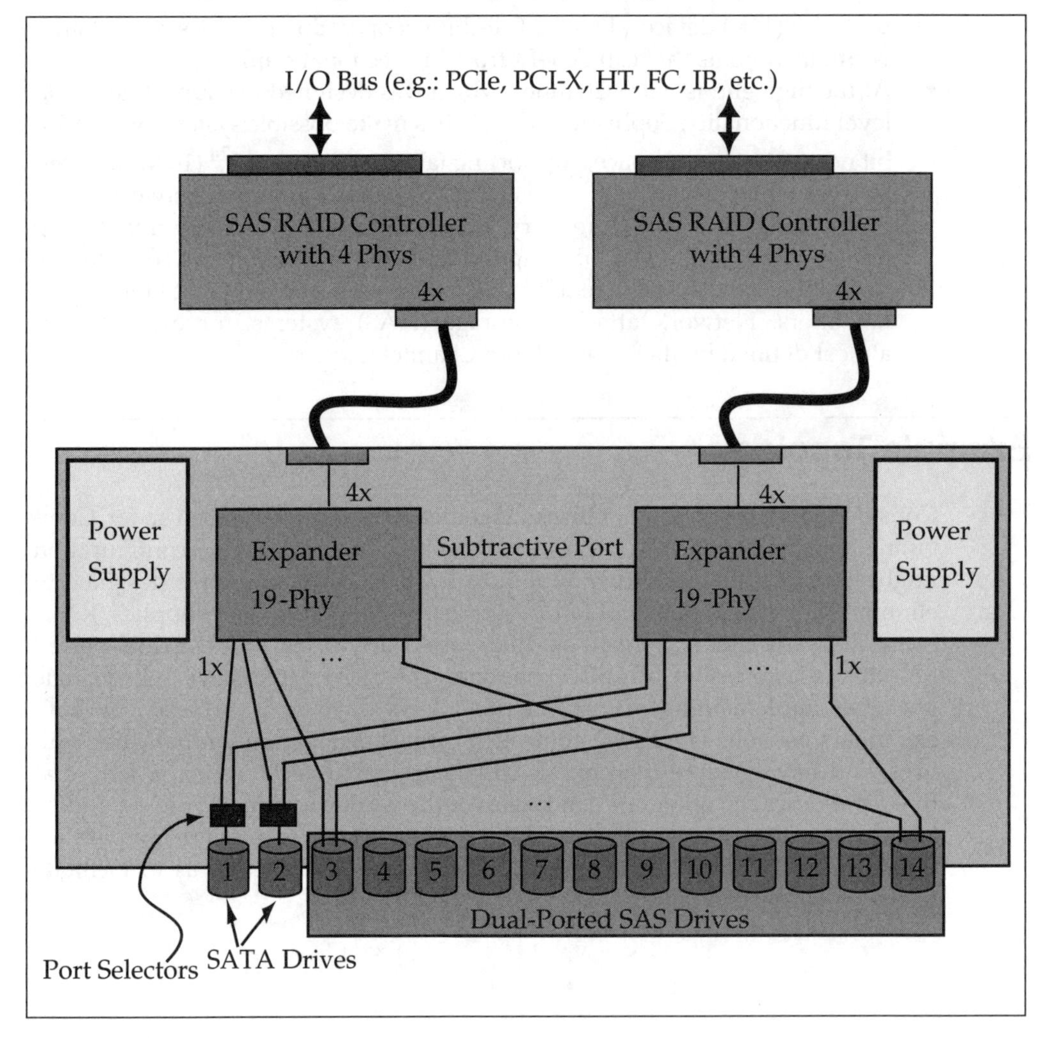

In describing this topology, it is worth noting that dual-ported SAS drives have advantages over SATA drives using a Port Selector. True dual-ported designs can process commands from both controllers independently and not just as a fail-over mechanism. This allows load balancing between the controller and provides improved performance and faster recovery time in the event of a failure. For Port Selectors, only one controller is chosen at initialization to access the drive and the other port remains inactive. When a failure occurs, the Port

Selector must be switched to give the remaining controller access to the drive, adding time to the recovery process.

Usage Model Summary

By now, several advantages of SAS over alternate transports should be clear.

1. SAS supports SATA devices and has greater flexibility than SATA. It is the logical choice for server storage systems that will use SATA or SAS. SATA drives will be preferred for near-line backup and other applications where capacity and lower cost are important, but it will still make sense to use a SAS infrastructure, since the infrastructure cost will be about the same for both SAS and SATA. For reference on this topic, "near line" refers to storage that is typically removable, allowing it to appear infinitely deep, since new mass storage devices can always be used to replace one that becomes full. The trade-off for this is that it takes time to access this storage for retrieval, since the needed data may not be on-line when it's needed.
2. SAS is the logical replacement for SCSI and retains compatibility with the SCSI protocol.
3. SAS includes Fibre Channel's high availability features, such as dual-ported devices, to provide higher connectivity, reliability and performance. Fibre Channel will be preferred for outside-the-box, long distance environments like SANs.

It seems a fitting conclusion to show the planned development of SAS over the next several years in Figure 1-8 as projected by the SCSI Trade Association. Discussions by the T10 Physical Layer working group regarding the next generation rate (6.0 Gb/s) were already under way at the time of this writing, so an increase to that speed looks likely for the near future. Higher speeds may yet present unforeseen difficulties, but the projections seem reasonable at this point.

Figure 1-8: SAS Developmental Roadmap

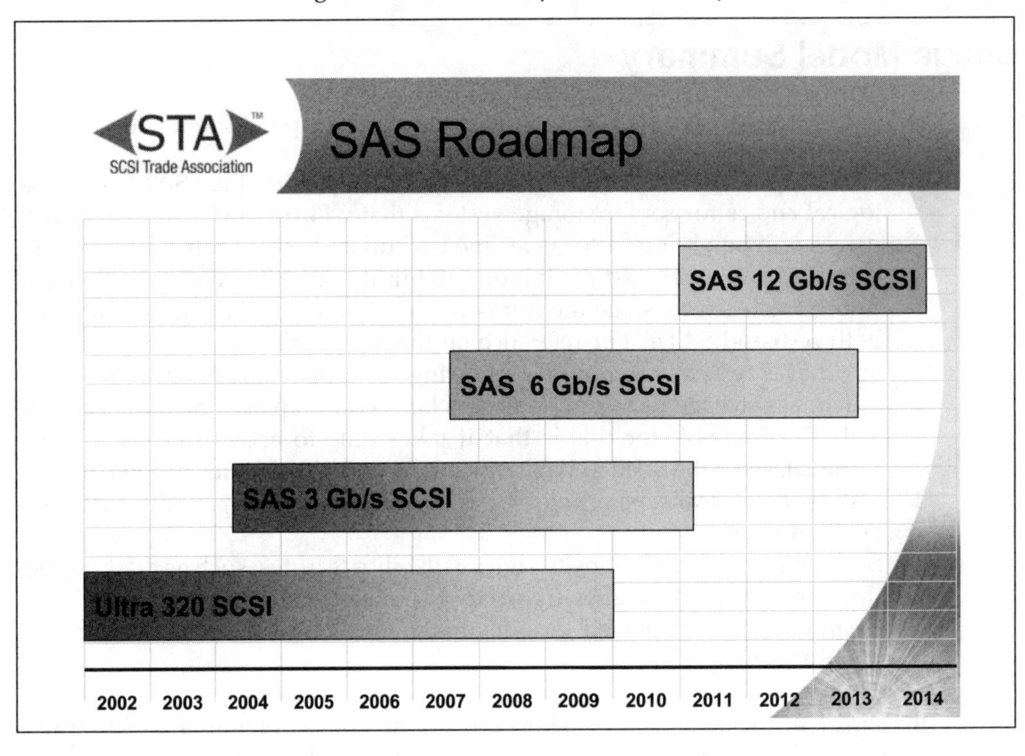

2 Origins of SAS and Background

The Previous Chapter

The previous chapter introduced the SAS solution and compared it to existing serial storage transports to provide the motivation for SAS.

This Chapter

This chapter discusses the SCSI, Fibre Channel and SATA background from which SAS was developed. While maintaining compatibility with its SCSI software base, SAS borrows from serial transports like Fibre Channel and SATA to develop a next-generation enterprise storage architecture.

The Next Chapter

The next chapter introduces the basic functions of SAS, explaining its method of operation from a very high level view. Terms are defined and examples presented to lay a foundation for understanding the basic operation of a SAS link. The layers of the SAS standard are introduced and their responsibilities and interaction are discussed.

Background for Serial SCSI

Until recently, there were three main storage IO technologies, each of which had a well-defined market. At the low end where cost was a primary concern, parallel ATA, developed for the PC market and its high volumes, was a good fit. In high-end implementations where complex topologies and high-performance storage systems were required, Fibre Channel became the standard. For applications where high performance was needed but topologies were not as demanding (such as enterprise storage), SCSI became the interface of choice. The following sections provide a brief look at each of these earlier transports.

SCSI Background

SAS was specifically designed as the replacement for SCSI (Small Computer System Interface). The precursor to SCSI first appeared in 1979 when Shugart Associates developed a drive interface bus referred to as SASI (Shugart Associates System Interface). In 1986 this was adopted as a standard called SCSI, and provided a bandwidth of about 2 MB/s. As shown in Table 2-1, over the years the standard was revised numerous times; first to SCSI-2, which defined a synchronous and wide (16-bit) bus, and later to SCSI-3, increasing the bandwidth to 20 MB/s. SCSI-3 also split the standard into several parts so as to avoid having to update the entire standard to implement future incremental changes. To facilitate such changes, the SCSI standards were grouped into several layers, as shown in Figure 2-1.

Table 2-1: History of Parallel SCSI

Interconnect	Year	Speed	Key Features
SCSI-1	1986	~ 2MB/s	Asynchronous, narrow (8 bit)
SCSI-2	1989	10 Mb/s	Synchronous, wide (16 bit)
		SCSI-3	
Fast-Wide	1992	20 MB/s	
Ultra	1995	40 MB/s	
Ultra-2	1997	80 MB/s	Low voltage differential signaling
Ultra-3	1999	160 MB/s	Cyclic Redundancy Code
Ultra-320	2001	320 MB/s	Paced, Packetized, QAS

Figure 2-1: Hierarchy of SCSI Standards

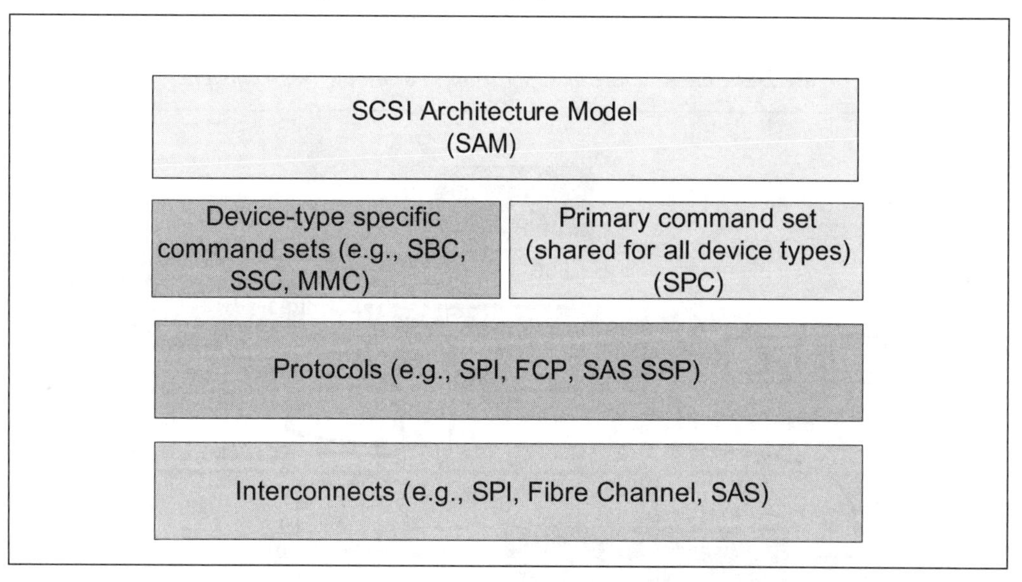

The overall definition of SCSI is contained in the SAM standard (SCSI Architectural Model), while the various command sets for each of the different device types supported are grouped into a command set layer that includes the SPC (SCSI Primary Commands) that are common to all devices, and others as required by specific devices. The third layer defines how the commands map to a particular protocol, such as SPI (SCSI Parallel Interface), or FCP (Fibre Channel Protocol), or SAS. Finally, the fourth layer defines the interconnects that allow devices to communicate between themselves using the protocols.

SCSI provided a number of advantages over previous disk interfaces such as ESDI (Enhanced Small Device Interface). An important one was that it off-loaded the low-level device details to the drives themselves. This had the effect of hiding the implementation details from system software and readily allowing the accommodation of newer devices as they became available. Also, unlike the older designs that only allowed one or two drives on a bus, SCSI handled up to 16 drives on a wide bus. These improvements came at a higher cost compared to the simpler designs like IDE (Integrated Device Electronics, which later became ATA - Advanced Technology Attachment), but for systems that needed the higher performance that was an acceptable trade.

In SCSI systems, an HBA is used to interface from the computer's system bus to the SCSI bus. This an important advantage because it decouples the SCSI bus from the system, so transactions can be simultaneously in progress on both the host system bus and the SCSI bus. A simplified legacy system picture, like the one shown in Figure 2-2, illustrates this concept.

Figure 2-2: Concurrent Bus Operation in a Simple SCSI System

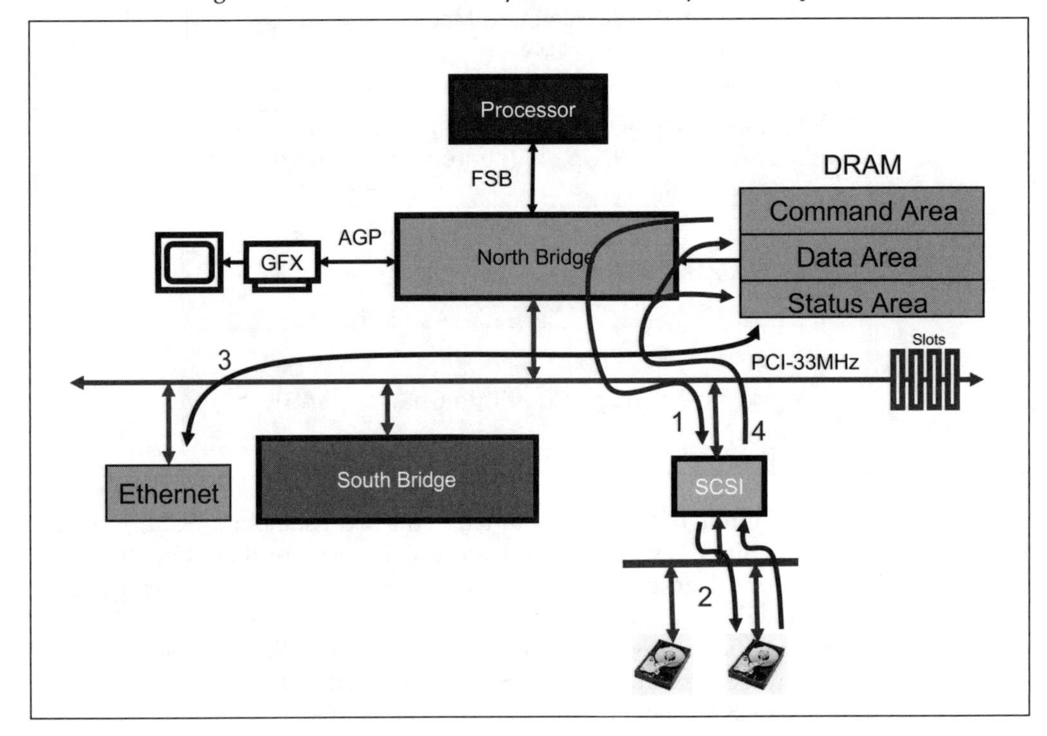

The sequence of events in this example would be as follows:

1. First, the HBA uses a PCI transaction to fetch a SCSI command from an area of memory designated for that purpose.
2. Next, the HBA begins execution of the command on the SCSI bus, retrieving data on a disk read, for example.
3. In the meantime, the PCI bus is available for other traffic, so while the disk transaction is in progress on the SCSI bus, traffic between the Ethernet card and system memory can proceed on the PCI bus.
4. When the SCSI transaction is completed, the data and status of the transaction can be written to their respective areas of memory by the HBA using another PCI transaction.

SCSI Definitions

It would be helpful to define some SCSI terms for the benefit of those new to SCSI. Many of these terms carry over directly to SAS or have analogous meanings. Figure 2-3 illustrates the context for some of these, and includes other terms such as Application Client and Device Server that are discussed later in Chapter 8, entitled "Application Layer," on page 193.

Figure 2-3: SCSI Objects

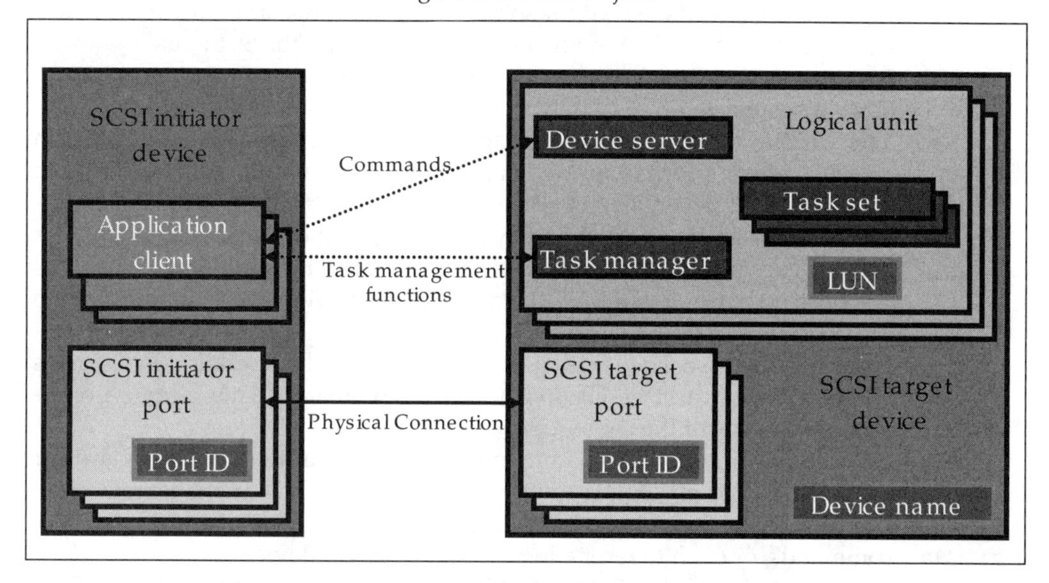

- **Initiator:** Device that can initiate SCSI commands and receive responses. In SCSI, initiators are relatively simple devices that yield control of transactions to the target device once the command has been sent.
- **Target:** Device that behaves as the receiver of SCSI commands, accepting or returning data and providing completion status. In SCSI the target is the more complex device and takes control of a transaction once the command has been received, deciding whether to disconnect before returning data and when to send read data or fetch write data.
- **Logical Unit:** Subsystem within a target that acts as a source or destination of data. A target may have several logical units, which are designated by Logical Unit Number (LUN), and must, at a minimum, implement LUN 0.
- **Nexus:** Derived from a Latin word that means to tie or to bind, a nexus describes a relationship between things. In SCSI, keeping track of the relationship between devices allows a target to reconnect to an initiator after

taking some action, and allows an initiator to know which target is responding for a given transaction. An I_T Nexus represents the relationship between an initiator and a target device. An I_T_L Nexus adds the logical unit number selected within the target, while an I_T_L_Q Nexus adds the tag value for each queued transaction when multiple transactions target the same logical unit from the same initiator.

- **Connect:** Describes the situation when an initiator successfully accesses a target device. Both devices will store the nexus information locally for future reference.
- **Disconnect:** Describes a temporary termination of the transaction by the target when it needs to wait for something (e.g.: a repositioning of the read/ write head assembly), allowing other devices to use the SCSI bus.
- **Reconnect:** Occurs when a target selects an initiator to continue a previously disconnected transaction.
- **Tag:** Unique to each command, tags allow multiple transactions to be in progress when a logical unit is targeted by the same initiator for multiple transactions. If permission is given by the device driver, the order of execution of the tasks can be modified by the logical unit to improve performance and the tag is used to identify which command it is servicing when the response is returned. For SAS, the tag is a 16-bit value that is unique within the I_T nexus.
- **Task:** Usually associated with a command, this is the operation in progress within a logical unit based on a received command. A task can be referenced by means of the tag associated with it.
- **Task Management:** Some commands are defined in the SAM standard for controlling tasks or logical units within a device. Task management commands allow an initiator to terminate an outstanding command or group of commands, or even to reset a logical unit or target device.
- **Command Descriptor Block (CDB):** Commands are encoded into a CDB for transmission in SCSI. The CDB formats are defined in the SPC standard (SCSI Primary Commands) and the length of the CDB is command dependent.
- **SCSI Domain:** As shown in Figure 2-4 on page 33, a domain consists of a group of initiators and targets that can communicate with each other over a service delivery subsystem (see next bullet item).
- **Service Delivery Subsystem:** A bus that complies with the SCSI Architectural Model (SAM) and provides the means by which devices communicate (including traces, cables, connectors, and any intervening devices).

As a note for reference in future chapters, Figure 2-3 illustrates some identifiers used by SCSI that are carried forward for SAS:

- The SCSI Port ID is replaced in SAS by the 64-bit SAS address for the port.

- The SCSI Device Name is also replaced by a SAS address. This address may be the same as the address used for the Port Identifier (as it is for expanders) or it could be unique to the device. This name is not used for addressing purposes the way the Port ID is used, but allows software a means of detecting that different Ports reside within the same device.

Figure 2-4: Simple SCSI Domain Example

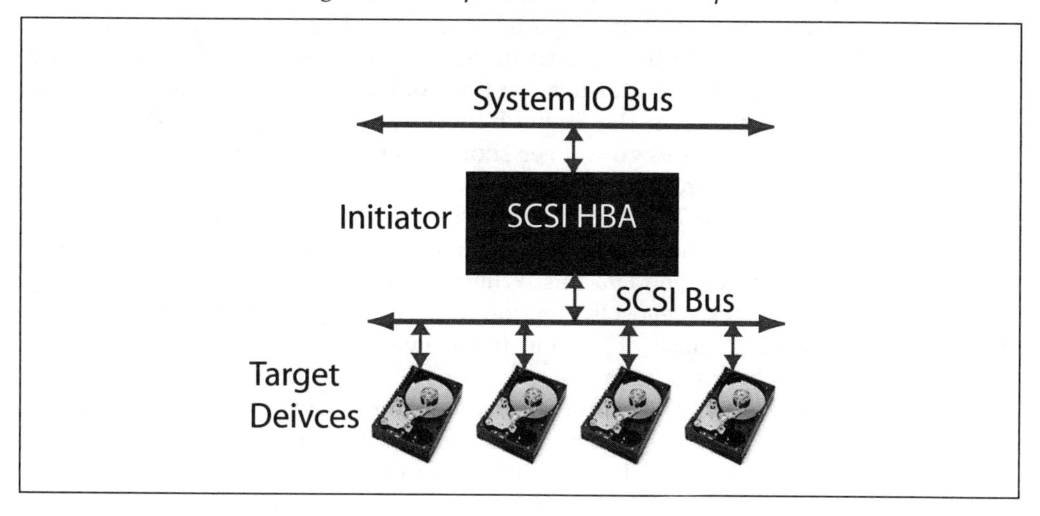

Problems with Parallel SCSI

Improvements to the SCSI model enabled it to increase in performance on a regular basis for many years, but the limitations inherent within the design precluded any additional improvements. These limitations are summarized below.

- **Insufficient bandwidth for future operation.** The current generation of SCSI supports up to 320 MB/s, but this bandwidth is shared by all the devices on the bus. If there are the maximum of 15 devices on the bus and heavy demand is fully utilizing the bus, the bandwidth available to each device could be reduced to only 21.3 MB/s. Since a typical enterprise hard drive can sustain data rates of 80 MB/s, this limits the number of devices that can effectively share the bus. A parallel SCSI version operating at 640 MB/s was considered, but was ultimately rejected due to the difficulty and high cost of implementation.
- **Limits of parallel bus design.** The reason SCSI could not be effectively enhanced to 640 MB/s is because it suffers from the same set of limitations

that all parallel bus designs face. Many of these are caused by the need to use a common clock between bus components; i.e., the same clock is distributed to all of the devices on the bus and one rising edge is used to drive the data while the next rising edge is used by the receiving device to latch the incoming data. Factors that affect the viability of a parallel design include:

- **Clock period:** As the frequency increases, the clock period is reduced. Eventually, the period becomes too small to transmit information reliably and receive it by the next rising edge of the clock.
- **Flight time:** The time required for a signal to travel from transmitter to receiver is affected by transmitter and receiver characteristics and by the length of the transmission trace or cable between them. As the frequency increases, the timing budget available for this is reduced, constraining the design to ever shorter transmission paths until it finally becomes impractical.
- **Signal skew:** The time difference between parallel signals is affected by transmitter characteristics, but more so by differences in trace length between parallel data bits. When the timing budget gets squeezed by higher clock speeds, the margin for error in signal skew is also reduced, making the task of routing traces ever more difficult and expensive until it becomes impractical.
- **Clock skew:** The difference between the arrival time of the reference clock at different devices in the system. This must be subtracted from the timing budget because the transmitter and receiver clocks may differ by this much. As the timing budget is reduced, this value must also be reduced as much as possible, adding complexity and cost to the board design.
- **Other issues:** that degrade with higher clock speeds include the power required to simultaneously switch many signals at the same time, and the cross-talk generated between the many data pins.

As illustrated in Figure 2-5, the combination of these issues can result in a timing budget violation at the receiver that causes incorrect data to be latched. Avoiding these problems requires very tight signal routing constraints that add significantly to the cost of a system design.

Figure 2-5: Problems with Parallel Bus Design

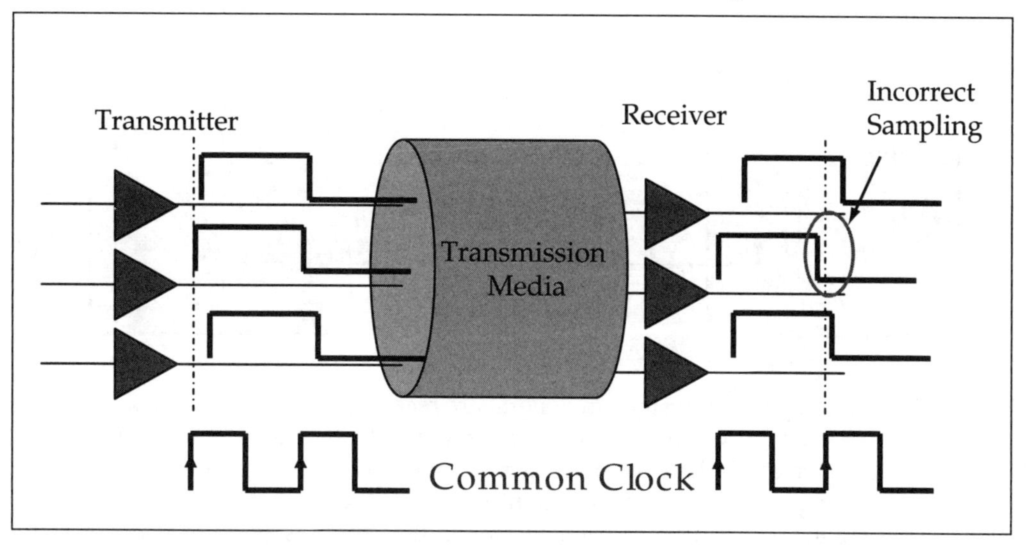

Source-Synchronous Clocking

Alternatively, some parallel buses like PCI-X 2.0 mitigated the problems of the common clock approach by changing to a source-synchronous clocking model (see Figure 2-6 on page 36). In this scheme, rather than using a common clock, the transmitter sends an internally-generated clock, or strobe, with the data and ensures that it is properly aligned to act as a clock for the data. If the system designer routes the strobe over very nearly the same path as the data, then it will arrive with approximately the same timing relationship at the receiver that it had at the transmitter, regardless of flight time or clock period. This scheme alleviates the immediate problems of parallel designs, but adds to an already high pin count and high power consumption. In addition, the problems of signal and clock skew are only postponed until frequencies increase enough that they again impact the timing budget excessively and the design reaches its limit.

Figure 2-6: Source-Synchronous Design

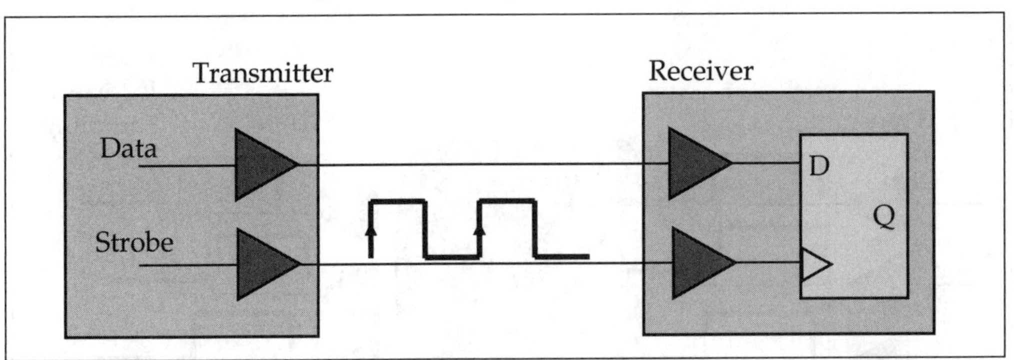

As a result, parallel designs in general are reaching their practical design limits and, consequently, newer designs are moving to the serial model. As is discussed later, serial designs solve the problems associated with parallel buses by embedding the transmission clock into the data stream for the receiver to use in latching the data. This approach eliminates the timing issues mentioned earlier, allowing serial designs to support much higher speeds in the future.

Fibre Channel Background

Fibre Channel is a very high-end transport compared to SAS, permitting much larger device counts and more complex topologies. Designed for very large storage systems, Fibre Channel supports long cables (10 km) and more sophisticated topologies, making it well-suited for applications like SANs (Storage Area Networks), as illustrated in Figure 2-7. A network of this type could be spread across different buildings and include multiple racks of drives.

Figure 2-7: Fibre Channel Storage Network

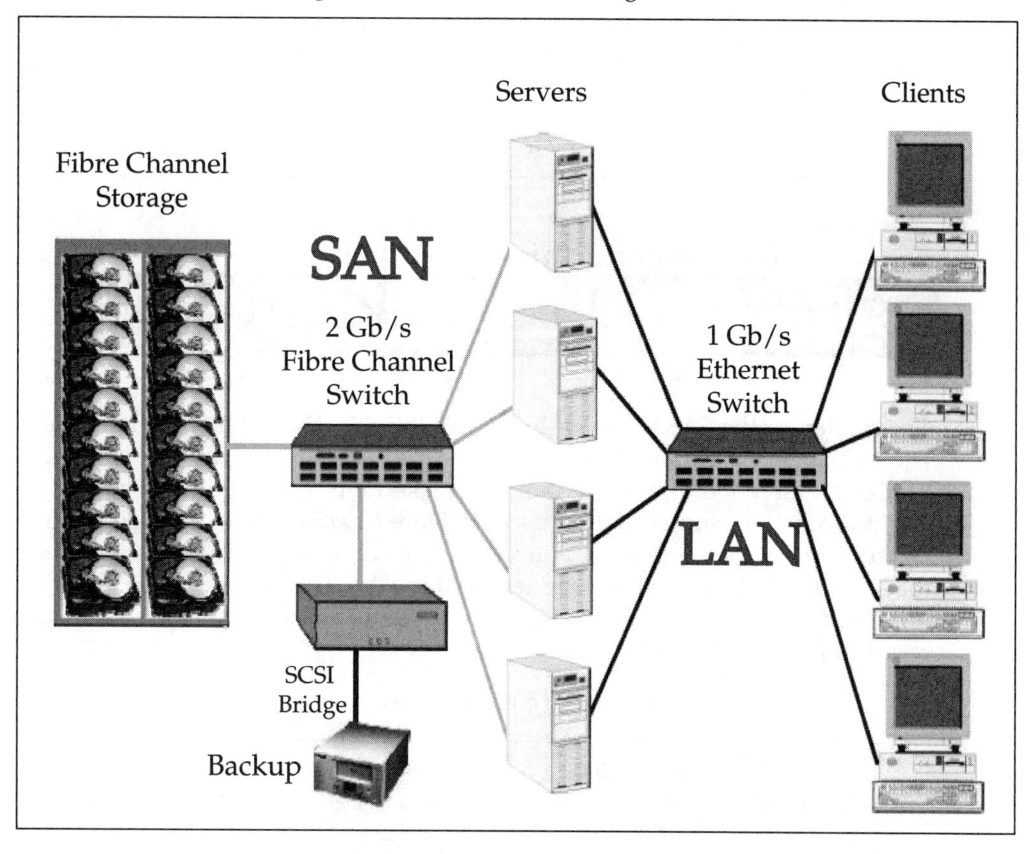

The market served by Fibre Channel is not the space that SAS was intended to target directly, so why discuss Fibre Channel here? Many of today's serial designs borrow heavily from earlier serial designs to leverage design effort and minimize repeated work, and SAS borrows largely from Fibre Channel. This can be seen in the format of the bitstream sent across the wire. Serial protocols send data packets one bit at a time, so the bitstream format must be organized into a pattern that is recognizable at the receiver. For Fibre Channel, this pattern is referred to as a Frame and it has several distinct parts as shown in Figure 2-8 on page 38, where the first bit to go out on the wire is shown on the left. As discussed later, both the beginning and end of the frame are marked by special characters called Primitives that indicate the Start Of Frame (SOF) and the End Of Frame (EOF). These are the first indicators of the frame structure — a valid frame must begin with SOF and end with EOF. The next item shown is the header for the frame, which contains the information such as the destination address, the transaction tag to uniquely identify this transaction out of all the outstanding transactions, etc. Following that are the data dwords for those frames that include data, and then a Cyclic Redundancy Code (CRC) value that is generated by the sender and checked by the receiver to aid in detecting any transmission errors.

Figure 2-8: Fibre Channel Frame

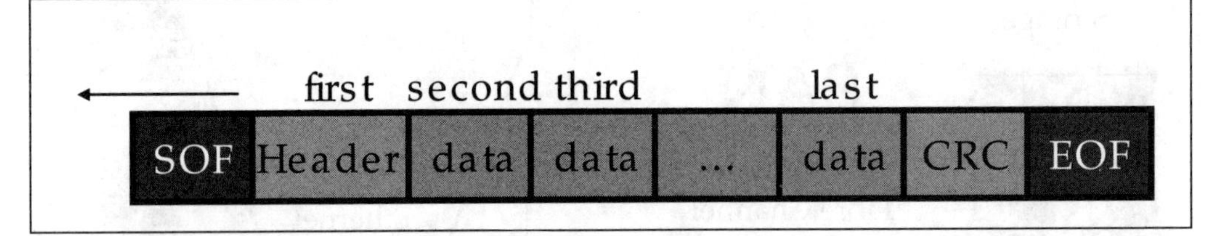

The header for the SAS frame is shown in Table 2-2. The fields show both their Fibre Channel definition (labeled FC) and SAS definition. The details of the header are described later; the point to make here is that the SAS header is intentionally very similar to that used by Fibre Channel. As can be seen in the figure, some of the fields are identical, some have modified values, and others that are used in Fibre Channel are reserved in SAS. This helps explain why the SAS header looks the way it does, and why, for example, there are so many reserved fields in the SAS header.

Table 2-2: SAS Frame Header

Byte	Fields (bits) 8 7 6 5 4 3	2	1	0
0	Frame Type (FC: R_CTL)			
1 - 3	Hashed Destination SAS Address (FC: Destination ID)			
4	Reserved (FC: CS_CTL)			
5 - 7	Hashed Source Address (FC: Source ID)			
8	Reserved (FC: Type)			
9	Reserved (FC: F_CTL)			
10	Reserved (FC: F_CTL)	Retry Data Frames	Re-trans-mit	Chang-ing Data Pointer

Table 2-2: SAS Frame Header

Byte	Fields (bits) 8	7	6	5	4	3	2	1	0
11	Reserved (FC: F_CTL)							Number of Fill Bytes	
12 - 15	Reserved (FC: Sequence ID, DF_CTL, Sequence Count)								
16 - 17	Tag (FC: OX_ID)								
18 - 19	Target Port Transfer Tag (FC: RX_ID)								
20 - 23	Data Offset (FC: Parameter)								
24 - m	Information Unit								
m - (n-3)	Fill Bytes, if needed								

Delivering a Frame

Fibre Channel supports several different delivery schemes, called Classes of Service, and each has advantages and disadvantages. Several of these are listed in Table 2-3 along with a description of their major features. Most Fibre Channel implementations use service class 3, presumably to prevent accesses between devices from tying up resources for long periods of time and to provide better sharing of network resources.

Table 2-3: Fibre Channel Classes of Service

FC Class of Service	Description
1	*Virtual circuit, full bandwidth* (like a telephone connection).
2	*Frame-routed, confirmed delivery* (ACKs), out-of-order frames possible.
3	*Frame-routed, unconfirmed delivery,* out-of-order and lost frames possible (since they can cause problems in practice, most switches use in-order delivery to be safe). Almost all FC implementations use Class 3.

Table 2-3: Fibre Channel Classes of Service

FC Class of Service	Description (Continued)
4	*Virtual circuit, fractional bandwidth.*
6	*Multicast*, allows data replication to several endpoints to facilitate high-reliability systems where replication is a common requirement.

By comparison, SAS takes a simpler approach and implements only the equivalent of service class 1. Since latency can be a factor for this class, it is important to limit the possible sources of it, and SAS accomplishes this by making the frame sizes relatively small and connections relatively short-lived. While the other service classes are packet based and therefore "connectionless", class one is a "connection-based" method that dedicates the resources between connected devices. Conceptually, this is similar to the way a telephone call is connected and has the advantage of speed, because once the path has been established there is no longer any competition for the resources. The disadvantage of this approach is that the dedicated resources are unavailable for use by other devices until they are released by the current connection. If the connection takes a long time, other devices may starve for bandwidth. This makes arbitration for network resources more important as well because, rather than examining every packet, the arbitration happens only once, when the connection is established, and stays in place until that connection is eventually closed.

Scalability is important in any peripheral system and especially so for serial transports, since they implement only point-to-point links between devices. In Fibre Channel, scalability is provided by means of switches which serve to fan out the buses and allow more devices to be connected into a network. However, switches are relatively complex and expensive devices. Since SAS implements simpler fabrics, it uses expanders, which are simpler and yet can accomplish much the same function. Figure 2-9 illustrates a simple topology that expanders make possible in a SAS environment. The figure illustrates some conceptual details that will be covered later, like the wide ports between the HBAs and the Fanout Expander, and the difference between a Fanout and an Edge Expander (see "Concepts for a More Complex Structure" on page 54).

Figure 2-9: Expanders Add Scalability

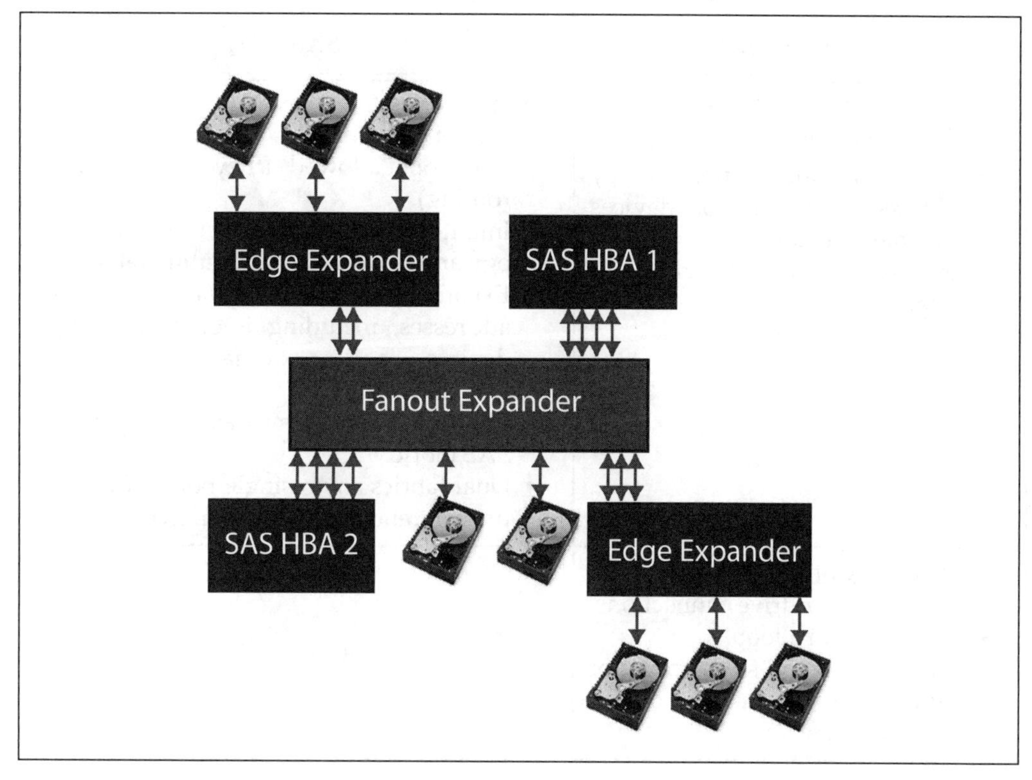

Finally, Table 2-4 compares the topological characteristics of Fibre Channel and SAS, highlighting the different market segments they target.

Table 2-4: Comparison of Fibre Channel and SAS

Fibre Channel	SAS
Simple or Complex Fabrics: • Cross-connected switches. • 2^{24} possibilities afforded by address => 16.8 million devices possible in a fabric. • Dual fabrics for no single point of failure.	Simple Fabrics: • Tree of expanders. • No loops allowed (they complicate routing). • Initiators perform discovery of topology and build program routing tables. • Expander sets have max of 128 addresses, including internal virtual devices and external, attached devices. • 128 * 128 = 16,384 max addresses in a SAS fabric. • Dual fabrics so no single point of failure can render the device inaccessible.
FC supports Arbitrated Loops • Often used for drive connections. • 127 devices in a loop. • Dual loops so no single point of failure can render the device inaccessible.	No loops permitted

ATA Background

Parallel ATA

Parallel ATA drives, intended for the single-user, personal computer environment emphasized low cost and capacity over speed or reliability. Only the simplest topologies were supported. A brief history of ATA development is given in Table 2-5 on page 43.

Table 2-5: Brief ATA History

Generation	Standard	Year	Speed	Key Features
IDE		1986		Pre-standard.
	ATA	1994		PIO (Programmed IO) modes 0-2, multiword DMA (Direct Memory Access) 0.
EIDE (Enhanced IDE)	ATA-2	1996	16 MB/s	PIO modes 3-4, multiword DMA modes 1-2, LBA (Logical Block Addressing).
	ATA-3	1997	16 MB/s	SMART (Self-Monitoring, Analysis and Reporting Technology).
	ATA/ ATAPI-4	1998	33 MB/s	Ultra DMA modes 0-2, CRC (Cyclic Redundancy Code), queuing, 80-wire.
Ultra DMA 66	ATA/ ATAPI-5	2000	66 MB/s	Ultra DMA modes 3-4.
Ultra DMA 100	ATA/ ATAPI-6	2002	100 MB/s	Ultra DMA mode 5, 48-bit LBA.
Ultra DMA 133	ATA/ ATAPI-7	2003	133 MB/s	Ultra DMA mode 6.

ATA got its start as the IDE (Integrated Drive Electronics) bus developed back in 1986, which moved the drive control logic from the system into the drive itself in an effort to improve the performance of PC disk drives. This was later adopted as a standard in 1994 by the T13 working group and renamed ATA (AT-Attachment, because it attached to the AT bus of the IBM PC-AT; AT stands for Advanced Technology). Similar to SCSI, the standard was revised every few years to add capabilities or bandwidth until 2003, when the ATA model shifted away from the parallel model to the serial model for many of the same reasons that SCSI did.

As shown in Figure 2-10, ATA also defined a layered architecture. At the highest level, ATA uses a register-delivery format to transfer commands, and also defines an ATA Packetized Interface (ATAPI) to handle other command sets, such as the SCSI SPC commands. The intermediate levels provide details of the device operation, much as they do for SCSI. At the lowest level, the interconnects are defined.

Figure 2-10: ATA Architectural Layers

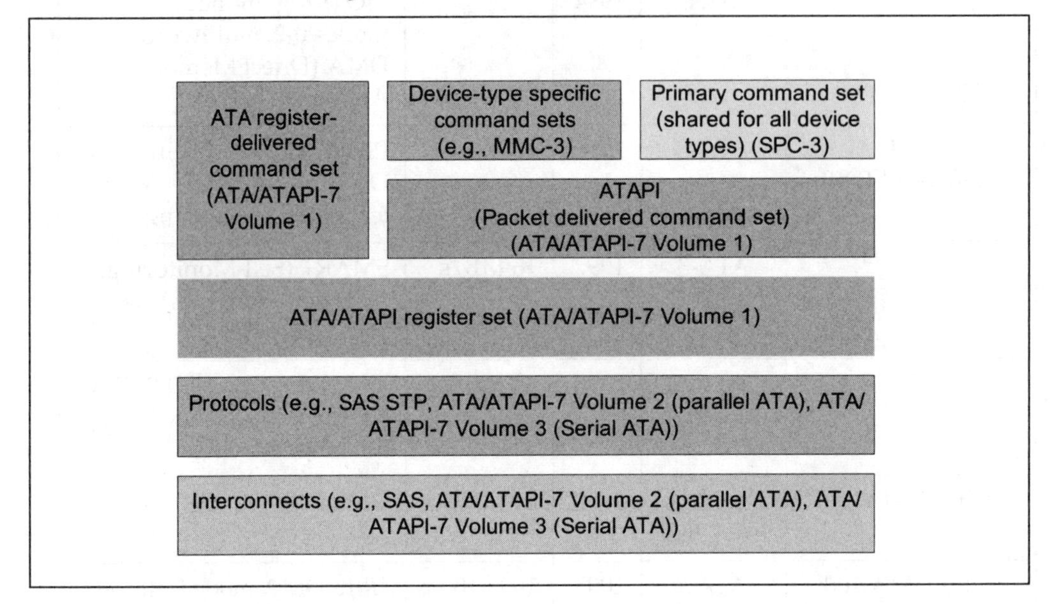

Serial ATA

The serial version of ATA was defined in 2002 by the release of the ATA/ATAPI-7 standard. This earlier version operated at 150 MB/s but, as can be seen in Table 2-6, later versions are planned to increase that bandwidth substantially. At the time of this writing, the SATA II standard was released by the private working group but not yet approved by the T13 standards body. Several products have been announced for it, including both chipsets and hard drives.

Table 2-6: SATA History

Generation	Standard	Year	Speed	Key Features
Serial ATA	ATA/ ATAPI-7	2002	150 MB/s	
Serial ATA II	ATA/ ATAPI-8?	2005?	300 MB/s	NCQ (Native Command Queuing)
Serial ATA III	ATA/ ATAPI-9?	?	600 MB/s	

SATA has obvious advantages for use in consumer desktop and laptop applications, including higher bandwidth and lower cost (due to the smaller cables and lower pin counts). This combination has also resulted in interest by the enterprise server market, especially since the projected bandwidth will be higher than parallel SCSI is currently able to deliver. Some factors have limited its usefulness in that space, however, some of which are addressed by SATA II:

1. First, servers typically have much higher reliability demands than consumer machines and this has led to the practice of minimizing the impact of any single-point-of-failure instances in the system. SCSI supported this with dual-ported drives that allowed a redundant HBA to take control of a drive if the primary HBA or one of a drive's ports should fail. However, SATA drives are more cost-sensitive and that precluded the possibility of adding another port to a drive. The SATA II definition includes a solution for this dilemma in two parts (see Figure 2-11 on page 46):
   - A Port Selector device that presents only one port to the drive but has two available for HBAs. It operates by allowing the first HBA that completes initialization on the link to be the active client, keeping the second connection inactive. The latecomer is allowed to take control and become active by sending a sequence of initialization codes to the device, which can be used to accomplish a fail-over operation.
   - A Port Multiplier device, which acts like a simple version of an expander and allows one SATA host to communicate with several drives.

2. Secondly, SAS provides expanders similar to Fibre Channel switches that allow the creation of simple networks and also allow HBAs to connect to more drives than they actually have ports to support. For SATA, the Port Multiplier does this function, using a field in the header of each packet to

determine which of several drives is the intended target of a transaction. The drives themselves believe they are continually connected to the host device (HBA). A port multiplier cannot be cascaded, however, so it does not offer the same level of scalability that an expander does.

3. Third, drive accesses in a server environment are typically much more random than those in consumer machines, and a fast seek time is important. SATA drives are designed for capacity rather than speed and typically have lower rotational frequencies and longer seek times, but the effect of this can be offset somewhat with the use of RAID (a Redundant Array of Individual [or Inexpensive] Drives that gives better performance or reliability than simple disk arrays). Another performance improvement can be achieved with the addition of Native Command Queuing (NCQ). This allows a drive to rearrange a set of queued commands so as to execute them in the order that minimizes head movement and yields the best overall performance. SCSI already had command queuing, but SATA II adds it in an effort to gain market share in the server space.

Figure 2-11: SATA Port Selector and Port Multiplier

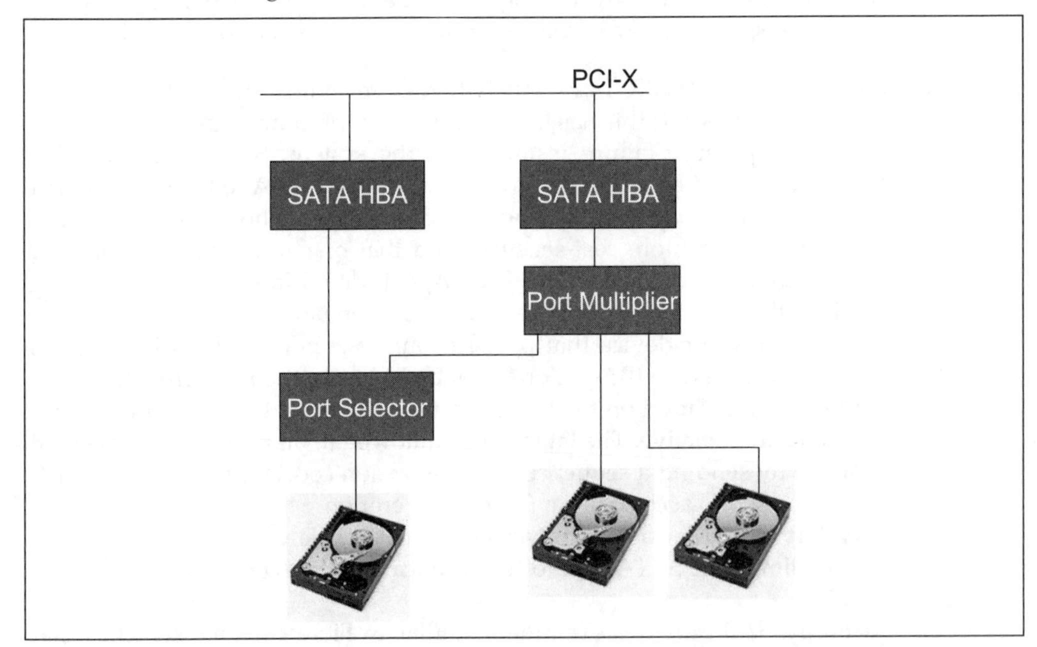

This discussion leads to a question: If SATA was able to solve the problems that limited its usefulness in servers and is lower cost than SAS, why not simply replace SCSI with SATA instead of SAS? Once again, the answer really involves two parts: the transport technology and the drives.

The SATA *transport* is designed to compete in the consumer market, so the design was kept simple and had to forego some features. For example, consider error reporting capability. SATA provides one 8-bit register for failure information, while a similar SCSI status record can be up to 18 bytes long. In addition, the transport is software-transparent with parallel ATA, so the bus inherits ATA's half-duplex protocol. The half-duplex bandwidth would be a performance constraint for systems that could queue up several commands on different drives and benefit from bi-directional traffic. By comparison, the SAS transport is full-duplex, supports all of the SCSI command sets, and is comparable in cost.

SATA *drives* offer the advantages of higher capacity and lower cost compared with SCSI. The off is a larger media for smaller actuators and magnets. Cost is also trimmed by reducing the size of the drive's write buffer. A SATA packet can be up to 8 KB in size and if the drive had to wait for all of the data to arrive and then check the CRC at the end to verify transmission accuracy it would need a buffer of that size. On the other hand, if the drive is allowed to commit the data to the media before it has all arrived, the buffer can be smaller. This does create a risk that a bad packet will be written to the media before the error is detected, but that trade-off is considered worth the cost savings. Disadvantages of SATA drives include:

- Drives are not dual-ported.
- Lower rotational frequencies result in longer seek times for random accesses.
- Lower MBTF (Mean Time Between Failures) - measured over 8-hours/day, 5 days/week operation.

By comparison, SAS drives have the following characteristics:

- Usually dual-ported.
- Fast seek times due to the smaller media that spins faster and has smaller actuators.
- Much higher MTBF — measured over 24-hours/day, 7 days/week operation.

This discussion can perhaps be summarized by observing that SATA is not a good replacement for SCSI. It would be cost-prohibitive to port existing SCSI code, and SATA drives do not support the performance or features that server drives typically require. On the other hand, the low cost of SATA drives, coupled with such server features as Port Selectors and Port Multipliers, make them attractive in situations where performance and reliability are less important than cost, leading to a logical mix of drive types as shown in Figure 2-12.

Figure 2-12: Flexible Storage Example

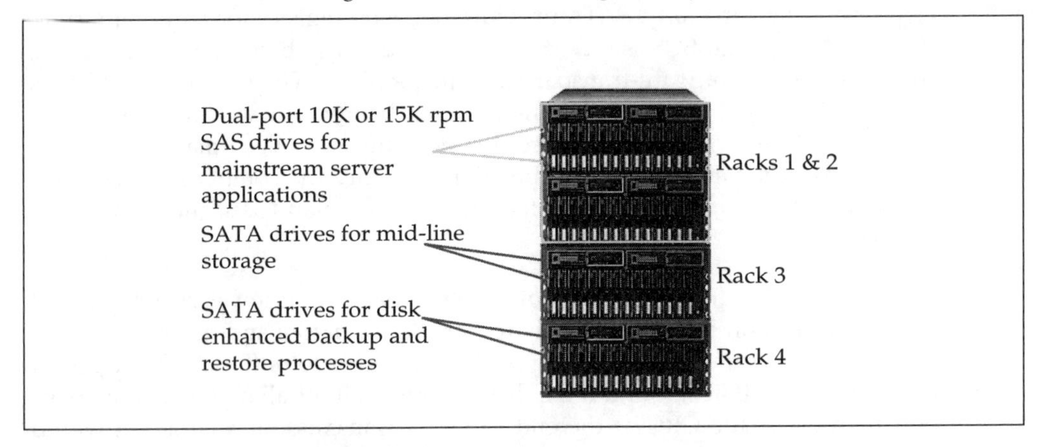

To achieve the best mix of alternatives, the SAS transport provides full compatibility with SATA drives. This allows support for both enterprise-class performance with SAS drives and low-cost storage with SATA drives in the same system. Since the cost of the SAS infrastructure is expected to be comparable to SATA, it seems likely that SAS will be preferred for the interface, and both types of drives will be used as needed by the system environment. This is attractive since it will simplify and standardize the storage infrastructure, allowing system administrators to change drive types as operating needs change, providing flexibility and opportunities for cost savings and innovation.

3 SAS Overview

The Previous Chapter

The previous chapter discussed the bus technology developments that motivated and led up to the development of SAS, noting that SAS borrowed ideas from serial transports like Fibre Channel and SATA to develop a next-generation enterprise storage architecture.

This Chapter

This chapter introduces the basic functions of SAS, explaining its method of operation from a very high level view. Terms are defined and examples presented to lay a foundation for understanding the basic operation of a SAS link. The layers of the SAS standard are introduced and their responsibilities and interaction are discussed.

The Next Chapter

The next chapter provides more definitions to facilitate a more detailed understanding of SAS link operation. The different types of devices and expanders are explored, leading to a discussion of topologies and domains, as well as a review of connections.

Comparison of SCSI and SAS Operation

SAS borrows from many I/O technologies, and those familiar with other serial protocols will find much that is similar in SAS. To understand SAS these people simply need to know which parts of a SAS system correspond to the parts of the transports they already know. Those familiar with SCSI will also find recognize many parts because SAS builds directly on the foundation of SCSI. Let's begin by looking at a parallel SCSI bus and describing the basics of its operation.

SCSI Example

Software Request

In Figure 3-1, a simple SCSI bus is illustrated with one initiator and several target devices. The host or client device runs an application program that requests service from a target (which acts as the server for those requests). To make the request, the client calls the SCSI device driver and the driver sends a command over the system I/O bus to the HBA, which is really just a bridge between the SCSI bus and the host system's bus.

Figure 3-1: Basic SCSI Bus Operation

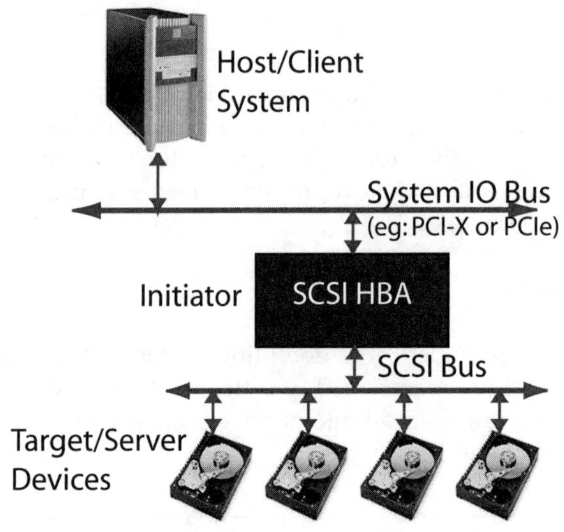

Host/Client System

System IO Bus (eg: PCI-X or PCIe)

Initiator

SCSI HBA

SCSI Bus

Target/Server Devices

Arbitration and Selection

The HBA, acting as the initiator, must use the shared SCSI bus to send the command. Since the bus is shared, arbitration is required to prevent more than one device from driving the bus at the same time. The initiator first needs to win the arbitration to be able to use the bus and may then select the target device. The SCSI protocol includes an arbitration phase and a selection phase for this purpose and the initiator drives its own ID for arbitration. If the initiator wins the arbitration, it next drives the target's ID to select that target for communication.

As an example, the ID for each SCSI device is typically just one out of 16 possibilities and is set in hardware with jumpers. SCSI ID values might be 7 for the initiator and 4 for the target.

Connection in Progress

Once a target is selected, it and the initiator both actively participate in the transaction and are said to be connected. When devices connect, they each store the ID of the other device for future reference (this is called establishing a nexus, which is the relationship between the initiator and target device). The nexus is useful to the target because it may choose to disconnect while servicing the request and then reconnect to the initiator later. To do that, it must know the initiator's device ID. The initiator needs the nexus because multiple targets might issue disconnects, causing it to have commands outstanding to several targets at the same time. When the responses are subsequently returned, it uses the nexus information to keep track of which target is responding.

Once a connection is established, the target takes control and decides when to transfer data for commands received from the initiator. Since SCSI is a half-duplex bus this means some handshaking is necessary for the initiator and target to take turns on the bus. The bus remains dedicated for the use of the two devices until the target releases it. Since the bus is shared, that means all other devices will have to wait until the current connection is shut down before the bus is again available. Several transfers might take place during the connection between the two devices but eventually the target will disconnect and the bus will then be free for other devices to use.

Wrapping Up

When the HBA has received the requested response from the target (such as read data) it informs the client that the command is completed. This would likely be done with an interrupt, that would invoke the device driver, which would report to the application client that the data is available in the appropriate buffer. The application would then fetch the data, completing that command sequence.

Corresponding SAS Structure: Simple Example

Now consider the simple SAS topology illustrated in Figure 3-2. SAS sets up and communicates in much the same way as SCSI, but with some differences.

Figure 3-2: Simple SAS Topology

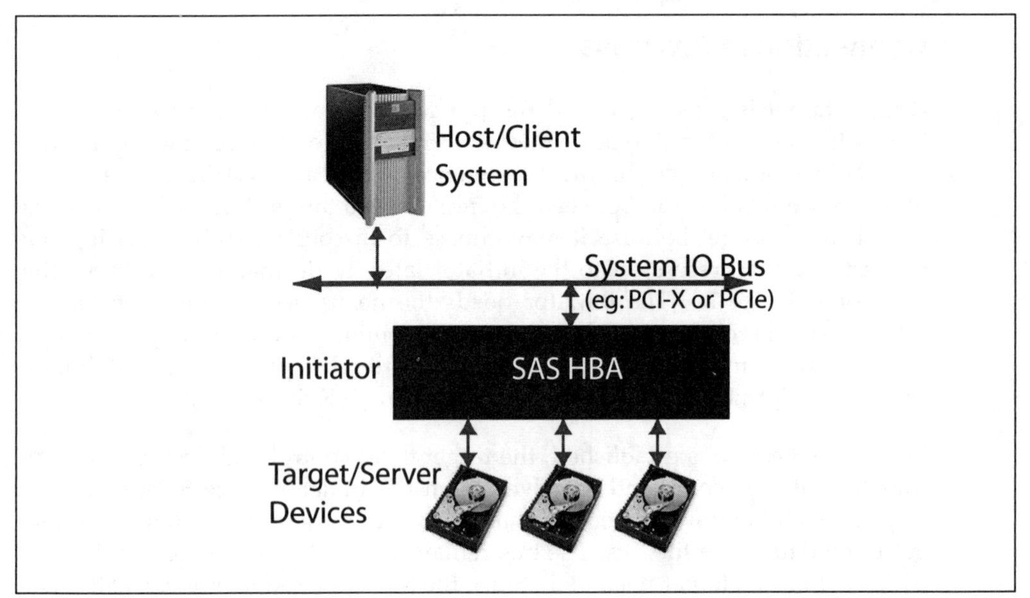

Definitions

SAS is a point-to-point bus and attaches two devices together. The connection points are referred to as *Ports* and every device will have at least one, while expanders and HBAs will likely have several. A Port can consist of just one *Phy* (the individual electrical interface to a link), or it may implement several. A Port that has only one Phy is called a *Narrow Port*, and a port that implements several is called a *Wide Port*. A *link* ties two Phys to each other and consists of one differential pair of wires for a transmit path and another pair for a receive path for a connection. As an illustration of wide and narrow ports, see Figure 3-3, showing an HBA with multiple Phys that might be set up either way.

Figure 3-3: Narrow and Wide Ports on an HBA

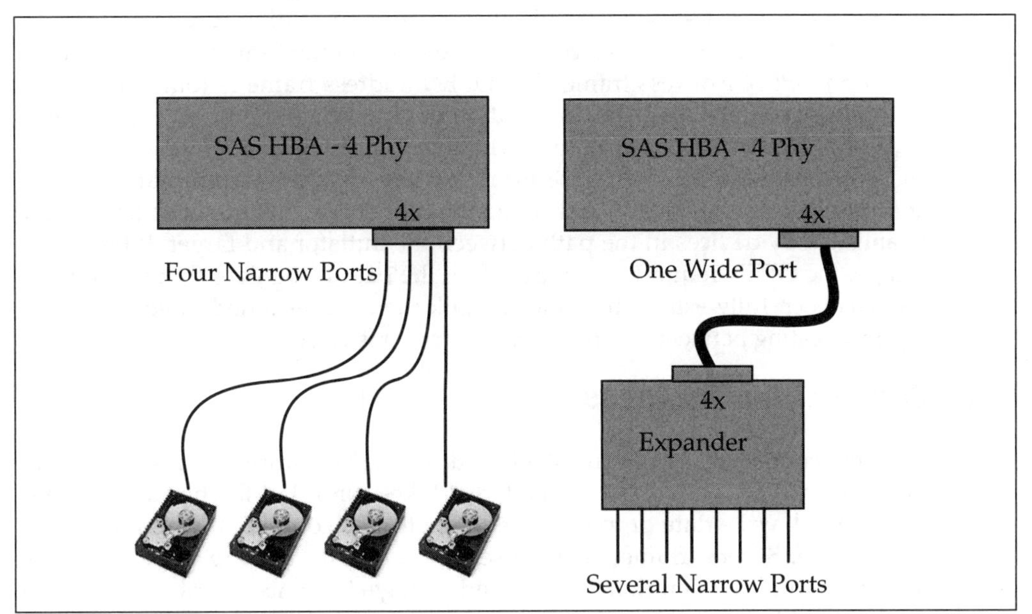

Arbitration and Selection

As before, the client sends a request to the driver which, in turn, forwards it to the HBA. The HBA in Figure 3-2 does not need to arbitrate for access to a shared bus because all the buses (links) are now point to point. However, to get service the HBA must still connect with the target. To do so it sends a connection request that includes the destination address, which is examined to determine to which Port the communication should be routed.

Each SAS device port is assigned a 64-bit SAS address, and requests are directed to a device based on its address. This address is assigned by the device manufacturer at the factory and is stored in hardware or firmware on the device. As part of the reset sequence, devices report this unique address to their link neighbor. Later, initiators execute a sequence of steps called the discovery process to read information from expanders and make a list of all the addresses accessible to them in the system (see Chapter 7, entitled "Discovery Process," on page 159). It is those addresses that are used to select a target device. To know which bus should be accessed for this request means the HBA also needs a mapping scheme to determine which addresses correspond to which bus. How this logic is implemented is vendor specific.

Establishing a Connection

Once the bus topology is known, a connection must be opened over it between the HBA and the destination device before communication can take place. To do that, the HBA port sends a connection request in the form of a special frame called an OPEN Address frame. The OPEN address frame is routed based on the address and arrives at the destination device. When the target receives this request, it responds by returning a primitive indicating that it either accepts or rejects the request. This response primitive has no address information and is not routed; it simply travels back along the connection that has been tentatively established by devices in the path between the initiator and target. If the target accepts the OPEN request, every device in the path recognizes that the connection has been fully established and the link then acts as a dedicated circuit for communicating between the two devices until it is closed.

Connection in Progress

Once the connection has been established, the nexus information is stored just as it was in SCSI. As with SCSI, the target takes control of the bus and decides when to pull write data or to send read data for the commands it receives from the initiator. Several frames may be sent in both directions, even at the same time (full-duplex operation is a big advantage for SAS), until one or both devices decide it's time to close the connection. Closing the connection when using SSP (Serial SCSI Protocol) involves having each device first indicate that it's done with the connection and then send a CLOSE primitive.

Wrapping Up

Just as with SCSI, when the HBA has received the requested response from the target (such as read data) it informs the client that the command is completed. This would likely be done with an interrupt that would invoke the device driver to report to the application client that the read data is available in the appropriate buffer. The application would then fetch the data, thereby completing the command sequence.

Concepts for a More Complex Structure

Consider the example of Figure 3-4, in which several HBAs and target devices are connected together with expanders (which are functionally similar to switches) to form a more complex network. The selection process becomes more interesting now because establishing a connection request between two devices may involve several intermediate devices as well. Before we can discuss the features that correspond to the SCSI model in this example, we'll need to cover a few more concepts.

Figure 3-4: Complex SAS Topology

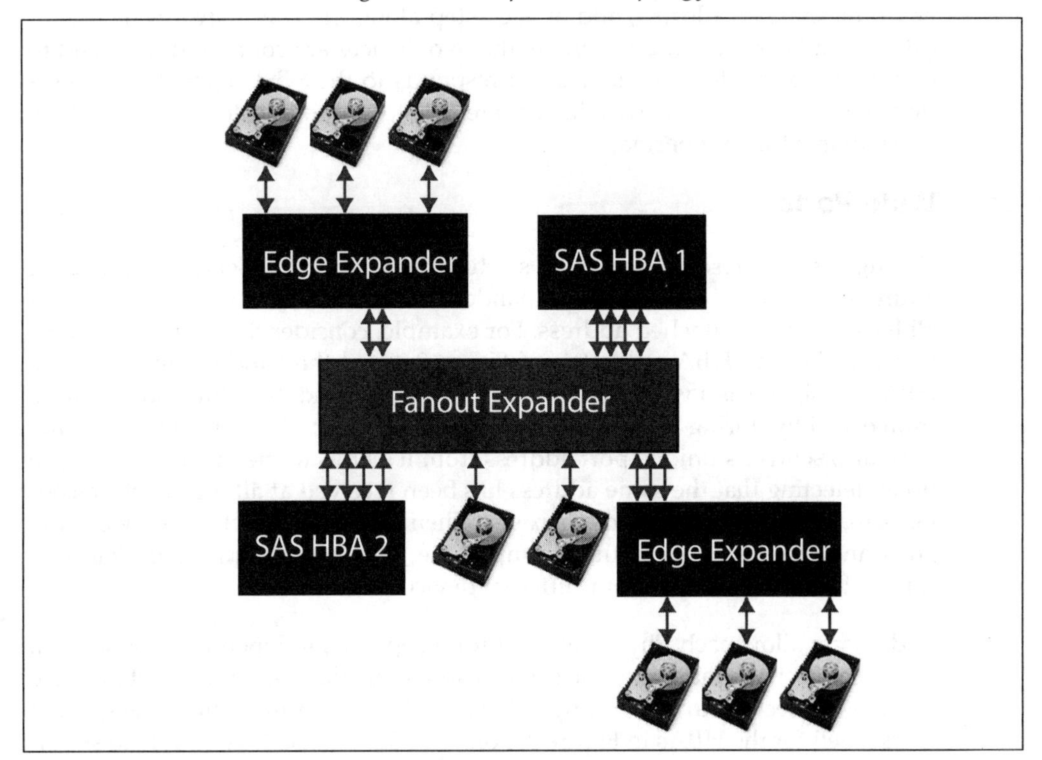

Routing the Requests

Most serial transports use point-to-point buses linked together through some form of routing device. The routing device in SAS is called an Expander which forwards service requests between the source and destination devices. Generally, there are two basic ways of accomplishing that:

- **Connection-based routing.** Devices establish a temporary dedicated path between the source and destination of the request. This yields the best latency for those devices but means others might have to wait for the connection to complete before they can get access.
- **Frame-based routing.** This method routes each individual packet one at a time. This avoids the problem of tying up the resources for a long time, but adds latency because the address of every packet must be evaluated for

routing.

The first method was chosen for SAS, most likely to help it adhere to its SCSI heritage as much as possible. Using this method, the devices route the request based on the SAS address, and at each step along the way they create a dedicated circuit connection until finally the two devices are connected from end to end with a dedicated circuit. This corresponds to the SCSI concept of connections very well, since the two devices are able to communicate as much as they like within a timeout period.

Wide Ports

During the link reset sequence at startup time, each Phy sends its SAS port address to its neighbor, allowing expanders to observe that several of their Phys all have the same attached address. For example, consider the four connections between the SAS HBA at the top of Figure 3-4 and the Fanout Expander. The HBA is designed as a wide port and therefore must send its unique port address from each Phy during link reset. The Fanout Expander, also designed as a wide port, also sends its unique port address from it's Phys to the HBA. Each device upon detecting that the same address has been received at all four ports, recognizes that a wide port connection exists. When making connections between the HBA and other devices in this example, the wide ports permit simultaneous connections to as many as four different devices.

Wide ports allow each Phy to be used for a separate, independent connection. Those connections may be to the same destination address, but it is not possible for one connection to use multiple Phys at the same time. This arrangement works well for the HBAs in Figure 3-4 on page 55 because they're able to simultaneously have several different connections in progress with the targets in the network.

Because of the potential for confusion on this point, let's reiterate a point made earlier: SAS does not allow multiple links to be used for one connection. Other architectures like PCI Express do allow this, and people familiar with those technologies may naturally suppose that SAS works the same way, but it doesn't. All communication in SAS happens across a connection, which is established as a dedicated circuit, or virtual wire, between one Phy in the requesting device and one Phy in the responding device.

Expanders

SAS expanders act like simple network switches that route connection request frames and then use connections to pass communication frames between devices. As illustrated in Figure 3-4 on page 55, there are two categories of expanders: Fanout expanders and Edge expanders.

- A SAS domain can only contain one Fanout Expander. By definition, a SAS domain is a tree structure and the Fanout Expander is the root of the tree. There are no devices that are hierarchically at a higher level. This type has to be able to keep track of all the possible addresses in the domain and consequently needs more memory for that purpose.
- Edge Expanders are simpler devices that can be cascaded to create more addressing possibilities. This expander type possesses a subtractive port, which is used as the default destination for any connection requests for which it cannot resolve the address. That means it doesn't need to track all the addresses in the network and can therefore be cheaper than a Fanout Expander.

Expanders receive connection requests on one Phy and attempt to establish an internal connection between that Phy and the destination Phy determined by examining the destination address of the request.

Corresponding SAS Structure: Complex Example

Arbitration and Selection

As before, the client sends a request to the driver which, in turn, forwards it to the HBA. HBA 1 in Figure 3-5 on page 58 sends a connection request onto the Port that it determines has a path to the destination address. In this case, because all of its Phys are attached to the same expander, any of them will be able to connect to any of the devices that are accessible to that expander.

Establishing a Connection

Consider the connection example in Figure 3-5. In this case, the connection request from HBA 1 arrives at the Fanout Expander, which informs the HBA that it has successfully received the request and is arbitrating the request by returning AIP (Arbitration In Progress). Next, it determines to which Port the request should be routed, and then forwards it onto that link. The next device in the path is an Edge Expander, and it behaves in much the same way. The edge expander next sends a confirmation that it is working on the request, which the Fanout Expander simply passes through to the originating device. Next, the Edge Expander determines the destination Port and forwards the request onto one of its links. Finally, the request reaches the targeted device and it sends a response.

Figure 3-5: Complex SAS Connection

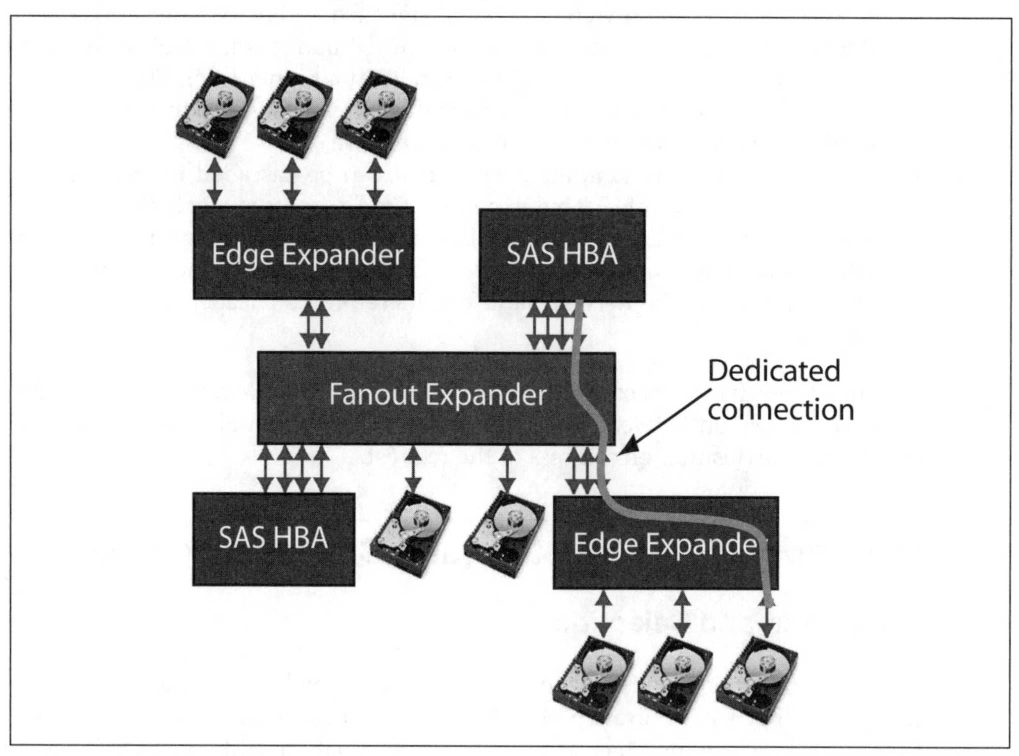

If the target accepts the request, the confirmation of that acceptance makes its way back through the connection that was tentatively established and informs the HBA that the connection has been established. The intermediate expanders also observe this fact and dedicate the internal resources to create a "virtual wire" between the HBA and the target device. At this point, the devices are connected. If the targeted device rejects the connection, the HBA will recognize the fact and the software will decide what to do next. Some connection requests can be retried, others cannot due to particular error conditions that the OPEN_REJECT primitive would specify as the reason for rejection. When the expanders see that the connection request was rejected, they break down the resources that were tentatively set up for the connection and free them for use by other devices.To help understand the sequence of these events, Figure 3-6 shows a ladder diagram illustrating the order of responses for each device. (To learn more of the details of expander operation, see Appendix A, entitled "Expander Devices" on page 505.)

Figure 3-6: Connection Request Ladder Diagram

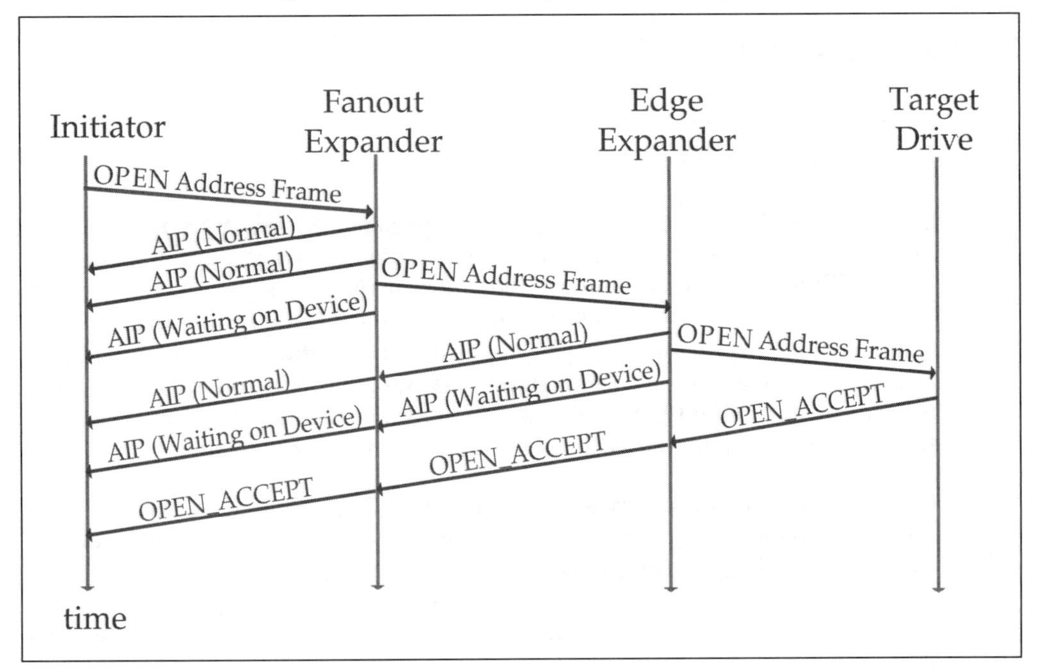

Connection in Progress and Wrapping Up

Once the connection has been established, the resources that provide a dedicated circuit between the HBA and target device remain allocated until the connection is closed. Since this HBA has several Phys, it could open connections to three other devices on its remaining three Phys and have four independent connections in progress at the same time. Beyond that, the process of exchanging information and operating on the bus is the same as for the simple example.

The Goal is to Communicate

The purpose of establishing a connection is to allow two devices to communicate. As we have seen, SAS maintains most of the SCSI protocol, but the serial interface introduces new requirements for sending commands and receiving corresponding responses. Since serial transports only send a bit at a time, the bits must be organized into logical groupings adhering to the format defined by the applicable standard. Some serial transports refer to these as *packets*; in SAS they are called *frames*. Establishing a connection allows two devices to exchange the frames that are used to send commands and the corresponding responses.

Example Scenario — Disk Read Request

Introduction to Operation

To connect with another device in order to exchange frames, SAS devices must execute several steps. The responsibility for implementing the logic necessary to perform those steps is split into smaller, more manageable parts called *layers* in the standard. Since the naming and function of the SAS layers has proven to be confusing to otherwise very intelligent people, the author has taken the liberty of giving the layers some "user-friendly" names for this introduction that more intuitively state what they do. The actual layer names are defined at the end of this section and are then used throughout the remainder of the book.

Consider the very simple case shown in Figure 3-7, where a SAS HBA is connected to a target device through a SAS fabric. The fabric could be any legal SAS topology, including several expanders between these two devices, but those details are not important at this point in the discussion. The steps that take place in the communication between the two devices are described in the sections that follow.

Figure 3-7: Diagram with User-Friendly Layer Names

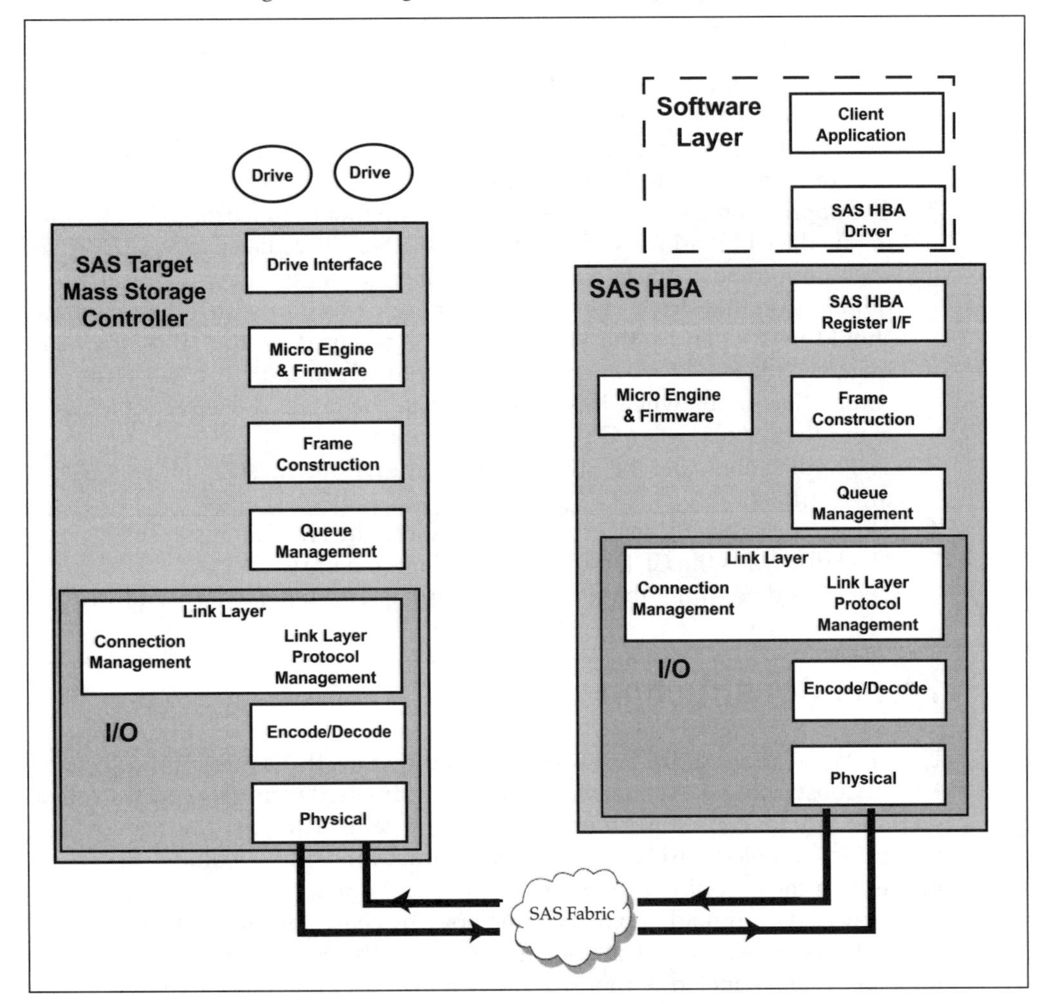

Software Layer

To begin with, an application program running on the client system requests service from a service provider (i.e., a SAS device that acts as the provider of one or more services). If we choose a disk read request for our example, this will be accomplished in the following manner.

1. The client application (e.g., a database program) issues a request to the memory allocator within the OS (i.e., malloc) requesting the allocation of three buffers in memory:
   a) A buffer in which the application will write a Command Descriptor Block (i.e., a data structure) defining the operation to be performed.
   b) A buffer into which the HBA will write the requested read data when it is received from the target.
   c) A buffer into which the HBA will write the completion status when it is received from the target device.
2. The application then writes the CDB into the first buffer. The CDB contents define the 64-bit address of the target disk controller, the specific LUN (logical unit number) attached to that controller, the start and end logical block numbers on that drive, the start memory address into which the read data should be written by the HBA when it is received by the HBA, the start memory address of the memory buffer into which the HBA will write the completion status when it is received from the target device and the command (in this case, it's a Disk Read operation).
3. The application calls the HBA driver and gives it the start address of the three buffers.
4. The driver writes those three parameters into the HBA's register set.
5. The HBA reads the CDB data structure from memory.
6. The HBA determines that one of its ports has a path to the target address.

Frame Construction

Under the guidance of the firmware executed by the HBA's microcontroller, the Frame Construction Layer creates a properly-formatted command packet called a Frame. Frames consist of groups of four bytes called dwords. The term dword is short for double-word, the Intel nomenclature for a 4-byte value. After bytes go through the encoding process, they are referred to as characters, and Figure 3-8 shows a dword made up of 4 characters. The characters are classified as one of two types, either control characters (labeled with a K in the nomenclature) or data characters (labeled with a D). The completed Frame will be forwarded to the queue management level.

Figure 3-8: Dword

first	second	third	fourth
character	character	character	character

Queue Management

At this level, outgoing frames are pooled into groups based on the destination address for which they are intended. When frames for a given address begin to arrive and get queued up, this layer sends a request to the Link Layer within an I/O block to open a connection to the destination device.

Link Layer

Connection Management Creates Open Request Frame

If the I/O block is not already busy managing an existing connection, the Connection Management logic creates a special frame (i.e. a packet) that requests a connection be opened, and forwards it to the Encode/Decode block. Recall that the connection request establishes a connection between the HBA and the target device. The request consists of an Open Request Frame that is routed by address to the target device. When the target device returns a response the hardware allocates the necessary resources to establish the dedicated connection.

Protocol Management

The Open Request frame is subject to the Link Layer Protocol Management logic. Part of the protocol management involves the creation of primitives that perform special functions such as signifying the beginning and end of each Frame. Most of these primitives are generated by the Link Layer of the sender and consumed by the Link Layer of the receiver.

Figure 3-9: Primitives

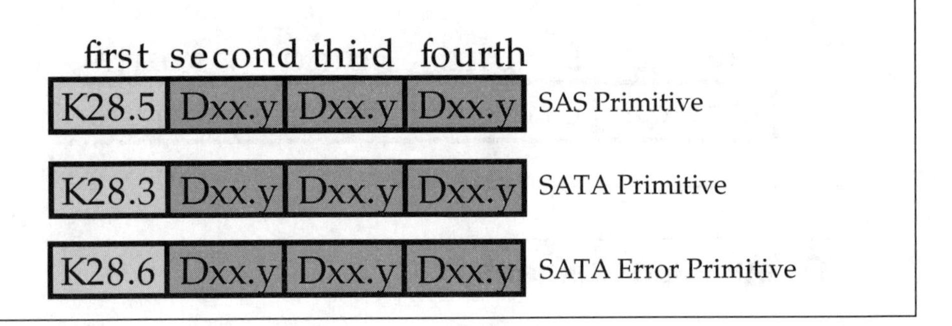

Primitives are easily recognized because they have a special control character in the first byte position (known as a control character), as shown in Figure 3-9, which illustrates both SAS and SATA primitives. For more details on primitives see the section called "Primitives" on page 284. The next step in the process is delivering the Open Request frame to the Encode/Decode block.

Encode/Decode Layer

In the Encode/Decode block various actions are taken to prepare the OPEN address frame for serial transmission. These steps are common to many serial transports, including 8b/10b encoding and bit-serializing of the frame.

Physical Layer

Finally, the serialized OPEN request frame arrives at the lowest layer, called the Physical Layer, where the electrical input and output buffers and transceivers reside. Here the bits are converted to the high-speed differential output and sent out across a cable or backplane.

OPEN Request and Response

When the OPEN request is transmitted to the neighboring device (see Figure 3-10), the high-speed bit sequence is presented to the receiver in the neighbor's Physical Layer. The incoming differential signal is used to recreate the transmitted bit stream, which is then presented to the Encode/Decode logic. At this level the logic decodes the data to recover the original dword stream and then forwards it up to the Connection Management logic. There, the recovered information is evaluated and determined to be a request to open a connection to the port on the target device. If the mass storage controller's upper layers have enabled it and if the requester is recognized as having permission to seek a connection with this device, then the Connection Management logic accepts the connection request and sends an ACCEPT primitive back to the requester.

Figure 3-10: OPEN Frame and Response

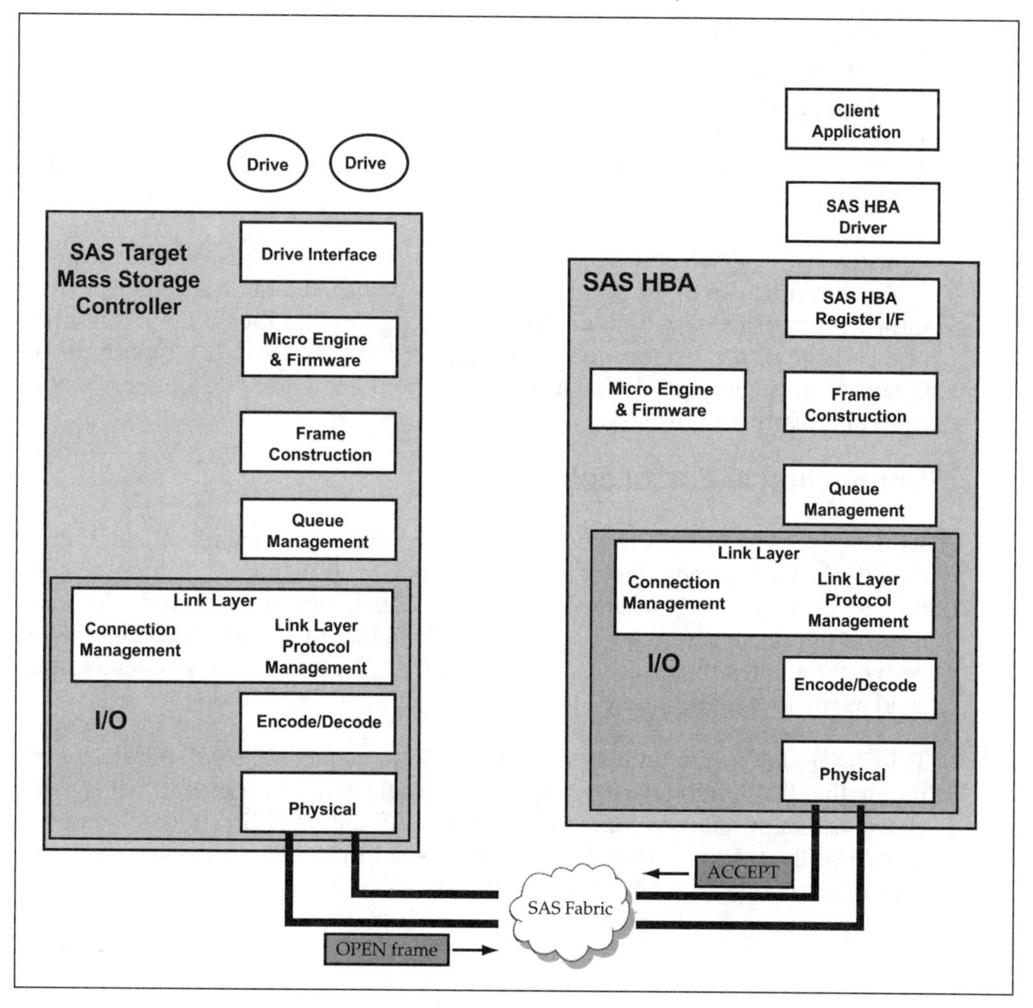

Accept Response Primitive Generated

The Connection Management layer creates an ACCEPT primitive and forwards it to the Encode/Decode logic. That layer encodes and serializes the data before passing it to the Physical Layer. The Physical Layer transmits the bit stream using its high-speed differential transmitter.

When this response arrives at the Connection Management logic in the HBA, a nexus between the two ports has been created. The nexus information can contain up to four parts, depending on the type of connection:

- Initiator port (I)
- Target port (T)
- The selected LUN (L)
- The tag of the task to be executed (labeled as Q because it's part of a Queued set of tasks)

A nexus that uses all four is described as an I_T_L_Q nexus, which means it stores the addresses of the initiator and target device, the LUN and the tag. This information is saved by both devices. In recognition that the OPEN request has been accepted, the Connection Management logic in the HBA reports to its Queue Management block that a connection to the intended destination is now open and ready for business.

Connection Is Established

At this point, the HBA is ready to forward the frame(s) currently queued up in the Queue Management block to the I/O block for transmission. Once the connection is established, whatever topology exists between the two devices has now become transparent and it appears to them that they have a dedicated wire between them (as illustrated in Figure 3-11). At this point, the two devices can send as many frames as they like within their timeout period on the bus.

This discussion began with an initiator having a request to send, but it's worth noting that the target device could also have data ready to transmit that is associated with a previous command. Since the SAS link is bidirectional, the target could use the newly-opened connection to send those data frames at the same time that it is receiving a new command.

Figure 3-11: Connection Establishes a Dedicated Path Between Devices

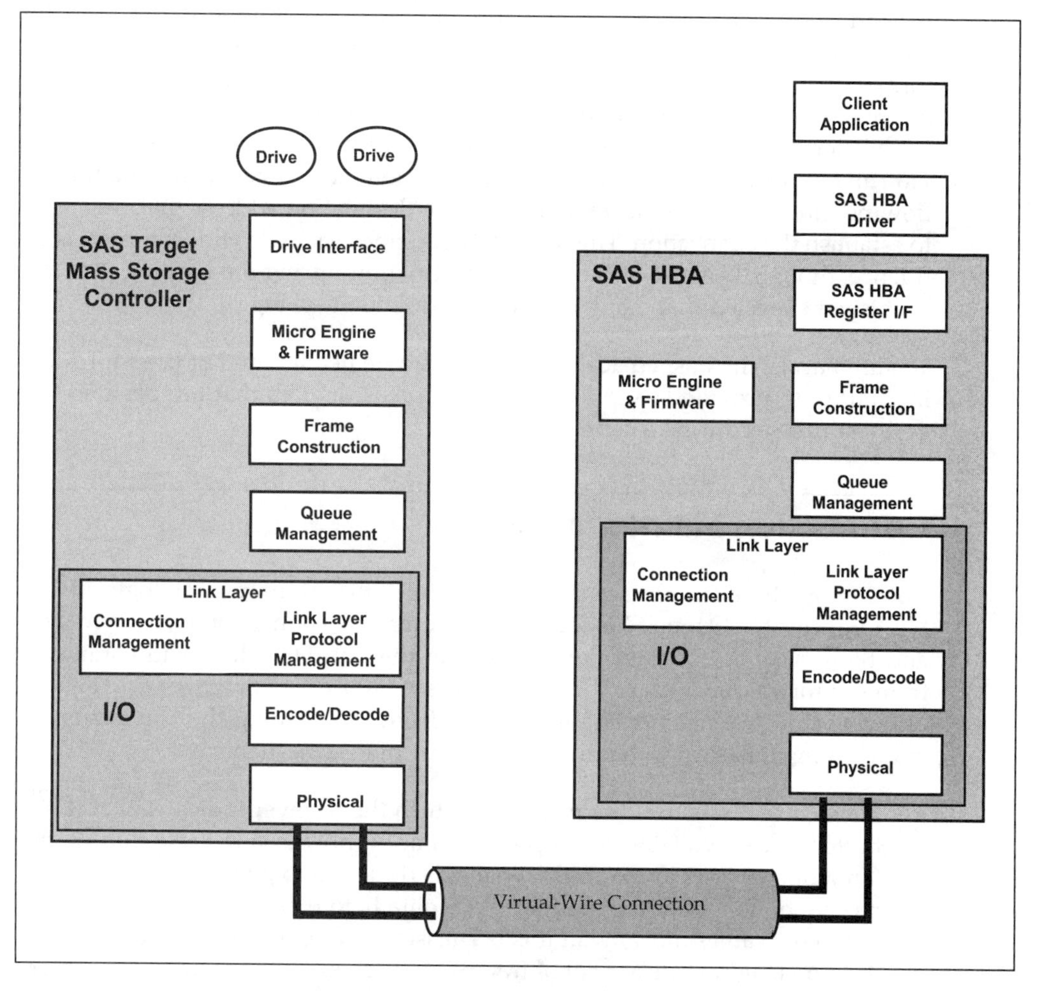

Frames Travel Connected Path (They're Not Routed)

The frames sent within a connection do not experience any "routing" per se, because determining the path from the source device to the destination device was already done when the connection was opened. Instead, they flow from source to destination through what is now a dedicated circuit.

The frames themselves do include a hashed version of the source and destination address, leading to some confusion that perhaps these addresses are used to route the packets themselves, but that is not the case. In fact, the hashing function that's used to reduce the address from 64 bits to just 24 bits causes some loss of information, so it is not a reliable version of the addresses anyway. Instead, hashed addresses are only provided for the simple reason that the space for a small destination and source address already existed in the header format that was borrowed from Fibre Channel (Fibre Channel uses 24-bit addresses and does provide for packet routing). Since the bits were already in the header, some vendors lobbied to have the addresses used in this way to provide an opportunity for devices in the connection path to verify that the frames flowing through it are in fact using the same destination address that was used to establish the connection. This verification cannot be made with complete confidence, though, because of the loss of information during the hashing process, so it is not expected that many devices will do this checking.

To summarize, the hashed addresses in the frame header are not used for routing, but only provided as a "courtesy" for those devices that are designed to verify addresses during a connection.

Connection Maintenance

Continuing the example scenario, the Connection Management logic in the HBA informs the Queue Management block that the connection is ready for use and the first of the queued data frames (in this case, the disk read command frame) is forwarded back to the I/O block (see Figure 3-12 on page 69). The role of connection management changes now, from establishing the connection to maintaining it. Basically, that involves the use of two mechanisms:

- Flow control which is the means by which the receiver indicates that it has buffer space available to receive a frame. With the one exception of the "first burst" case, in which the system is designed to guarantee a minimum receive buffer space for the first write data before any flow control is sent, outgoing frames must await this permission before they can be sent.
- Acknowledging safe arrival of frames at the receiver. Most frames are interlocked, meaning they must await the successful acknowledgement of the previous frame's reception before they may be transmitted. In our example, no previous data frames have been sent, so no acknowledgement is needed.

Figure 3-12: Command Frame Sent to the Target

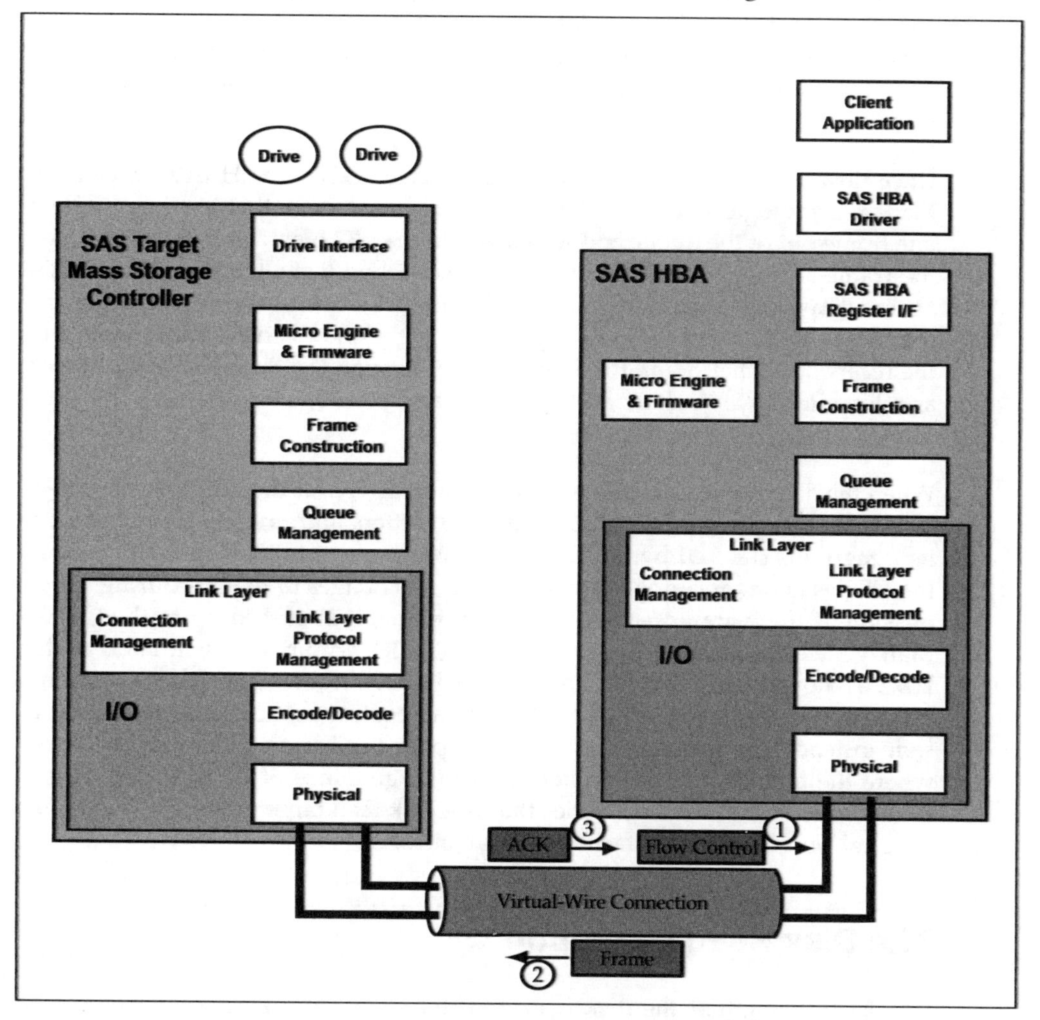

Data Frame Transmittal and Reception

Flow control is handled a little differently depending on what type of transaction is being executed. For a write, the initiator (e.g.: HBA) must wait on the target (e.g.: a mass storage device) to indicate both that it has buffer space to accept write data, and that it is ready to accept one or more frames. For reads, it's assumed that the initiator has allocated the necessary buffer space before sending the command and the only flow control needed is an indication of readiness to accept frames. For our example, once the HBA sends a flow control frame indicating that it's ready for data frames, these conditions are satisfied. This flow control information is only generated and used by the connection management logic within the initiator and target Phys, and is transparent to the higher layers.

Once flow control verifies sufficient buffer space exists, the HBA's Connection Management logic signals the Queue Management block that it's time to drain one frame out of the queue and forward it to the I/O block for transmission. As the frame is being loaded into the Encode/Decode logic, the connection management layer adds an SOF (Start of Frame) primitive at the beginning of the frame and an EOF (End of Frame) primitivc at the end to give a frame context to the receiver. At that point, the frame is sent through the Encode/Decode block and Physical Layer buffers and is transmitted serially over the wire (as illustrated in Figure 3-12 on page 69).

When the data frame containing the command arrives at the target mass storage controller and passes through the physical buffers and Encode/Decode block, its integrity is checked by the Connection Management block by verifying that the CRC is good, meaning there have been no changes to the bits during transmission. If there are no errors within the frame, it is passed up to the Queue Management block and an acknowledge (ACK) primitive is sent back to the HBA acknowledging that the frame arrived safely. If there had been a problem, the frame would have been discarded and a negative acknowledgement (NAK) sent instead. The frame is next passed up to the Frame Construction block, where the target's microcontroller, under the guidance of its firmware, disassembles the frame and determines that is a disk read targeting one of the LUNs (Logical Unit Numbers) attached to this controller.

The Disk Read Operation

It is fairly likely that the disk read will require a repositioning of the drive's read/write head assembly and this mechanical action will take a long time compared to the frame transmission. In that case, the target SAS mass storage controller device would likely choose to close the connection rather than leaving it open and preventing other devices from being able to use the connection resources during that time. For simplicity, however, let's assume that the device is able to fetch the data quickly (perhaps from a read-ahead cache within the controller, for example).

The Read Data Is Returned in a Data Frame

The first block of read data is placed in a data frame and is transmitted back to the HBA. The header of the data frame includes the context for this transaction, including the amount of data and the tag associated with the command that resulted in this data.

The HBA Processes the First Read Data Frame

Upon reception, the HBA's firmware-based microcontroller looks up the start address of the data buffer in system memory based on the tag value, and writes the read data to memory. It decrements the overall read data transfer count, but the transfer count hasn't yet been exhausted. The memory address pointer is updated to point to the next available location in the memory data buffer.

The Final Read Data Frame Is Returned and Processed

The target mass storage controller continues to read data from the target LUN, packetizes the data into frames and sends them back to the HBA. The HBA continues to write the returned read data to memory until the final frame is returned and the transfer count is exhausted.

The Connection Is Closed

Finally, the last step for the two devices is to close the connection. The HBA's Connection Management logic causes a DONE primitive to be transmitted to the target port on the mass storage controller. Upon receipt of the DONE, the Connection Management logic in the mass storage controller causes a matching DONE to be transmitted back to the HBA. Upon receipt of DONE, the HBA's Connection Management logic sends a CLOSE primitive. The target also sends a CLOSE, because the devices don't have to wait for CLOSE before they send it. Once the devices have both sent and received CLOSE, the resources are released and become available for other connections.

Completion Status Is Written to Memory

The HBA's firmware-guided microcontroller causes the disk read operation's completion status to be written into the system memory buffer using the stored memory address pointer.

The Client Application Is Notified

The HBA's firmware-guided microcontroller then generates an interrupt to the host system processor, causing the processor to execute the interrupt handler within the HBA Device Driver. The handler reads a status register within the handler and determines that a completion notification has been deposited in memory. The driver reads this information and, using an application ID stored with the status completion notice, it contacts the client application program and informs it that the requested read data has successfully been deposited in memory. The application then consumes (i.e., uses) the data.

Summarizing the Sequence

To summarize the sequence of the frames and primitives that are exchanged in this process, consider the ladder diagram shown in Figure 3-13. Here the connection has already been established and now the flow control aspect of the connection is illustrated. If the connection was opened by the initiator, the first thing that needs to happen is that the target needs to send at least one flow control credit to the initiator so it can receive the command frame. This is done by sending an RRDY (Receiver Ready) primitive. Several of these can be sent to tell the initiator that several buffers are available for data transfer, but in this example, only the one is needed. (for more on this topic, see "Flow Control" on page 346). In response, the initiator sends the command and follows that with several RRDY primitives to indicate a readiness to accept several frames coming back.

Figure 3-13: SSP Read Request Example

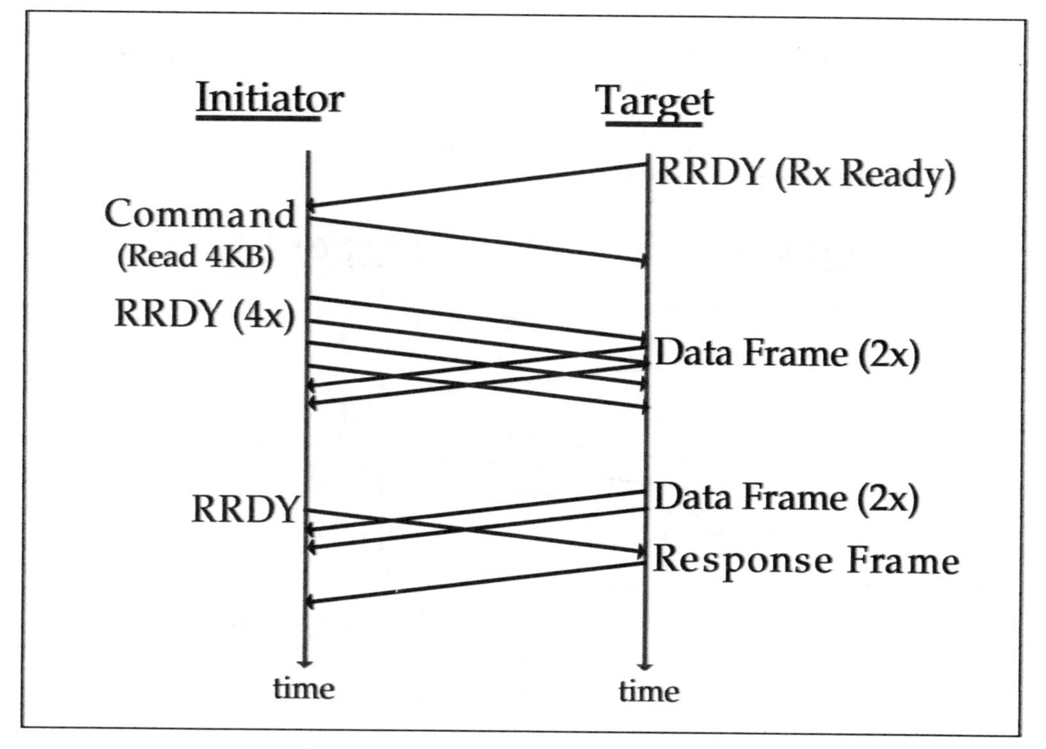

The target responds to the read request and the indications of available buffer space in the initiator by sending data frames. If the read was asking for 4KB of data, as shown in the example, the target would need to send at least 4 data frames to complete the transfer, because each of them can only be 1KB at most for SSP. Once all the data has been received, the initiator would expect to receive a response frame from the target, reporting on the status of the operation. That would require permission, in the form of an RRDY, so one more must be sent before the response frame can be expected.

Example Scenario — Disk Write Request

A similar case is shown in Figure 3-14, but this time the command is a write. As before, the connection is already open, so what is shown here are the command and data frames, along with the flow control exchange. Like the read example, a frame can't be sent unless an RRDY was first received to give it permission to be sent. The difference in this example is that the target has one more frame type it sends: the XFER_RDY frame. Each RRDY primitive sent indicates that the receiver can accept one frame, which means it must have a 1KB frame buffer available since the frame could legally be that large. The XFER_RDY frame is used to report how much overall buffer space is available in the target to accept write data from the initiator.

Figure 3-14: SSP Write Request Example

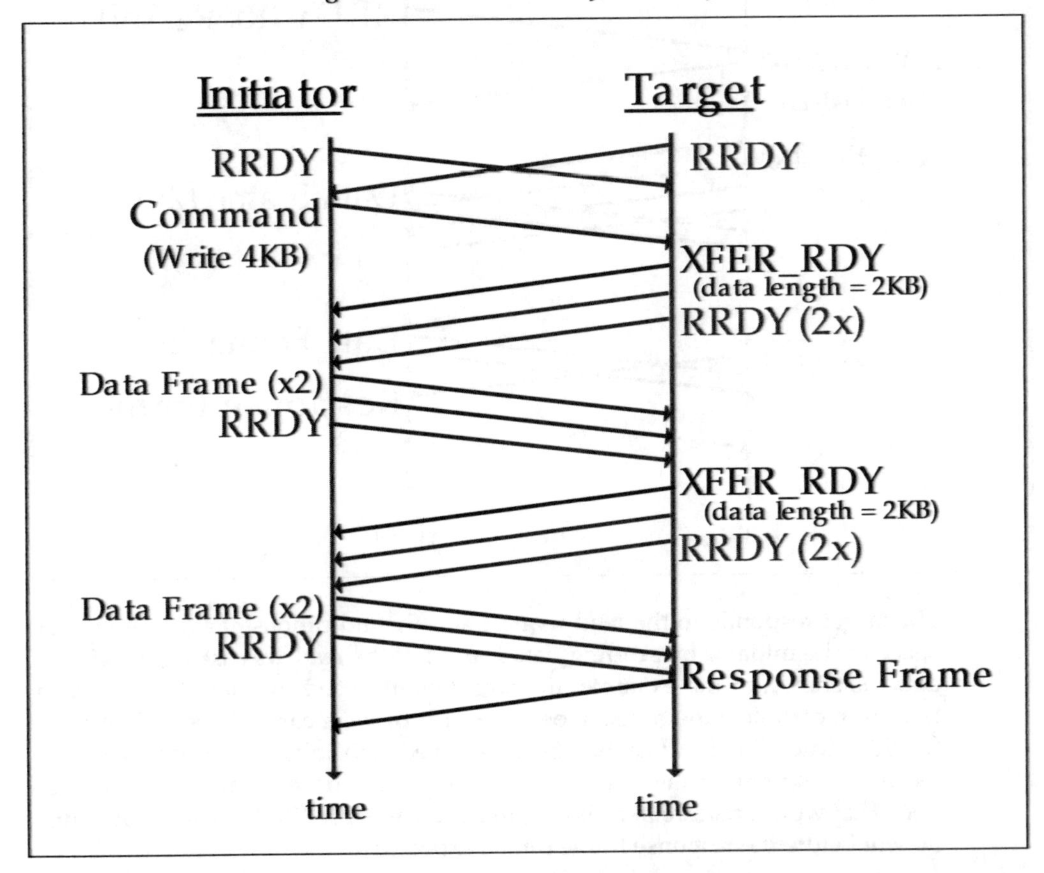

This information does seem to overlap a little, but the initiator cannot begin to send the write data until it receives an XFER_RDY specifying that at least part of the needed space is available. The reason this information is not needed for the read command is because the initiator is expected to have sufficient buffer space available before sending the request, so that should never be an issue. This example is described in detail in "Flow Control" on page 346.

The Real Layer Names

Having described the parts of a SAS device in terms of their functions, let's now look at the actual layer definitions, as shown in Figure 3-15, as the standard defines and uses them. Since more parts of the system are shown than just those that make up the SAS layers, the SAS layer names are highlighted.

Figure 3-15: Actual SAS Layer Names

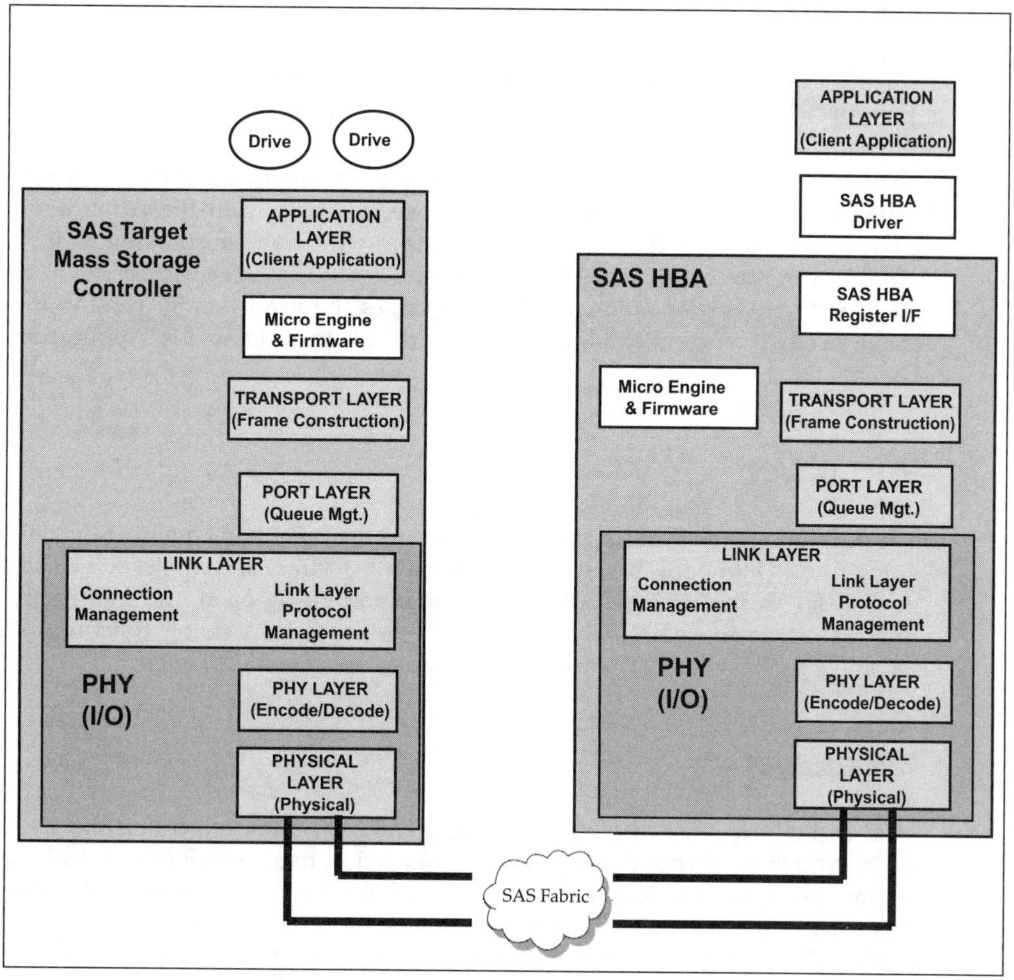

Application Layer

Starting at the top, the official name for the software layer is the Application Layer. For this layer the standard defines just the changes that were made to the SCSI mode and log pages in support of the serial interface. These pages provide configuration information about the devices, including control parameters and status, just as they do for SCSI devices. This layer translates the command from the device driver into the procedure call format that SCSI uses and passes that to the next layer.

Transport Layer

The logic that performs the frame construction function is called the Transport Layer. In essence, it receives outgoing procedure calls from the Application Layer and repackages the various arguments into the frame format that will be used for serial transmission. When the frame is ready it's forwarded down to the next layer. For incoming packets it reverses the processes by parsing the frame contents and assembling a procedure call to send to the Application Layer.

Port Layer

The next layer is the Port Layer, and it performs the function of queuing the outgoing frames into pools based on the destination address and requesting a connection for them. Once a connection to that address is open, the frames are drained out to the next layer. There really is no corresponding function for incoming frames; these are simply passed up to the Transport Layer.

Link Layer

Next is the Phy, consisting of three layers. The first of these layers is the Link Layer, which performs the function of connection management as described before. It receives a request for a connection from the Port Layer and takes the necessary actions to establish the connection on the wire. Once the connection is in place, this layer then has the responsibility to manage it by injecting primitives into the flow as needed and verifying flow control and acknowledgement of frames for the protocol being used. For incoming traffic the Link Layer responds to a connection request by accepting or rejecting it and, if accepted, it manages the connection operation in the same way as before.

Phy Layer

The next level is the Phy Layer and there's no doubt the nomenclature gets a little confusing at this point. That's one reason the layers were introduced with functional names instead of the names the standard uses. The Phy Layer resides within a block called the phy, and implements the Encode/Decode functions for sending and receiving the frames.

Physical Layer

At the lowest level of the hierarchy are the high-speed analog buffers that perform the differential signaling onto the transmission medium. For this layer, the standard defines both the electrical characteristics of the buffers and the signaling environments they drive.

4 Device Types and Topologies

The Previous Chapter

The previous chapter introduced the basic functions of SAS, explaining its method of operation from a very high level view. Terms are defined and examples presented to lay a foundation for understanding the basic operation of a SAS link. The layers of the SAS standard are introduced and their responsibilities and interaction are discussed.

This Chapter

This chapter provides more definitions to facilitate a detailed understanding of SAS link operation. The different types of devices and expanders are explored, leading to a discussion of topologies and domains, as well as a review of connections.

The Next Chapter

The next chapter begins with the necessary background to understand the architecture of narrow versus wide ports. It then describes the layered architecture of devices, which behave differently depending on whether the device uses narrow or wide ports. Next, details of the layered architecture within a narrow port are presented, and the final section describes the layer implementations of wide ports.

Introduction

Prior to discussing the various SAS device types and topologies, there are several terms and concepts used in the discussion of SAS that need a brief introduction. These are presented here in what is considered enough depth to facilitate understanding of the issues discussed in this chapter.

SAS Address

Each Phy has a SAS address assigned to it at the factory. The addresses used in SAS are 64-bit units that consist of three parts, as listed here (see also Figure 4-1):

- A 4-bit identifier assigned by the Naming Address Authority. This value is the same for SAS and Fibre Channel, which is 5.
- An IEEE-assigned 24-bit company ID
- A 36-bit Vendor-Specific Identifier

Figure 4-1: SAS Address

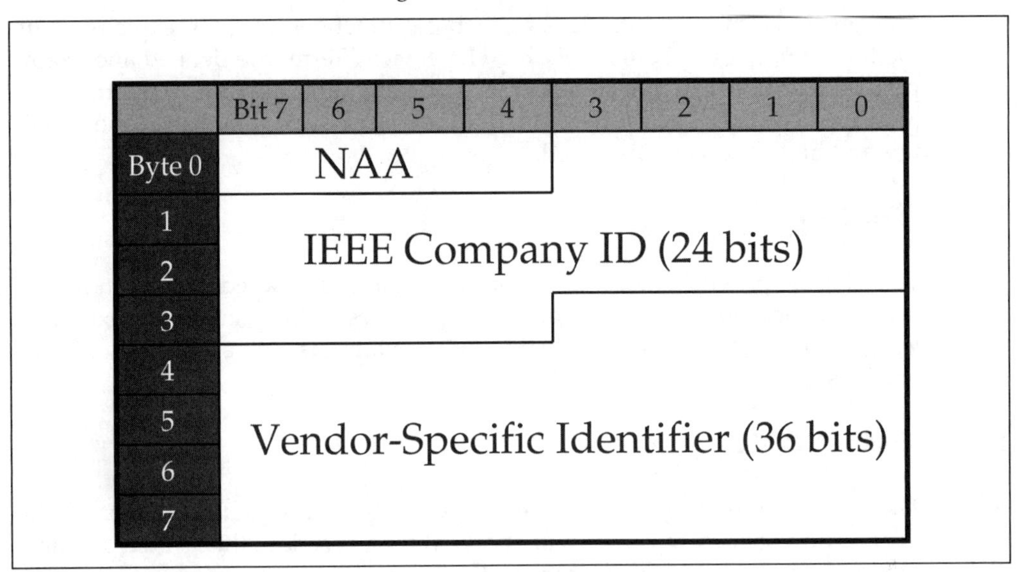

Phy - The Interface to the Fabric

Enlarging on the Phy and Port definitions, it's helpful to note that the Phy is the logic that includes the transceiver that sends and receives the bits on the wire. When two devices are attached it creates a *link*, as shown in Figure 4-2. A link consists of a send path and receive path together and is described as being full-duplex because it allows transmission in both directions at the same time.

Figure 4-2: SAS Phy and Link Example

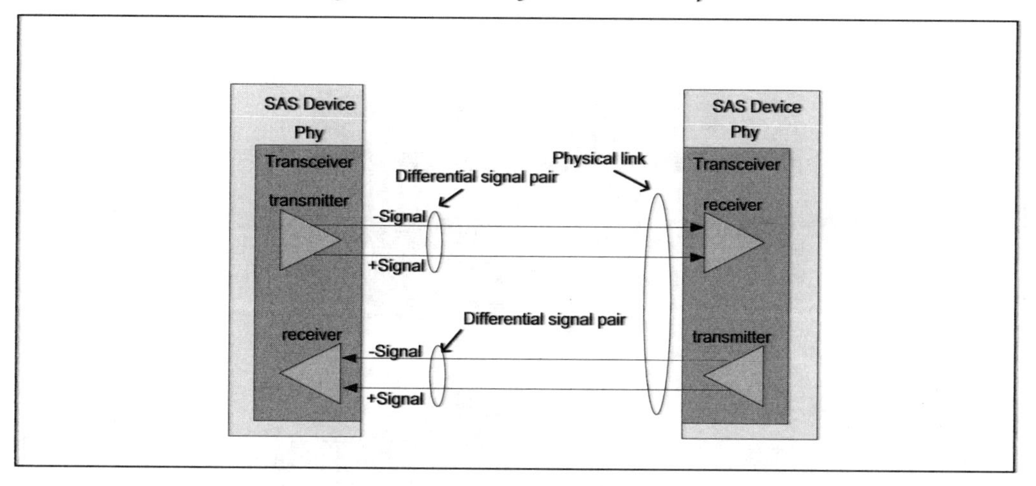

The transmitters and receivers use differential signaling because it provides improved noise immunity and signal integrity (see Chapter 17, entitled "Physical Layer," on page 411). Few parallel interfaces could afford to use differential, in spite of its advantages, because the double pin count it imposes per signal would make them too expensive. Serial designs, however, have fewer pins and need the lower voltages differential offers to reduce the power that would otherwise be required by the very high switching speeds involved.

End Devices

There are two types of SAS devices: end devices and expanders. According to the standard, a device that's not an expander, such as a disk drive, tape drive, or HBA, is an end device. End devices act as initiators or targets and do not have the ability to forward transactions to other devices. Disk drives are an example of an end device and might be directly attached to an HBA or they could be indirectly attached through an expander, as shown in Figure 4-3.

Figure 4-3: Direct and Expander-Attached Devices

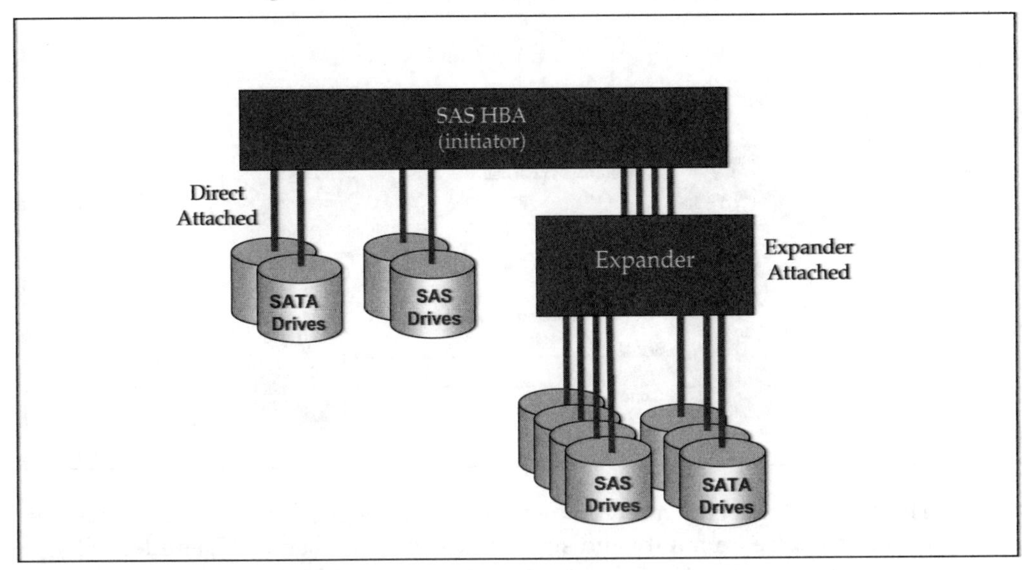

Expander Devices

Expanders provide a function similar to switches in Fibre Channel by allowing a system to scale. They can also save cost because they provide the ability to connect more drives to an HBA than its ports can directly support and expander ports are expected to be inexpensive compared to HBA ports (see Appendix A, entitled "Expander Devices" on page 505 for more on expanders). Expanders fall into one of two broad classes: Edge expanders designed for relatively simple routing, and Fanout expanders intended for more extensive connection routing possibilities. Each type is introduced later in this section. First, the fundamental functions of expanders are discussed.

Expander's Crossbar Function

Expanders contain several components including expander Phys and an expander function that acts as a crossbar switch to allow routing of SAS connections between the phys. To illustrate the concept of a crossbar switch to those who may be new to it, consider Figure 4-4, which shows a model of the internal circuitry. Basically, the switch provides a path between any two Phys. There are six Phys in the example, so there could be at most three connections in progress at one time, and the potential paths for those are shown by the vertical lines that represent a bi-directional link (two differential wire pairs). The conceptual means for making such a connection is to gate the signal from the source Phy onto one of the internal wire pairs and then gate it from the other wire of that pair to the destination Phy.

Figure 4-4: CrossBar Switch Conceptual Diagram

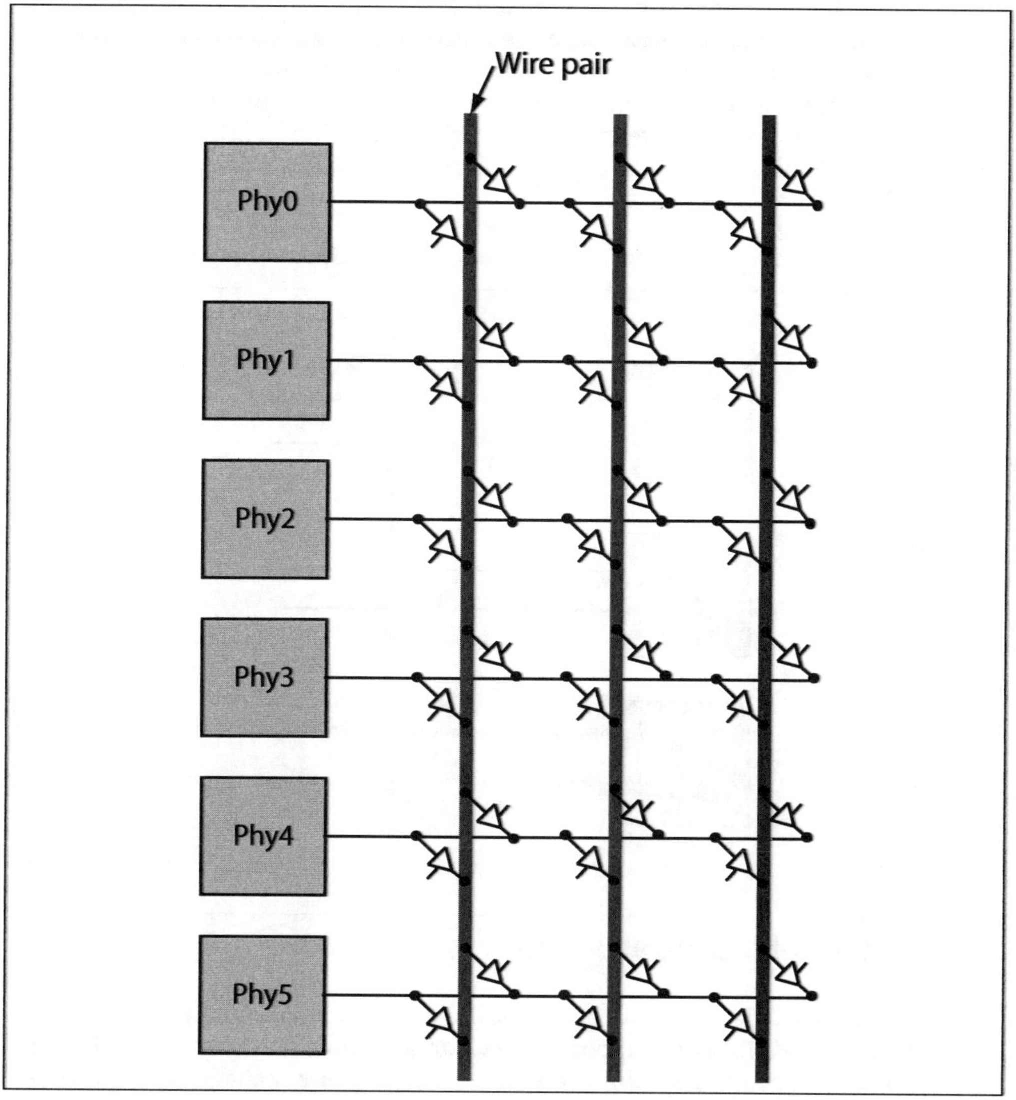

It is a two-step process to establish the connection for an expander. First, the incoming request is accepted and routed to the destination Phy. Second, the response comes into the destination Phy and is routed back to the source Phy. Once the request has been sent and the response shows that it was accepted, the two Phys are connected to each other with only the gates in the path delaying the bidirectional signals. The expander makes the path across it appear transparent between the Phys.

Figure 4-5 illustrates Phy1 connected to Phy3 with the bi-directional link now shown in more detail as two separate differential paths. Now it can be seen that the wider vertical lines actually represent a pair of wires. The gates provide both a transmit and a receive path to allow frames to flow both directions at once (the closed gates are circled to highlight them). In addition, it's easier to see in this illustration that any Phy of the expander can be connected to any other Phy.

Figure 4-5: Connected Path Between Source and Destination Phy

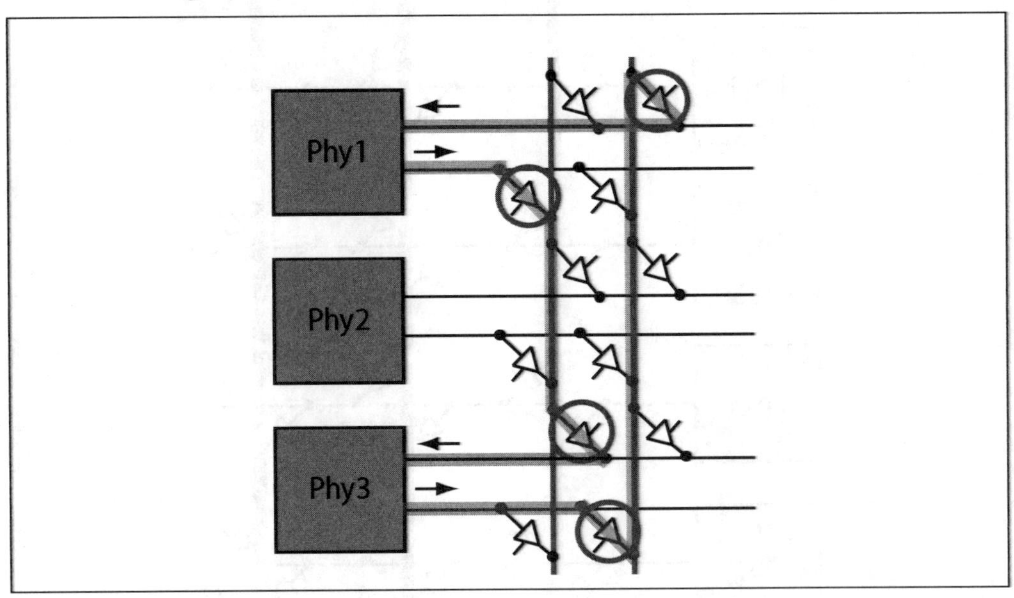

Internal Expander Ports

As shown in Figure 4-6, an expander must also contain a system management protocol (SMP) port to support system configuration, and may optionally contain an internal target for functions such as enclosure management. Expander phys may also optionally include bridges that would allow them to support SATA target devices, as shown in the bottom right corner of the illustration. All expander phys are assigned the same SAS address, but they have a unique Phy identifier to keep track of them.

Figure 4-6: Expander Architecture Example

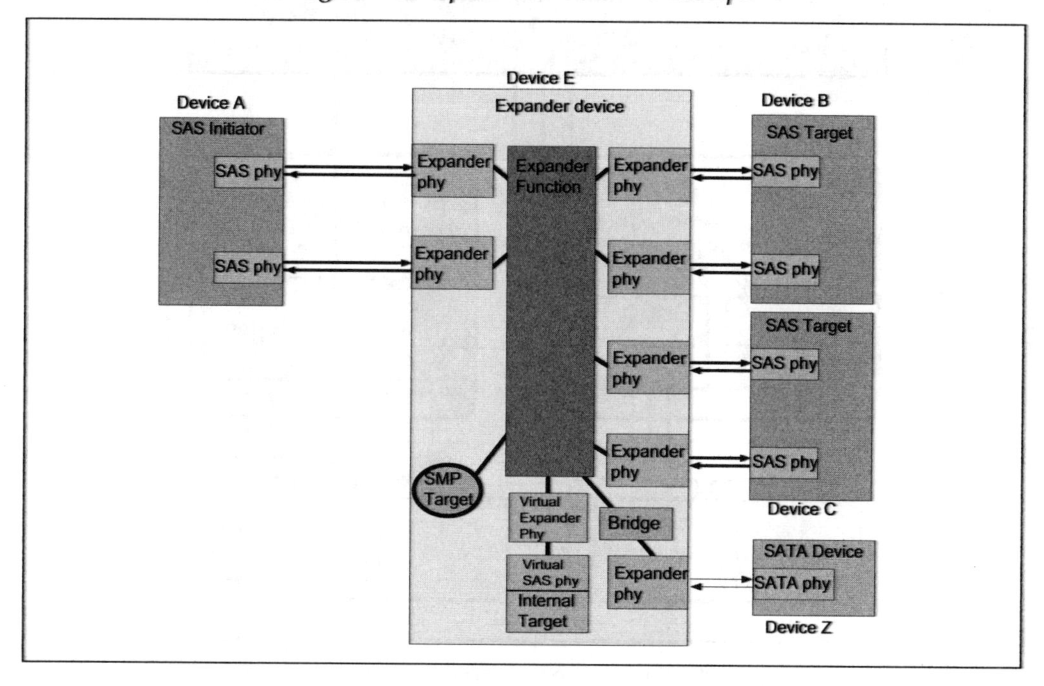

Edge Expanders

General

Edge expanders, as the name implies, reside at the "edges" of a topology and interface with the end devices found there. However, they can also be cascaded to form deeper hierarchical topologies. These two somewhat incompatible ideas are more easily understood if we remember that edge expanders are always assembled into "edge expander device sets" which may include just one or several edge expander devices, as illustrated in Figure 4-7 on page 86. Within the set, the expanders may be cascaded, but at the boundaries are only end devices. The standard does not define how these sets may be constructed, but gives some guidelines. Basically, the set overall can only contain at most 128 addresses, has end devices at the boundaries, and can have one subtractive port.

Figure 4-7: Edge Expander Set

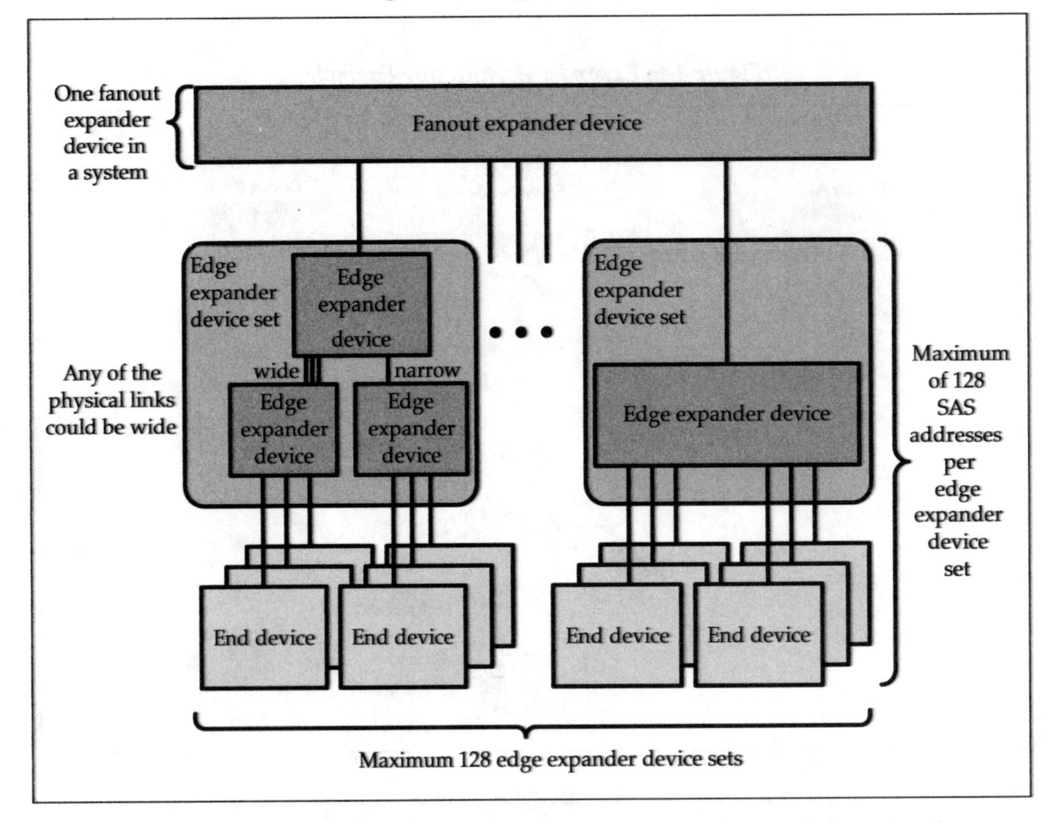

This subtractive port is one way that edge expanders are kept simple, because it becomes the destination of any connection request for which the address cannot be resolved. Having a default port is another way of saying that the expander set is not required to know all the addresses in the system, allowing it to use less memory for storing addresses and making it less expensive. Wide ports between expanders are allowed, but there can be no loops among the expander connections, which helps achieve two design goals for expanders and SAS topologies: simplicity and low cost. The subtractive port of an edge expander set may be connected to a fanout expander or another edge expander set, or an end device. Figure 4-7 shows the fanout expander case, Figure 4-8 on page 87 shows the largest topology possible without using a fanout expander, and Figure 4-9 on page 87 shows the case of a single edge expander.

Figure 4-8: Two Edge Expander Sets Attached by Subtractive Ports

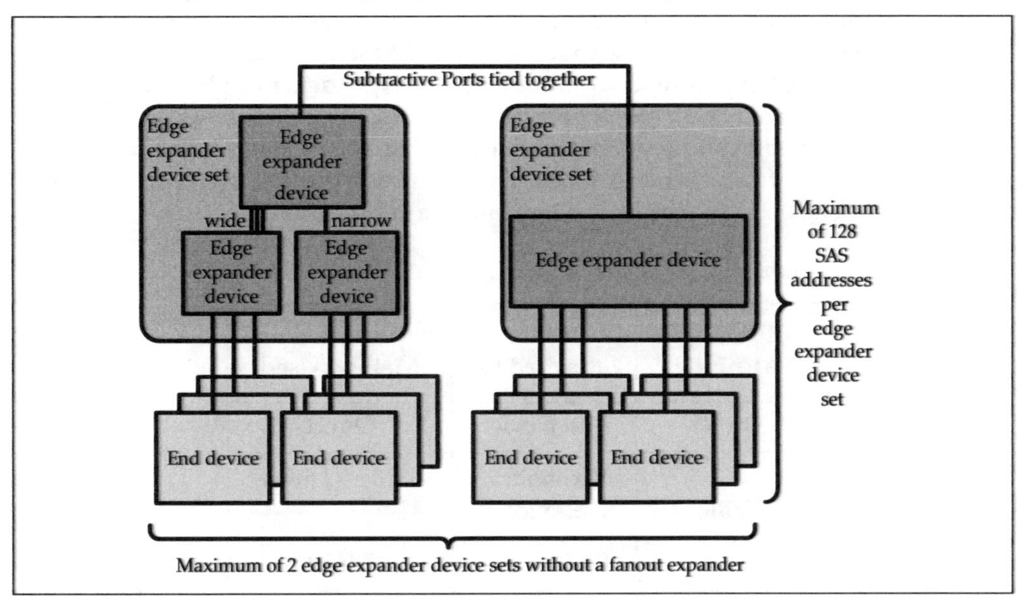

Figure 4-9: Single Edge Expander Set

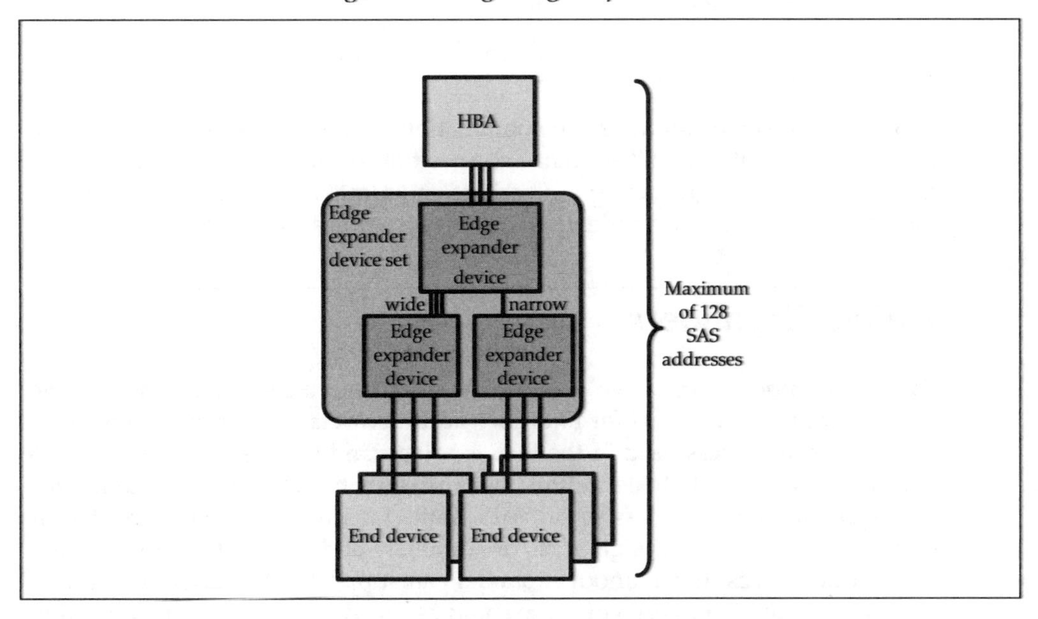

Routing Methods

Edge expanders have three routing methods available to them as listed in Table 4-1: Direct, Table, and Subtractive. Requests to addresses of end devices that are connected directly to an expander are routed based on the list of direct-attach addresses. Addresses reported through other expanders must be maintained in an address table and requests are routed based on the contents of that table. Requests to addresses that don't reside in either place default to the subtractive routing port if there is one. Fanout expanders have the first two options but not the last one because they do not implement a subtractive port.

Table 4-1: Expander Routing Attributes and Methods

Routing Attribute	When attached to	Routing Method Used
Direct	End Device	Direct
Table	Expander Device	Table + Direct
	End Device	Direct
Subtractive	Expander Device	Subtractive (+ Direct)
	End Device	Direct

A SAS storage architecture is the combination of these various devices. There must be endpoints like HBAs that act as initiators, and endpoints like drives that act as targets. Connecting the various endpoints is the function of the service delivery subsystem, made up of expanders, cables, and traces.

Fanout Expanders

Fanout expanders don't have a subtractive port and consequently don't have the luxury of a default port for unknown addresses. As a result, they must have a list of every address used in the SAS topology and will need a large look-up table to track them all. By definition, there can only be one fanout expander in a SAS system, which has less to do with limitations of the architecture than it does with meeting the design goals of simplicity and low cost. The maximum number of devices that a fanout expander can support is 128, as shown in Figure 4-7 on page 86, and each of those could be an edge expander set supporting up to 128 addresses, making the largest possible number of addresses for a SAS topology 128 times 128 or 16,384.

If there is no fanout expander, there can be no more than two edge expander sets in the system connected to each other through their subtractive ports. End devices can be attached at any level in the hierarchy of expanders but there must not be multiple paths that an expander can see to access them. This leads to a discussion about the legal topologies for SAS and the domains that can be created.

Domains

A network may be composed of several domains. A domain is a logical concept for establishing which devices are able to communicate with each other, and there are a few rules defining them. As shown in Figure 4-10, a SAS domain may include both SAS end devices and expander devices. Note that all devices linked to an expander are in the same domain by definition, since a connection can be routed between any phys on an expander. By contrast, a SATA domain comprises only SATA devices, usually just a SATA host connected to a SATA endpoint. Figure 4-11 on page 90 illustrates an expander that actually resides in both domain types.

Figure 4-10: SAS Domain Example

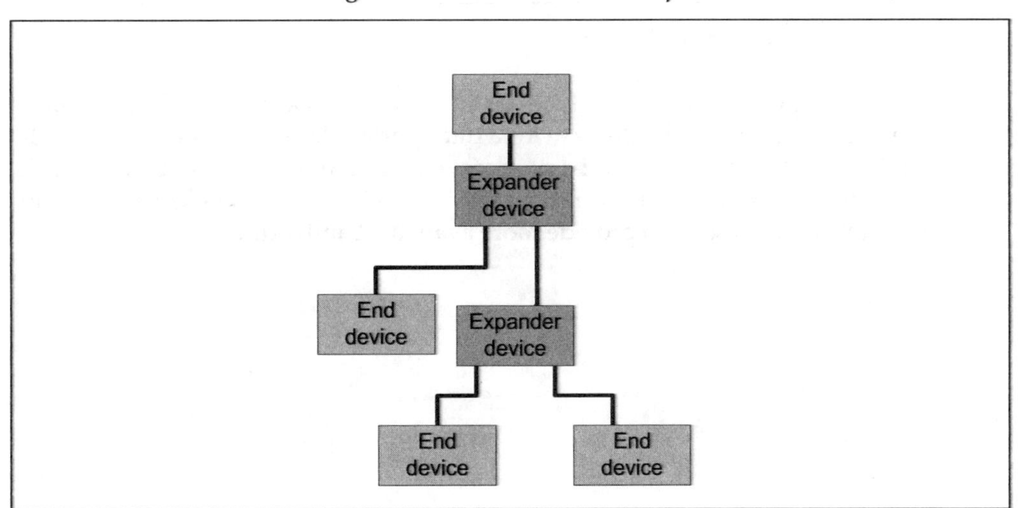

Figure 4-11: SAS Domain Bridged to a SATA Domain

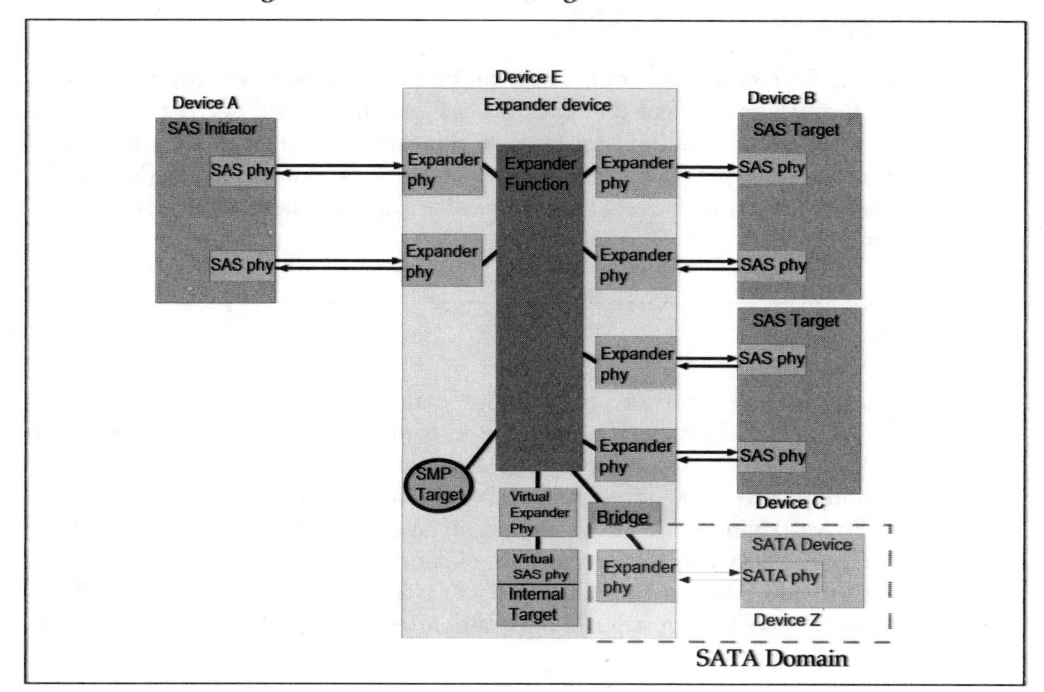

Dual Citizenship

A single SAS device can actually reside in more than one domain if it has multiple ports. Such would be the case for a dual-ported drive, as shown in Figure 4-12. On the other hand, a multi-ported device can use the same address on each port and permit a wide-port instead, which means all of its links would be in the same domain so as to provide more available bandwidth.

Figure 4-12: Dual-Ported Device in Two Domains

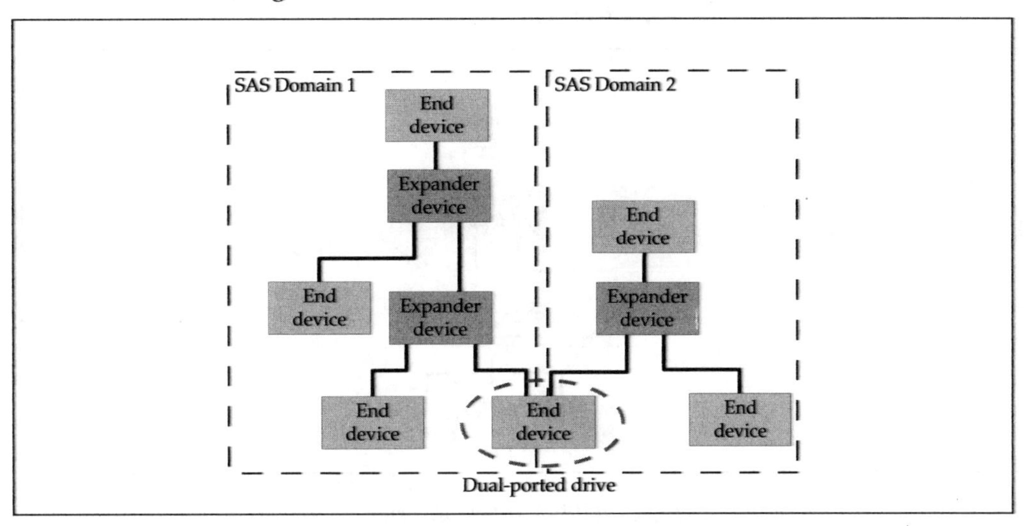

Topology Restrictions

When discussing SAS topologies, it is important to note several rules regarding legal construction of domains that serve to reduce the cost of the network by limiting its complexity.

Limited Addressing

First, as mentioned earlier, the number of SAS addresses that may be used by an edge expander set is limited to 128, and that includes addresses from attached devices as well as those addresses used internally for virtual Phys within an expander.

Dual Port Configurations

Second, as shown in Figure 4-13, it is permissible for a device to have a wide port in order to provide a redundant path or better bandwidth. However, it is not acceptable for an expander to have more than one path available to an end-point device, as Figure 4-14 illustrates. Software will disable one path to fix this multipath problem if it is detected.

To clarify this rule: while it is acceptable for an end device to have more than one path available to reach another end device, it is not acceptable for expanders to have a choice about which path to take to the same device.

Figure 4-13: Wide Port Example

Figure 4-14: Multi-path Error

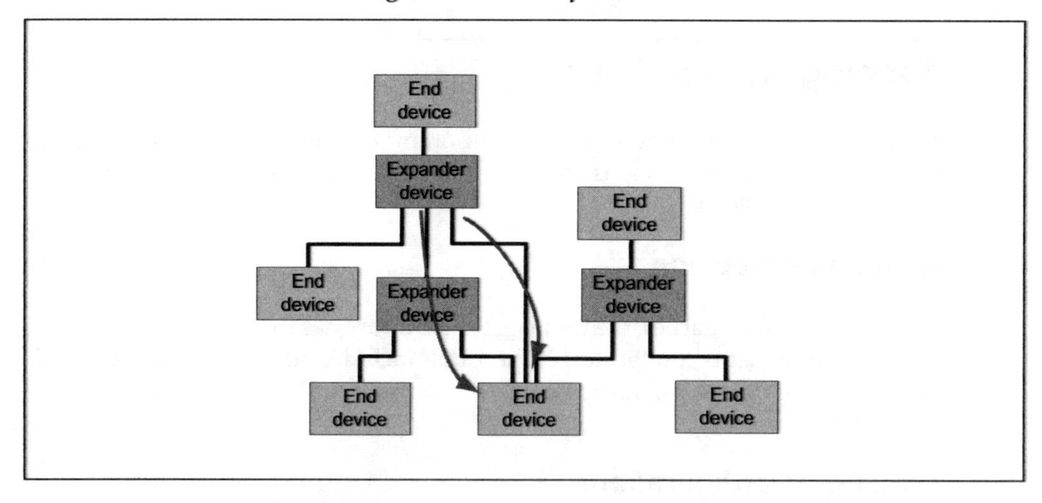

No Loop Topologies

Third, along the same lines, Figure 4-15 illustrates a loop error in the topology. Loops are not allowed in the paths between expanders, both to maintain simplicity in the topologies and because of the very simple method that expanders use to inform devices in the domain about detected changes to the fabric. For example, when an expander detects that an address has been added or removed, it sends a broadcast message on all the rest of its SAS ports to inform connected devices that a change has occurred. Each initiator must then query the expanders to learn what has changed. If two expanders have more than one path to each other, this can result in an infinite loop of change broadcasts as one broadcasts the change, then the other sees the broadcast and interprets it as another change and repeats the process by broadcasting back to the first one. The fix for this case is similar to the previous one: disable one of the paths to prevent the loop condition.

Figure 4-15: Expander Loop Topology Error

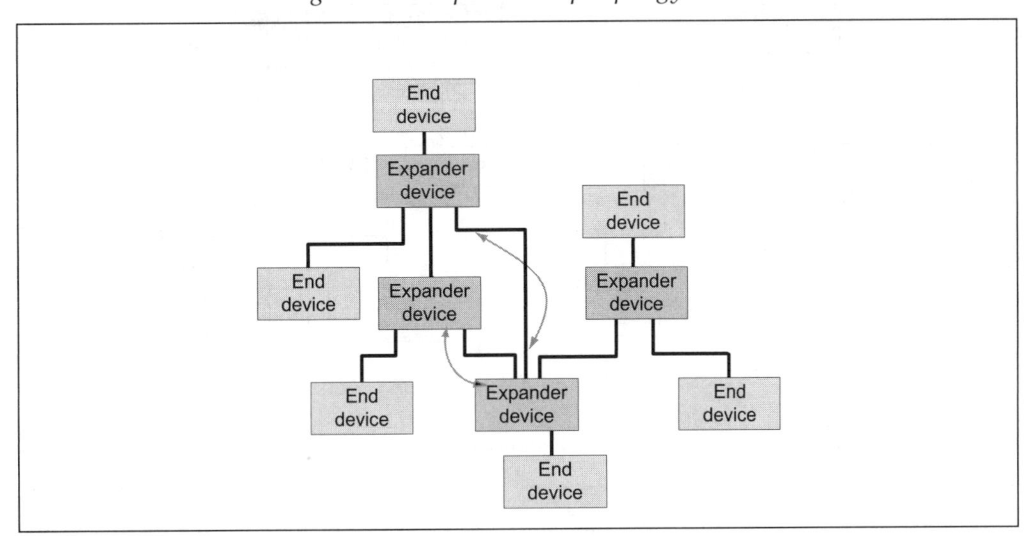

Expander Limitations

There can only be one fanout expander in a SAS domain although, as mentioned earlier, it can access as many as 16K SAS addresses in the system.

If no fanout expander is used, then only two edge expander sets can be connected together, with their subtractive ports connected to each other.

Endpoint-to-Endpoint Connections

One last rule to help define a domain is that one endpoint attached to another endpoint is defined as a separate domain.

A Domain Quiz

Armed with these rules, consider the following example. The network shown in

Figure 4-16 on page 94 has several domains and also includes errors. How many domains and how many errors are present in it?

Figure 4-16: Domain Quiz

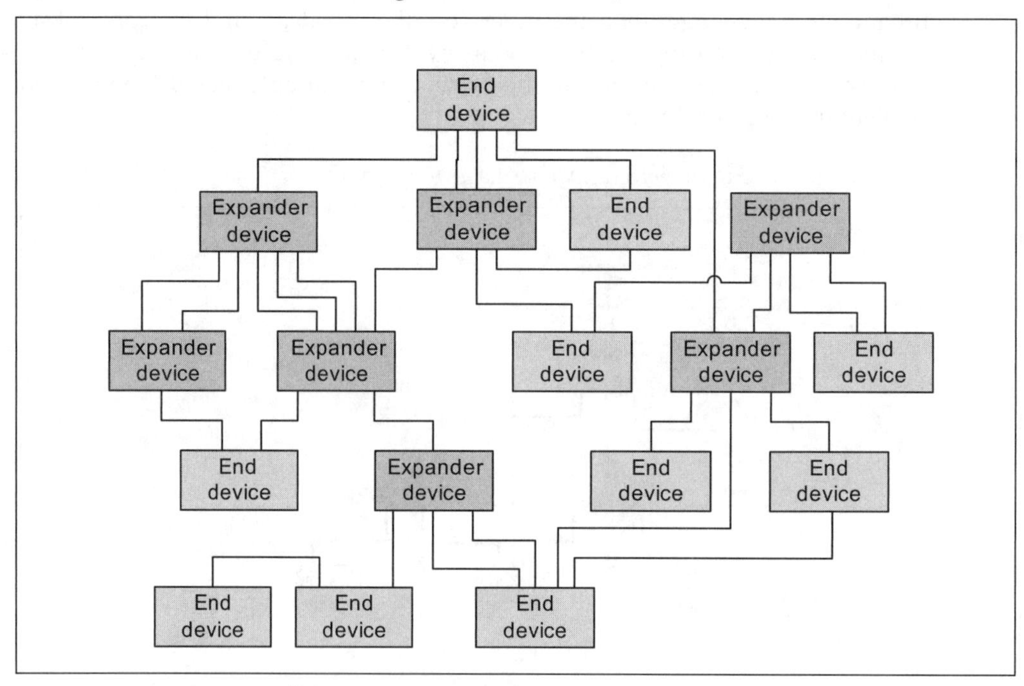

The solution to this puzzle is shown in Figure 4-17 on page 95, where the highlighted areas show that there are in fact six domains. The circles highlight two problem areas caused by allowing expanders to see more than one path to the same endpoint. Breaking the path marked by the upper circle will keep the expander just below it from seeing two paths to the end device at the top of the drawing, and breaking either path to the circled end device on the left would prevent the expanders above it from seeing a choice of two paths to reach it. Note that the topmost end device still has two paths it can use to reach the end device on the bottom right. Recall from the earlier discussion about multi-path errors that this is not an error condition because there are no expanders that have a choice about which path to take to connect these two devices.

Figure 4-17: Domain Quiz Solution

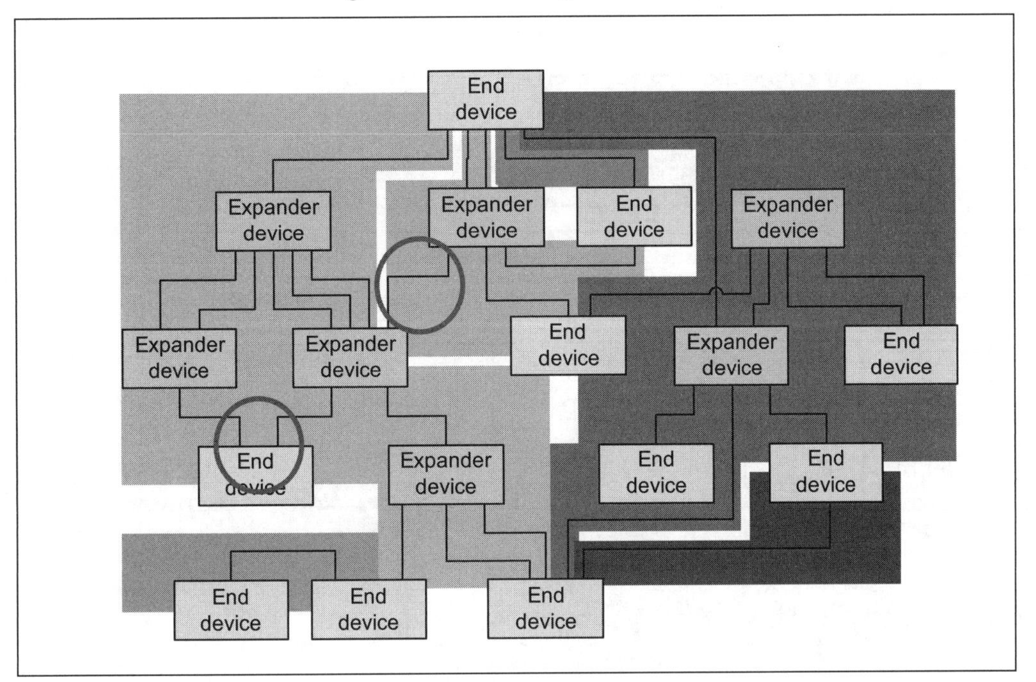

The domain examples used to this point have been somewhat arbitrary in order to facilitate illustration. A more realistic domain example is shown in the example considered earlier and repeated in Figure 4-18 on page 96. Here, several small form factor, dual-ported drives are shown installed together in a rack-mount implementation intended to eliminate single-point-of-failure issues. Each drive resides in two different domains with separate expander sets, separate power supplies and even separate HBAs.

Figure 4-18: Realistic Domain Example

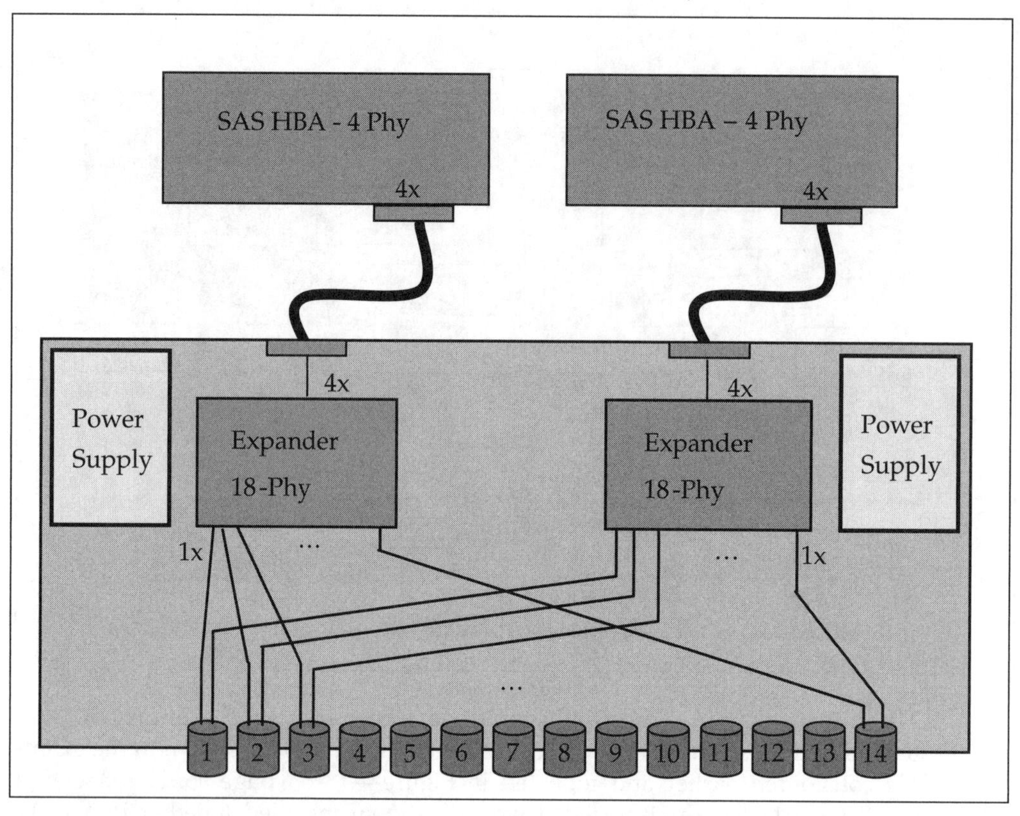

Connections Review

SAS communications take place between devices using frames that travel over a *connection*. A connection is a temporary circuit between an initiator and target that is established when one device issues a connection request using an OPEN Address frame and the targeted device accepts the request by responding with an OPEN_ACCEPT primitive (a primitive is a single-dword packet used for maintaining protocol - see "Primitives" on page 284). Connection requests contain the address of the targeted device and are routed to the appropriate port by expanders based on that address. When a request has been accepted, the resources used to establish it are dedicated for the use of the connected devices until the connection is closed. To close a connection, the devices will normally exchange DONE primitives and then CLOSE primitives.

Figure 4-19 illustrates a simple topology with two connections in progress. From this it can be seen that multiple connections are possible when wide ports are present, since they provide multiple paths for connections.

Figure 4-19: Connection Example

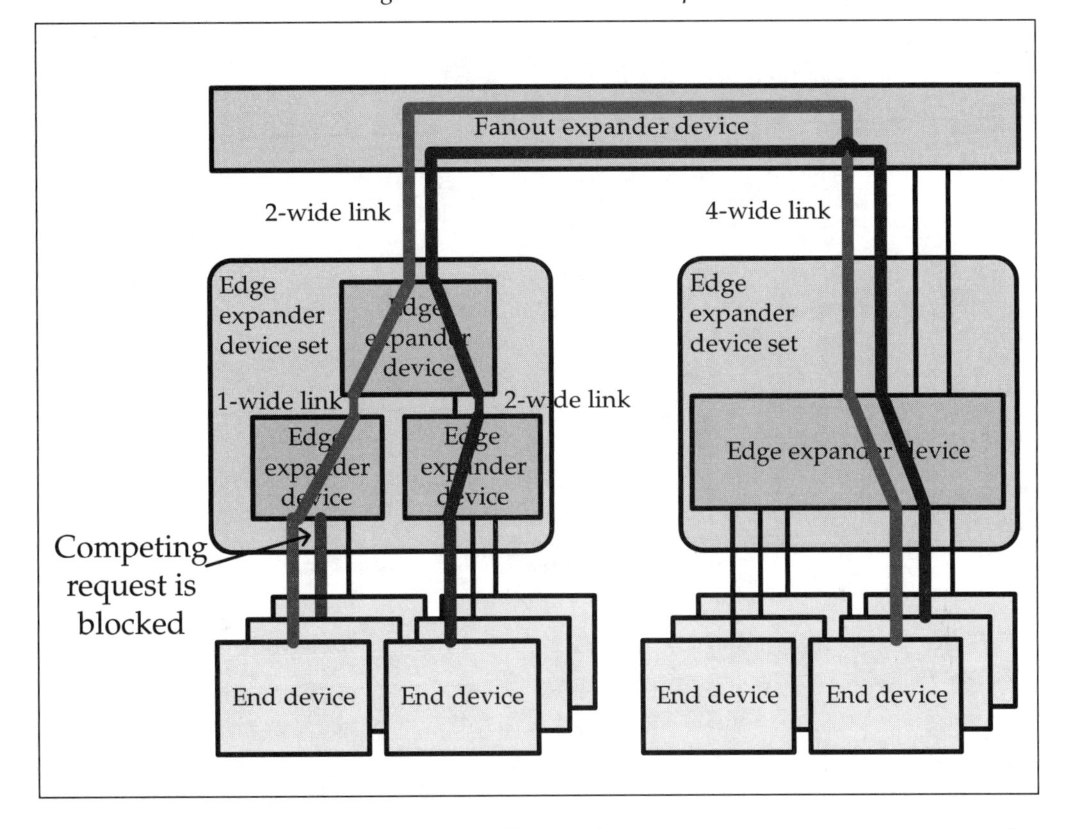

These connections can be to different destinations, as shown here, or to the same destination if the target has a wide port. Wide ports, though, will typically only appear on HBAs or RAID controllers to allow them to connect to several drives. As mentioned before, SAS drives will typically have dual narrow ports.

A bottleneck can be seen at the lower left expander, because it serves three devices potentially competing for access to the narrow port that serves the rest of the system. In this example, a second connection request from an attached device is forced to wait for the current connection to complete before it can make progress. If both requests arrive at the expander at the same time, it must arbitrate between them. This process is covered in Chapter 14, entitled "Link Layer - Arbitration," on page 333.

5 The Layered Device Architecture

The Previous Chapter

The previous chapter provided more definitions to facilitate a detailed understanding of SAS link operation. The different types of devices and expanders were explored, leading to a discussion of topologies and domains, as well as a review of connections.

This Chapter

This chapter begins with the necessary background to understand the architecture of narrow versus wide ports. It then describes the layered architecture of devices, which behave differently depending on whether the device uses narrow or wide ports. Next, details of the layered architecture within a narrow port are presented, and the final section describes the layer implementations of wide ports.

The Next Chapter

The next chapter describes the steps by which devices initialize the link for communications. This is a hardware-based process at the beginning, and establishes whether a neighboring device is present, what type it is, what link rates it supports, and its SAS address. Once that is completed, there are steps that must be taken by application software to discover the SAS topology and configure the devices.

Introduction

Background

This chapter is divided into three parts. The first part discusses the concepts and terms that are important to understanding the implementation of narrow versus wide ports. Next, we'll look at the layers as they are implemented in the simplest case: a device that only implements a single narrow port. In the third part, we'll consider the layers as implemented in a more complex case: a device that implements one or more wide ports.

Phys and Ports

Before launching into a discussion of the layers, it will help to have a clearer definition of some terms. The term Phy is used in the standard with respect to the interface between a device and the service delivery subsystem (e.g.: cable, backplane, etc.). In the standard the Phy is shown to include the Link Layer and Phy Layer as one logical block. (Don't be confused by the fact that the Phy contains the Phy Layer - the terms *Phy* and *Phy Layer* mean different things.) In a small departure from that format, the Phy definition we will use in the book adds the Physical Layer to the Phy block, as is shown in Figure 5-1 on page 101. The reason for making this slight change is that the Physical Layer contains the differential transmitter and receiver for the interface and is logically the last piece between the rest of the Phy and the outside world. This is not quite in keeping with the standard, but seemed more intuitive for a tutorial book.

Types of Phys

The generic term "Phy" incorporates all the possibilities that a Phy could include, but the standard lists some variations that are used to clarify details about usage. For example, a Phy that interfaces to a SATA subsystem can also be called a SATA Phy, while a Phy that interfaces with a SAS subsystem is referred to as a SAS Phy. They are also labeled according to protocol in some places in the standard. Thus, a Phy may be labeled an SSP Phy, SMP Phy or an STP Phy. For simplicity, unless the situation warrants the use of another term for clarity, this book will use the generic term "Phy" to represent all these types of possible Phy implementations.

Figure 5-1: Layers In a Device with One Narrow Port

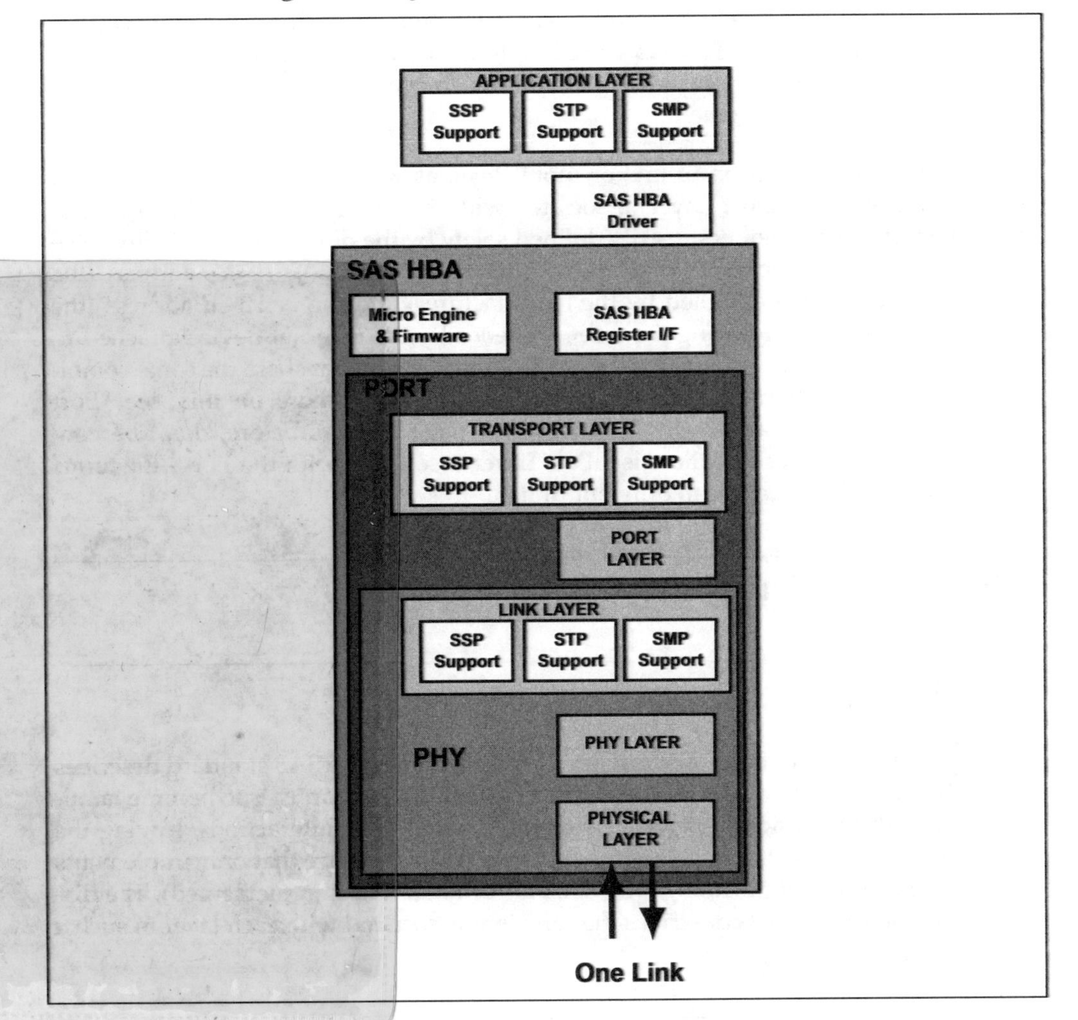

Phy Characteristics

A SAS Phy must support both SSP and SMP protocol and can optionally support STP. A Phy can be used as an initiator Phy or target Phy or both. Each Phy has a 64-bit SAS address associated with it that is programmed by the vendor at the factory, and a unique Phy identifier (a device-specific number starting at 0 and going as high as 127) within the device. During the reset sequence, each

Phy sends an Identify frame to its neighbor to communicate its characteristics, including: protocols supported, address, and Phy identifier. A designer may choose to implement multiple Phys within a single device and assign the same address to all of them (as would be typical in an HBA design), or assign a different address to each Phy (as would be likely in a dual-ported disk drive). The reason for choosing one addressing approach over the other has to do with the desired port arrangement.

A Port is a collection of one or more Phys, as well as the upper layers (Port Layer and Transport Layer) associated with that group of Phys. The organization of a port is not necessarily defined solely by the device design. A Phy actually has two addresses that are of interest: its own 64-bit SAS address (the internal address assigned by the manufacturer) and the attached address (the address reported during the reset sequence by the external device attached to this Phy). A Port is defined to be a collection of Phys that share the same combination of addresses, both source and attached (for more on this, see "Port Assignments Change with Topology" on page 113). As before, don't be confused by the fact that there is a Port Layer associated with the Port - the terms *Port* and *Port Layer* mean different things.

A Device with One Narrow Port

General

In keeping with many modern interface definitions, the SAS standard describes the functionality as a series of layers. The goal in this chapter is to become familiar with the basic operation of these layers and their interactions, leaving the details for later chapters. Figure 5-1 shows an HBA device that only implements one narrow port (meaning only one bidirectional link is implemented). The discussion that follows describes the functions associated with each layer in such a device.

Layer Overview

A layered architecture facilitates a modular design and allows for easy re-use of modules between designs. It is important to note that the SAS standard does not tightly specify some layer responsibilities, thereby giving designers freedom in implementation specifics.

The layers communicate with each other by passing requests, indications, confirmations, and other messages to each other, and their behavior is described in the SAS standard primarily by means of state machines. The state machines are discussed within the chapter for each layer. For now, we'll present just a brief description of the layers, beginning at the highest layer.

Application Layer

General

The Application Layer of the SAS standard comes in three flavors, SSP (Serial SCSI Protocol), SMP (Serial Management Protocol), and STP (SATA Tunneled Protocol). Support for SMP is required for a SAS initiator because that protocol is used to execute the Discovery Process (see Chapter 7, entitled "Discovery Process," on page 159). For a SAS target-only device, just SSP support is required, because a designer might choose to forego an SMP interface to save cost (the same information is available from mode pages; for more on this, see "Software Initialization" on page 140). For an initiator that supports SATA, all three protocols would probably be necessary because, as an initiator, it would need SMP to do discovery and it would need STP to access SATA drives. The Application Layer is intended to preserve the software interaction with the device as much as possible, and only describes changes that were necessary to the protocol elements in support of each protocol for SAS.

SSP (Serial SCSI Protocol)

The interaction of this layer is represented in the SAM-3 (SCSI Architecture Model) standard by means of procedure calls with arguments supplied by the caller, and SAS carries this model forward. The SAM-3 standard also defines the format of many optional mode, log, and sense pages for configuring or reading status information from devices and some of these had to be changed to support SAS functionality. These page formats and the changes described for them are discussed in detail in Chapter 8, entitled "Application Layer," on page 193. One function of these pages is to include information about how some errors are to be handled, such as whether a command that encountered trouble should be reissued or not. Finally, a new feature was added to assist with the power requirements of spinning up several drives together. The primitive NOTIFY (ENABLE SPINUP) takes precedence over every other command for a drive and prevents a SAS drive from spinning up until this primitive has been received. This gives the software better control over the spinup sequence and protects against power supply overload caused by having too many drives spin up at the same time.

STP (SATA Tunneled Protocol)

For SATA devices, SAS implements the SAS Tunneled Protocol (STP). A tunnel mechanism allows packets associated with one network protocol to be transmitted over a different type of network in specially formatted packets. Once an STP connection has been established, to each other the two connected devices appear as a SATA host and SATA target and communicate using the SATA-specific protocol. The two connected devices behave as SATA devices and any intermediate expander devices in the path simply pass the frames through without change. Consequently, there are no SAS-specific Application Layer features defined for STP at all.

SMP (SCSI Management Protocol)

The SAM-3 standard describes a list of seven management functions that could be requested by an application, driver, or OS, such as ABORT TASK and QUERY TASK. SAS enlarges on that foundation by defining a separate management protocol that defines additional functions. One of the main reasons for adding this functionality is to give expanders in the system a simple method for discovering which addresses are visible to them. These management functions facilitate the discovery process in a SAS network by making it easy for initiators to query devices and expanders and learn what type of device they are, how many Phys they contain, etc.

Transport Layer

The main job of the Transport Layer is to construct the frames that will be sent over a connection. The contents of the frames vary among the three different protocols, but a common type would the one shown in Figure 5-2, where the frame contains information about its contents in the header and contains data in the body. Some frames will have no data at all (e.g.: SMP frames or SSP command frames) but, if they do carry data, the maximum is 1KB for SSP and 8KB for STP.

Figure 5-2: Frame Construction

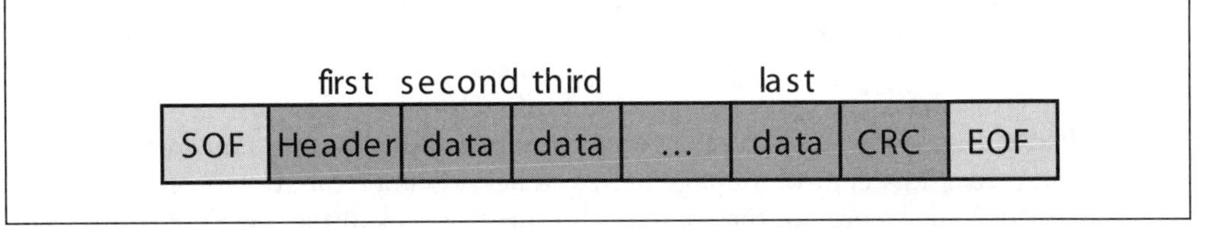

One other interesting aspect of the Transport Layer is that, if this device supports the optional Transport Layer Retries for SSP frames, it will keep a copy of outgoing frames until they have been acknowledged. That way, if the frame fails on the link for some reason a copy is available for a replay operation (see "SSP Error Handling" on page 233).

Port Layer

The function of the Port Layer is fairly simple for the narrow port example. Frames are forwarded from the Transport Layer and queued up into pools based on the destination address. When at least one frame has been queued, a connection to the destination address request is needed. If the connection already exists, the frame can be transmitted, but if not it will need to be opened first. To do that a request is sent to the link layer to open a connection using the requested protocol. If the connection succeeds, the link layer reports it and the frames for that address can now be drained out of the port layer pool and transmitted onto the link. If the connection has trouble, the request to open it may need to be reissued, and the Port Layer handles this task.

Link Layer

The biggest part of the standard is devoted to the Link Layer, the heart of the SAS architecture. Its functions include establishing and maintaining connections between devices. As part of this process, the Link Layer responsibilities also include:

- Sending address frames to request connection establishment.
- Adding a CRC value to each packet for reliable detection of transmission errors.
- Generating primitives as needed (for example, ACK and NAK for confirm-

ing reception of a frame) and adding them to the outbound flow of dwords.
- Checking and removing primitives from the incoming flow.
- Scrambling the transmitted bytes to reduce EMI.
- Handling the identification and hard reset protocols.
- Managing clock skew and rate matching.

Much of what distinguishes the three protocols — SSP, STP, and SMP — is handled in this layer. Supporting a connection once it has been established involves things like flow control management and acknowledgement of received frames, and those tasks are not the same for all three. For example, an SMP connection only sends one request and receives one response before closing, so it has no need for flow control or acknowledgement. For more on the details of the link layer see Chapter 12, entitled "Link Layer - Serial Support," on page 299.

Phy Layer

General

The Phy Layer performs the following basic functions:

- When the Link Layer provides the serial byte stream representing a frame to the Phy Layer, the Phy Layer's 8b/10b Encoder encodes each 8-bit byte into a 10-bit character.
- The resulting stream of 10-bit characters are supplied to a Serializer that generates a serial bit stream that is supplied to the differential transmitter in the Physical Layer.
- When the Physical Layer receives an inbound bit stream from the cable, its differential receiver converts the differential signals into a digital bit stream and feeds it to the Deserializer in the Phy Layer.
- The 10-bit character stream produced by the Phy Layer's Deserializer is in turn fed to the 10-bit/8-bit Decoder which decodes the 10-bit characters back into 8-bit bytes.
- The Phy Layer then feeds the resulting byte stream to the Link Layer for further processing.
- The Phy Layer is also responsible for the generation of the special bit patterns used to initialize the two ends of the link immediately after a reset.

8b/10b Encode and Decode

The encoding performs several useful functions for serial transmission:

1. It embeds a clock into the data stream by ensuring sufficient "transition

density". By recovering this clock at the receiver, serial transmissions avoid the need for a shared system clock and the problems of flight time and clock skew associated with parallel designs.

2. It serves to balance the number of ones and zeroes sent across the wire. Serial transmission media often include a capacitor in the transmission line to block the DC component of the signal between transmitter and receiver, and this is true for SAS in some implementations. If a long string of ones or zeroes were sent, the capacitor might charge up and affect signal integrity. Balancing the highs and lows prevents this from becoming a problem.
3. It provides for simple detection of most transmission errors, since many of the possible 10-bit encodings are not used. If a valid 10-bit character experiences an error during transmission, it is likely to change into an illegal character and is therefore easily recognized as invalid at the receiver.

Initialization

Before any transfers can take place across a link, the link must be initialized to establish at what speed the neighbors can communicate, and what protocol they will use. This is done using OOB (Out Of Band) signaling that simply consists of patterns of activity followed by idle time. "Out of band" is perhaps not the best description for this, since the signals use the same path as ordinary transmissions, but the name conveys the idea that they are not part of the normal data stream and have characteristics that are recognizable even before the link has been initialized. During the time when a transmitter is sending OOB, it sends a burst of special bit patterns which are detected by the receiver as edge transitions. At this point the receiver cannot yet recognize a frame. When the transmitter stops sending these bursts and simply leaves the differential voltage at the common mode voltage, the receiver detects no activity and measures the time until the edges begin arriving again.

After being reset, receivers cannot recognize more than this because devices must take certain steps to prepare for communications before they can make sense of the bit pattern. The first step in this preparation is to send and receive the OOB patterns COMINIT, COMWAKE (if a SATA target is detected), and COMSAS, as shown in Figure 5-3. The length of time the link is inactive between bursts communicates the information to the device, somewhat like Morse code. To learn more about this process, refer to the section on the "Introduction" on page 125.

Figure 5-3: OOB Example

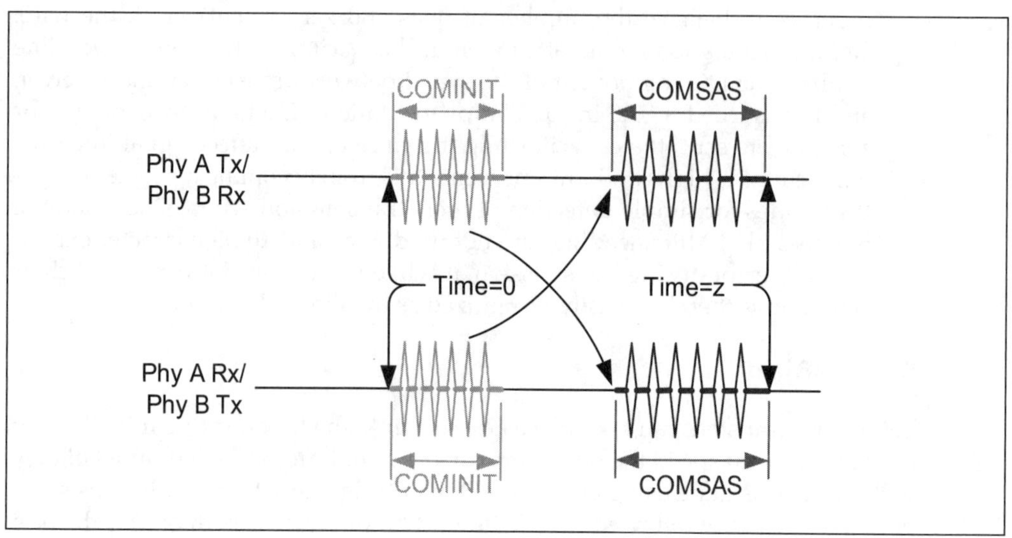

Physical Layer

The Physical Layer is described in two parts:

- The differential transmitter/receiver. For outgoing traffic, this handles the bit stream supplied by the Phy Layer and drives it out as a high-speed differential signal over the cable. When the bit stream representing a frame is received, the Physical Layer's differential receiver accepts the incoming bit stream and sources it to the Phy Layer for processing.
- The external, passive portion of a link, meaning the service delivery subsystem (e.g.: cables and connectors). It borrows elements from other serial transport designs and has been specifically designed to be physically compatible with the SATA cable interface for the internal signaling environment (see Chapter 18, entitled "Cables and Connectors," on page 433, for a discussion of signaling environments). Unlike SATA, however, SAS cables are often designed with two sets of signals to support dual-ported drives.

Transmission Sequence

Refer to Figure 5-4 during the following discussion. At the highest level in the hierarchy, the Application Layer issues commands to the lower layers and receives the resulting data and completion responses. For an HBA, the Application Layer consists of the client software application and the device driver.

Figure 5-4: Layers In a Device with One Port

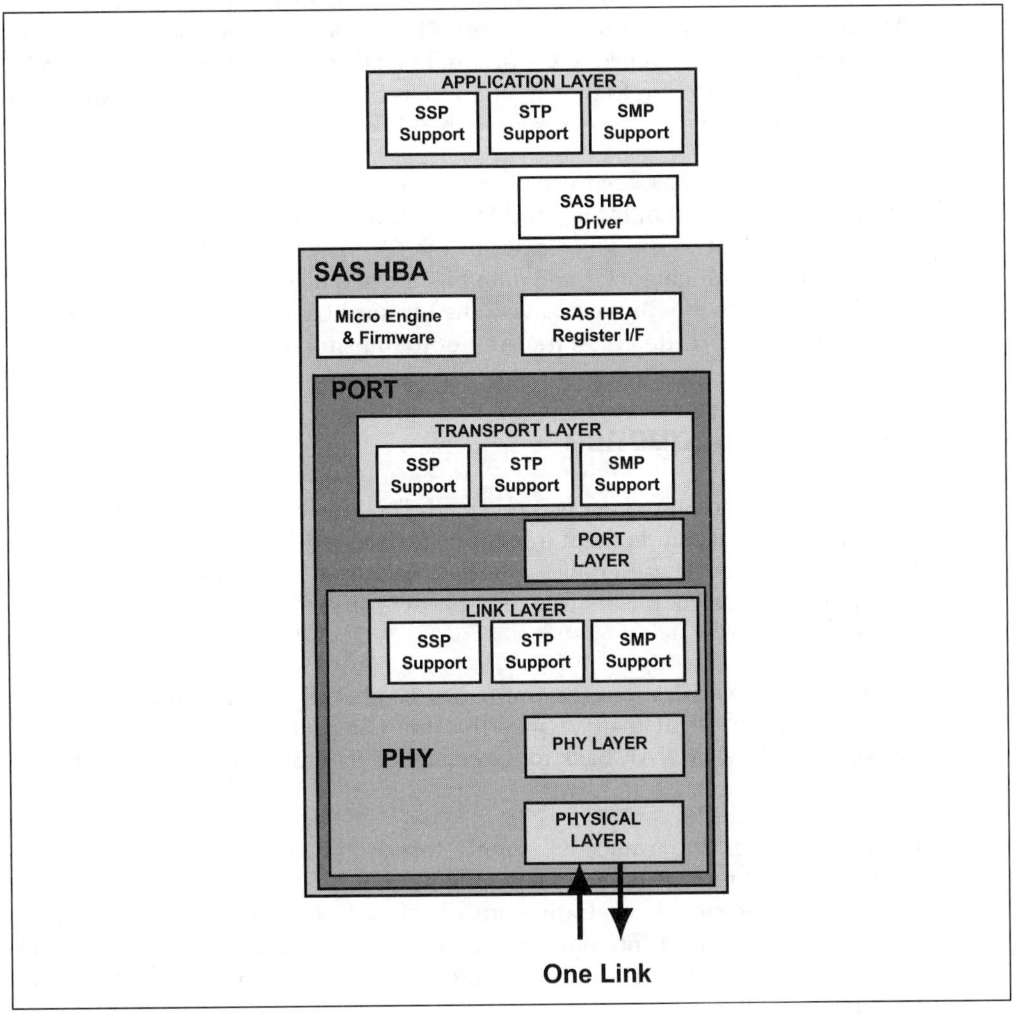

For a SAS adapter other than an HBA (e.g., a mass storage controller), the Application Layer consists of the device-specific logic and software that provides the interface between the adapter's Transport Layer and the internal targets (e.g., disk drives). Outgoing traffic requests are passed to the Transport Layer which translates them into the proper frame (packet) format for transmission and forwards them to the Port Layer.

In the Port Layer, outbound frames are queued up in pools based on destination address. In Figure 5-4, the SAS port in this device only contains one Phy, so the Port Layer just acts as a frame queue and sends an Open Connection request to the Link Layer when one or more frames have been queued for transmission. Once a connection is opened to the destination address (i.e., the Link Layer indicates that the connection to the target port has been established), the frames can be drained out of the queue and sent to the Link Layer.

Once a connection has been established, the frame is sent to the Link Layer which adds SOF (start of frame) and EOF (end of frame) primitives to the frame and then passes it to the Phy Layer. In the Phy Layer, each 8-bit byte is converted into a 10-bit character, the data bits are serialized, and the bit stream is then forwarded to the Physical Layer. The Physical Layer receives the digital bit stream and uses its differential transmitter to transmit it out onto the cable.

Reception Sequence

For received frames, the process is reversed. The Physical Layer receives the differential signals, converts them into a bit stream, and forwards that to the Phy Layer. The Phy Layer deserializes the bits back into a 10-bit character stream and decodes those characters into an 8-bit byte stream, which it then forwards to the Link Layer.

The Link Layer verifies that the frame has good SOF and EOF primitives and then strips them off. It then verifies that the CRC for the frame is good and transmits an ACK or NAK back to the sender. If the frame was good, the frame is forwarded up to the Port Layer.

In the Port Layer, the frames are simply forwarded to the Transport Layer as messages with arguments that contain all the information from the frame. The Transport Layer stores the frames into local memory, parsing the frame to recover the fields used internally by the device. Finally, the device signals an interrupt to invoke its device driver and tell the application layer software to fetch the contents of the memory.

A Device with One or More Wide Ports

General

Let's now consider the more complex case shown in Figure 5-5, illustrating a wide port with four Phys. The internal details are only shown for one of the Phys, but each of the four Phys contain identical logic blocks.

The difference in the roles played by the layers now is that, unlike in the port with a single Phy, the Port Layer has the option to choose any of the four Phys when creating a connection. In this example, it is assumed that all four are attached to the same address, so a connection targeting that address can use any of the Phys to connect with it. This means more connections can be open at the same time, resulting in better performance if the system can support it. As counterbalance to this argument, though, recall that multiple connections to a specific drive wouldn't give better performance because the drive can't support a higher rate.

Layer Description

The operation of the layers within a Phy are unchanged for a wide port, but there are some comments to make regarding the Transport Layer and Port Layer.

Transport Layer

The behavior of this layer is not changed for a wide port, but it's important to note that there is one transport layer for each port. If a device has Phys that could be used independently or grouped into wide ports, it would need to implement a separate transport layer (set of logic and state machines) for each Phy. If some of the Phys were grouped together into a wide port then some of the transport layer blocks would go unused.

Figure 5-5: Layers in a Device with One Wide Port

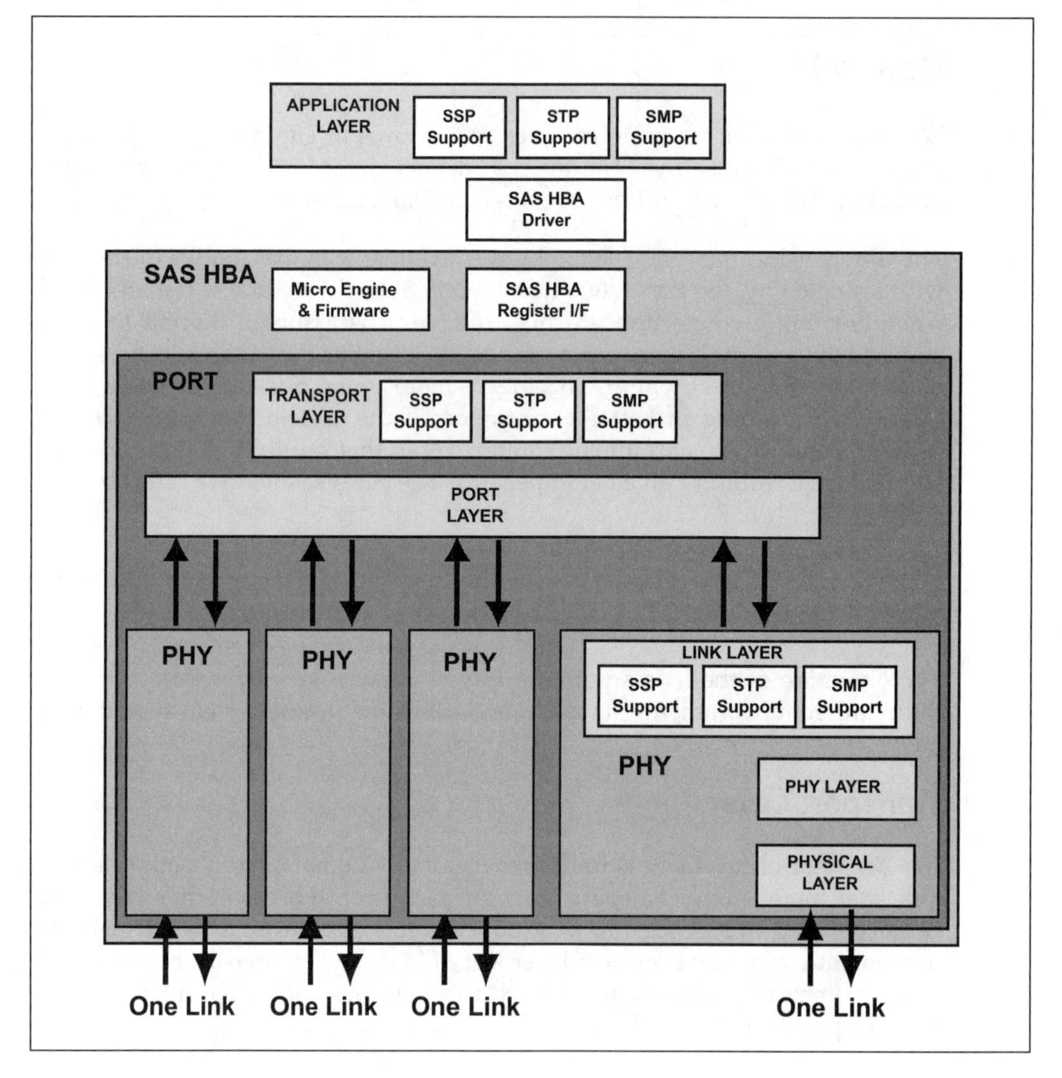

Port Layer

There may be several Phys associated with a port, all with the same address, and they are all possible avenues for an outgoing connection. One of the jobs of the Port Layer is to distribute the outgoing connections to the available Phys (if it has more than one to work with), and this is done in a manner similar to a telephone call center. In that model, all the calls are directed to the center and more than one of the clients may be calling the same number. As illustrated in Figure 5-6, a received call is queued and routed to the next available operator automatically, so all of the operators appear to the clients to be located at one phone number.

Figure 5-6: Port Layer Call Center Model

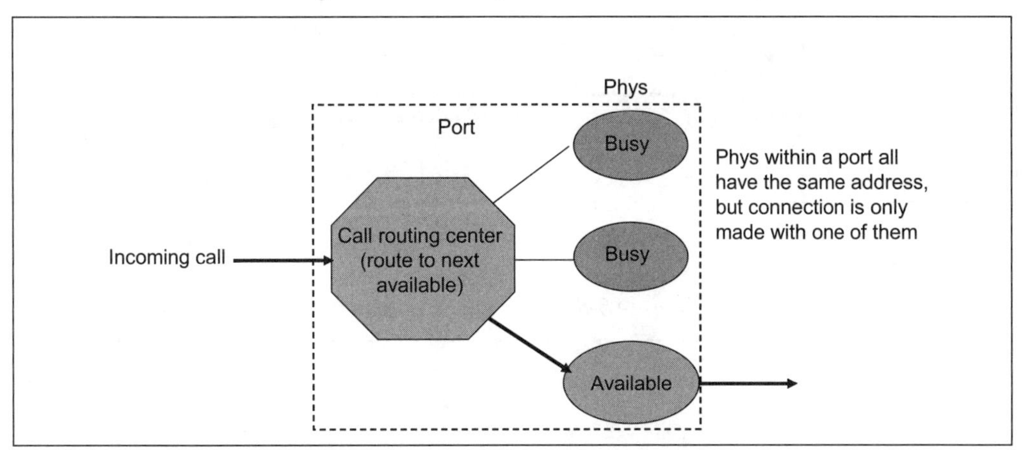

For SAS, outgoing frames are forwarded from the Transport Layer to the Port Layer of a Port and queued up there for transmission. Next, the Port Layer checks for an available Phy to use for transmission. There are a couple of possible results. For example, it may be that one Phy already has a connection open to the desired destination address, which would mean that this frame can simply be routed to that Phy. Otherwise, a connection will need to be opened, so a request is forwarded to the Link Layer to handle that operation. The standard states that the actual method used for selecting a Phy will be vendor specific.

Port Assignments Change with Topology

Since the definition of a port is partly based on the address of the remote Phy to which a Phy is attached, the assignment of ports for a device can change depending on the topology into which it has been installed. A port might contain only one Phy, as illustrated in Figure 5-7 or it might contain several Phys, as shown in Figure 5-8. If several Phys in a device all detect the same remote attached address after a link reset, then they are grouped together into a single port, and it is referred to as a wide port. A wide port offers the possibility of better performance because a device can use it to open more than one connection at the same time, even to the same device. However, an important distinction is that, unlike other serial transports such as PCI Express, a wide port cannot combine several Phys for use in the same transaction.

Figure 5-7: Single-Phy Port

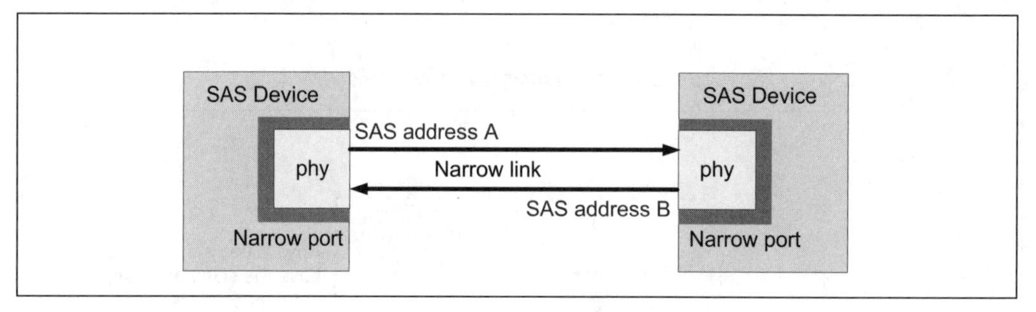

Figure 5-8: Wide Port Example

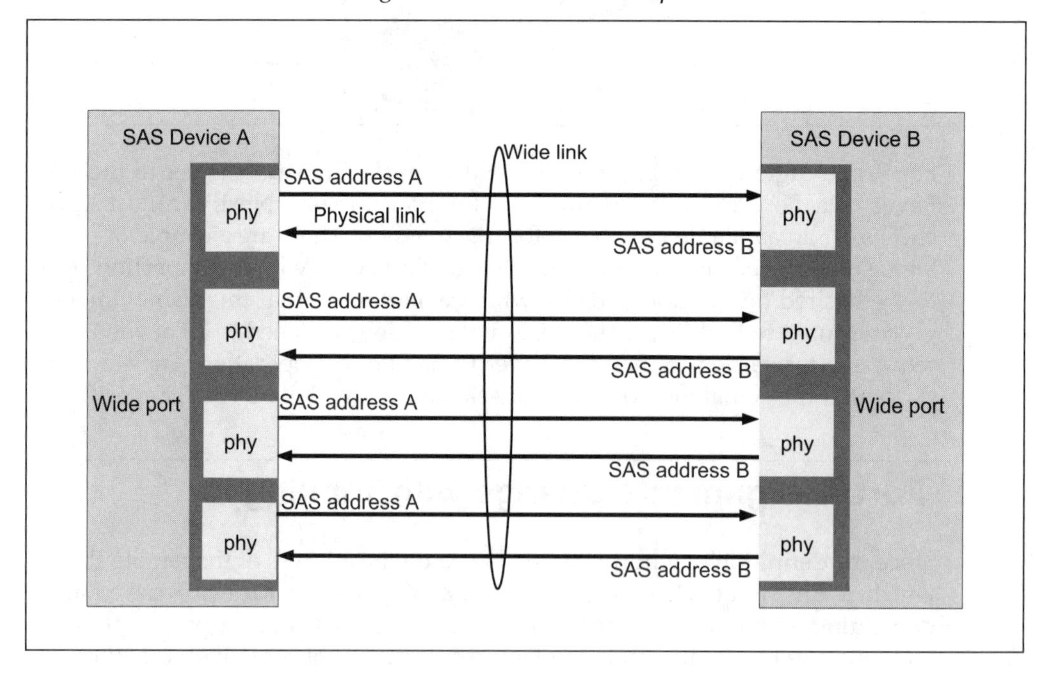

If a device contains several Phys that do not connect to the same external address, then they are split logically into ports based on the addresses to which they are attached. For example, in Figure 5-9, device A has four Phys, two of which see the external address B and two of which see address C. The resulting configuration in device A is two ports that each contain two Phys. If all the Phys of Device A were attached to different remote addresses, the resulting configuration would consist of four separate ports each containing a single Phy.

Figure 5-9: Multi-Port Example

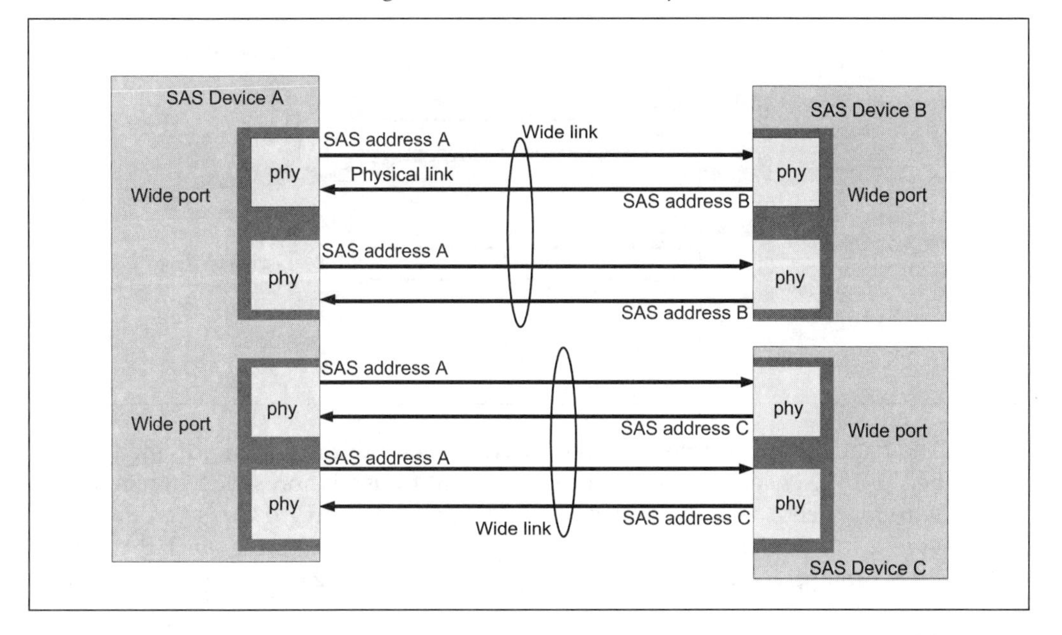

One last example in Figure 5-10 shows a likely implementation for a dual-ported disk drive, in which the drive forces two ports by assigning different addresses to its Phys. Since the local addresses for the two Phys are not the same, they can never be grouped into the same port even if they see the same attached address. In this case, the expectation is that the drive should have two distinct ports that connect to different HBAs to eliminate a single point of failure for accessing the drive. It's possible that a disk drive could be designed to use a wide port, but it's very unlikely because most drives are unable to supply enough data to support two connections at the same time. A single enterprise drive can typically only support data rates of about 75 to 80 MB/s, so even if two Phys were available to transfer data at the same time, that extra bandwidth would simply go unused.

Figure 5-10: Dual-Ported Drive Example

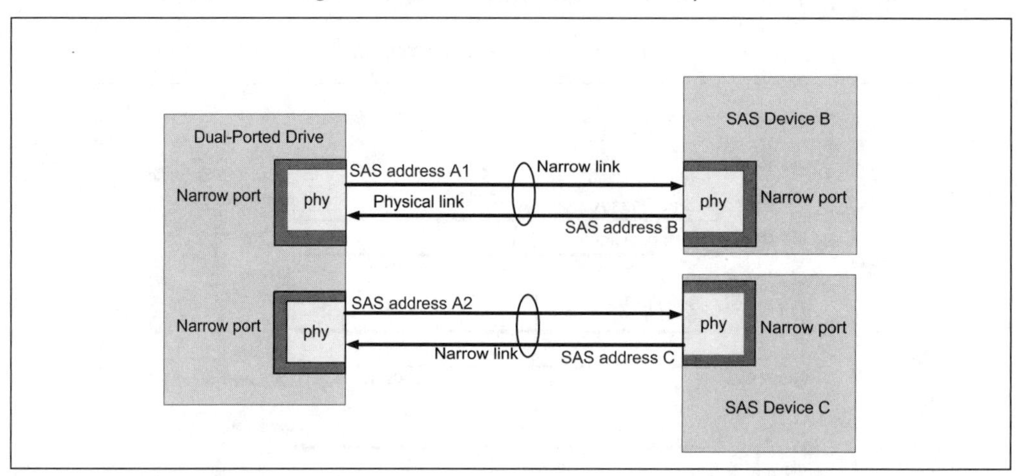

The bandwidth a single Phy can provide is simply the bit rate divided by 10, because the encoding scheme used for serial transmission sends 10 bits on the wire for each byte to be transmitted. A Phy running at 3.0 Gb/s can thus provide a full-duplex 300 MB/s data transfer rate. For example, an HBA with 8 Phys running at 3.0 Gbits/s can support a full-duplex 2400 MB/s bandwidth.

Wide and Narrow Ports

Let's return to the comment made earlier: an HBA will be designed to support wide ports while a disk drive will not. The reason for this has to do with providing more connection opportunities and avoiding single points of failure in a storage subsystem. Consider the example implementation shown in Figure 5-11, in which a rack of 14 disk drives is connected in a subsystem designed to eliminate single points of failure. To maximize the effectiveness of this strategy, each drive needs to be dual ported and be accessible by two different HBAs. If any one path in the system fails, the drive will still be accessible to the system.

Figure 5-11: Example System with Failover Support

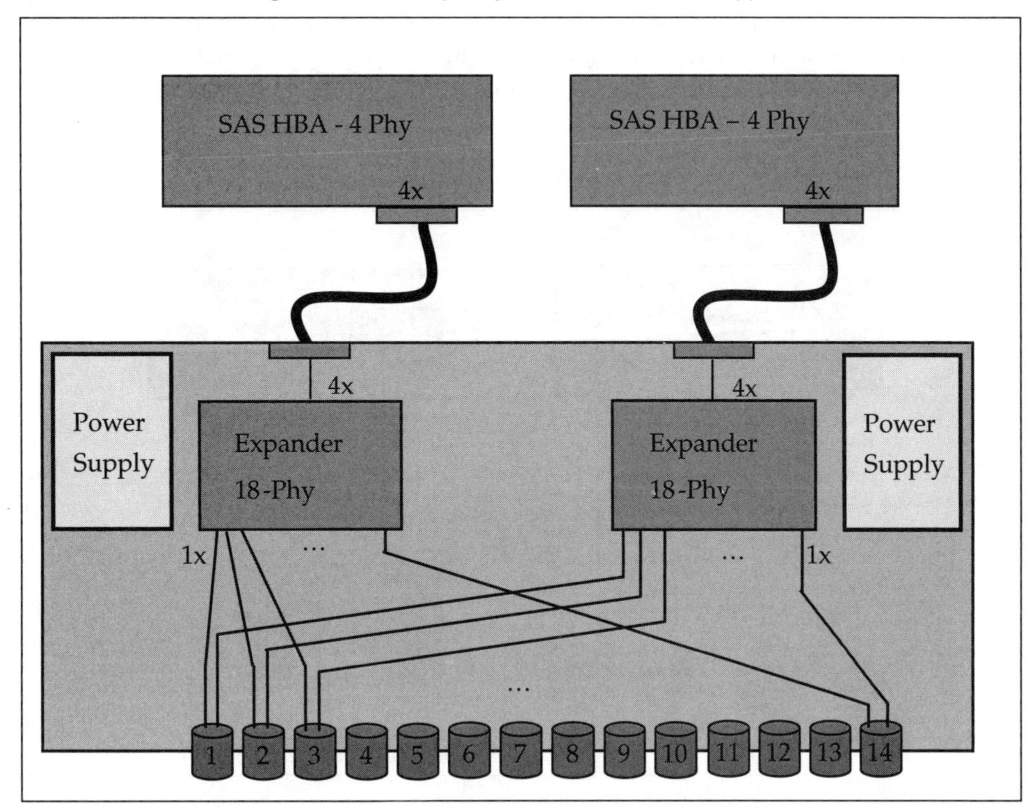

In Figure 5-11, both HBAs are shown with wide ports containing four Phys, allowing each of them to access up to four drives at the same time. There are more than four drives in the system, though, so an expander is used to act as a switch that scales up the number of accessible drives. The goal of expanders is to increase the number of connection possibilities available to a device, allowing a connection to be established between any one of its Phys to any of the other of its Phys (for more on expanders, see Appendix A, entitled "Expander Devices," on page 505). The expanders are also attached to each other through their subtractive ports to provide a path that allows the two HBAs to communicate with each other to stay synchronized in terms of their operation. A subtractive port is the path an edge expander chooses as the destination for a connection request when it cannot resolve the address. This simplifies the expander because it has a default path and therefore doesn't have to track all the addresses in the system. The point is that it's advantageous for HBAs to have wide ports.

It's not required that an HBA use all of its Phys to create a wide port like the one just described. The Phys could be attached to different attached addresses like the example on the left in Figure 5-12, where the HBA ends up with four narrow ports instead of a single 4-wide port because there are devices with different addresses attached to it. As illustrated in the diagram, the same HBA could have 4 individual ports, or a single wide port depending on what is attached to it.

Figure 5-12: HBA with Narrow Ports or One Wide Port

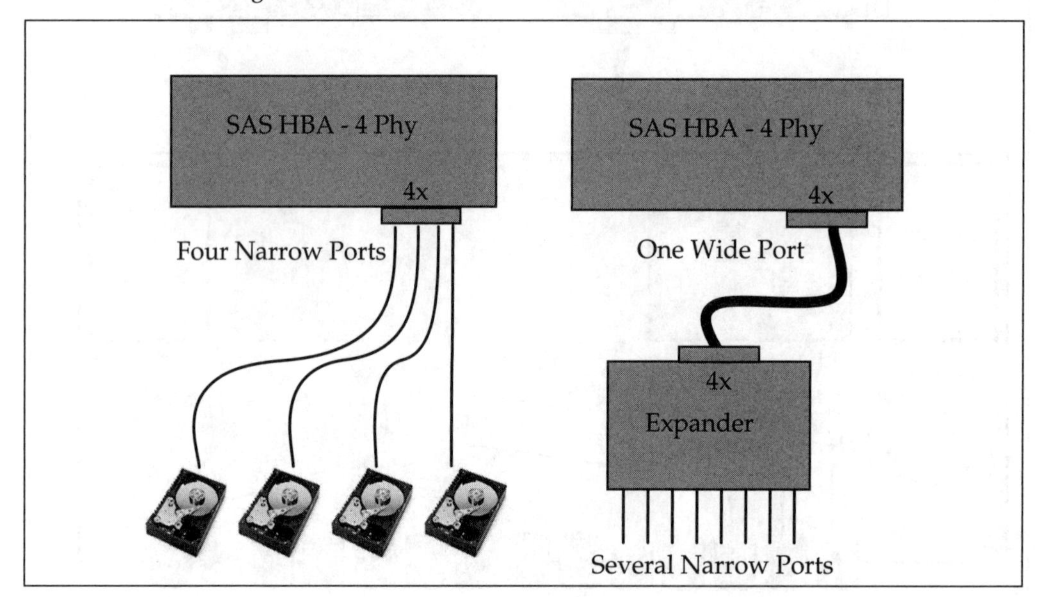

By contrast, a disk drive or mass storage device can benefit from two Phys, but not, ordinarily, from a wide port. There are two reasons for this:

1. First, as mentioned earlier, high-speed, enterprise-class drives can only sustain data rates of 75 to 80 MB/s, so there's no motivation to implement more than one 300 MB/s port on a drive; it would never be able to use the bandwidth.
2. It's very important that the drive be able to avoid single points of failure, so there is motivation for a second Phy to provide a fail-over mechanism. This is typically handled by building two Phys into the target device, but assigning them different source addresses at the factory. That forces them to always be seen as two separate, narrow ports and precludes them from being grouped into a wide port that might create a single point of failure.

An implementation of the wide port example in Figure 5-11 might look like the illustration shown in Figure 5-13. While several different cable schemes are available (see Chapter 18, entitled "Cables and Connectors," on page 433), two HBAs are each shown connected with four-wide ports to the same backplane to provide a connection path from each HBA to each of the dual-ported drives.

Figure 5-13: Example Implementation of a Wide-Port HBA System

Illustration courtesy of Molex

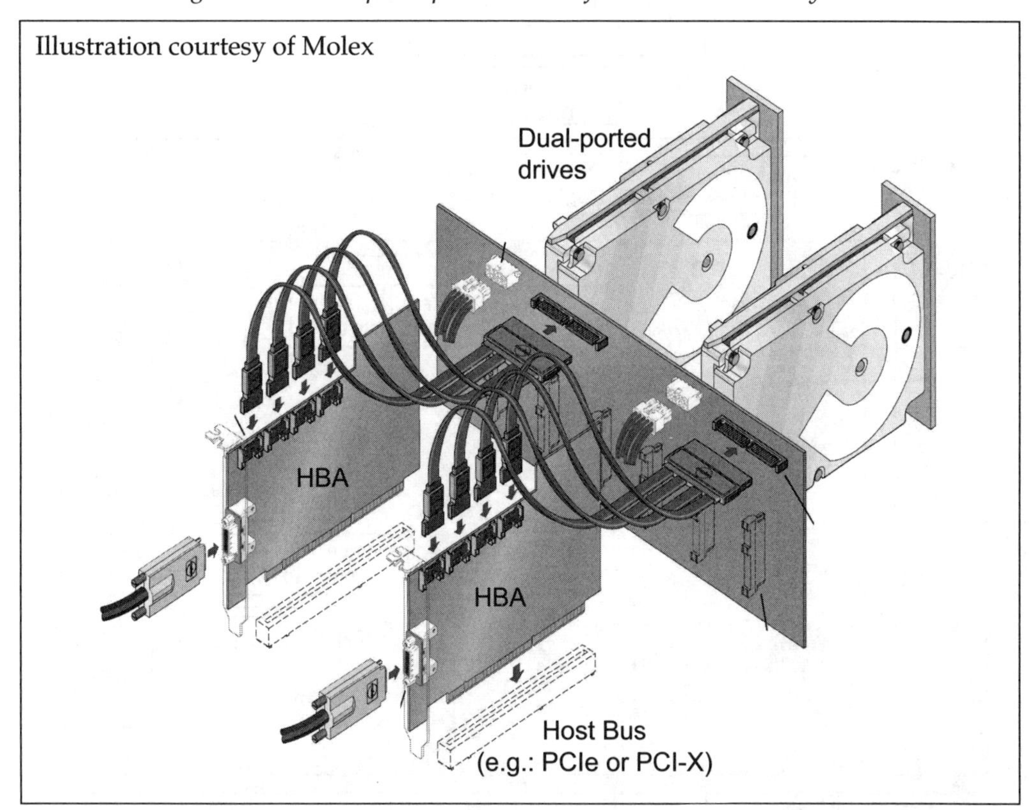

Taking our layer illustration one step further, consider the drawing in Figure 5-14, which shows a device with several Phys that have been grouped into three different ports. As before, the details of the other ports are not shown, but they would each contain Phys consisting of the same logical blocks. Here it can be seen that a port is actually made up of the Phys within it as well as the Port Layer and the Transport Layer. The device has three different attached addresses to which a request can be routed. It is the destination address of a request that determines which port the request will be passed through.

Figure 5-14: Layer in a Device Containing Several Ports

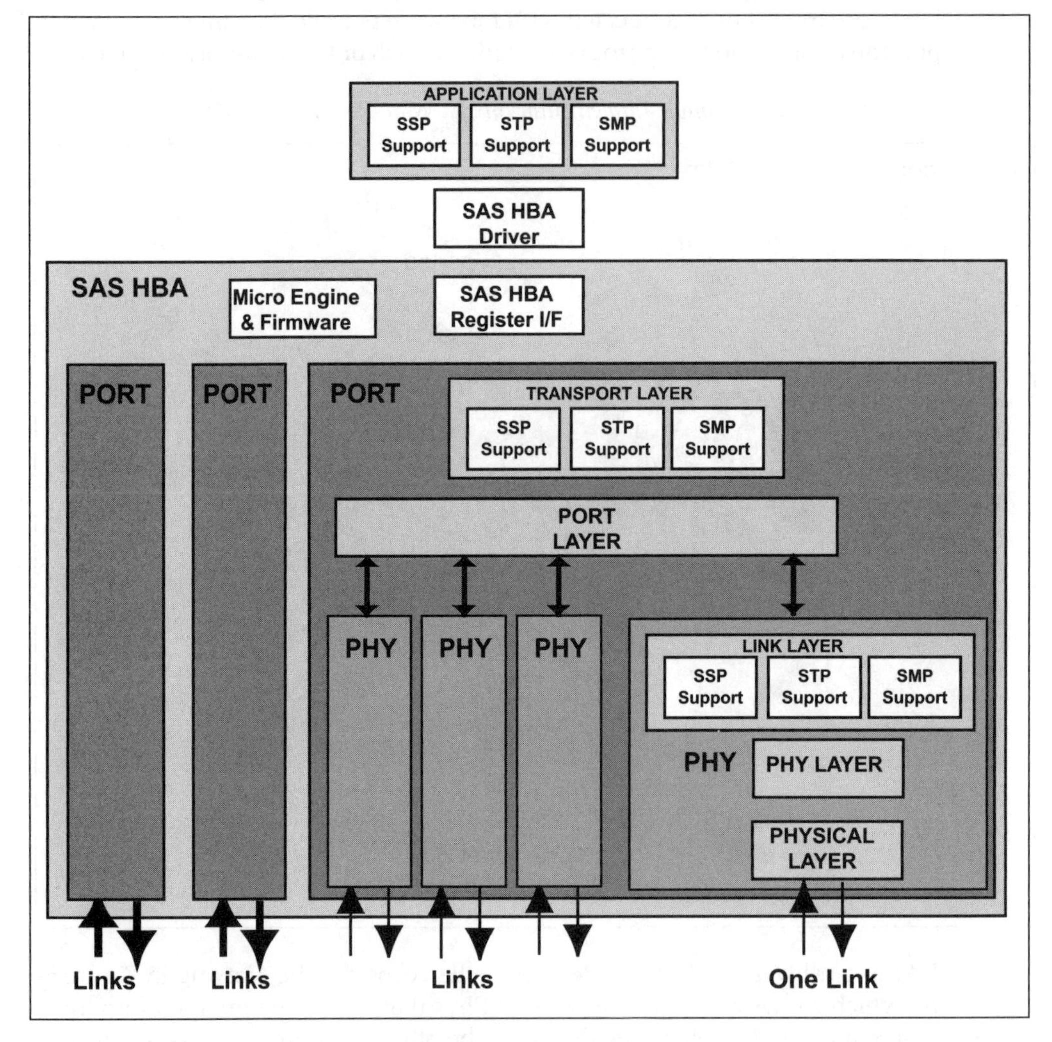

In summary, a *Phy* is the logical block that performs all of the functions of the Link, Phy and Physical Layers. There can be several Phys within one *Port* if they all have the same factory-assigned addresses and all see the same address reported by the attached neighbors. There can be several Ports within a SAS device and, if so, an outgoing transaction is routed to the port that allows it to connect to the destination address. The Port within a device is selected based on the destination address of a request, the Phy within the Port is selected based on availability, and the connection is finally established between the source Phy and the destination Phy.

Part 2: Initialization and Discovery

6 SAS Initialization

The Previous Chapter

The previous chapter gave the necessary background to understand the architecture of narrow versus wide ports. It described the layered architecture of devices, which behave differently depending on whether the device uses narrow or wide ports. Next, details of the layered architecture within a narrow port were presented, and the final section described the layer implementations of wide ports.

This Chapter

This chapter describes the steps by which devices initialize the link for communications. This is a hardware-based process at the beginning, and establishes whether a neighboring device is present, what type it is, what link rates it supports, and its SAS address. Once that is completed, there are steps that must be taken by application software to discover the SAS topology and configure the devices.

The Next Chapter

The next chapter describes the process by which initiators and self-configuring expanders learn which addresses and types of devices are accessible to them in the system. Every initiator must go through this process after a reset or after seeing a BROADCAST (CHANGE) indication. If an expander is visible to an initiator, and it has an address table then, unless the expander is self-configuring, the initiator will need to update the table with the addresses that are accessible to that expander.

Introduction

There are two parts to initializing a SAS device. The first is hardware based and happens after a reset. Devices on either end of a link will automatically begin the process of detecting whether another device is present, whether it is a SAS or SATA device, and at what speeds the interface may be run. There are some steps that have to take place before a receiver can recognize dwords as information from the transmitter, and those are accomplished by the hardware initialization process. The second part is software initialization, and this optional step is under the control of the application software. It consists of reading configuration information from the device and writing values into that space to set up the desired parameters for the device.

Hardware Initialization

General

The goal of hardware initialization is to accomplish the following steps:

1. Detect the presence of an attached device and determine whether it is a SAS or SATA device.
2. Negotiate the highest common transmission rate supported by both devices, using the proper method for a SAS or SATA device type.
3. Identify information about the attached device, including its SAS address.

SAS devices participate as peers in this process rather than having one designated as the controlling device, partly because it's not known ahead of time what type of device will be attached. Even so, there is a difference in the responsibilities of the different device types. End devices only need to attempt the initialization process once after reset. The attached device may not be ready, but after that first attempt the end device can simply wait for some other device to begin the process since there must be an initiator in the system that will access it. If the initialization process doesn't succeed the first time, initiators will repeat it at a vendor-specific rate to check for newly-attached devices. Expanders (both fanout and edge expanders) likewise must continually repeat the process if it fails. It's important to note that this activity only takes place between the two neighbors on either end of the point-to-point link. For example, OOB is not propagated across an expander.

OOB Signaling

The first step is accomplished using what is called Out of Band (OOB) signaling. After a reset, receivers need a regular stream of incoming data so they can lock onto the embedded clock within it and recover meaningful symbols. However, before a SAS device can do that, it has to determine whether there is a device attached and whether SAS or SATA protocol will be used, since the process for using them is different. To find out, an approach was chosen that is very similar to that used in SATA, in which the devices exchange "chirps" or bursts of activity on the link. This only needs to be recognized by the receiver as activity or quiet time on the link, rather than the encoded bytes used in normal transmission, so a squelch detect circuit can do the job. The pattern of activity and quiet time indicates the presence of a device and communicates its type.

Speed Negotiation

The next step is to negotiate the transfer speed on the link. This is a protocol-specific process, but the devices now know which type of device is attached and will follow the proper sequence to achieve speed negotiation. As part of this process, since a steady stream of data is received by both devices, dword synchronization is achieved and receivers can begin to detect valid symbols and meaningful dwords in the data stream.

Identify Sequence

The third and last step is to gather information from the attached device, such as its address and protocol capabilities. SAS devices exchange this information with each other by sending an address frame called the Identify frame after the first two steps have been completed. SATA devices, on the other hand, have no corresponding step because SATA doesn't use addresses. Instead, target devices expect to be connected to only one SATA host, either directly or through a port multiplier. If a SATA target is attached to a SAS device, there will need to be a bridge in one of them to act as the liaison between them, supplying an Identify frame to initiators within the SAS network on behalf of the SATA target.

All of these steps together are taken whenever the Phy is reset. There are levels of reset for a device, but all of them involve this part, referred to as the Phy Reset Sequence, and will result in the hardware initialization steps.

Reset Sequences

SAS devices have more than one level of device reset, as listed here and illustrated in Figure 6-1:

- Hard Reset - resets the entire device, including all the layers.
- Link Reset - resets only the link and Phy Layers of a device. This includes a Phy reset and sending of the Identification Sequence.

- Phy Reset - resets only the Phy Layer of a device and includes only OOB and speed negotiation.

The Link and Phy resets are most interesting to us at this point because it is within these sequences that the hardware initialization steps we've described so far take place. As shown in Figure 6-1, the Phy reset involves sending OOB and performing speed negotiation, while the Link reset includes that as well as sending the Identify frame.

Figure 6-1: SAS Link Reset Sequence

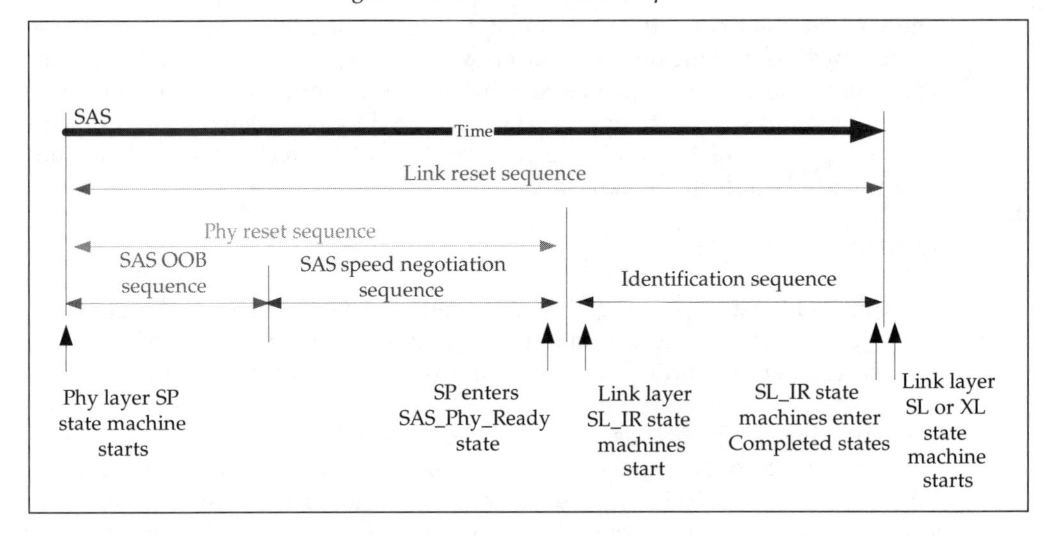

OOB (Out of Band) Signaling

For both SAS and SATA, the hardware initialization process begins with OOB signaling. Pronounced either as letters or as a funny-sounding syllable, OOB can be misleading because the term might be understood to mean that a dedicated signal is used rather than the normal data path. However, the SAS OOB signals do travel within the normal data path. The reason they are called OOB is because the signaling takes place before the receiver has been prepared to recognize dwords and so it is not part of the normal transmission process. Let's consider what is involved in the process of OOB communication.

OOB Mechanism

OOB signaling is accomplished by the absence of activity from the transmitter, during which the differential voltage is essentially zero, followed by burst times during which an ALIGN(0) primitive is transmitted. The bursts are indistinguishable at the receiver as anything other than non-idle traffic, but that is sufficient for the moment; their arrival indicates that a device is attached and that the initialization process can proceed. The receiver only needs a squelch-detect circuit to be able to detect the sequence of idle and burst activity on the link, and an example of this sequence is illustrated in Figure 6-2.

Figure 6-2: OOB Signaling

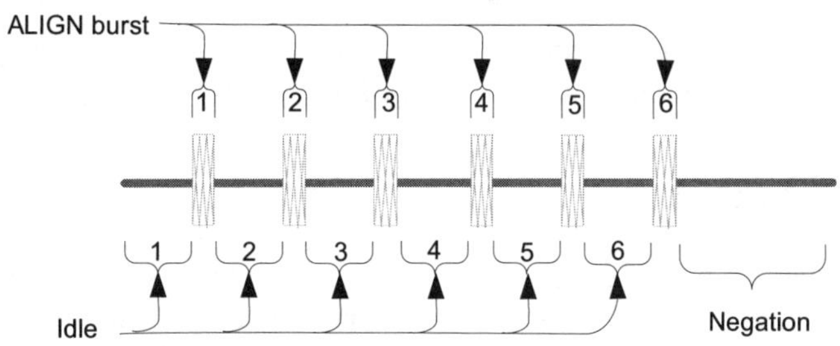

OOB Transmission

To accomplish OOB signaling, transmitters send a pattern of 6 idle/burst pairs followed immediately by a longer idle time referred to as negation time, as shown in Figure 6-2. The times for these OOB activities are specified in terms of the OOBI (Out of Band Interval). The OOBI is based on the clock tolerance of the first generation (G1) SAS speed of 1.5 Gb/s, and is defined as ranging from 666.600ps to 666.733ps. The burst times are always a fixed length and defined in the standard as 160 OOBI, which works out to a range between 106.66ns to 106.68ns. The idle and negation times are also defined in terms of the OOBI, and these are what change to convey one of three OOB meanings as summarized in Table 6-1 on page 130. The goal, of course, is that these different Idle and Negation times should be easily distinguished from each other.

Table 6-1: Transmitter OOB Timing

OOB Signal	Burst Time	Idle Time	Negation Time
COMWAKE	160 OOBI (106.66 - 106.68ns)	160 OOBI (106.66 - 106.68ns)	280 OOBI (186.65- 186.69 ns)
COMINIT/ COMRESET	160 OOBI (106.66 - 106.68ns)	480 OOBI (319.0 - 320.0 ns)	800 OOBI (533.28 - 533.39 ns)
COMSAS	160 OOBI (106.66 - 106.68ns)	1440 OOBI (959.9 - 960.1 ns)	2400 OOBI (1599. - 1600. ns)

OOB Reception

The receiver is only looking for 4 OOB idle/burst pairs out of the 6 that are sent by the transmitter. Once it detects 4 pairs, it considers the event to have been detected, but it's not completed until the corresponding negation time is also seen. The same event cannot be detected again until after the negation time has been seen. Figure 6-3 illustrates a receiver detecting a COMWAKE event, showing both the point at which the information is detected and where it is completed.

Figure 6-3: Receiver OOB Detection

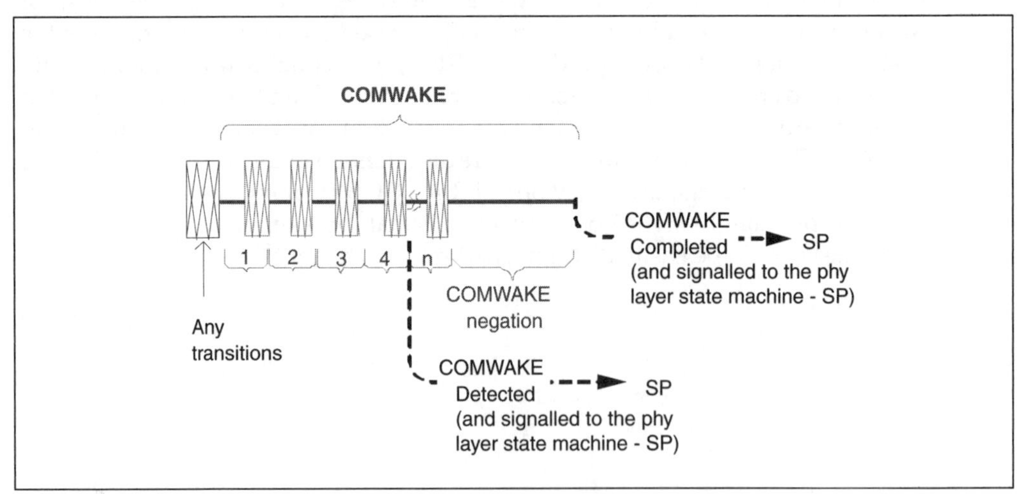

As mentioned earlier, the receiver is not checking burst times, which are constant anyway. Instead, it only looks at the idle and negation times to see the intended information as summarized in Table 6-2 and Table 6-3 below.

Table 6-2: Receiver OOB Idle Detection Timing

OOB Signal	May Detect	Shall Detect	Shall Not Detect
COMWAKE	55 to 175 ns	101.3 to 112 ns	less than 55ns or more than 175 ns
COMINIT/ COMRESET	175 to 525 ns	304 to 336 ns	less than 175ns or more than 525 ns
COMSAS	525 to 1575 ns	911.7 to 1008	less than 525ns or more than 1575 ns

Table 6-3: Receiver OOB Negation Detection Timing

OOB Signal	Shall Detect
COMWAKE	> 175 ns
COMINIT/ COMRESET	> 525 ns
COMSAS	> 1575 ns

SAS OOB Protocol

The standard shows three examples of SAS OOB timing, but they can be summarized by saying that all SAS devices send COMINT after reset and wait for COMINIT or COMSAS in return. The timing of receiving one of these patterns depends on which device comes out of reset first. If expander or initiator Phys do not see a response to their COMINIT transmission, they will resend it repeatedly at a vendor-specified rate. End devices, on the other hand, don't repeat the process. They send COMINIT once and then simply wait for another device to initiate the process later if no response is seen the first time.

One of the timing examples from the standard is recreated in Figure 6-4, where the sequence of sending and receiving COMINIT, followed by sending and receiving COMSAS can be readily seen. Receipt of COMSAS is understood by SAS devices as an indication that the neighboring device is another SAS device.

If COMSAS is not received, that would indicate the presence of either a SATA device or else a SAS device that is not responding.

Figure 6-4: SAS OOB Sequence

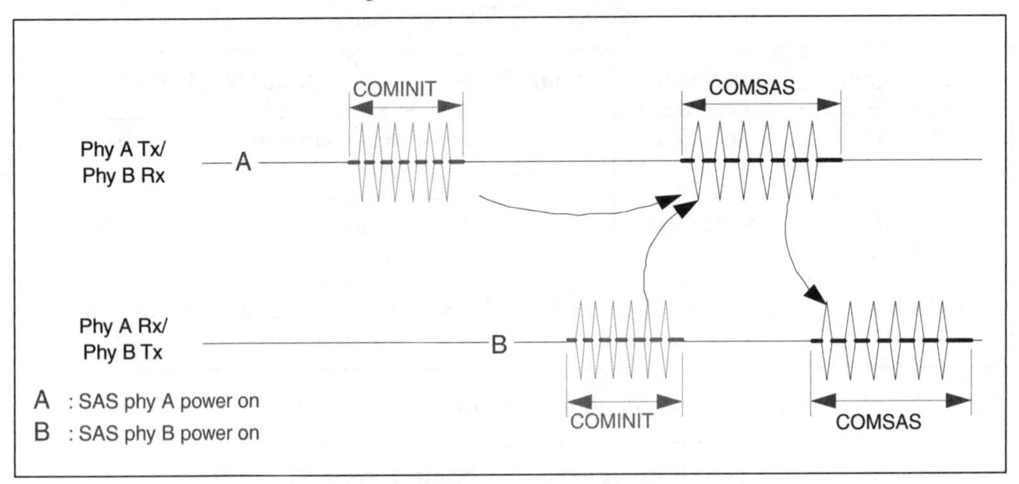

As illustrated in Figure 6-5 on page 133, a SATA device might not recognize or respond to a COMSAS OOB at all. Another possibility is that it might misinterpret the COMSAS as another COMWAKE and resend the COMINIT. Either response is understood by the SAS device to indicate that a SATA device is probably attached. The next step, as shown in the figure, is to send the COMWAKE pattern to see whether the device will respond to SATA OOB. Note that an attached SATA device can only be a target and not a host, according to the standard, because SAS only support targets. The SAS device may optionally be able to detect if a SATA Host has been illegally attached and report that in the Phy Mode Descriptor of the Protocol-Specific Port mode page for the device.

Figure 6-5: SAS to SATA OOB

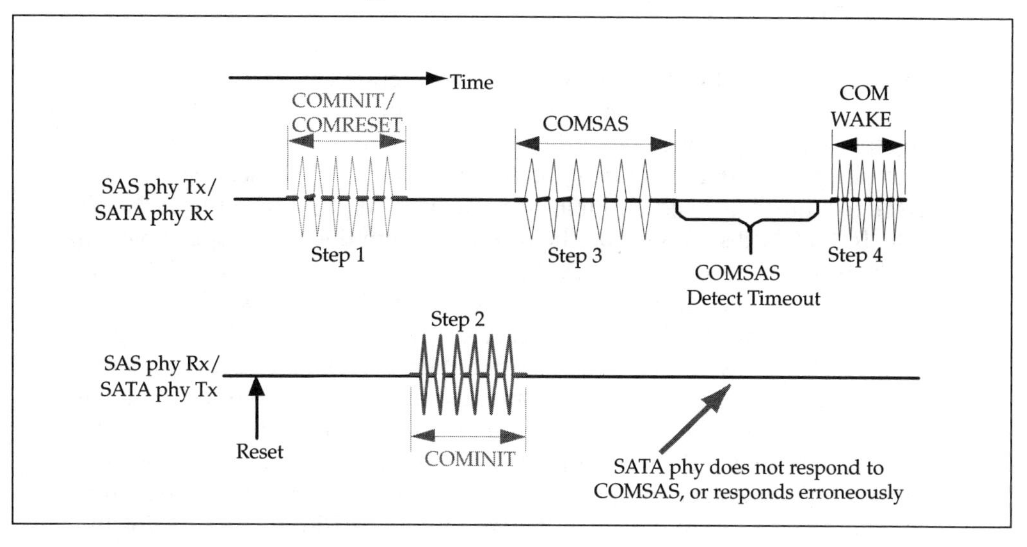

Speed Negotiation

After the initial OOB patterns are sent and the device recognizes the attached device type, the next step is to negotiate the operational speed of the link. This is accomplished by sending a pattern at the desired rate to the neighbor and listening for the response.

Speed Negotiation Process

This process starts with each transmitter sending primitives at the lowest speed. After verifying that speed, both will change to the next higher speed and repeat the process until either all supported speeds have been attempted or a speed is found that does not work. Although there may be several steps involved, once the process is complete the devices will have verified all the speeds that they can mutually support rather than just the highest common speed. This information might be useful later if the link experiences trouble and the system wishes to shift the link to another supported speed. A potential drawback to this approach is that it can take significantly longer to complete than the SATA speed negotiation process (see Chapter 20, entitled "SATA Initialization," on page 489). This is because it takes time to go through all the possible speed steps, and because SAS implements a fairly long recovery time between those speed steps to allow PLLs (Phase-Locked-Loop clock synchronizing logic) to make adjustments for the next speed.

Peer Operation

In going through the process, SAS devices operate as peers rather than in host and target roles. One reason for this is that they won't know what their role in the topology is going to be until later. An expander Phy, for example, may be attached to an initiator, a target, or another expander. Consequently, a symmetric algorithm was needed. First, both devices send ALIGN(0)s at the slowest rate. If ALIGN(0)s are seen on the receiver within the SNLT (Speed Negotiation Lock Time), then they send ALIGN(1)s until the SNTT (Speed Negotiation Transmit Time) is completed. If ALIGN(1)s are also received, this rate window succeeds, otherwise it fails. If it succeeds, wait for the RCD (Rate Change Delay) time of 500µs, then increase the speed to the next rate and repeat the process. If the rate window fails, reduce the speed to the previous working rate and try again. This sequence is repeated until all the rates have been verified or until both a supported and an unsupported rate are found. As an aside, the very long RCD recovery time between rate windows was requested by some members of the working group to ensure sufficient time for a PLL to prepare for the next rate.

Example

The example shown in Figure 6-6 on page 135 illustrates this process. One device starts sending ALIGN(0)s at the Generation 1 rate of 1.5 Gb/s but does not see them on the receiver. After the SNTT time, that rate is understood to be not working, so the rate is increased to the Generation 2 value of 3.0 Gb/s and ALIGN(0)s are sent again. This time, the neighboring device is also sending ALIGN(0)s and these are received before the SNLT (Speed Negotiation Lock Time) expires. In response, each begins sending ALIGN(1)s and receives them before the SNTT expires, confirming that the G2 rate window is supported. Based on that, they cease transmission for the RCD time, then try again at the next higher Generation 3 speed, which will likely be 6.0 Gb/s. (At the time of this writing the next generation speed had not yet been defined, but the T10 Phy working group was discussing the issues that would be involved with using 6.0 Gb/s as the third generation rate.)

The standard requires that a device participate in speed negotiation windows up to its highest supported rate plus one. In this example, the highest supported rate is the G2 rate, but the device "participates" in the next higher rate by sending nothing during that time. The expectation is that the other device will recognize that there was no response and back down to the previously working rate.

Figure 6-6: SAS Speed Negotiation Example

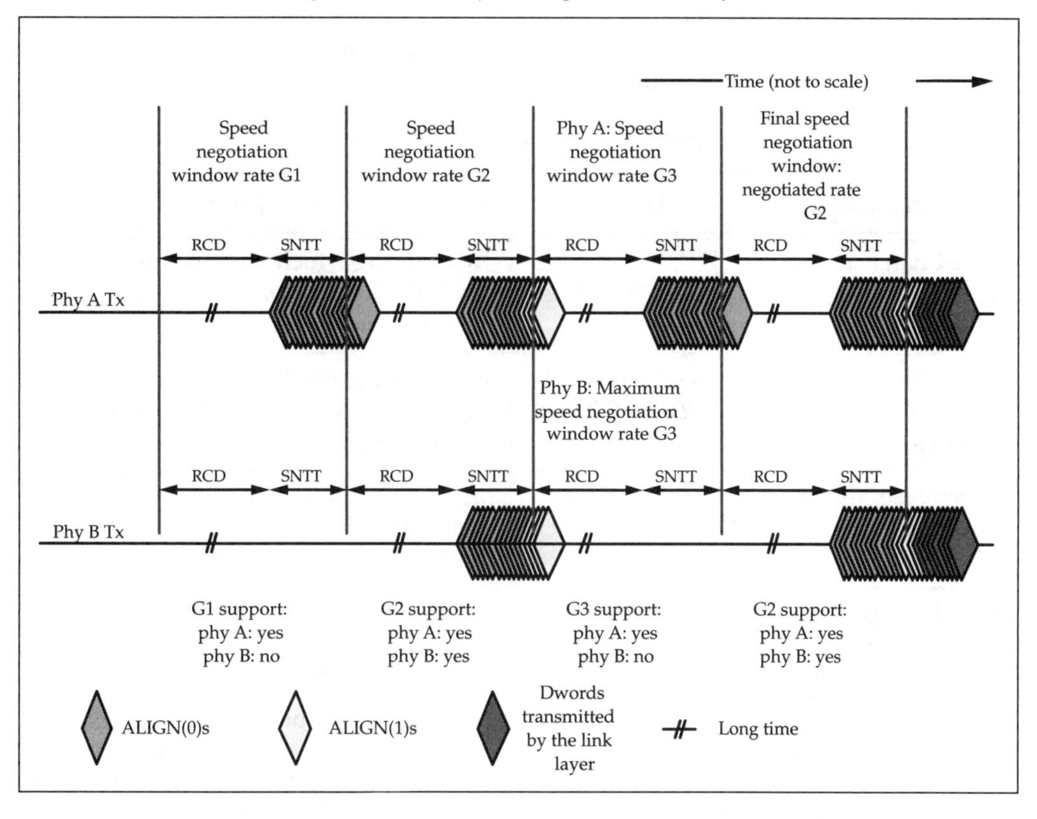

If neither device supported that higher frequency they'd both be quiet during that rate window. Detecting a rate that does work and then a rate that doesn't work defines the highest supported link rate for both devices.

When the G3 rate window is attempted in this example, one device does not support it and sends nothing. The other device sends ALIGN(0)s, but doesn't receive any coming back before the SNTT expires. Both devices recognize that the current rate window has failed and, in response, they retreat to the previous working rate and try it again. If this rate works the second time, then that becomes the negotiated rate. It is not expected that the repeated rate should fail but, if the Phy fails to achieve dword synchronization during the final speed negotiation window, the entire process has failed and the two devices will start again from the beginning. This unlikely event is referred to as a Phy Reset Problem and may be counted and reported in the corresponding field of the Report

Phy Error Log Page or the SMP Report Phy Error Log page.

The overall process of SAS speed negotiation is fairly slow, requiring about 1.8ms for 1.5 Gb/s and 2.4ms for 3.0 Gb/s. The times allocated for each step are defined in terms of the OOBI, as listed in Table 66 of the standard and repeated here for convenience in Table 6-4.

Table 6-4: SAS Speed Negotiation Timing

Parameter	Time	Description
Rate Change Delay Time (RCDT)	750,000 OOBI (499.95 - 500.05 μs)	Time during which the transmitter sends D.C. idle between speed negotiation windows.
Speed Negotiation Transmit Time (SNTT)	163,840 OOBI (109.21 - 109.24 μs)	Time during which ALIGN(0) or ALIGN(1) is sent during the speed negotiation sequence.
Speed Negotiation Lock Time (SNLT)	153,600 OOBI (102.39 – 102.41 μs)	Max time for a transmitter to send ALIGN(1) if a rate window is to succeed.
Speed Negotiation Window time	913,840 OOBI (609.17 – 609.29 μs)	RCDT + SNTT

It may happen that a SAS device attempts to communicate on the link and receives no response. Target devices will only try once to announce their presence; if no reply is seen to their COMINIT, they'll wait for an initiator to begin the process. Expanders are expected to try again within 500ms, since both targets and initiators may be waiting on them to detect new devices. For clarification, detecting new devices is based on receiving OOB signaling from the device. Initiators must continuously attempt to get the OOB working, at a rate of not less than 10ms between attempts.

SAS Link Initialization Example

To bring together the concepts discussed so far, consider the example shown in Figure 6-7 on page 137, which has an expander attached to a SAS initiator, a SAS target device, and a SATA target. As a starting point, assume Device B powers up first and is the first to send its OOB pattern. In the example, the expander is not yet prepared to participate and so Device B sees no response.

Since it is a target device, it has done its duty and can now simply wait for an initiator in the system to re-initiate the process for it some time later.

Figure 6-7: Initialization Example

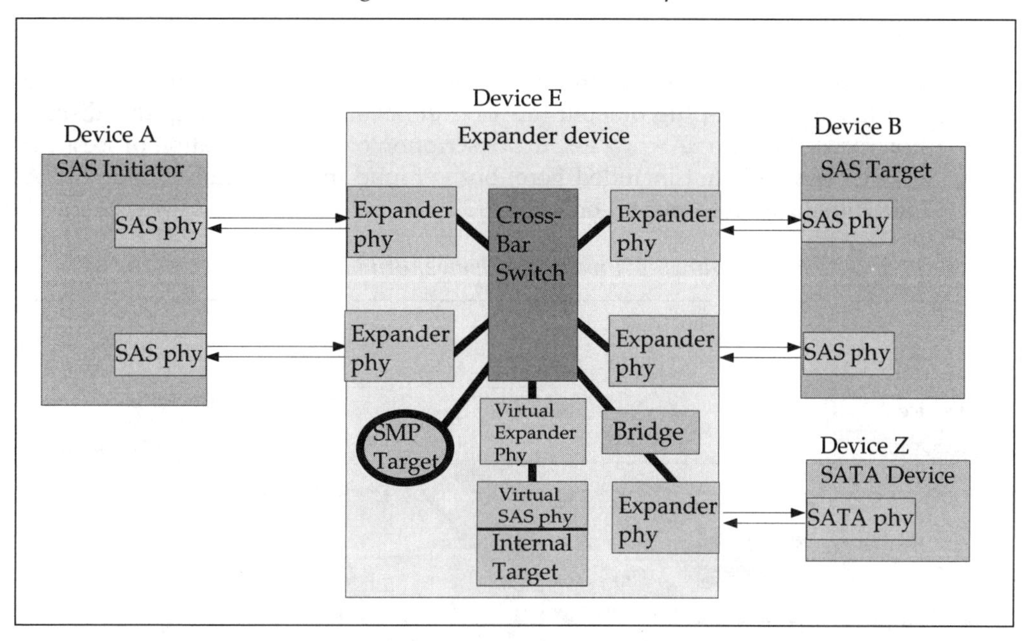

Next, assume Device A powers up. It also sends OOB and gets no reply, but since it is an initiator, it will need to periodically keep trying the OOB, at a vendor-specific rate. When Expander device E powers up, it begins the link reset sequence (see Figure 6-1 on page 128) by sending COMINIT on all its Phys, probably all at the same time. Device A responds with COMINIT and COMSAS as expected, and resolves the speed negotiation at a compatible rate to complete the Phy reset sequence. Next, the two devices exchange the Identify address frames to inform each other of their SAS address and device type. That completes the link reset sequence.

Device B will respond in the same way and learn the same information about its attached device: that it is an expander device with a certain address and supported link rate. The expander (for more detail on expander behavior, see Appendix A, entitled "Expander Devices," on page 505) will see the devices complete initialization at different times, and each subsequent case will result in the expander sending a BROADCAST (CHANGE) primitive on every port except the one that detected that change. For example, as shown in Figure 6-8 on page 138, if device A completes initialization first, and then B, that means A will see a BROADCAST (CHANGE) primitive to indicate that something has changed in the system topology after it finished initialization. As an initiator, device A will then need to query the expander to learn what has changed. (The means for doing this is described in Chapter 7, entitled "Discovery Process," on page 159.)

So far, device Z has still not initialized, so the expander will continue to retry that link at the hot-plug timeout rate of every 500ms. To help keep this discussion focused on the SAS process, the description of the initialization process for a SATA device is not included here, but is found in the section called "SATA Link Initialization Example" on page 495.

Figure 6-8: Broadcast (Change) Primitives

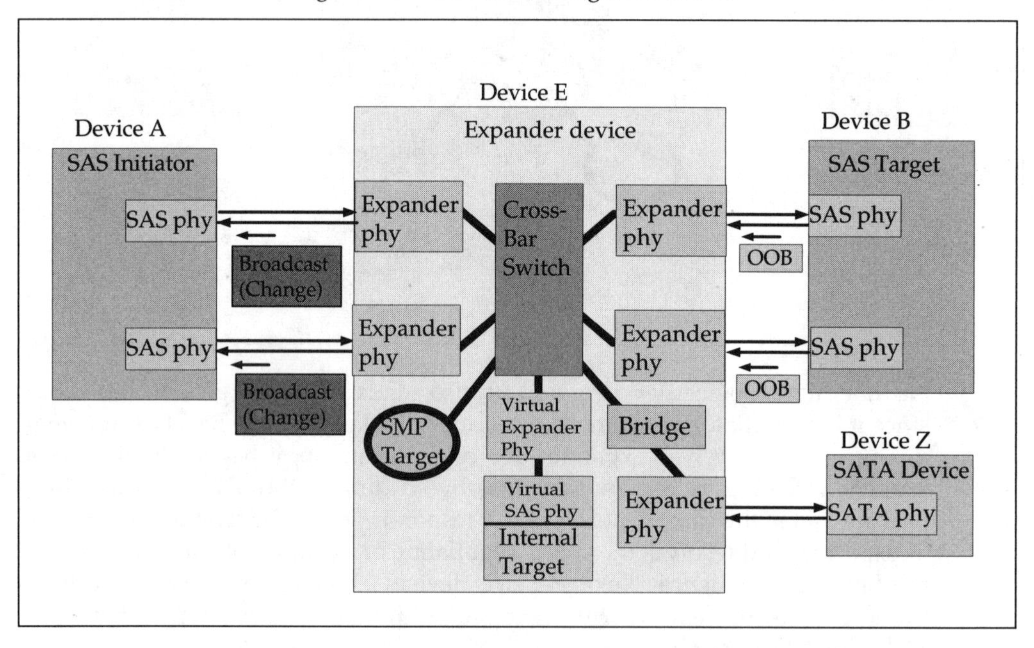

As a first step in the discovery process device A queries the expander to learn how many Phys it contains and what their associated SAS addresses are. To do that, it sends an SMP REPORT GENERAL command to the expander to get the number of Phys. Then it sends an SMP DISCOVER request for each of those Phys, starting with Phy0 and incrementing forward until it has reached the number reported. In this example, device A learns that the initiator has 6 Phys available, two of which connect back to itself. Of the others, one is an internal SAS Phy, one has no device currently attached, and two are attached to device B. The initiator can read that device B is an end device, has a wide port with two

Phys attached to the expander at a given rate, and supports SSP protocol. There are no other expanders in the domain and thus no need for the initiator to map any table entries for the expander. At this point device A could send an OPEN request to access device B or to the internal Phy in the expander.

When device Z does initialize, the expander informs the rest of the system that a new device has come online by sending a BROADCAST (CHANGE) primitive on all the ports except the one that detected the change. Recall that this broadcast only informs the system that some change has occurred and contains no information about what that change was (in keeping with the design goal of keeping expanders simple and inexpensive). It's up to the initiators in the system to respond to this notification by repeating as much of the discovery process as necessary to learn what has changed.

Device B has no responsibilities when it sees the broadcast. As a target device, it is not tracking the topology and simply waits for access from initiators. The same thing is true for the internal Phy of the expander, which is also only a target. Device A, though, is an initiator, and will need to repeat the discovery process to find out what has changed. In doing so, it learns that an address has been added for a new SATA device. This is a good point to mention that SATA devices do not themselves implement the 64-bit SAS address that is needed for access in a SAS topology. Instead, the device containing the bridge from SATA to SAS must supply that address, and in this case it is the expander bridge that will do it. This artificial address might be created by using the SAS address of the expander as a base value and offsetting it by the Phy number, for example.

Phy Failure Example

Next, assume one of the two Phys on device B fails, as shown in Figure 6-9 on page 140. When the expander detects this change it will again be necessary to send a BROADCAST (CHANGE) primitive on all the other ports. As before, this is only really interesting for device A, which will again need to repeat the discovery process to verify all the paths it can access and find out what has changed. For this case there have been no address changes, but the path to device B had been a wide port and now it is narrow. That doesn't really affect the topology much, since device A just needs to know which addresses it can see, but now only one connection at a time can be established with device B, instead of two at a time.

Figure 6-9: Working Phy Fails, Causing Broadcast (Change)

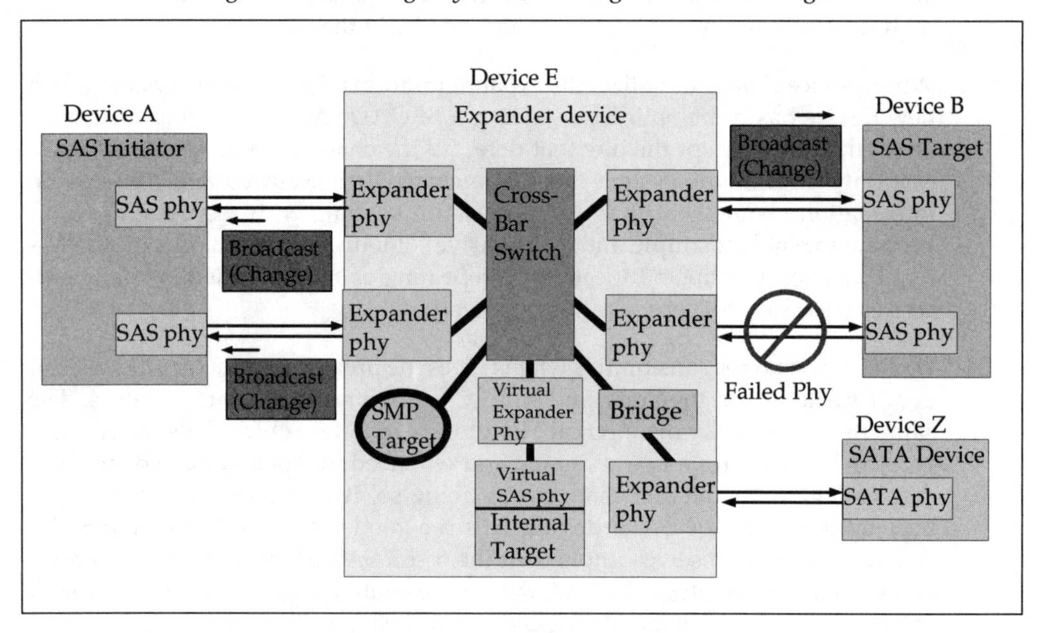

The expander's internal or virtual SAS target port, typically included to implement enclosure services, will also have a unique SAS address. The logic associated with the enclosure services processor could directly access the services, or could convert the SCSI commands to another protocol, like I^2C, that is commonly used for these services. However, I^2C is slow (only 1-bit wide and running at 100KHz), so better performance will be achieved if this is implemented as a full target device. Another note along these lines is that the standard only documents SSP using standard SCSI for accessing the device and does not include SMP. The reason for choosing SSP over SMP for access is that SMP is limited to 1K frames per function and so might not provide enough payloads.

Software Initialization

General

When a system starts up, a software routine will be called to scan the buses and find out the number and type of devices installed. Then, before an application is able to make full use of a target device, it must learn the operating parameters. For SCSI, and consequently for SAS as well, parameters are defined in a few broad categories (see the SPC-3 standard), such as Diagnostic parameters, Log parameters, and Mode parameters. This device-specific information is found by accessing the local memory contained in a device's Logical Units. The information is organized into blocks called *pages* and some pages are also defined to have *subpages*.

Configuration

The pages that are most interesting for our discussion here are the Mode pages, because they contain the configuration details for the device and allow the software to read and program it. Some of these pages are used by all devices while others are only valid for specific device types. The pages used depend on the device type. A partial list of the mode pages employed by a disk drive is shown in Table 6-5 on page 141. Referring to that list, we can see that page code 08h in the table contains information about the caching properties for the device. This area allows software to enable or disable functions for the disk as needed, like read caching, write caching, and prefetching. There's no reason that changing the interface would affect what the drive needs to do in this regard, so this page can remain unchanged from its use in SCSI.

Another example is page code 02h that lists the parameters affecting the behavior of this device with regard to the process of disconnecting from the bus and reconnecting later. This SAS page must change from the SCSI implementation because the serial bus must deal with different issues.

The mode pages are read with a MODE SENSE command and written with a MODE SELECT command, just as they are in SCSI.

Table 6-5: Partial List of Mode Parameter Pages for Disk Drives

Page Code	Name	Description
02h	Disconnect/Reconnect Page	For all device types, this determines the behavior of the target with respect to freeing the bus.
03h	Format Page	For disk drives, this gives information needed to format the medium.

Table 6-5: Partial List of Mode Parameter Pages for Disk Drives

Page Code	Name	Description (Continued)
04h	Disk Drive Geometry Page	For disk drives, this gives the fixed geometry information.
08h	Cache Page	Controls the use or write caching or read prefetching, reports the size of available cache memory.

Parameter Storage

Typically, a logical unit maintains three copies of these parameters, referred to as:

- **Current** – the parameters the device is currently using. These values are stored in RAM and are lost when power is removed from the device.
- **Default** – these values are fixed in ROM for the device to use as factory-installed defaults.
- **Saved** – this set of parameters is stored in non-volatile memory and is available for use at power-up. When the device is powered up, the saved values are copied into the current parameters for operation. At the manufacturer, the default values are copied to the saved values and are used until new parameters are written. These factory default values can also be restored to the saved space with a SCSI command.

Most of the Application Layer chapter in the SAS standard describes mode page modifications that depend on the protocol. For SSP, the SAS interface introduces new issues with respect to the existing SCSI interface, so some of these pages require adaptations to include parameters specific to SAS. Note that the mode pages are considered optional, but provide much useful information.

Mode Pages and Log Pages

Disconnect-Reconnect Mode Page — 02h

The first such modified page is the Disconnect-Reconnect mode page, which every transport modifies for its own purposes. Different protocols choose which fields they want to support. Page 02h and its field definitions are shown in

Table 6-6 below and described in the text that follows it.

Table 6-6: Disconnect-Reconnect Mode Page

	Field(s)		
Byte 0	PS	SPF (0)	Page Code (02h)
1	Page Length (0Eh)		
2 to 3	Reserved		
4 to 5	Bus Inactivity Time Limit		
6 to 7	Reserved		
8 to 9	Maximum Connect Time Limit		
10 to 11	Maximum Burst Size		
12 to 13	Reserved		
14 to 15	First Burst Size		

PS – Page Save. When read, indicates whether the target is able to save page contents into non-volatile memory when instructed to do so by an initiator, as defined in SPC-3. A diagnostic program can put settings into this page and tell the device to save and use them rather than its own internal defaults. This is useful for cases when drives are turned off and back on, and need to remember their operational parameters. The device will use its internal default settings unless there is a saved page it should use. Writing this bit with a Mode Select command will save the settings of this page if the device is able to do so.

SPF – SubPage Format. The standard ran out of mode page codes, and consequently subpages were added to increase the number of available pages. Since the subpage code field is one byte in size, up to 256 subpages may be defined for each page. A zero in this field indicates a legacy mode page, in which case there is no subpage code.

Page Code – value of 02h = Disconnect-Reconnect mode page

Page Length – the length of this page is 0Eh bytes, counting only what comes after this length indicator byte.

Bus Inactivity Time Limit – the longest time a target can keep a connection open without sending a frame, in units of 100us. If the timer expires, the target must issue a DONE primitive. This timer is only concerned with outgoing frames; incoming frames do not reset it. Note that simply sending a DONE does not mean the connection will be closed immediately. If the other Phy in the connection still has frames to send, it continues to do so. The DONE only obligates it to reply with DONE if it goes longer than 1ms without sending a frame.

Maximum Connect Time Limit – the longest time a target can keep a connection open overall. Again, the units are in 100us increments and if the timer expires, the target must issue a DONE primitive. When doing streaming data over a very efficient connection, the connection could potentially remain open forever while there is data to send. This parameter limits that possibility to avoid starving other devices for bandwidth. As before, simply sending a DONE does not mean the connection will be closed immediately. If the other Phy in the connection still has frames to send, it continues to do so. The DONE only obligates it to reply with DONE if it goes longer than 1ms without sending a frame.

Maximum Burst Size – the largest amount of data that can be transferred within a connection without transferring at least one frame for a different I_T_L_Q nexus. The reason for this is to force pauses in the data transmission to allow other devices a chance to communicate. For example, an intelligent target might supply large amounts of data for a long time and over multiple commands. This parameter limits how much data can be sent for the previous command, preventing one very large request from starving out the next request, and instead causing the device to alternate between competing requests. SAS devices should not need this; it is carried over from SCSI and left in for legacy support. The Bus Inactivity Time Limit and Maximum Connect Time Limit mentioned above are more useful for SAS.

First Burst Size – indicates the amount of data an initiator is allowed to write to a target prior to receiving an XFER_RDY confirmation that the device is ready to receive it. Targets designed to accept an unsolicited write block of this size use this field, and the meaning is akin to an implicit XFER_RDY. This option was designed for high-latency environments like iSCSI, in which the time spent waiting on confirmations would have a significant impact on performance. Low-latency environments like SAS do not need this and should not use it. While its use is legal in SAS, there is little motivation to support it either from the HBA side or the target side.

Protocol-Specific Mode Page — 19h (Short Page Format)

Next is the Protocol-Specific mode page that allows the Application Layer to control a few interesting SAS features for this device. The short-form page is shown in Table 6-7 below and its fields are described in the text that follows it.

Table 6-7: Protocol-Specific Mode Page - Short Page Format

Byte	7	6	5	4	3	2	1	0
0	PS	SPF (0)	Page Code (19)					
1	Page Length (6h)							
2	Reserved			Ready LED Meaning	Protocol ID =6h			
3	Reserved							
4-5	I_T Nexus Loss Time							
6-7	Initiator Response Timeout							

Page Code – 19h is the code for the Protocol-Specific mode page

Ready LED Meaning – The behavior of the LED for a drive is based on the setting of this bit as summarized in Table 6-8 on page 145.

Protocol ID – 6h indicates SAS. The entire list of protocols is defined in the SPC-3 standard and is repeated here for convenience in Table 6-9.

Table 6-8: Ready LED Meaning

Power Condition	Bit = 0	Bit = 1
Active or Idle	Normally on, but flashes when processing commands	Normally off, but flashes when processing commands
Standby or Stopped	Normally off, but flashes when processing commands	
Spin up or down	Toggle off or on with period of and 50% duty cycle	
Formatting Media	Toggle off and on in vendor-specific manner	

Table 6-9: Protocol Identifiers

Code	Protocol Identifier
0h	Fibre Channel
1h	Parallel SCSI
2h	Serial Storage Architecture (SSA)
3h	IEEE 1394 "Firewire"
4h	Remote Direct Memory Access (RDMA)
5h	iSCSI
6h	SAS
7h	Automation/Drive Interface Transport Protocol (ADT)
8h	ATA Packet Interface (ATAPI)
9h - Eh	Reserved
Fh	No protocol specified

I_T Nexus Loss Time – This supplies the time that a target should wait before giving up when attempting to reopen a connection to an initiator that earlier requested a response. If a target has a read DATA frame, XFER_RDY frame, or a RESPONSE frame to send to an initiator and tries to open a connection to the original initiator but the OPEN request fails for some reason (OPEN REJECT received or no response or OOB fails, or any problem that would prevent it from connecting to the initiator), then allow this much time, in milliseconds, before giving up and declaring the I_T nexus lost. The recommended setting for this value is 2000 ms, but a setting of zero implies a vendor-specific value, while a setting of all F's means there is no timeout and the device should simply keep trying forever.

The purpose of this timer is to recover from the case when a drive has received a command but has somehow been disconnected from the host requester. Giving up on the transaction allows the device to release resources that would otherwise remain allocated indefinitely. An example would be a drive that had a port fail while a request was in progress but has a second backup port available. Without a timeout like this, the performance for the second port would be poor because buffers would be tied up while waiting to give the response to the earlier request, limiting their use for subsequent requests. Note that I_T nexus loss will mean that all commands for that I_T nexus are aborted, and a unit attention condition is created for that I_T nexus with an additional sense code of I_T NEXUS LOSS OCCURRED.

Initiator Response Timeout – If a target has already sent an XFER_RDY but the initiator is taking too long to respond with the write data, then resources are needlessly tied up. If this timeout, measured in milliseconds, occurs without a response, then simply abort the command with CHECK CONDITION status (2h), sense code of ABORTED COMMAND (Bh), and an additional sense code of INITIATOR RESPONSE TIMEOUT (4Bh/06h). A value of zero in this field means there is no timeout and the target should wait indefinitely. Note that this is essentially timing the initiator, which might actually be doing useful work on another I_T_L_Q nexus even though this target is not seeing a response. Consequently, it should be used with care.

Discussion on Timeouts.

After discussing link timeouts, a question sometimes arises as to whether any mode pages define higher-level timeouts, such as a maximum time permitted for completing a read command. The short answer is no, since neither SCSI nor ATA address that issue at all. Instead, an OS will generally have an OS-specific timeout for such things. Beyond that, OEMs often place timeout requirements on targets they qualify (shorter than expected OS timeouts), but there is no standard for it. The timeouts can be command-specific as well - a FORMAT UNIT command or REWIND (for tapes) might take hours, while an INQUIRY command is expected to complete quickly. The time also depends on the type of Media since, for example, a disk drive takes longer to respond than RAM does. There is an exception to this general rule, though, because the MMC command set defines some optional timeouts for each command that can be enforced.

Protocol-Specific Mode Page — Long Page Format

There is also a long-format Protocol-Specific mode page defined which contains more information about the particular Phys contained in the device. This subpage is also referred to as the Phy Control and Discover subpage because it provides a means of accessing the same information in a device for the discovery process that an SMP DISCOVER request would. As we will see in Chapter 7, entitled "Discovery Process," on page 159, getting information from a complex device like an expander is accomplished using SMP requests. However, supporting SMP functionality adds cost to an end device, so an important use of this page is to provide a means of reporting the discovery information without requiring that end devices implement an SMP target. This subpage provides information on all the Phys for this device, as shown in Table 6-10 below and described in the text that follows it.

Table 6-10: Protocol-Specific Mode Page - Long Format

Byte	Field(s)		
0	PS	SPF (1h)	Page Code (19h)
1	Subpage Code (01h)		
2 to 3	Page Length		
4 to 6	Reserved		
7	Number of Phys		
8 to n	First SAS Phy mode descriptor (see Table 6-11)		
n to m	Next SAS Phy mode descriptor		
m to last	Last SAS Phy mode descriptor		

SPF – The SubPage Format indicates whether there will be more information given as a subpage of a given page. When set to 1, it indicates this is a subpage definition, and the particular subpage will be identified by the subpage code. Subpage 0 is the original legacy page; subpages 1 - FEh represent new pages, while subpage code FFh is used by MODE SENSE to "read all subpages".

Page Code – 19h is the code for the Protocol-Specific mode page

Subpage code – 01h indicates the long subpage

Page Length – number of bytes in this page, not including the bytes prior to the last indicator byte (meaning the total minus 3 bytes)

Number of Phys – indicates how many Phys are contained in this device and thus how many Phy mode descriptors will follow in this page

Phy Descriptors – Each Phy in the device will have a Phy descriptor, with fields as shown in Table 6-11 and described in the following text.

Table 6-11: SAS Phy Mode Descriptor

	Bit 7	6	5	4	3	2	1	0
Byte 0	Reserved							
1	Phy Identifier							
2 to 3	Reserved							
4	Rsvd	Attached Device Type			Reserved			
5	Reserved				Negotiated Physical Link Rate			
6	Reserved				Attached SSP Init Port	Attached STP Init Port	Attached SMP Init Port	Attached SATA Host
7	Reserved				Attached SSP Target Port	Attached STP Target Port	Attached SMP Target Port	Attached SATA Device
8 to 15	SAS Address							
16 to 23	Attached SAS Address							
24	Attached Phy Identifier							
25 to 31	Reserved							
32	Programmed Min Physical Link Rate				Hardware Min Physical Link Rate			
33	Programmed Max Physical Link Rate				Hardware Max Physical Link Rate			
34 to 41	Reserved							
42 to 43	Vendor Specific							
44 to 47	Reserved							

Phy Mode Descriptor

Several fields refer to an "attached" Phy. This information about the neighboring device is reported by the other device after a hard reset, and this is done by sending an IDENTIFY address frame. SAS devices will do this, but SATA devices will not.

Phy Identifier – the number assigned to this Phy that must be unique within the device. The numbers for end devices are not specified by the standard, which means designers should not make assumptions about the numbering scheme that a given device will use. For expanders, though, the Phys are to start with Phy0 and increment forward through the available Phys without gaps. If gaps were allowed, then every discovery process would have to go through all 128 possibilities every time.

Attached device type – Several fields in the descriptor describe attributes of the device attached to this Phy, as listed in Table 6-12. This is the information sent to this Phy by its neighbor with the Identify frame. If an end device is attached, an initiator can open connections to it using protocols that this descriptor indicates are supported. If an expander is attached, initiators would need to open SMP connections to it and continue the discovery process by examining the Phys of the expander.

Table 6-12: Reported Device Types

Value	Description
000b	No device
001b	End device
010b	Edge expander
011b	Fanout expander
all others	Reserved

Negotiated link rate – the physical link rate that resulted from speed negotiation by this Phy during the link reset sequence, or the state of the Phy if it is not yet running at speed. This entire table (see Table 6-13) is really only for an expander device, since reading this page from an end device will only report 1.5 or 3.0 Gb/s. The other entries make sense for an expander, though, because it might be able to see a Phy that has not yet resolved its rate.

Table 6-13: Negotiated Link Rate

Value	Negotiated Physical Link Rate
0h	Unknown - place holder for application client data structure
1h	Phy is disabled (via the Phy Control function)
2h	Phy Reset Problem

Table 6-13: Negotiated Link Rate

Value	Negotiated Physical Link Rate (Continued)
3h	SATA in spin-up hold state
4h	SATA Port Selector, rate not yet negotiated
8h	1.5 Gb/s
9h	3.0 Gb/s

- ***Unknown*** – This could be used as a place holder in an application client's data structure until it has had a chance to query the Phys.
- ***Phy Reset Problem*** – results when the speed negotiation fails during link reset (see Figure 6-10 on page 152). Speed negotiation is described in more detail in the Phy Layer chapter but, to summarize it, SAS tries speed negotiation with the slowest supported rate and, if that works, goes to the next higher rate and tries again. This process finds all the supported speeds, and the highest one that is unsupported, then tries the highest supported speed again. The last speed negotiation window is expected to work. If it fails, the Phys must rerun the Phy reset sequence from the beginning in hopes of a better result. This event is reported here and a count is maintained in the Phy Reset Problem Count field of the REPORT PHY ERROR LOG function. If it keeps failing, an initiator accessing the expander via another Phy can discover the problem and use the PHY CONTROL functions programmed Min/Max Physical Link Rate fields to try to avoid the failing rate.

Figure 6-10: Phy Reset Problem

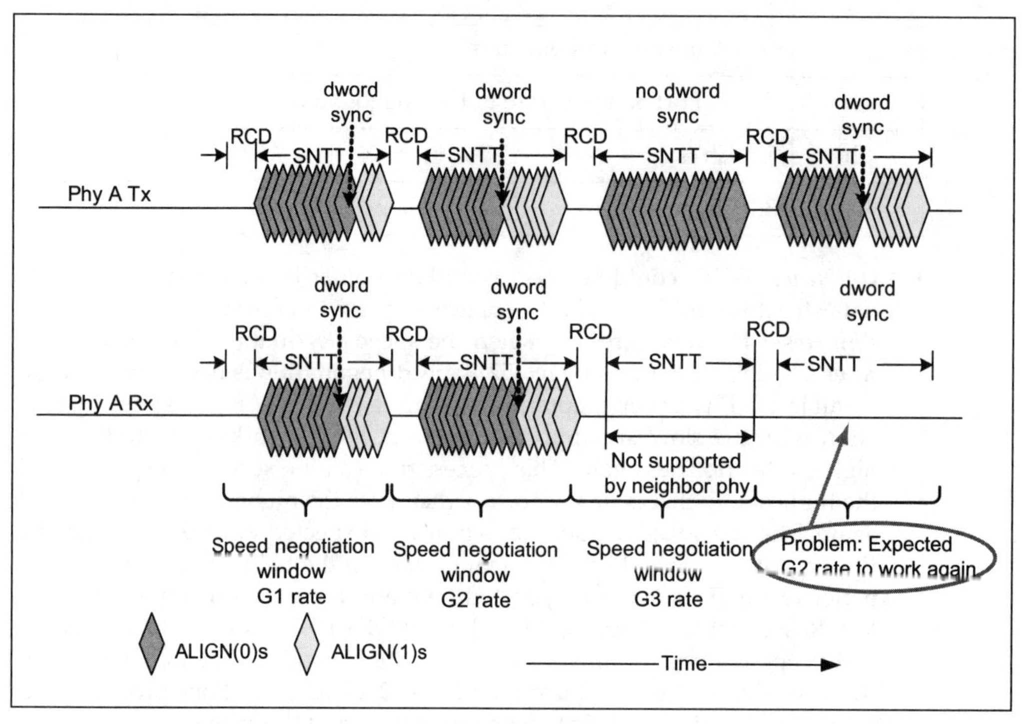

- *SATA Spin-up* – In the best case, SATA drives spin up automatically after finishing speed negotiation and reaching the PHY Ready state. Since they don't wait for permission from the system there is a risk when they are used in a multi-drive environment, since several could spin up at the same time. Drives use much more power when spinning up than they do during normal operation, so allowing several to spin up at once would require a larger power supply than would be needed for run time operation. The simplest way to avoid this problem is to postpone finishing the speed negotiation, rather than doing it automatically. For example, if an expander detects a SATA drive during the OOB sequence, it would not complete the reset sequence and instead report the situation in this field. After that, it would be waiting for software to request a link reset to finish the process and proceed.
- *SATA Port Selector* – The meaning of this code is that a port selector has been detected but the speed has not yet been negotiated. Interestingly, the response to the SMP DISCOVER request is identical to the contents of this

mode page in every area, except that it also includes a bit called "Attached SATA Port Selector" in bit 7 of byte 7. It may be that this bit will be added to this mode page as well in the future, but at the time of this writing, it was not. In the discussion on the DISCOVER response (covered in Chapter 7), it is observed that this bit is combined with the Attached SATA Device bit as shown in the Table 6-14. For background, it is helpful to know that a Port Selector allows two hosts (HBAs) to access the same SATA drive, providing fail-over capability, as illustrated in Figure 6-11. The first host device to finish OOB with the port selector becomes the active device and the latecomer is inactive. The secondary host can later take over the primary position to access the target device if needed.

Figure 6-11: SATA Port Selector

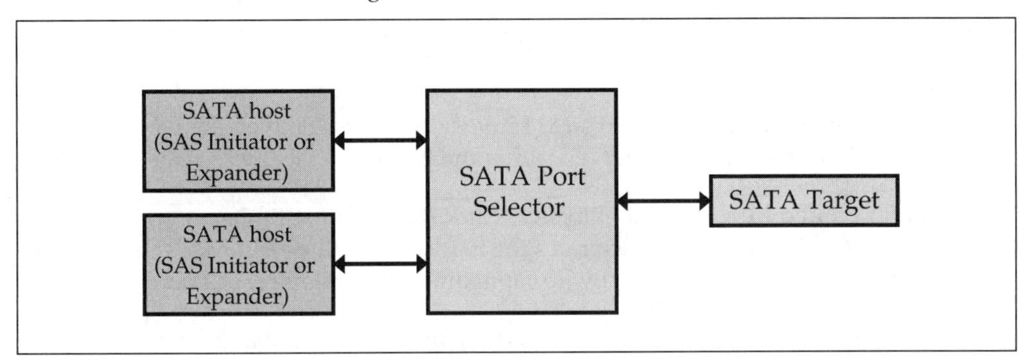

Table 6-14: SATA Port Selector Meaning

Attached SATA Port Selector bit	Attached SATA Device bit	Description
0b	0b	No SATA device of port selector attached
0b	1b	SATA device attached, no port selector
1b	0b	Attached Phy is a port selector and either: a) the attached Phy is the inactive host Phy, or b) the attached Phy is the active host Phy, but there is no SATA device ready behind the selector
1b	1b	The attached Phy is the active host Phy of a port selector and there is a SATA target device visible behind it.

Continuing our discussion of the fields of the Phy Mode Descriptor, we look next at the bits indicating whether the attached device is an initiator or target and which protocols it supports.

Attached Initiator/Target Ports – The bits shown in bytes 6 and 7 of the descriptor indicate whether the attached device can act as an initiator or target or both, and which protocols it supports. All 6 cases can be true at the same time.

SAS Address – The 64-bit SAS address transmitted by this Phy during an identification sequence.

Attached SAS Address – The 64-bit SAS address received by this Phy during an identification sequence.

Attached Phy Identifier – The unique Phy number for the Phy of the attached device.

Hardware Min and Max Physical Link Rate – These convey the hardware rate capabilities for this local Phy (i.e.: what the link is physically capable of doing).

Programmed Min and Max Physical Link Rate – These limits are programmed by software to indicate which rates the hardware is allowed to use. These can be equal to or less than the hardware capabilities of the device,

Vendor-Specific – None yet specified. Typically, standards authors leave these fields undefined so vendors can use them for whatever they like.

Protocol-Specific Log Page — 18h

Switching now to the log pages defined by SPC-3 and adapted for SAS, consider log page 18h, the Protocol-Specific Log Page, which reports logical unit information. As defined by SPC-3, these log pages are accessed by the commands LOG SENSE (for reads) and LOG SELECT (for writes), permitting a device to report Phy error conditions without including an SMP port for that purpose.

As shown in Table 6-15, the page includes protocol-specific log parameters. The format of the parameters is shown in Table 6-16 and the fields are described in the text that follows it. One parameter table is needed for each of the ports of the device, and the port that each table describes is indicated by the parameter code, which is also the relative port identifier.

Table 6-15: Protocol-Specific Log Page

Byte	Field(s)
0	Page Code (18h)
1	Reserved
2 to 3	Page Length
4 to n	Protocol-Specific log parameters

Table 6-16: Protocol-Specific Log Parameters

Byte	Field(s)	
0 to 1	Parameter Code (relative target port identifier)	
2	Parameter Control Bits	
3	Parameter Length	
4	Reserved	Protocol Identifier (6h)
5 to 6	Reserved	
7	Number of Phys	
8 to n	Phy log descriptor	

Description of the fields in the Log Parameter table above:

Parameter Code – 16-bit field indicating the port of the device. Ports are numbered from 1 to FFFFh, generally starting with 1.

Parameter Control Bits - These are unchanged from their definitions in SPC-3.

Parameter Length – specifies the number of bytes in this page after this length byte, so in this case it will be n-3.

Protocol Identifier – set to 6h for SAS.

Number of Phys – indicates the number of Phys in this SAS target port only, rather than the number in the device overall, and indicates how many Phy log descriptors will follow.

Phy Log Descriptor – contains many of the same fields as the Mode Descriptor described earlier, but also some that are unique. The Phy Log Descriptor is shown in Table 6-17, and the fields that have not already been described earlier are described here.

Table 6-17: SAS Phy Log Descriptor

	Bit 7	6	5	4	3	2	1	0
Byte 0	Reserved							
1	Phy Identifier							
2 to 3	Reserved							
4	Rsvd	Attached Device Type			Reserved			
5	Reserved				Negotiated Physical Link Rate			
6	Reserved				Attached SSP Init Port	Attached STP Init Port	Attached SMP Init Port	Reserved
7	Reserved				Attached SSP Target Port	Attached STP Target Port	Attached SMP Target Port	Reserved
8 to 15	SAS Address							
16 to 23	Attached SAS Address							
24	Attached Phy Identifier							
25 to 31	Reserved							
32 to 35	Invalid Dword Count							
36 to 39	Running Disparity Error Count							
40 to 43	Loss of Dword Synchronization							
44 to 47	Phy Reset Problem							

Description of the fields in the Phy Log Descriptor table above:

Invalid Dword Count – This indicates the number of invalid dwords that have been detected on this Phy. The count stops at the maximum value of FFFF

FFFFh and does not wrap around. Invalid dwords are any that do not fit into valid patterns, and could be caused by in-flight corruption or by errors at the Phy Layer of the sender or receiver. For example, a control character in any position besides the first byte of a dword, an illegal character in any position (for more on legal and illegal characters refer to 8b/10b encoding in the Phy Layer chapter), or a disparity error would all result in invalid dwords.

Running Disparity Error Count – This counts receiver errors, too, but only this particular classification of them. Disparity generation and checking is described in more detail in the Phy Layer chapter. This counter tracks the number of these events since the last reset sequence and stops at the maximum value of FFFF FFFFh rather than wrapping around to zero.

Loss of Dword Synchronization – This indicates the number of times the Phy has lost dword synchronization and had to repeat the link reset sequence to recover it. This count also stops at the maximum value of FFFF FFFFh.

Phy Reset Problem Count – The number of times the Phy has failed the final speed negotiation window of a Phy reset sequence. Recall from the earlier discussion of this issue that the last speed negotiation is supposed to succeed. If it does not, the speed negotiation sequence will have to be repeated. If that process iterates repeatedly, it would indicate an ongoing problem with the transmission path. This count stops at the maximum value of FFFF FFFFh.

7 Discovery Process

Previous Chapter

The previous chapter described the steps by which devices initialize the link for communications. This is a hardware-based process at the beginning, and establishes whether a neighboring device is present, what type it is, what link rates it supports, and its SAS address. Once that is completed, there are steps taken by application software to discover the SAS topology and configure the devices.

This Chapter

This chapter describes the process by which initiators and self-configuring expanders learn which addresses and types of devices are accessible to them in the system.

The Next Chapter

The next chapter describes the Application Layer of the SAS layered design. This layer is largely implemented as driver-level software rather than directly as hardware, and is intended to be fully backward compatible with the SCSI application model. Some background for that model is presented to provide sufficient context for the discussion, and the changes that were needed in the Mode and Log pages for SAS devices to support a serial transport are described.

Introduction

The process by which initiators in a SAS network find out which devices are accessible in the system is called the Discovery Process. There can be as many as 16,384 addresses in a SAS topology and every initiator has to be aware of which are visible to it. Expanders play a big role in the process because they can be cascaded into sets which allow scaling of the topology. The expanders themselves may or may not take an active role in the discovery process, depending on whether they were designed to be self-configuring. The reason for this option is that expanders are intended to be as simple and inexpensive as possible. Normally it falls to the initiators to go through the steps, working with the expanders to which it has access to check all the possible paths for addresses. Once that is done and the initiator has constructed its own address map, it will then need to update the expanders with that address information.

Example Topology

Consider the example topology shown in Figure 7-1, in which several edge expander sets are linked together with a fanout expander. This is not intended to be a realistic implementation, but simply illustrates what is possible. To clarify the discussion that follows, note that all the expanders are identified with a number, while all the end devices and the one HBA are identified with a letter. For our purposes, these identifiers will correspond to the SAS addresses of the devices. Also observe that, in this example, the expander phys are numbered sequentially in a counter-clockwise rotation starting with Phy 0 at the top.

Figure 7-1: Example SAS Topology

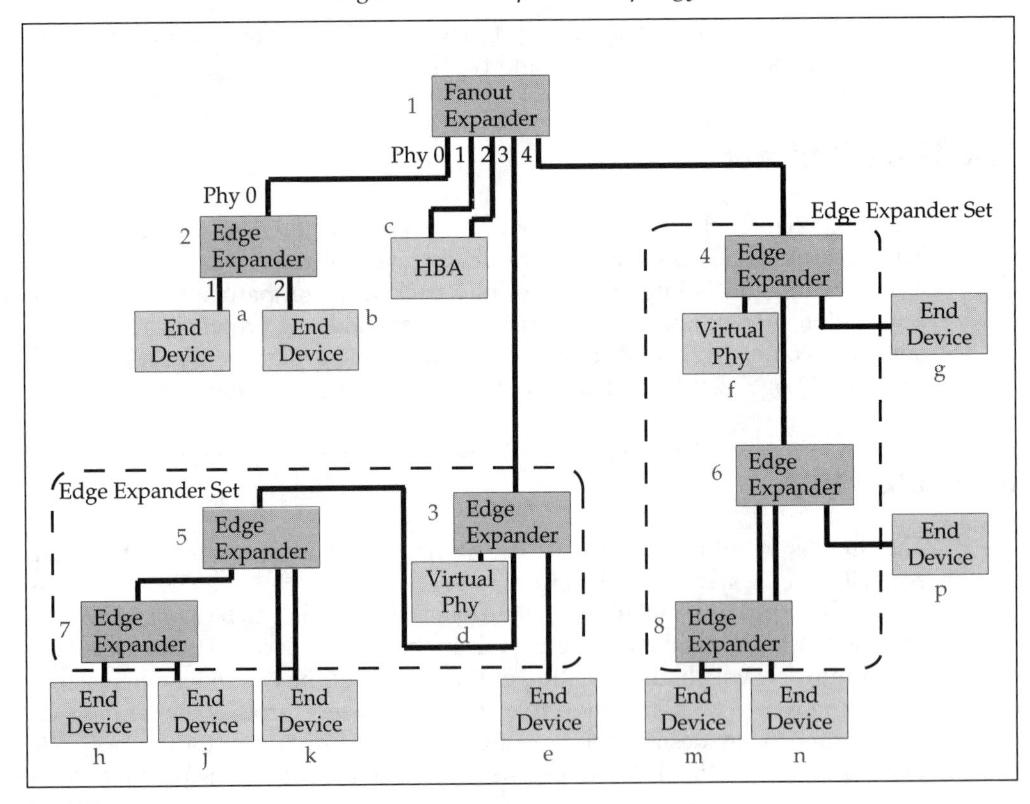

Identify Sequence

When the phys each complete their link reset sequence, they will have exchanged Identify frames and are therefore aware of the attached device's address and device type (expander or end device). For example, the fanout expander in this example sees addresses as shown in Figure 7-2. Phys 1 and 2 see that an end device is detected, so there will be no further addresses on those paths. In fact, both phys see the same address so they are grouped together into a single wide port. The other 3 phys all detect an expander attached, so an address table will be needed for this expander, updated with the addresses that turn out to be accessible through those other expanders. Edge expander phys can use one of three routing methods: direct attach, table routed, and subtractive routed (see Appendix A, entitled "Expander Devices," on page 505). Fanout expanders are not permitted to have a subtractive-routed port, and a table-routed port will support both an end device or edge expander set attached to it, so it makes sense that fanout phys are always table routed.

Figure 7-2: Fanout Expander Addresses

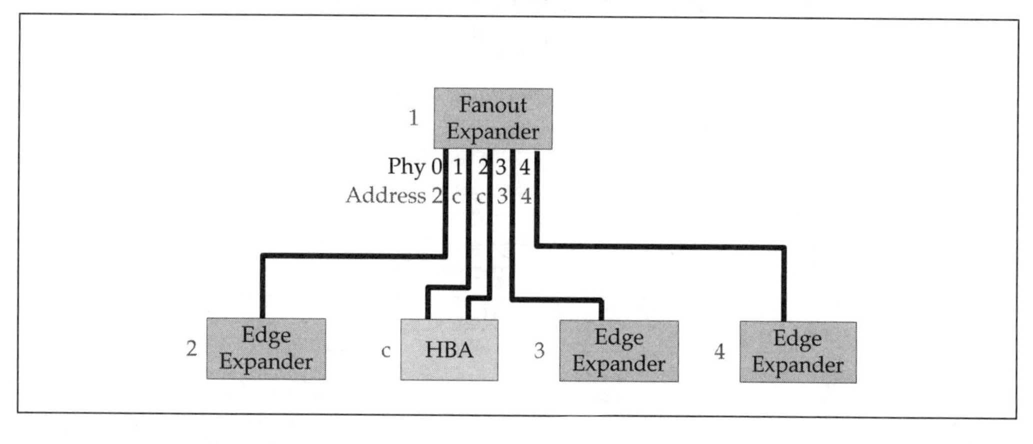

Discovery

The next step is to learn the other addresses in the system, and the simplest way is by using SMP requests. If attached expanders are self-configuring, then the initiator's task of learning the addresses will be reduced somewhat, because they will not need to write the expander routing tables. This allows initiators to get some of the address information they need by simply reading the table that a self-configuring expander builds. So a logical first step is to discover whether or not attached expanders have implemented self-configuring capability, and this can be done by sending an SMP REPORT GENERAL request to the expander.

Report General Request

The SMP Report General Request permits an initiator to query an expander to determine a variety of information including whether it is self-configuring. Recall that SMP transactions are much simpler and less open-ended than SSP or STP interactions. Once an SMP connection is established with the destination address the initiator is allowed to send one request and receive one response, after which the connection must be closed. The REPORT GENERAL request format is shown in Table 7-1 on page 162. The contents and format of the response from the device is shown in Table 7-2 on page 162. The details of all the fields will be discussed later; what is of interest now are the low-order bits of byte 10 that explain whether the expander is self-configuring. The bit labeled "Configurable" indicates whether the routing table can be configured by external devices (bit set to one), or is self-configuring (bit cleared to zero). The bit labeled "Configuring" only has meaning if the table is self-configuring, because it indicates whether the self-configuration process has completed. If this bit is set, then the expander is still in the process of self-configuring.

Table 7-1: SMP Report General Requests

Byte	Field(s)
0	SMP Frame Type (40h)
1	Function (00h)
2 to 3	Reserved

Table 7-2: Report General Response

Byte	Field(s)
0	SMP Frame Type (41h)
1	Function (00h)
2	Function Result

Table 7-2: Report General Response

Byte	Field(s) (Continued)		
3	Reserved		
4 to 5	Expander Change Count		
6 to 7	Expander Route Indexes		
8	Reserved		
9	Number of phys		
10	Reserved	Configuring	Configurable
11 to 27	Reserved		

How To Read the Routing Table

To read the contents of an expander's routing table, an initiator has only to send one SMP request REPORT ROUTE INFORMATION for each index of each Phy in the expander. This request permits an initiator to obtain the entire list of addresses. Unfortunately, the information is insufficient to serve the needs of the initiator because the table only records the address and a disable bit to indicate whether the address will be used. Initiators need to know the device type, connection rate, and other information about the devices they wish to access, so they'll still need to send a request to each device for this information.

The fields of the REPORT ROUTE INFORMATION request are shown in Table 7-3 on page 163, and the routing table being accessed is shown in Table 7-4.

Table 7-3: SMP Report Route Information Request

Byte	Field(s)
0	SMP Frame Type (40h)
1	Function (13h)
2 to 5	Reserved
6 to 7	Expander Route Index
8	Reserved

Table 7-3: SMP Report Route Information Request

Byte	Field(s) (Continued)
9	Phy Identifier
10 to 11	Reserved

Table 7-4: Expander Routing Table

Expander Route Index	Phy Identifier			
	0	1	...	n
0	Entry	Entry		Entry
1	Entry	Entry		Entry
...				
M	Entry	Entry	...	Entry

Note that the Route Index and Phy Identifier in the request specify one entry in the table, and each entry represents the address that Phy could see, plus the enable/disable bit. If the Phy is attached to an expander, then there could be many addresses accessible to that phy, limited only by the number of indexes supported by the routing table.

The response to the REPORT ROUTE INFORMATION request is shown in Table 7-5 on the following page.

Table 7-5: Report Route Information - Response

Byte	Field(s)
0	SMP Frame Type (41h)
1	Function (12h)
2	Function Result
3 to 5	Reserved
6 to 7	Expander Route Index
8	Reserved

Table 7-5: Report Route Information - Response

Byte	Field(s) (Continued)	
9	Phy Identifier	
10	Reserved	
11	Disabled	Reserved
12 to 15	Reserved	
16 to 23	Routed SAS Address	
24 to 39	Reserved	

Notice that in bytes 6, 7 and 9, the table index and Phy identifier are repeated as a confirmation of the selection, and that the corresponding address stored in the routing table is given in bytes 16 to 23. In addition, the responding device reports the results of the operation in the Function Result field of byte 2, and the possible results are listed in Table 7-6 on page 165.

Table 7-6: List of Function Results

Value	Function Result	Description
00h	SMP Function Accepted	Good result
01h	Unknown SMP Function	Target doesn't support the request
02h	SMP Function Failed	Request failed for some reason
03h	Invalid Request Frame Length	Request frame length was invalid
10h	Phy Does Not Exist	Phy Identifier was out of range, for functions including a Phy Identifier field
11h	Index Does Not Exist	Expander Route Index was out of range (or the specified Phy doesn't have a routing table at all), for functions including an Expander Route Index field

Table 7-6: List of Function Results

Value	Function Result (Continued)	Description (Continued)
12h	Phy Does Not Support	REPORT PHY SATA requested, but no SATA device attached
13h	Unknown Phy Operation	Unknown PHY CONTROL Phy Operation request

Discovery Process Overview

Returning now to the example topology with which we began this chapter, we will walk through the discovery process to show how it works. Assume first that the expanders are not self configuring. As an aside, expanders that are not self configuring are simpler and incur less design risk, which early designs would prefer, but that slows the discovery process somewhat. Discussions with leaders in the SAS community lead the author to believe that future expander designs likely will be self configuring.

Start with Report General

To start the process, every initiator that detects an attached expander after reset will need to open an SMP connection to that expander and read the addresses that the expander itself has detected. To do this, it will first probably want to know how many phys are contained in the expander, and this is obtained via the REPORT GENERAL request. This was shown earlier, but is repeated here for ease of reference when describing the fields in greater detail (see Table 7-7 and Table 7-8).

Table 7-7: SMP Report General Request

Byte	Field(s)
0	SMP Frame Type (40h)
1	Function (00h)
2 to 3	Reserved

Table 7-8: Report General Response

Byte	Field(s)		
0	SMP Frame Type (41h)		
1	Function (00h)		
2	Function Result		
3	Reserved		
4 to 5	Expander Change Count		
6 to 7	Expander Route Indexes		
8	Reserved		
9	Number of Phys		
10	Reserved	Configuring	Configurable
11	Reserved		
12 to 19	Enclosure Logical Identifier		
20 to 27	Reserved		
28 to 31	CRC		

Report General - Fields

- **Frame Type:** Setting this field to 40h indicates an SMP request, while a value of 41h indicates an SMP response.
- **Function:** In the request this indicates which type of request was sent. In the response it echoes the requested value as a confirmation that it was received correctly.
- **Function Result:** Status of the response - a value of 0 confirms that the request had a good result - see Table 7-6 on page 165 for the full list of values that could be returned.
- **Expander Change Count:** This field tracks how many times this expander has initiated a BROADCAST (CHANGE) on its phys. The intent was to help reduce the amount of activity generated whenever a broadcast does occur. As background on this, whenever an initiator sees a BROADCAST (CHANGE) primitive, it must take steps to ascertain what has changed in

the system. In a system like the one in Figure 7-1 on page 160, this could take some time, since every Phy of every expander will need to be checked. It is also true, however, that one event type that will cause an expander to send a broadcast is receiving a broadcast from another expander. If initiators somehow knew that a particular expander was not the initiator of the broadcast the discovery task could be reduced because there would be no need to check the phys of that expander. The change count value provides such a mechanism. If a broadcast was seen by an initiator but the change count for an expander is the same as it was the last time it was checked, then that expander is unlikely to have been the one that saw the actual change. Based on that, an initiator would not need to check the phys of this expander and the discovery process can skip to the next expander. It should be noted that this is an indicator rather than a fail-safe mechanism for detecting changes because it is a 16-bit counter that wraps around when it reaches the maximum value. There might have been 2^{16} changes since the last time the value was checked, wrapping the counter all the way back around to where it was. Although this is unlikely it is possible, and needs to be considered when making a decision based on this count value.

- **Expander Route Indexes:** This gives the maximum number of indexes for a Phy in this expander. The Phys may not use all of them, but this represents how many entries are available for each Phy.
- **Number of Phys:** This reports the highest-numbered Phy in this device. The understanding is that the actual number of Phys included in this device ranges from 0 to this number, but may skip some Phy numbers along the way, such as any vacant phys. Vacant phys are those which the SMP target port cannot access for some reason, even though they are within the range from zero to the reported number of phys. The fanout expander in Figure 7-3 might report this value as 4, meaning that Phy 4 is the highest numbered phy. Since the Phy numbering starts at zero, this means there could be as

many as 5 phys in this expander.

Figure 7-3: Fanout Expander Addresses

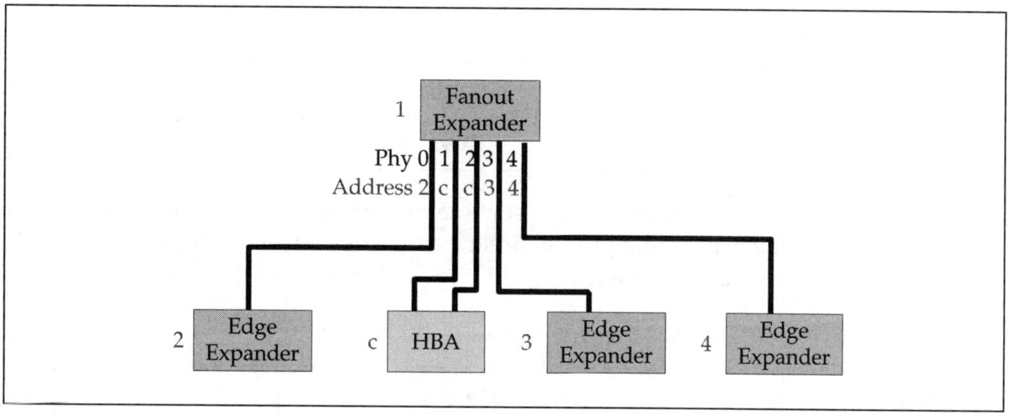

- **Configurable:** Set to one indicates the table can be configured by external initiators which implies, more significantly, that this is not a self-configuring expander. If it is cleared to zero, the expander *is* self-configuring.
- **Configuring:** Set to one indicates the self-configuring table is in the process of setting itself up with all the addresses it can find.
- **Enclosure Logical Identifier:** This identifies the enclosure, if any, in which the device is located, as defined by SES-2. A value of zero indicates that no enclosure information is available.
- **CRC:** This is the Cyclic Redundancy Code used to provide a robust means of checking for transmission errors.

Using the Discover Request

The next step for the initiator will be to send an SMP DISCOVER request, as shown in Table 7-9, specifying one of the phys in the expander, starting with Phy 0. The process is repeated while incrementing the Phy number through the number of Phys reported in the SMP REPORT GENERAL response.

Table 7-9: Discover Request

Byte	Field(s)
0	SMP Frame Type (40h)
1	Function (10h)

Table 7-9: Discover Request

Byte	Field(s) (Continued)
2 to 8	Reserved
9	Phy Identifier
10 to 11	Reserved

The response to the Discover request contains a great deal of information about the device attached to this phy, as described in the text that follows. Table 7-10 on page 170 lists the field definitions of the first 15 bytes of the response.

Table 7-10: Discover Response - part 1

<table>
<tr><th>Byte</th><th colspan="3">Field(s)</th></tr>
<tr><td>0</td><td colspan="3">SMP Frame Type (41h)</td></tr>
<tr><td>1</td><td colspan="3">Function (10h)</td></tr>
<tr><td>2</td><td colspan="3">Function Result</td></tr>
<tr><td>3to 8</td><td colspan="3">Reserved</td></tr>
<tr><td>9</td><td colspan="3">Phy Identifier</td></tr>
<tr><td>10 to 11</td><td colspan="3">Reserved</td></tr>
<tr><td>12</td><td></td><td>Attached Device Type</td><td>Reserved</td></tr>
<tr><td>13</td><td colspan="2">Reserved</td><td>Negotiated Physical Link Rate</td></tr>
<tr><td>14</td><td colspan="2">Reserved</td><td>Attached Initiator Port bits</td></tr>
<tr><td>15</td><td>Attached SATA Port Selector</td><td>Reserved</td><td>Attached Target Port bits</td></tr>
<tr><td>16 to 55</td><td colspan="3">(see Table 7-14)</td></tr>
</table>

Discover - Fields

- **Function:** The value of 10h indicates the DISCOVER request and response.
- **Phy Identifier:** Specifies which Phy is to be reported. Figure 7-4 on page 171 shows how this might be useful, since either topology "a" or "b" could exist in the links between the devices. The ability to read the attached Phy identifier clarifies it in case it should be needed for addressing problems later.

Figure 7-4: Use of Phy Identifier to Clarify Topology

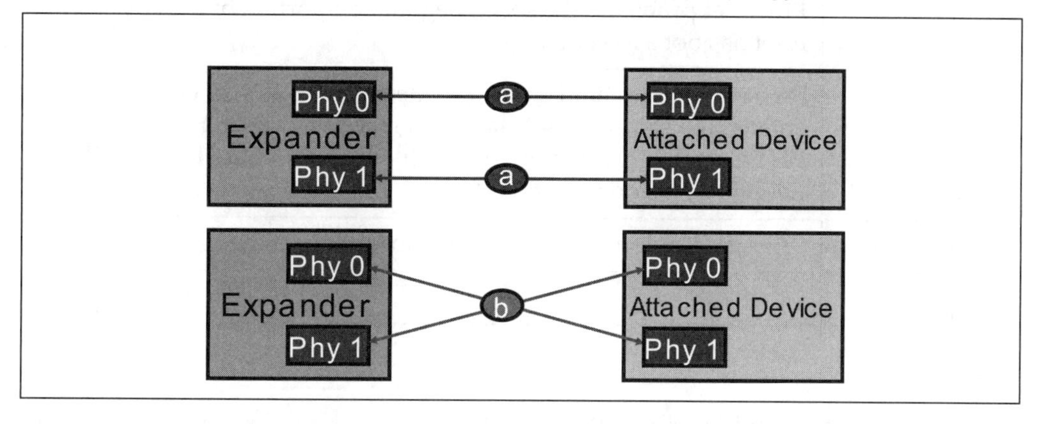

- **Attached Device Type:** This reports the type of device that is attached, according to Table 7-11 on page 171.

Table 7-11: Attached Device Types

Value	Attached Device
000	No device attached
001	End Device
010	Edge Expander
011	Fanout Expander

- **Negotiated Physical Link Rate:** This is the result of the speed negotiation process between the neighbors on the link, and is encoded according to

Table 7-12 below.

Table 7-12: Negotiated Link Rate

Value	Negotiated physical link rate
0h	Unknown - place holder for application client data structure before this Phy has been queried
1h	Phy is disabled - either because of a problem, or because an SMP PHY CONTROL request was used to disable it
2h	Phy reset problem - the speed negotiation portion of the Phy reset has not succeeded
3h	SATA in spin-up hold state - Phy detected a SATA device, entered the spin-up hold state, and is waiting for an SMP PHY CONTROL function to send it a Link Reset or Hard Reset to move on from this state.
4h	SATA Port Selector detected, rate not yet negotiated
8h	1.5 Gb/s
9h	3.0 Gb/s

- **Attached Initiator/Target Port bits:** These six bits indicate whether the attached device can operate as an initiator or target or both for each of the three protocols supported by SAS: SSP, STP, and SMP. It's helpful to point out that, even though an attached SATA Host can be detected and reported here (SATA initiator), support for it is outside the scope of the SAS standard.
- **Attached SATA Port Selector:** This bit indicates that a port selector has been detected. When set, its full meaning is determined in combination with the Attached SATA Device bit, as shown in Table 7-13 below.

Table 7-13: SATA Port Selector and Device Indications

Attached SATA Port Selector	Attached SATA Device	Description
0	0	No port selector or device detected.
0	1	SATA device Phy detected.

Table 7-13: SATA Port Selector and Device Indications

Attached SATA Port Selector	Attached SATA Device	Description (Continued)
1	0	Attached Phy is a port selector host Phy and either: a) attached Phy is the inactive host phy, or b) attached Phy is the active host Phy but the SATA device on the other side is not present or not ready.
1	1	Attached Phy is a SATA port selector active host Phy and a SATA device is detected on the other side of it.

The remainder of the discover response fields are shown in Table 7-14 below, and described in the text that follows.

Table 7-14: Discover Response - part 2

<table>
<tr><th>Byte</th><th colspan="3">Field(s)</th></tr>
<tr><td>0 to 15</td><td colspan="3">(see Table 7-10)</td></tr>
<tr><td>16 to 23</td><td colspan="3">SAS Address</td></tr>
<tr><td>24 to 31</td><td colspan="3">Attached SAS Address</td></tr>
<tr><td>32</td><td colspan="3">Attached Phy Identifier</td></tr>
<tr><td>33 to 39</td><td colspan="3">Reserved</td></tr>
<tr><td>40</td><td colspan="2">Programmed Min Rate</td><td>Hardware Min Rate</td></tr>
<tr><td>41</td><td colspan="2">Programmed Max Rate</td><td>Hardware Max Rate</td></tr>
<tr><td>42</td><td colspan="3">Phy Change Count</td></tr>
<tr><td>43</td><td>Virtual Phy</td><td>Reserved</td><td>Partial Pathway Timeout Value</td></tr>
<tr><td>44</td><td colspan="2">Reserved</td><td>Routing Attribute</td></tr>
<tr><td>45</td><td>Reserved</td><td colspan="2">Connector Type</td></tr>
<tr><td>46</td><td colspan="3">Connector Element Index</td></tr>
<tr><td>47</td><td colspan="3">Connector Physical Link</td></tr>
</table>

Table 7-14: Discover Response - part 2

Byte	Field(s) (Continued)
48 to 49	Reserved
50 to 51	Vendor specific
52 to 55	CRC

- **SAS Address:** The 64-bit SAS address of the reporting device.
- **Attached SAS Address:** The 64-bit SAS address of the device attached to this phy.
- **Attached Phy Identifier:** The Phy number of the Phy attached to the reporting phy.
- **Hardware Min/Max Rate:** This is the range of physical link rates that the hardware of the reporting Phy will support (see Table 7-15).
- **Programmed Min/Max Rate:** This is the range of link rates that the software has programmed this Phy to use. The range can be equal to or less than the range supported by the hardware (see Table 7-15).

Table 7-15: Physical Link Rate Values

Code	Programmed Rate	Hardware Rate
0h	Not Programmable	
8h	1.5 Gb/s	1.5 Gb/s
9h	3.0 Gb/s	3.0 Gb/s
All others	Reserved	Reserved

- **Phy Change Count:** Much like the Expander Change Count field described earlier for the REPORT GENERAL response, for expander phys this field counts the number of times this particular Phy has been responsible for causing a BROADCAST (CHANGE) primitive to be sent from this expander. Its purpose is the same; to give initiators a way to quickly tell whether this Phy needs to be checked further when doing the discovery process to track down the source of the change.
- **Virtual Phy:** When set, this bit indicates that this Phy is internal to the device, and so the attached device is also internal. When set to zero, it indicates that this Phy is a physical Phy and the attached device is external.

- **Partial Pathway Timeout Value:** This indicates the partial pathway timeout that will be used by this expander Phy when resolving potential deadlock conditions by attempting pathway recovery. The value is measured in microseconds and can be programmed from 00h to FFh, but the recommended default value is 7 µs. To learn more about this condition and how SAS approaches this problem, refer to Chapter 14, entitled "Link Layer - Arbitration," on page 333.
- **Routing Attribute:** This indicates the type of routing that the expander can use with this phy, as shown in Table 7-16. This attribute is not allowed to change based on the attached device type, but could be established at reset in a vendor-specific manner, such as loading the values from a EEPROM to set them up based on the system in which the device is installed.

Table 7-16: Routing Attribute Field

Code	Attribute Name	Description
0h	Direct Routing	Only for attached end devices. Expanders are not supported on this phy
1h	Subtractive Routing	Subtractive routing used if an expander is attached, or direct routing used if an end device is directly attached
2h	Table Routing	Table routing used if an expander is attached, or direct routing used if an end device is directly attached
All others	Reserved	

- **Connector Type:** Indicates the type of connector used to access the phy, as reported by the enclosure services process for the enclosure. The full list of connector values is in the SES-2 standard, but a partial list showing the ones currently defined for SAS is given in Table 7-17 below.

Table 7-17: SAS Connector Types

Code	Description	Max Number of Physical Links
01h	SAS external receptacle, such as SSF-8470	4
02h	SAS external compact receptacle, such as SSF-8088	4
10h	SAS internal wide plug, such as SFF-8484	4
11h	SAS internal compact wide plug, such as SFF-8087	4
20h	SAS Backplane receptacle, such as SFF-8482	2
21h	SATA-style host plug	1
22h	SAS plug, such as SFF-8482	2
23h	SATA plug device	1

- **Connector Element Index:** Indicates the element index of the connector use to access this phy, as reported by the enclosure services process. Refer to the SES-2 standard for more on this.
- **Connector Physical Link:** Indicates the physical link in the connector used to access this phy, as reported by the enclosure services process. Refer to the SES-2 standard for more on this.

When the SMP DISCOVER response has been read for every Phy in the expander, the next step is to find all the phys that have an expander attached to them and repeat the process with those expanders. That is, send a REPORT GENERAL request to the address of the attached expander to learn how many phys it contains, then send repeated DISCOVER requests to it to learn the details of each of its phys. Addresses found this time are the first level beyond the direct connection to the original expander, and will need to be written into the entry of the routing table for that phy. In the table, the index indicates something about the level of the new addresses relative to the original expander. If another expander is discovered at this level, the process will need to be repeated again to search for the addresses beyond.

Creating An Address Map

If an expander has a routing table, (e.g.: a fanout expander required to use table routing), and if it is not self-configuring, initiators will need to update the table. Initiators basically create a map of the topology as they go through the discovery process and, once it is complete, the values can then be written into address tables as needed. The writers of the SAS standard decided that there would be no "master" device in this process; instead every initiator goes through the same process. Consequently, several initiators could all make updates to the routing table of an expander at different times, which means it is very important that they all do it the same way to avoid losing information when overwriting values. Toward this end, the discovery order was spelled out in the standard and can be summarized as follows: the expected order of discovery is "breadth-first", meaning that all the entries for one level (starting with Phy 0 for each device) should be checked before proceeding to the next level.

Once an initiator has completely traversed the topology it can access, it then updates the routing tables of any expanders that were not self-configuring. This is done by using the SMP CONFIGURE ROUTE INFORMATION request to specify the address that should be written into the table, and the Phy identifier and index that will specify the entry of the table to be written, as shown in Table 7-18 below.

Table 7-18: Configure Route Information Request

Byte	Field(s)
0	SMP Frame Type (40h)
1	Function (90h)
2 to 5	Reserved
6 to 7	Expander Route Index
8	Reserved
9	Phy Identifier
10 to 11	Reserved

Table 7-18: Configure Route Information Request

Byte	Field(s) (Continued)	
12	Disable Expander Route Entry	Reserved
13 to 15	Reserved	
16 to 23	Routed SAS Address	
24 to 39	Reserved	

The Disable Expander Route Entry bit in byte 12 of this request indicates whether the expander is allowed to use this Phy for routing addresses. If this bit is set, the ECM (expander connection manager) will not be allowed to route connection requests to this phy.

Discovery Process Detailed Example

Returning now to the example topology (see Figure 7-5, duplicated here for ease of reference) this section details the steps required to find all the accessible addresses and update the expander routing tables. To begin with, consider the fanout expander at the top of the diagram.

Figure 7-5: Example SAS Topology

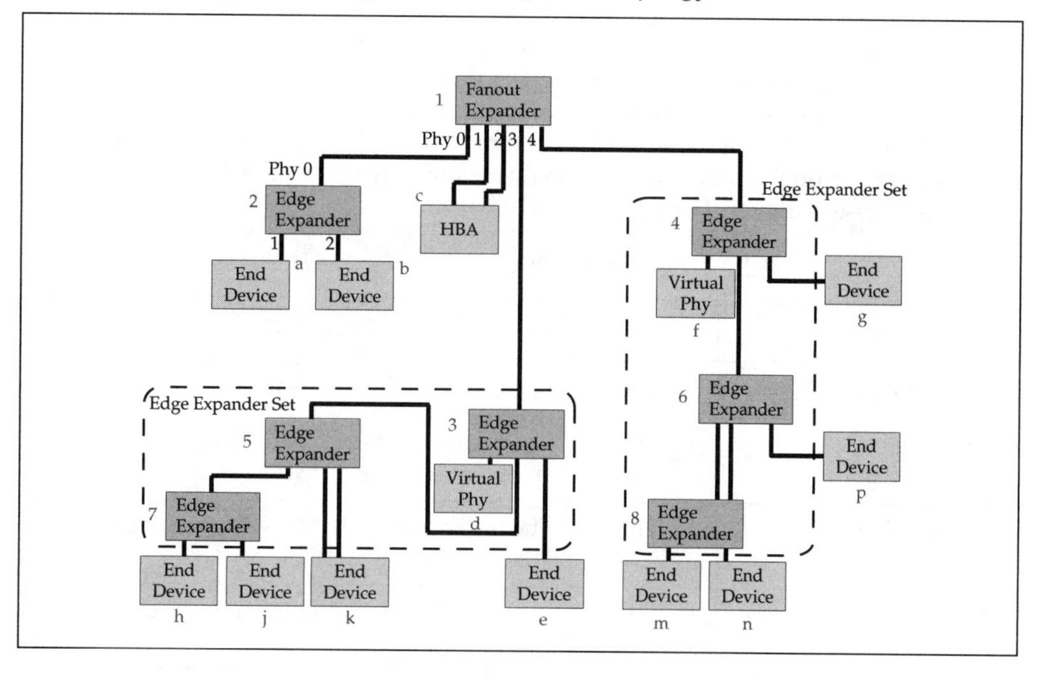

Assuming for purposes of discussion that none of the expanders are self configuring, an initiator will need to read its Phy values to determine the next step to be taken. Device "c" is the one HBA and initiator in this example, and it will perform the typical sequence:

- Open an SMP connection to the fanout expander.
- Send a REPORT GENERAL request.
- Receive and parse the response.
- Close the connection.

The response reports that this expander implements 4 Phys, meaning the Phys are numbered from 0 to 4 for a maximum of 5 Phys (some of the Phy numbers may not be implemented, so the total Phys could be less than 5). Assume the response also shows the Configurable bit set, meaning that this expander is not self-configuring.

Discovery of Level 0

The next step will be to discover what is attached to the expander itself. In terms of configuring the routing information for the expander, the addresses which are directly attached to it are considered to be in Level 0 of the hierarchy. As a clarifying point, the numbering of levels is from the point of view of the expander that is being configured rather than from a system perspective. To find the Level 0 addresses, the HBA opens another SMP connection to the fanout expander and sends a DISCOVER request for Phy 0 and closes the connection. This process is repeated for each of the possible Phys. In this example, Phy 0 of the fanout expander has an edge expander attached to it as shown in Figure 7-5 on the previous page, so the response for Phy 0 would include values like those shown in Table 7-19.

Table 7-19: Example Discover Response Fields

Field	Value	Description
Attached Device Type	010b	Attached device is an edge expander
SAS Address	1h	The SAS address of this Phy (all the Phys of an expander will have the same address)
Attached SAS Address	2h	The SAS address that this Phy sees from the attached device
Attached Phy Identifier	0h	Phy 0 of the attached device is attached to this Phy

Since the attached device is an expander, further discovery of its attached addresses will be necessary, but that will have to wait until later. The rule is always to complete the level currently under investigation before moving the next level (breadth first, then depth), so the DISCOVER request will need to be repeated to examine Phy 1 of the expander, then Phy 2, and so on to complete Level 0. That process yields the results shown in Table 7-20.

Table 7-20: Fanout Expander Direct-Attached Devices

Fanout Expander Phy	Attached Device	Attached SAS Address
0	Edge Expander	2
1	SSP Initiator, End Device	c
2	SSP Initiator, End Device	c

Table 7-20: Fanout Expander Direct-Attached Devices

Fanout Expander Phy	Attached Device (Continued)	Attached SAS Address
3	Edge Expander	3
4	Edge Expander	4

Discovery of Level 1

Having completed the discovery of all the devices directly attached to the fanout expander itself (Level 0), the next step will be to repeat the process for the next level away from the expander (Level 1). To do that, the HBA will repeat this same process of opening SMP connections to query each of the attached expanders. That lets the HBA (the initiator) create a list of the addresses attached to each of those expanders, which are then used to configure the routing table for the fanout expander. The contents of the resulting table are shown in Table 7-21. Notice that only Phys 0, 3 and 4 of the fanout expander have table entries, because Phys 1 and 2 aren't attached to expanders and therefore don't need table entries. Level 1 includes expanders "2", "3", and "4", and the table entries will be the addresses that they report as attached to their Phys.

Table 7-21: Fanout Expander Partial Routing Table - Level 1

	Phy 0	Phy 1	Phy 2	Phy 3	Phy 4
Index 0	1			1	1
Index 1	a			d	f
Index 2	b			5	6
Index 3				e	g
Index 4					
Index 5					

To understand the table contents, examine the first column for Phy 0 and refer to Figure 7-6 on page 182. Phy 0 of the fanout expander is connected to edge expander 2, and when that expander's Phys are queried, the results show SAS address "1" on Phy 0, address "a" on Phy 1, and address "b" on Phy 2. Since that is the order of the Phy numbers, that is the order in which they are discovered and written into the table. Continuing this process across Level 1 of the topology results in discovering the addresses accessible to the expanders one level away from the expander whose table we're trying to program, until all of the Level 1 addresses have been filled in.

Discovery of Level 2

Moving to Level 2 in the hierarchy, the initiator will open SMP connections to the next set of expanders and repeat the process to discover the addresses that they can access. Doing so explores the addresses two levels away, for expanders 5 and 6. Writing the results back into the fanout expander's routing table results in a modified table as shown in Table 7-22.

Figure 7-6: Hierarchical Levels in the Example Topology

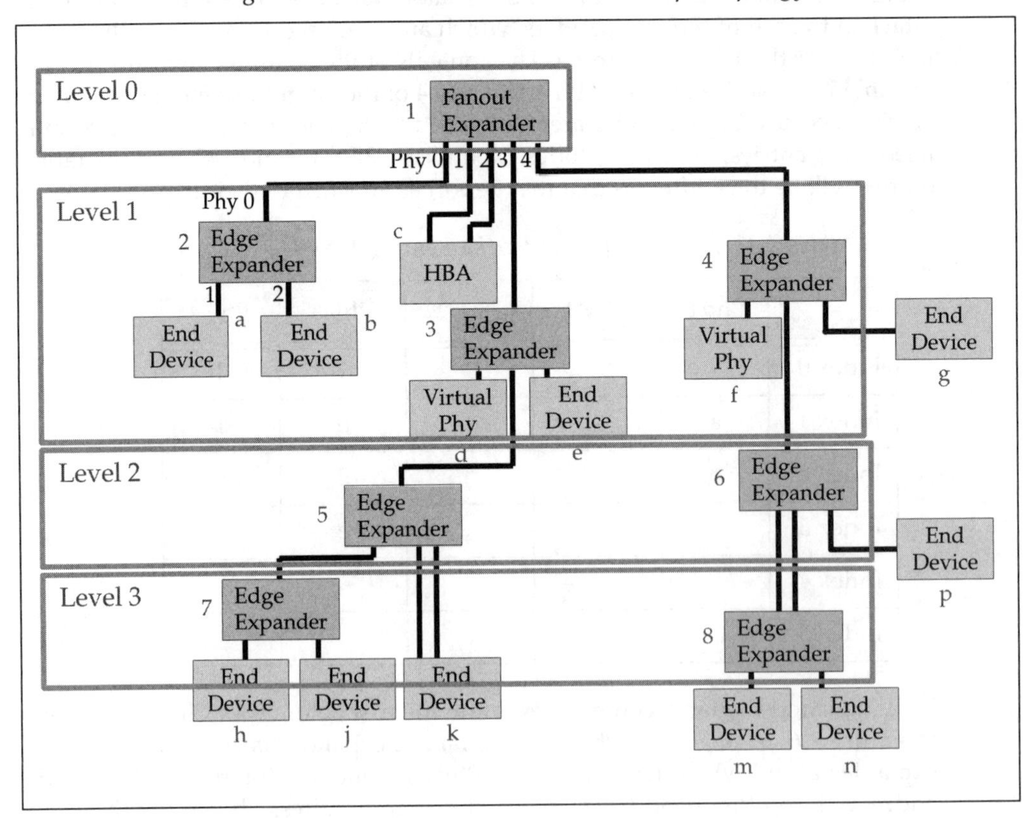

Table 7-22: Fanout Expander Partial Routing Table - 2nd Level

	Phy 0	Phy 1	Phy 2	Phy 3	Phy 4
Index 0	1			1	1
Index 1	a			d	f
Index 2	b			5	6
Index 3				e	g
Index 4				3	4
Index 5				7	8
Index 6				k	8
Index 7				k	p
Index 8					

Discovery of Level 3

Finally, the last level of expanders to discover in this example is Level 3, and that is explored by once again repeating the discovery process to each of the two expanders at that hierarchical level. Discovering all of these addresses and writing them into the fanout expander's routing table results in the final version shown in Table 7-23 on page 184. Even though Phys 1 and 2 have no table entries, an initiator must still be able to read their contents from the table. Of course, the contents will simply indicate that those table entries are not valid.

Improving Efficiency of the Routing Table

A quick look at Table 7-23 reveals that the basic table is not terribly efficient in its use of memory space. Since the standard requires that software be able to read the table as a two-dimensional matrix, but does not specify how it must be implemented, there are some opportunities to correct the inefficiencies. For example, the fact that several blank entries are maintained just to provide a simple version of the two-dimensional matrix of the table is wasteful. There are also some entries that are not interesting because they simply refer to the previous level of expander. For example, at index 0 of Phy 4 the device reports the address of the fanout expander above it. This is not a useful address for the fanout expander, which doesn't need its own address in the routing table.

Table 7-23: Fanout Expander Complete Routing Table

	Phy 0	Phy 1	Phy 2	Phy 3	Phy 4
Index 0	1			1	1
Index 1	a			d	f
Index 2	b			5	6
Index 3				e	g
Index 4				3	4
Index 5				7	8
Index 6				k	8
Index 7				k	p
Index 8				5	6
Index 9				h	6
Index 10				j	m
Index 11					n

Redundant entries, such as the entries for index 6 and 7 of Phy 3, also waste space since routing decisions only need to know that an address is available. The standard writers recognized these opportunities as well, so the standard does support optimization, but states that its implementation will be vendor specific.

Such optimizations would not be difficult to imagine. For example, if all the redundant and self-referencing addresses are removed, the number of indexes required for the table is reduced with no loss of information, as shown in Table 7-24 on page 185. There is still room for optimization in this example because blank entries remain, so another version of the table to optimize this a step further would be as shown in Table 7-25 on page 185. This table has the advantage of being able to allocate memory as needed for the addresses available to each phy.

Table 7-24: Fanout Expander Routing Table Optimized

	Phy 0	Phy 3	Phy 4
Index 0	a	d	f
Index 1	b	5	6
Index 2		e	g
Index 3		7	8
Index 4		k	p
Index 5		h	m
Index 6		j	n

One last optimization would also be an intuitive step in this process. Using the table during normal operation is an address look-up process: OPEN requests arrive specifying a destination address and need to be routed to the appropriate Phy. As a result, it would make sense to organize the table in that format, as shown in Table 7-26. Here, when an address is presented, the lookup process is as simple as possible.

Table 7-25: Fanout Expander Routing Table, Further Optimized

Phy, Index	Attached Address
0,0	a
0,1	b
3,0	d
3,1	5
3,2	e
3,3	7
3,4	k
3,5	h

Table 7-25: Fanout Expander Routing Table, Further Optimized

Phy, Index	Attached Address
3,6	j
4,0	f
4,1	6

Table 7-26: Address-Based Route Table Example

Destination Address of Incoming Request	Connection will be Routed to
a	Phy 0
b	Phy 0
d	Phy 3
5	Phy 3
e	Phy 3
7	Phy 3
k	Phy 3
h	Phy 3
j	Phy 3
f	Phy 4
6	Phy 4

Discovery of Next Expander

Consider the routing table that would be constructed inside edge expander "3" (see Figure 7-7 on page 188). This expander has four Phys, so Level 0 will consist of the four addresses that are directly attached. Because this is an edge expander, it has a subtractive port that it must use to connect to the fanout expander, and that is Phy 0 in this example. The beauty of a subtractive port is that the expander does not need to store all the accessible addresses in the system. Instead, any connection requests with an address not found by this device are routed to the subtractive port by default.

Since Phys 1 and 3 are attached to end devices, only Phy 2, attached to an expander, could have addresses that need to be tracked in the table. Looking again at Figure 7-7 shows that there are two levels of expanders attached to Phy 2, so when the initiator steps through this process it would first find all the addresses at Level 1 and then move on to find all the addresses at Level 2. Going through that process, an initiator would create a list of addresses and write them into the routing table for expander "3" as shown in Table 7-27. Note that there are more addresses and levels hierarchically above expander 3, but those are accessed through the subtractive port and do not need to be listed in the table.

Figure 7-7: Discovery Process for Expander 3

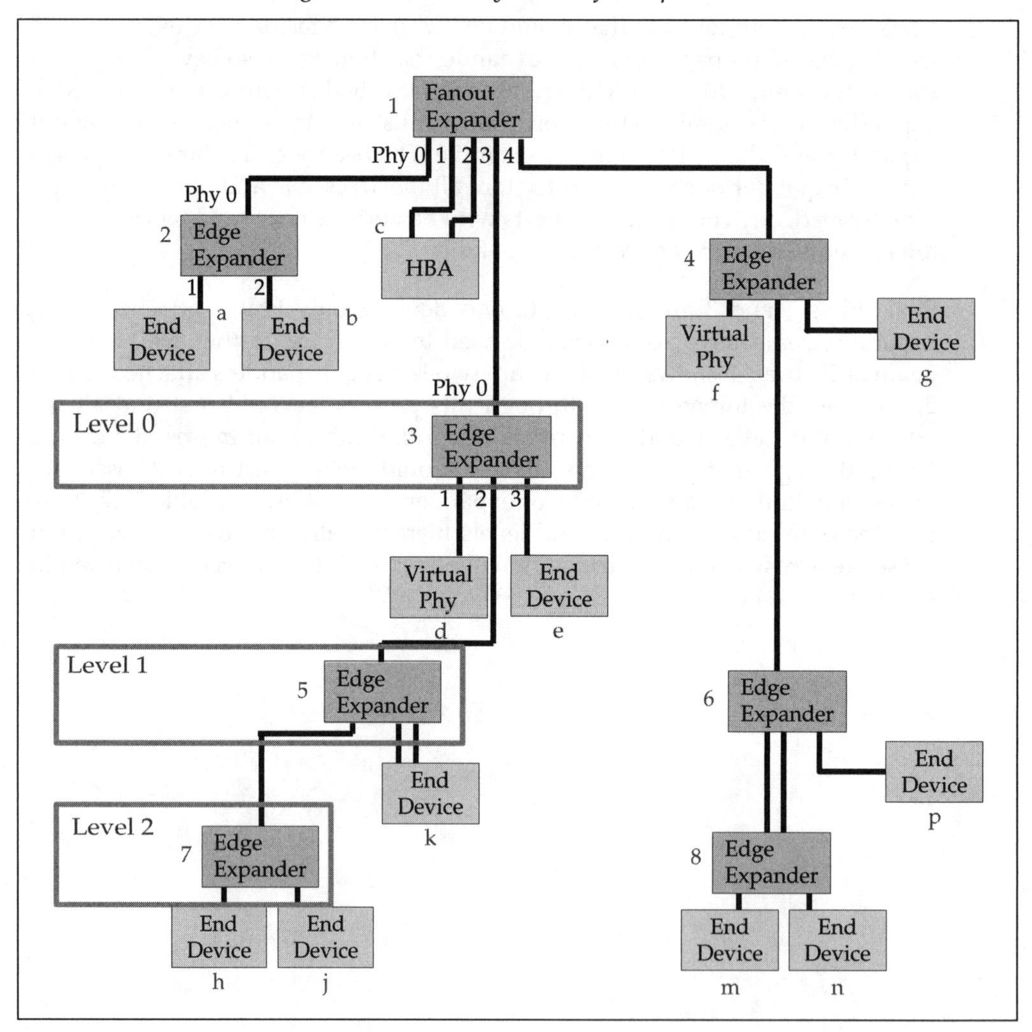

Table 7-27: Edge Expander 3 Routing Table

	Phy 1	Phy 2	Phy 3
Index 0		3	
Index 1		7	
Index 2		k	
Index 3		k	
Index 4		5	
Index 5		h	
Index 6		j	

As before, this table can be optimized if the management application client for this device supports it. Going through the same process as we did for the fanout expander would yield an optimized routing table such as the one shown in Table 7-28. As expected, all the known addresses will route to Phy 2 and any other addresses will route to the subtractive port.

Table 7-28: Edge Expander Optimized Routing Table

Address	Routes to
7	Phy 2
k	Phy 2
h	Phy 2
j	Phy 2

Summary

To summarize the discovery process: initiators and self-configuring expanders will need to send an SMP REPORT GENERAL request to the neighboring expanders to learn how many Phys they implement and how deep their tables can be. The routing table can be read with an SMP REPORT ROUTE INFO request and written by using an SMP CONFIGURE ROUTE INFO request. Finally, an SMP DISCOVER request is used to learn the detailed information about the device attached to each Phy of the expander.

It should be noted that even though SMP requests have been used throughout this section to describe this process, end devices are not required to implement an SMP target. Much of the same information is available from them via Mode and Log pages and it would add cost to include an SMP target in an end device. However, expanders are required to implement an SMP target to facilitate the discovery process.

Part 3: SSP and SMP Protocols

8 *Application Layer*

The Previous Chapter

The previous chapter described the process by which initiators and self-configuring expanders learn which addresses and types of devices are accessible to them in the system.

This Chapter

This chapter describes the Application Layer of the SAS layered design. This layer is largely implemented as driver-level software rather than directly as hardware, and is intended to be fully backward compatible with the SCSI application model. Some background for that model is presented to provide sufficient context for the discussion, and the changes that were needed in the Mode and Log pages for SAS devices to support a serial transport are described.

The Next Chapter

The next chapter describes the function and responsibilities of the Transport Layer of the SAS hierarchy. This layer receives requests from the Application Layer modeled as function calls, creates frames to support the requested action and queues them until they are completed. The frames are then passed down to the next lower layer, which is the Port Layer.

Context for Application Layer

An understanding of the SAS layered architecture begins with the Application Layer, which consists of all the software above the Transport Layer, including applications, file system drivers, class drivers, SCSI and subsystem drivers, and miniport drivers. Much of this is beyond the scope of the SAS standard and this book, but it is helpful to describe the context for it and look at what requirements SAS places on the drivers beyond what they already do to support a particular protocol.

In general, the Application Layer passes commands to the Transport Layer, informing it about the packet protocol to be used and the type of command or response to send. For example, a software request to send a SCSI command becomes an SSP COMMAND frame, while a request to learn about the devices attached to an expander becomes an SMP DISCOVER frame. The relationship between the various layers of the SAS architecture is shown in Figure 8-1, where clause 10 of the SAS standard describes the Application Layer at the top of the diagram. As can be seen, there are aspects of most layers that are specific to the particular protocol being used, and this is true of the upper layers as well. For discussion, we will begin with the SCSI Application Layer.

Figure 8-1: SAS Architecture Layers

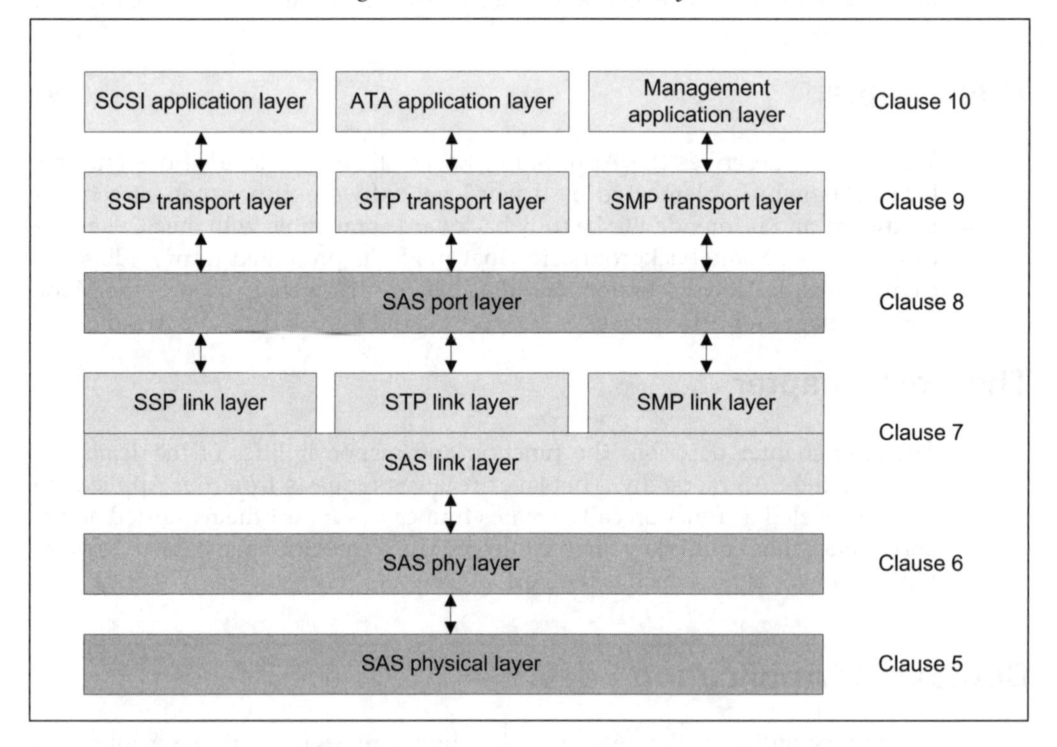

The SCSI Model

It will be helpful for those unfamiliar with the basics of SCSI if we provide some brief review of SCSI application and transport functions here. Those already acquainted with SCSI may wish to skip ahead to the section "SCSI Power Conditions" on page 203. To learn more about SCSI and purchase copies of the numerous standards that define it, refer to the INCITS web site at http://www.incits.org. Helpful information can also be obtained from the SCSI Trade Association site at http://www.scsita.org/. Last of all, review drafts of revisions to the standard that are currently under consideration are available from the T10 technical committee web site at http://www.t10.org, though it is important to note that INCITS is the official body that sells the final approved version of the standards. (T10 draft copies may also become unavailable to non-members at some point in the future.)

To begin our review note that at the higher-level (illustrated with dotted lines in Figure 8-2), SCSI transactions are understood to take place between application clients that make requests, and servers that service those requests. Clients are SCSI initiator devices and servers are SCSI target devices.

Figure 8-2: SCSI High Level Model

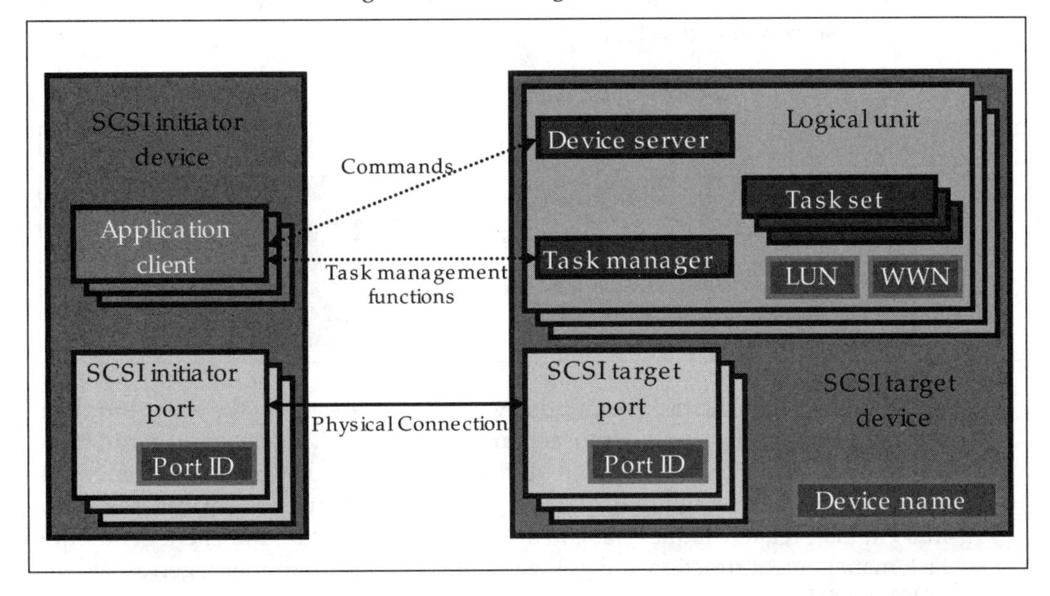

Referring to Figure 8-2, several of the SCSI identifiers associated with a device are shown, and the list below summarizes them with their corresponding value in SAS:

- **Port ID:** A unique address within the SCSI domain for each port. In SAS the 64-bit SAS address associated with a port serves as its port ID. A device may assign several phys with the same SAS address to allow them to be grouped into a wide port. The Port ID is the SAS address value that is reported by the Identify frame as part of the link reset sequence.

- **Device Name:** For SAS this is again a SAS address. This address is not reported in the Identify frame, although there is some discussion in the standard working group to change this so it is reported with the 2.0 version of SAS. For now, the only way for software to learn the Device Name is by reading the proper Mode page. The purpose of this value is to provide application layer software a means of telling which ports and logical units are in the same target device. Since the Device Name and Port IDs are all required to be unique values, a device may have several SAS addresses associated with it.
- **LUN:** A target device may contain several logical units, referred to by Logical Unit Number (LUN).
- **WWN:** Each logical unit also has a World-Wide Name (WWN) that is reported in the Vital Product Data page, and this is the same as it is in SCSI.

A data transfer begins when an application client sends a command to a device server, as shown in Figure 8-3.

Figure 8-3: SCSI Command Processing

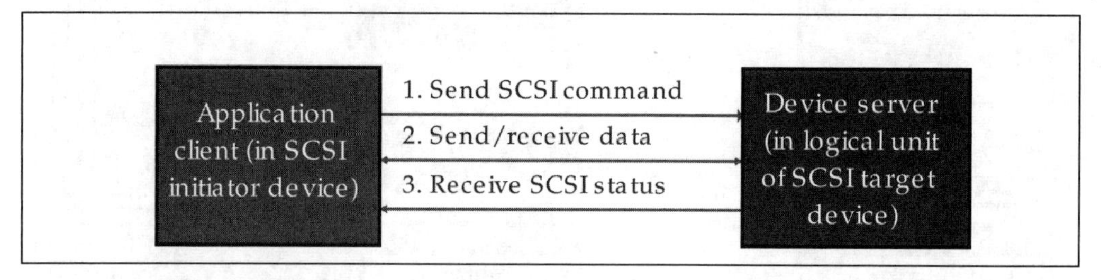

The server accepts the task, responds by sending or receiving the data, and then returns a status value for the transaction. Servers contain a task manager to handle the set of tasks they can queue up for execution, and SCSI defines a method for the client to manage that queue by using task management functions. To make a task-related request, such as "abort current task", the client sends the task management function and gets a simple response from the target, as shown in Figure 8-4.

Figure 8-4: Task Management Sequence

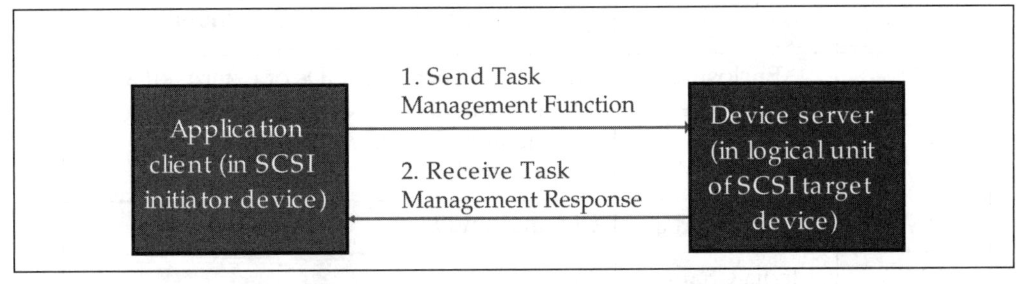

SCSI Commands

There are four groups of commands defined by SCSI:

1. **Non-data** commands, such as the TEST UNIT READY command
2. **Write** commands, such as writes to a disk. Write data is called Data Out because it is going out from the initiator's point of view.
3. **Read** commands, such as reads from disk. Read data is called Data In.
4. **Bi-directional** commands, in which data is both sent and received. Many OS's do not support this yet, but it can be useful in support of some RAID implementations. For example, the initiator might send data that the drive would then XOR with existing data already present and return the result.

SCSI also defines several command sets, one of which — SPC (SCSI Primary Commands) — defines commands that are implemented by all devices. The other command sets are optional depending on the type of device and its anticipated use, as shown in Table 8-1.

Table 8-1: SCSI Command Sets

Standard	Name	Types of Device that Implement the Command Set
SPC	Primary	All
SBC	Block	Disk drives
SSC	Streaming	Tape drives

Table 8-1: SCSI Command Sets

Standard	Name	Types of Device that Implement the Command Set (Continued)
SES	Enclosure Services	Enclosures, such as JBODs or external RAID. This command set allows communicating with an enclosure to read status of fans, power supplies, etc.
MMC	Multi-media	CDs and DVDs
SMC	Media Changer	Tape libraries
SCC	Controller	RAID controllers
OSD	Object	Object-based storage devices

Four SPC commands are required in every logical unit, as listed in Table 8-2 below. The INQUIRY command, as one example, returns information about the target device, including which command set it supports.

Table 8-2: Required SCSI Commands

Name	Types of Logical Units Using It
Inquiry	Returns miscellaneous information about the logical unit, including Device Type (disk, tape, etc.), Vendor ID, Serial Number, Vital Product Data
Report LUNs	Returns a list of the logical unit numbers present in the SCSI target device (LUN 0 is mandatory)
Request Sense	Returns logical units current sense data (obsolete, since most modern devices return the sense condition automatically with error indication)
Test Unit Ready	Returns GOOD if the logical unit is ready to accept media-access commands

Data Transfer

For SCSI commands that involve data transfer, the transfer is controlled by the logical unit. When an application client sends a command, it must be ready to participate in the data exchange at any time, but when the logical unit receives the command, it can wait as long as it wants before sending the read data or fetching the write data. The client is not allowed to "push" the data to the target, and this reduces the requirements for the target by eliminating the need to reserve buffer space for unexpected data. SCSI does allow an exception to this rule, though; using the "first burst" feature that guarantees the target will have at least a minimum buffer space to accept unsolicited data. This exception is more important for high-latency transport protocols like iSCSI than it is for a low-latency protocol like SAS. The SAS protocol does carry this concept forward but, while it is possible to use it for SAS, there is little motivation to support it from either the HBA side or the target side.

Having said that, it is worth noting that application clients maintain separate data buffers for read data and for write data (see Figure 8-5). This is even more important for SAS transfers because they are full duplex and need to support traffic in both directions at once. A separate buffer scheme is not mandated by the standard, but timely full-duplex operation is necessary for SAS to function without severe constraints. Once a connection is made, a device could receive data at the same time as outgoing data is being sent. If the device cannot provide a receive buffer while sending data, the protocol will not operate properly.

Figure 8-5: SCSI Data Transfer Buffers

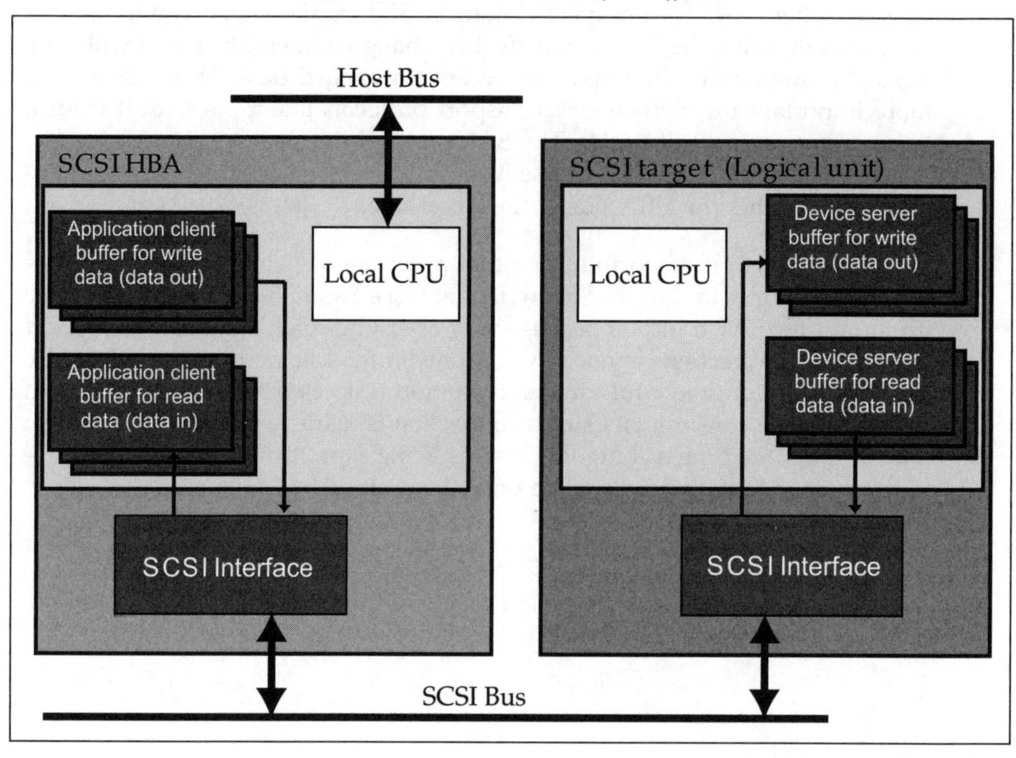

After a command has been serviced by the logical unit, a status code is returned, and the most common status codes are listed in Table 8-3 on page 200. If the code was 02h – CHECK CONDITION – then Sense data is also returned to explain what the trouble was. The complete list of sense keys is contained in SPC, but a list of common keys is presented in Table 8-4 on page 201.

Table 8-3: Common SCSI Status Codes

Value	Status	Description
00h	Good	Command completed successfully
02h	Check Condition	Command failed. Sense data (a structure of more than 8 bytes) is returned with the status indicating the reason for the failure.

Table 8-3: Common SCSI Status Codes

Value	Status	Description (Continued)
08h	Busy	Command refused - logical unit is temporarily busy (unknown reason). Try again
28h	Task Set Full	Command refused - logical unit is busy with other commands. Try again after a command completes (if that can be determined).
18h	Reservation Conflict	Command refused - logical unit is reserved by some other initiator port for the time being.

Table 8-4: Common Sense Keys

Value	Key	Description
0h	No Sense	No additional information.
1h	Recovered Error	Command succeeded, but logical unit recovered from an error to do so, such as an abnormally high number of retries when reading from disk.
2h	Not Ready	Logical unit was not ready for the command, for example the drive was not spinning when a read was requested.
3h	Medium Error	Non-recovered error, such as unrecoverable media area
4h	Hardware Error	Non-recovered error, such as bad controller
5h	Illegal Request	Problem with command, such as bad field in CDB
6h	Unit Attention	Command ignored, some other even needs to be reported
Bh	Aborted Command	Command was aborted for some reason.

Task Management

The task management functions mentioned earlier are defined in the SAM-3 standard and listed here in Table 8-5. Note that these all have a nexus associated with them, allowing them to manage a logical unit or a task within the task queue for that logical unit. SAM-3 defines command and task management processing, using a transport protocol "service procedure call" model. This model defines the interface between the application client and its SCSI initiator port, as well as the device server and its SCSI target port. For SAS, it defines the interface between the Application Layer and the Transport Layer. As a result, the SAS standard does not define the Application Layer much at all, assuming it is compliant with the SAM-3 model of the transport protocol services. The Transport Layer is defined, though, using the state-machine description style in many places in the SAS standard to describe behavior.

Table 8-5: SCSI Task Management Functions

Command	Scope	Description
QUERY TASK	I_T_L_Q	Check whether specified command is still being processed. Used for NAK recovery, to see whether command was received.
ABORT TASK	I_T_L_Q	Abort a specific command
ABORT TASK SET	I_T_L	Abort all commands from an initiator
CLEAR TASK SET	I_T_L	Abort all commands from all initiators
CLEAR ACA	I_T_L	Clear an Auto Contingent Allegiance condition
LOGICAL UNIT RESET	I_T_L	Reset the logical unit
I_T NEXUS RESET	I_T	Causes I-T Nexus loss in target. Logic behaves as if unable to open initiator before nexus loss timer expired.

SCSI Power Conditions

The next area the standard addresses with respect to the SCSI Application Layer is the control of the power for drives. As mentioned earlier, disk drives consume much more power while spinning up than they do when active, and this can be an issue in an enclosure with many drives, as shown in Figure 8-6, since a drive that only uses about 20 watts when active might need as much as 50 watts peak during spin up. If they all spin up at the same time, the resulting power load could exceed the power supply capacity, requiring a larger supply just to support spinup, or causing problems during spinup. To prevent these problems, the drives need to spin up in an orderly fashion.

Figure 8-6: Multi-Drive Enclosure

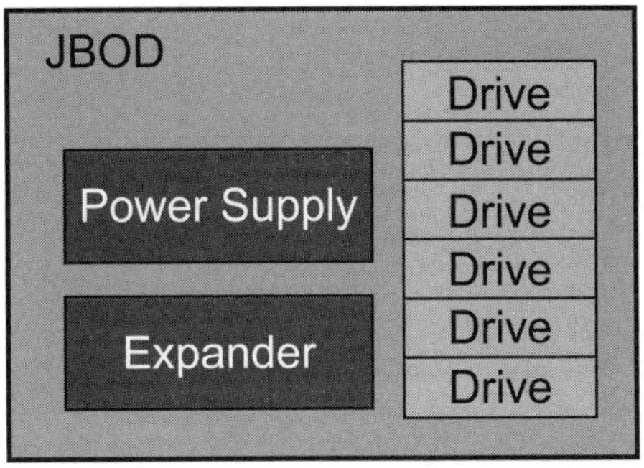

SATA Spin-Up

Support for staggered spin up is optional for SATA II, so some SATA drives won't support it and will simply spin up automatically after a power on. Those drives would not be appropriate in a system with many drives where an orderly spin up sequence is important to avoid overloading the power supply. For drives that do support this feature, the solution chosen was to define pin 11, normally the Ready Indicator, as the spin up control indicator. If pin 11 is grounded by the host, this indicates to the drive that it is allowed to spin up automatically. If pin 11 is instead pulled high, the drive should postpone spin up until speed negotiation completes on the link, or later if the ATA Power Up In Standby feature is used (see ATA/ATAPI-7 volume 1). The host can delay completing the link reset until the proper time and the drive will not spin up until then. Pin 11 will normally be pulled high in a server system where a staggered spin up is important. The pin can also be used as an Activity output signal after spinup if it was not grounded by the host.

SAS Spin Up

SAS drives do not spin up automatically. Instead they must wait for the NOTIFY (ENABLE SPINUP) primitive to give them permission. This is illustrated by Figure 8-7, which shows the application layer state machine involved in spinning up a drive. Notice that the only two paths in the machine to reach the Active state require a NOTIFY (ENABLE SPINUP) to make that transition. For reference, Table 8-6 describes all but the Powered_On substate of the Power Conditions State Machine.

Figure 8-7: Power Conditions State Machine

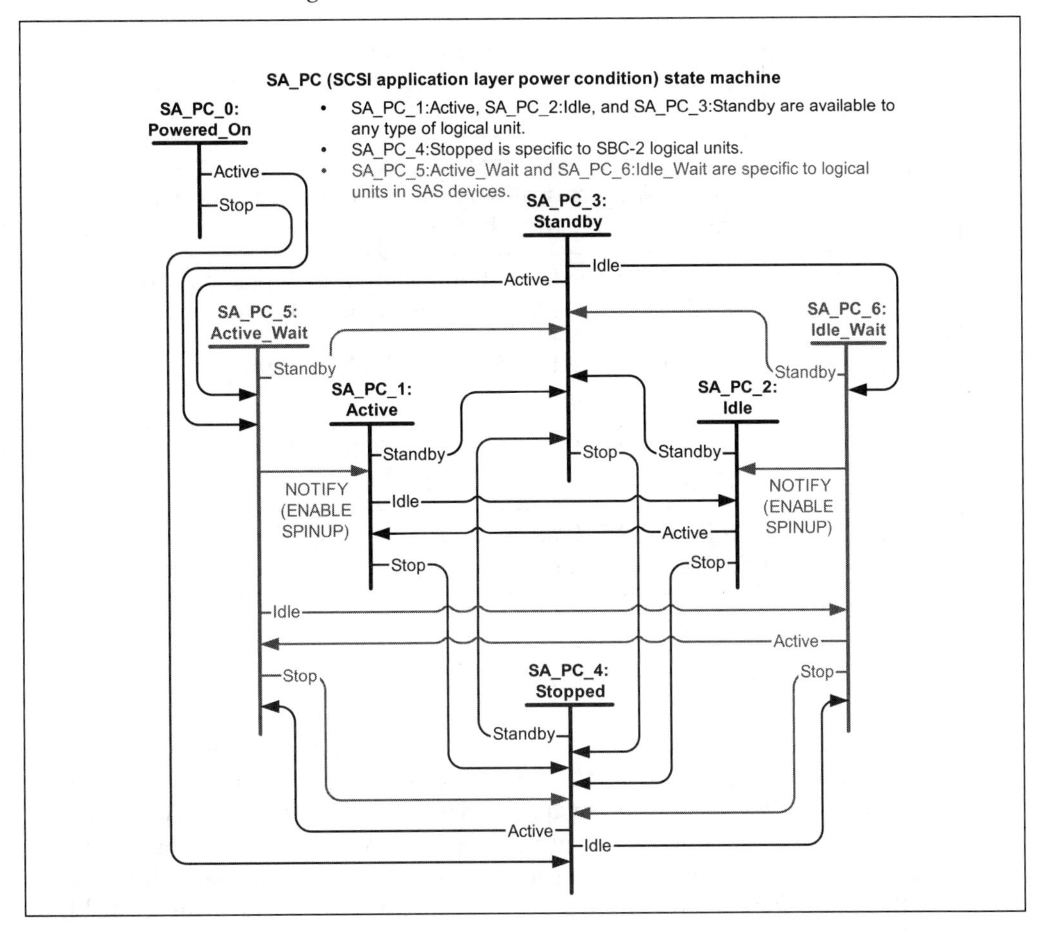

Table 8-6: Power Condition - State Description

State	Description
Active	Fully operational - media is spinning
Idle	Operational - media is spinning. Longer command latency. Automatically transitions to Active as needed to process a command.
Standby	Media is stopped. Automatically transitions to Active or Idle as needed to process a command.
Stopped	Media is stopped. START STOP UNIT command required to restart.
Active_Wait	**New for SAS**: Waiting for a NOTIFY (ENABLE SPINUP) to enter Active state
Idle_Wait	**New for SAS**: Waiting for a NOTIFY (ENABLE SPINUP) to enter Idle state

SMP Application Layer

For SMP, the SCSI management functions were used as the foundation for a new protocol model. The SAM-3 standard describes a list of management functions that could be requested by a SCSI device, such as ABORT TASK, QUERY TASK, etc. SAS expands significantly on that foundation by defining a separate management protocol containing more functions and better capabilities. Some of these new functions are used for discovering which addresses are available to the system at start up, or learning which have been added or removed when changes are broadcast. They provide initiators a straightforward method for scanning addresses and facilitate the discovery process in a SAS network. This method is explained further in Chapter 7, entitled "Discovery Process," on page 159.

Software for the initiator uses a management application client to send the SMP commands, and in the target device a management device server is used to respond to them. The list of commands or functions available is as follows:

Report General – Returns general information about the device, such as mode pages, phys, and addresses.

Report Manufacturer Information – Returns vendor and product ID.

Discover – Returns information about a particular phy, such as address and device type of the device attached to it.

Report Phy Error Log – Returns error count for this Phy in four areas. These were described earlier in the section on the Phy log descriptor of the protocol-specific Log page, and are simply listed here. Counts instances of Invalid dwords, Disparity errors, Loss of dword synchronization, and the Phy reset problem.

Report Phy SATA – Returns information about the SATA state for this phy. This SMP function is only implemented by expanders with SATA bridges and by SMP ports that share a SAS address with a SATA port. Fields contained in this report:

- Affiliations Supported – indicates whether this port supports the SATA functionality intended to give an initiator dedicated access to this target until the affiliation is cleared.
- Affiliation Valid – set to one when this Phy is maintaining an affiliated initiator address and the affiliated STP initiator SAS Address field in this report is valid.
- STP SAS Address – reports the SAS address of the STP target port that contains this phy.
- (Initial) Register Device to Host FIS – contains the contents of the initial of these type FIS's. For a bridge, this is provided by the attached SATA device after a link reset sequence. For a native STP target port in an end device, this is directly reported to the initiator instead. The first byte of this field will be initialized to zero whenever the Phy is reset (lost dword synchronization or link reset sequence or power up), and will be set to 34h when the first Register – Device to Host FIS has been received.
- Affiliated STP Initiator SAS Address – address of the initiator port that currently has an affiliation with the STP target port containing this phy.

Report Route Information – Returns the entry in the routing table for a specified entry of a specified phy. By iterating this command, an initiator can read the entire contents of the address routing table in an expander.

Configure Route Information – Writes an address into a specified entry of the routing table for a specified Phy of an expander.

Phy Control – Used to supply timeout values to a specific Phy or to give the Phy a link reset or a hard reset.

9 Transport Layer

The Previous Chapter

The previous chapter described the Application Layer of the SAS layered design. This layer is largely implemented as driver-level software rather than directly as hardware, and is intended to be fully backward compatible with the SCSI application model. Some background for that model was presented to provide sufficient context for the discussion, and the changes that were needed in the Mode and Log pages for SAS devices to support a serial transport were described.

This Chapter

This chapter describes the function and responsibilities of the Transport Layer of the SAS hierarchy. This layer receives requests from the Application Layer modeled as function calls, creates frames to support the requested action and queues them until they are completed. The frames are then passed down to the next lower layer, which is the Port Layer.

The Next Chapter

The next chapter describes the Port Layer of the SAS architecture along with the state machines used in the standard to explain its behavior, and the messages passed to and from it in support of the other layers.

Transport Layer Perspective

There is a Transport Layer section for each of the three protocols supported - SSP for SCSI command support, STP (SATA Tunneled Protocol) for SATA support, and SMP (Serial Management Protocol) for management functions. Before getting into the details of the Transport Layer, it will be helpful to review the location of the Transport Layer within the layered hierarchy of SAS using a functional example. Figure 9-1 shows a block diagram of a device that implements three ports, one of which shows the internal functional blocks. When the application issues an outgoing command, the Application Layer at the top sends the request to the SAS HBA Driver, which communicates the request to the HBA's Register Interface. Next, a port is selected based on the destination address, and the request is forwarded to the Transport Layer of that port.

Figure 9-1: Functional Block Diagram of Layers

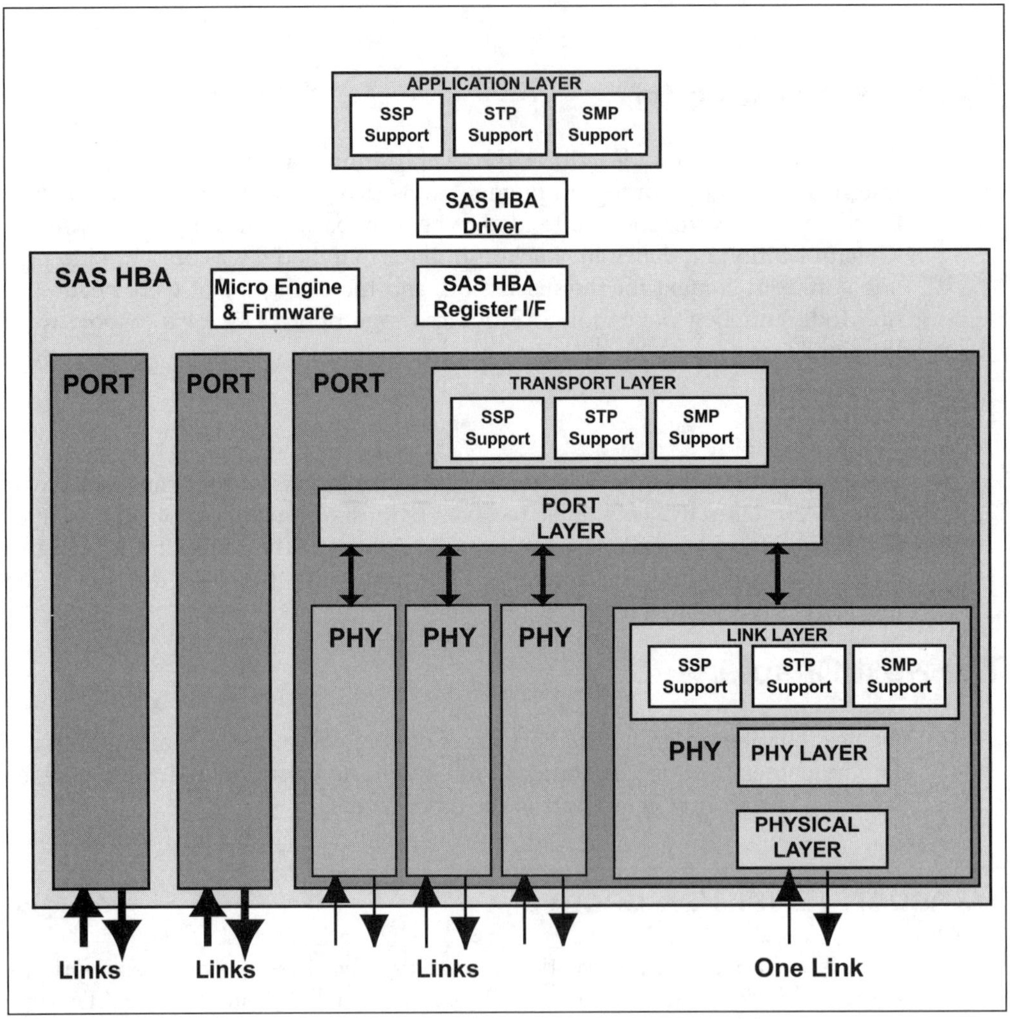

There is just one Transport Layer block for each port of a SAS device, even in the case of a wide port that implements several phys like the one in the example. However, the Transport Layer supports three separate protocols:

1. SSP for SCSI Command support
2. STP for SATA support
3. SMP for management functions.

The Transport Layer responsibilities include passing requests and confirmations between adjacent layers, as well as handling some Link Layer errors. Perhaps its most interesting job is to construct frames in support of the request. The format of the frames is protocol specific, so let's consider them in the context of each protocol.

SSP (Serial SCSI Protocol) Transport Layer

This section focuses on the SSP portion of the Transport Layer beginning with the packet, or Frame format. SSP, of course, must mimic SCSI operations as much as possible, so the content of the frame must contain all the information for a SCSI transfer as well as the information needed for the serial protocol.

SSP Frames

As shown in Figure 9-2, SSP frames are bracketed by an SOF (Start of Frame) and EOF (End of Frame) primitive. These make it clear to the receiver where each frame begins and ends. The loss of either of these during transmission will invalidate the frame since the receiver would be unable to distinguish the frame boundaries. The other contents of the frame include a header that gives information about the frame, followed by up to 1024 bytes of data, if any, and lastly a CRC.

Figure 9-2: Overall SSP Frame

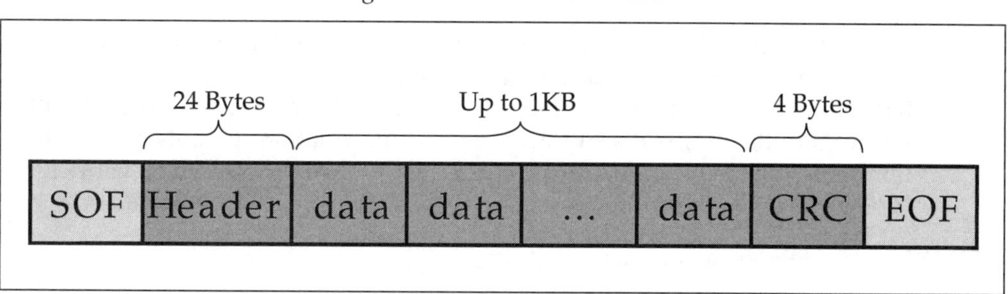

The header communicates the purpose of this frame and how it will be serviced. For SSP, the contents of a header are the first 24 bytes of the SSP Frame Contents as shown Table 9-1, and the fields it contains are described in the text that follows it.

Table 9-1: SSP Frame Contents

<table>
<tr><th>Byte</th><th colspan="4">Field(s)</th></tr>
<tr><td>0</td><td colspan="4">Frame Type</td></tr>
<tr><td>1 to 3</td><td colspan="4">Hashed Destination SAS address</td></tr>
<tr><td>4</td><td colspan="4">Reserved</td></tr>
<tr><td>5 to 7</td><td colspan="4">Hashed Source SAS address</td></tr>
<tr><td>8 to 9</td><td colspan="4">Reserved</td></tr>
<tr><td>10</td><td>Reserved</td><td>Retry Data Frames</td><td>Retran smit</td><td>Changing Data Pointer</td></tr>
<tr><td>11</td><td>Reserved</td><td colspan="3">Number of Fill Bytes</td></tr>
<tr><td>12 to 15</td><td colspan="4">Reserved</td></tr>
<tr><td>16 to 17</td><td colspan="4">Tag</td></tr>
<tr><td>18 to 19</td><td colspan="4">Target Port Transfer Tag</td></tr>
<tr><td>20 to 23</td><td colspan="4">Data Offset</td></tr>
<tr><td>24 to m</td><td colspan="4">Information Unit (Corresponds to Frame Type)</td></tr>
<tr><td>m to (n-3)</td><td colspan="4">Fill bytes, if needed</td></tr>
<tr><td>(n-3) to n</td><td colspan="4">CRC</td></tr>
</table>

The CRC is computed by the transmitter with a standard mathematical algorithm based on the header and data, and verified by the receiver. This method basically creates many bit changes in the CRC field for every bit change in the header and data. This doesn't give enough information to allow error correction, but provides a robust error check mechanism. The receiver verifies the CRC value when the entire frame has arrived.

The use of an error-correcting code would might have seemed desirable since it would reduce the need for retries of corrupted frames but it is not common in serial transports. CRC is the only link transmission error detection scheme used in serial transports with which the author is familiar. Whatever motivated those older designs to use CRC, new architectures like SAS may have chosen to follow this industry standard practice to reduce design effort and risk.

SSP Frame Header Fields

- **Frame type:** Indicates the purpose of this frame (see Table 9-2). Commands and Task management header types are sent from initiator to target, while XFER_RDY and Response types are returned from the target to the initiator, and Data headers go both ways. The sequence of these transfers is the same as it is for SCSI. A few examples are listed here:
  - Read Command, Data from Target, Response
  - Write Command, XFER_RDY, Data to Target, Response
  - NonData -- Command, Response

  While these can be uninterrupted transaction sequences, the SCSI target is allowed to disconnect at any time and reconnect later to finish the sequence.

Table 9-2: Frame Type Field

Value	Description
01h	DATA
05h	XFER_RDY
06h	COMMAND
07h	RESPONSE
16h	TASK management
F0 - FFh	Vendor Specific
All others	Reserved

- **Hashed Destination and Source Addresses:** When a connection is requested between two devices, the destination address specified in the OPEN request is used to route it. Once the connection is established, there is no need for address information in the subsequent frames because they simply flow over the dedicated path and no routing takes place. Still, there is the possibility that a device might attempt to use an existing connection to send a frame targeting a different address than the device which has been connected. To provide an opportunity to check for this, the standard authors chose to include in the header a compressed form of the addresses for both source and destination. These hashed addresses allow devices to verify that the frame is still using the same addresses that were accepted with the request. As mentioned earlier, these fields exist in the SAS header because it is modeled on the Fibre Channel header. The fields are 24 bits wide because these fields are only 24 bits in the Fibre Channel header. To compress the 64-bit SAS addresses for use in those fields, it was decided to put them through a process called *hashing* to reduce them to a 24-bit value. Hashing is an imperfect solution, though, because some 64-bit addresses will hash to the same 24-bit value, creating a risk that some incorrect values might appear valid. It is not mandatory for a device to check these fields, and at the time of this writing it was not expected that many vendors would do so in the early round of products.

- **Retry Data Frames:** Only used with XFER_RDY frames, this informs the initiator whether it is permissible to retry write DATA frames that fail.
- **Retransmit:** This bit indicates whether this frame is a retransmission of an earlier frame that experienced a failure. It is only used with XFER_RDY, TASK, or RESPONSE frames.
- **Changing Data Pointer:** (See the description in the section on Data Offset.)
- **Number of fill bytes:** The SAS protocol does all transfers in groups of four bytes called dwords. If the total number of bytes in a frame is not evenly divisible by four, then up to three bytes may need to be added to make it so. To make it easier for the receiver to see when this has been done, this field indicates how many bytes were added. The only frames that are not naturally 4-byte aligned are DATA frames and RESPONSE frames, and for them the fill bytes will be added at the end, just before the CRC value. For all other frames the number of fill bytes will be zero.
- **Tag:** When an initiator sends a command, it creates a 16-bit tag value associated with it that can be used to identify the results that come back for it. Since several commands may be queued up before responses start coming back, the initiator needs a way to associate each response with its original context, so a 16-bit tag value is used for this purpose. The target puts the corresponding tag into the frame when returning the data or response, and the initiator can use that to quickly look up the context for it. Initiators actually use a second tag, too, called the Initiator Connection Tag that serves a somewhat similar purpose when a connection request arrives at the initiator. That tag will be discussed later.
- **Target Port Transfer Tag (TPTT):** Inherited from Fibre Channel, this optional tag accomplishes a similar function on the target side, providing a

short-cut for the target to associate the buffer space for this transaction. A target could have several commands in progress, all of which have an XFER_RDY outstanding, so that the data for several write transactions may arrive at any time and in any order. The target must associate this context quickly when the data begins to arrive, and it is much easier to do that if there are only a small number of possible contexts. If the target had to associate the full tag with its local context, it would need a Content Addressable Memory (CAM) and would take longer to look it up. Note that TPTT only has meaning for writes; for reads the TPTT is set to zero

- **Data Offset:** This field only has meaning for DATA frames and is ignored otherwise. It contains the application client buffer offset as defined in the SAM standard and is set to zero for the first read or write data transfer. If additional data frames are needed to complete the request, the subsequent frames will have a data offset value that equals the sum of the data offset and data length of the previous transfer. As one might surmise, this is really just a check that the data pointers are in sync between the sender and receiver. If an SSP initiator port receives a frame of read data with an unexpected offset value, the frame will be discarded. All the subsequent DATA frames received for that command will also be discarded and the application client will abort the command. If an SSP target port receives a frame with a bad offset, it will also discard the frame and terminate the command by sending a RESPONSE frame indicating a CHECK CONDITION status, sense code ABORTED COMMAND, and additional sense code set to DATA OFFSET ERROR. Any subsequent write data for that command is discarded.
- **Changing Data Pointer:** Used to indicate that the target is resending a DATA frame with a Data Offset field that may not be sequential with reference to that of the previous frame. Ordinarily, the Data Offset field is used as a confirmation that no data frames have been lost by verifying that the data offset increases sequentially from the previous frame. This bit indicates the rule just described does not apply; if that check fails for this frame, it is not to be considered an error. The reason is that the data was considered to have a problem and is being retransmitted in an effort to correct the problem.
- **Information Unit (IU):** This section represents the information corresponding to the frame type. For DATA frames, this contains the data bytes to be sent. For COMMAND frames, it contains the CDB (Command Descriptor Block), Task attributes, the logical unit being addressed and other information about the command. RESPONSE frames include status, sense data, and response code. XFER_RDY frames provide an offset and data length, while TASK management frames indicate the logical unit, the function to be executed, and the tag of the task to be managed.

- **Fill Bytes:** These are bytes that were added to make the frame aligned on a dword or four-byte boundary. The number of them was specified in the NUMBER OF FILL BYTES field, and the contents of the bytes is vendor specific.
- **CRC:** The Cyclic Redundancy Code that is appended to every frame that was computed based on all the bytes between the SOF (start of frame) and EOF (end of frame) primitives. This is computed by the sender's Link Layer and checked by the receiver's Link Layer.

Example of TPTT Usage

Consider the following example, shown in Figure 9-3 on page 217, that illustrates the use of both tags discussed so far. Here, the initiator has created a local command context buffer using one of its available tag locations to store the pointers for this structure, such as starting addresses for data-in and data-out buffers. When the initiator sends the command frame to the target, it includes the CDB and other information, and the tag value as well, which the diagram shows as 175. Assume for this example that the command will be a data write.

When the target receives this frame, it creates a command context buffer of its own where it stores the CDB and tag, and sets up the pointers to its own memory locations for receiving the write data for this command. This information is stored locally in the target and referenced with the Target Port Transfer Tag (TPTT), shown as a value of 7 in the drawing.

Figure 9-3: Target Tag Example

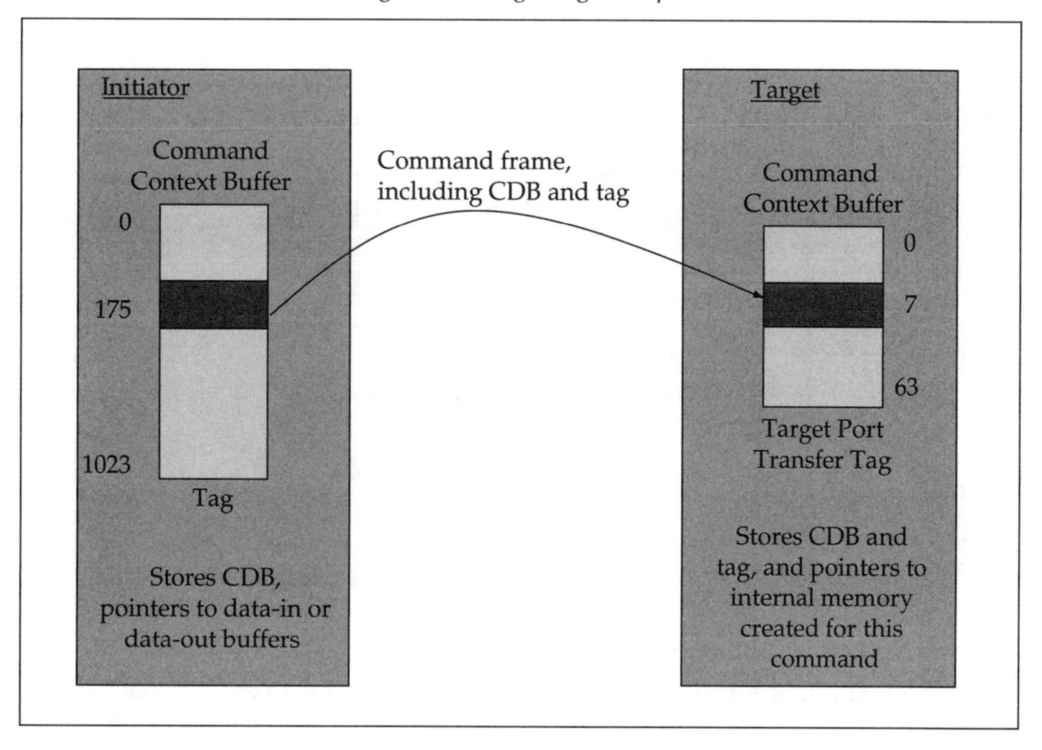

Referring now to Figure 9-4 on page 218, step one, once the target has its internal pointers ready, it sends an XFER_RDY frame back to the initiator to pull the data for the write command. This frame includes the tag the initiator gave it with the original command and also includes the target's tag, the TPTT. Since the use of TPTT is optional, the initiator does not know whether the target is making use of it or not, but still needs to memorize the TPTT value and echo it back with the frame when sending the data.

Figure 9-4: Target Tag Example, part 2

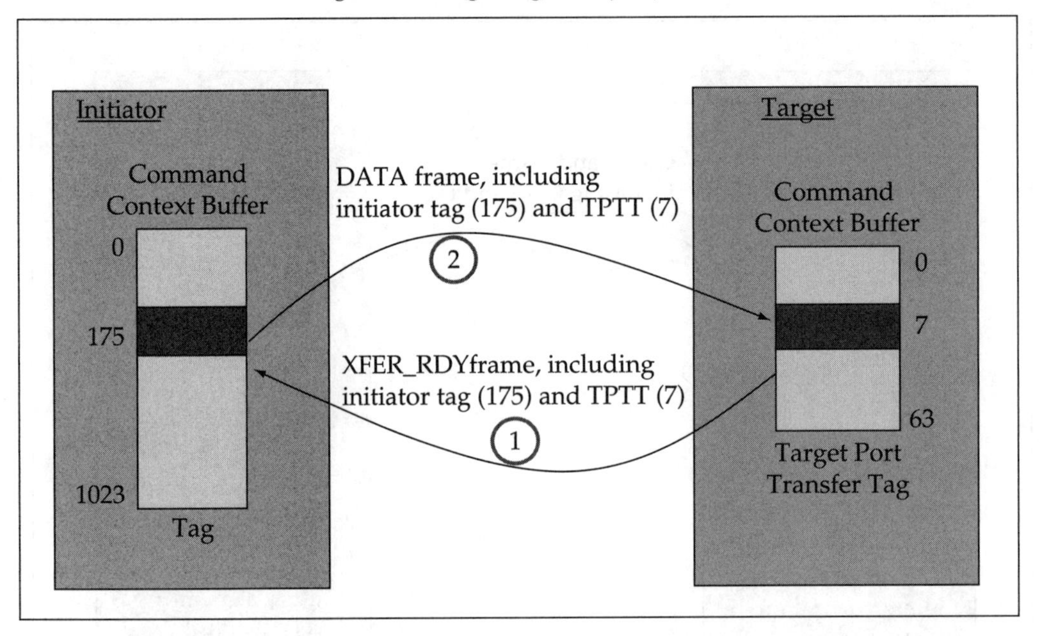

When this frame arrives, the initiator uses the tag value to quickly look up the context of this command. Finding the pointers for the data, it initiates a transfer out from the memory location they refer to. In step 2, the initiator now has the data ready and knows that permission has been given to send up to 1KB of data to the target. So it sends a DATA frame that once again includes the initiator's tag, but also includes the TPTT for the target's use. When the frame arrives at the target, the TPTT permits a quick lookup of the memory structure for the data, allowing it to be put into the proper buffer with minimal delay. The time needed for this lookup is important to the device that is receiving the data, because there is not much time between the arrival of the frame header indicating what is going to happen and the arrival of the data coming in at a high rate of speed. It would take longer for the receiver to recreate the context based on the address and tag of the sender than from its own internal tag. Thus the motivation for the TPTT.

Interestingly, the target is allowed to change the TPTT for every XFER_RDY it sends, even for multiple responses to the same original command. Continuing our example with Figure 9-5 on page 219, assume the first write command was for a transfer that was larger than 1KB and will require more than one

XFER_RDY to complete. If that is followed by another write command that arrives before the first is completed, then the tags might get re-used.

Figure 9-5: Target Tag Example - Part 3

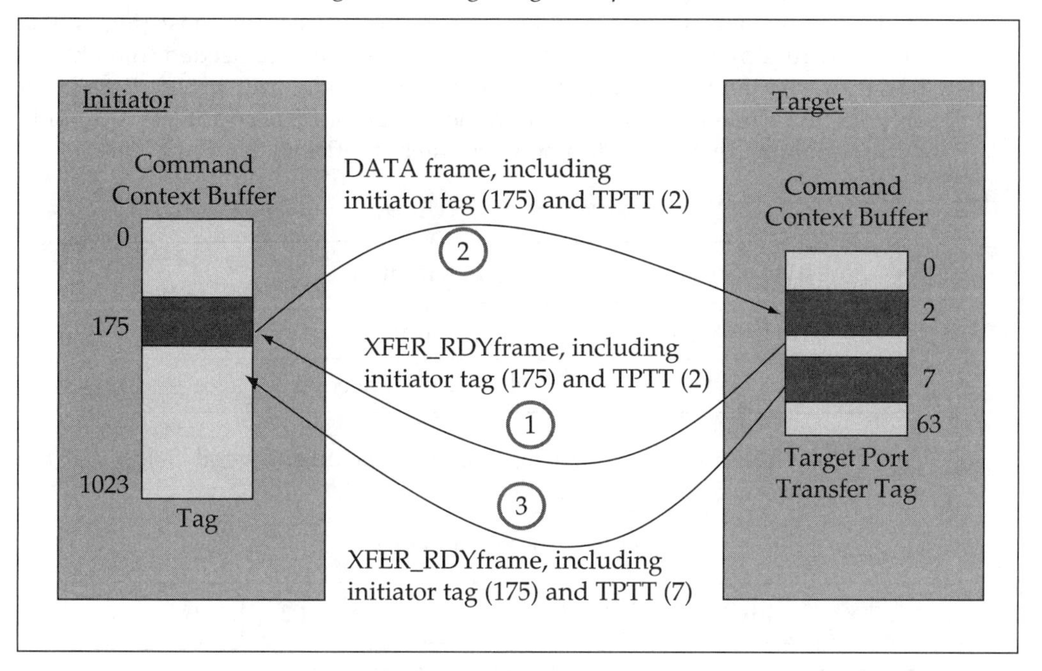

If the target's first XFER_RDY uses a TPTT value of 2 for the first write response, then the initiator echoes that value in the header when it sends the data. Once the target looks up that TPTT, finds the pointers and stores that data away, that TPTT is once again available.

Assume next that the target is ready to send an XFER_RDY for the second write command. Since entry 2 of the TPTT is available, it could use that value for this second XFER_RDY. Finally, before the data for the second write is returned, assume that the target is ready to fetch the next part of the data for the first write command. When it sends the XFER_RDY this time, it will have to include a different TPTT value, because entry 2 is already in use. As a result, the initiator will see an XFER_RDY with the tag for the first write command that now has a different TPTT. All this means, though, is that the initiator must latch the TPTT value every time it sees an XFER_RDY, rather than expecting to see the same one for all the XFER_RDYs that relate to the same command.

Details of Information Units

Next let's examine the Information Units one at a time to see what they contain and how they are arranged in the frame header. It's easiest to start with the DATA IU, shown in Table 9-3, because it's a simple structure, consisting of data from 1 to 1024 bytes, plus up to three fill bytes if they are needed to make the frame an even number of dwords (evenly divisible by four bytes). Recall that only the Data frame and Response frame can possibly need fill bytes, so only those two frames may include a non-zero fill bytes field.

Table 9-3: SCSI DATA IU

Byte	Field(s)
0 to n	Data
(up to 3 bytes)	Fill bytes, if needed

The COMMAND IU, as shown in Table 9-4, includes several fields that are described below it.

Table 9-4: COMMAND IU

<table>
<tr><th></th><th>Bit 7</th><th>6</th><th>5</th><th>4</th><th>3</th><th>2</th><th>1</th><th>0</th></tr>
<tr><td>Byte 0 to 7</td><td colspan="8">Logical Unit Number</td></tr>
<tr><td>8</td><td colspan="8">Reserved</td></tr>
<tr><td>9</td><td>Enable First Burst</td><td colspan="4">Reserved</td><td colspan="3">Task Attribute</td></tr>
<tr><td>10</td><td colspan="8">Reserved</td></tr>
<tr><td>11</td><td colspan="6">Additional CDB Length in dwords</td><td colspan="2">Reserved</td></tr>
<tr><td>12 to 27</td><td colspan="8">CDB</td></tr>
<tr><td>28 +</td><td colspan="8">Additional CDB Bytes</td></tr>
</table>

- The **Logical Unit Number** (LUN) specifies which of the logical units within the target device is being addressed by this command. Targets can have several LUNs, which must start with LUN 0 and should be in sequential, ascending order for legacy support.

- Next is **Enable First Burst** which, when set, allows the initiator to send one burst of write data without waiting for the customary permission to be granted by an XFER_RDY frame from the target. The size of data it is allowed to send is given by the First Burst Size field in the Disconnect-Reconnect mode page. If this field in the mode page is non-zero or changeable, and the logical unit and target port indicate they comply with SAS 1.1 or later, as reported by the INQUIRY data version descriptors, then the Enable First Burst bit can be set.
  It is not expected that this function will find much application in SAS, because it is intended for systems that experience long latencies, like iSCSI or Fibre Channel. In those environments, the delay from sending the command to getting permission to send data could be long, reducing effective bandwidth, and so it makes sense to implement this capability. For SAS, though, latencies are expected to be short due to the limited size of the topology. Consequently, there is no need for a first burst capability, and its use is discouraged.

- The **Task Attribute** field specifies the transaction priority ordering policy that should be followed for this command. These are defined by the SAM standard, and this field uses those definitions as shown in Table 9-5.

Table 9-5: Task Attributes

Code	Task Attribute	Description
000b	SIMPLE	This task is to be managed according to the SAM rules for simple task attribute. Basically, the target determines the ordering based on what will give best performance overall.
001b	HEAD OF QUEUE	This task is to be managed according to the SAM rules for a head of queue task. This command should become the next one executed regardless of other queued simple commands.
010b	ORDERED	This task is to be managed according to the SAM rules for an ordered task. In this case, it is the initiator who determines the order of execution.
011b	RESERVED	

Table 9-5: Task Attributes

Code	Task Attribute	Description (Continued)
100b	ACA	This task is to be managed according to the SAM-3 rules for *Auto Contingent Allegiance*. In earlier SCSI designs if a failure occurred the device would only hold on to the sense data for that failure until another command was received. If several commands were queued up, the failure data could be lost. The solution was ACA, which meant that if the target saw a failure it would refuse any other commands from the initiator until the initiator received the Check Condition and sent a CDB with the ACA task attribute. It is ***not needed for SAS***, because the target automatically sends any sense data with the RESPONSE frame.
101b - 111b	RESERVED	

- The **Additional CDB Length** field contains the length in dwords (four bytes) of the Additional CDB field.
- The combination of **CDB** and **Additional CDB** fields together contain the CDB to be interpreted by the selected logical unit. The contents of the CDB are defined in the SCSI command standards such as the SPC standard.The next frame type to be discussed is the RESPONSE IU, which is shown in Table 9-6. The individual fields in it are described in the text that follows.

Table 9-6: Response IU

	Bit 7	6	5	4	3	2	1	0
Byte 0 to 9	Reserved							
10	Reserved						DataPres	
11	Status							
12 to 15	Reserved							
16 to 19	Sense Data Length (bytes)							
20 to 23	Response Data Length (bytes)							
24 +	Response Data or Sense Data							

- The **DataPres** field indicates whether there is data present with this response frame. The values of this 2-bit field are shown in Table 9-7.

Table 9-7: DataPres Values

Value	Description
00b	No sense or response data
01b	Response data included - this is sent for every TASK frame and in response to errors in the Transport Layer handling of a COMMAND frame.
10b	Sense data included - for commands that complete with sense data to return, such as a CHECK CONDITION status.
11b	Reserved - not legal to have both Response data and Sense data at the same time. RESPONSE frame with this setting will be discarded.

- The **Status** field is simply the SCSI status codes defined in the SAM-3 standard. A list of common status codes is reproduced here for convenience in Table 9-8.

Table 9-8: Common Status Codes

Status Code	Status	Description
00h	GOOD	Device server successfully completed the task
02h	CHECK CONDITION	Indicates that sense data has been delivered
08h	BUSY	Logical Unit is temporarily unable to accept a command. Recommended that the application client try the command again later.
28h	TASK SET FULL	Logical Unit has at least one task in progress and insufficient resources to accept another.

Sense data is only present if the status is CHECK CONDITION, and its format is defined in the SPC standard. The most common fixed-length format for it is 18 bytes and includes a SENSE KEY and ADDITIONAL SENSE

CODE. For example, if an initiator attempts to send linked commands to a device that does not support them, the result will be as follows: Status = Check Condition, Sense Key = Illegal request, Additional sense code = Invalid field in CDB.

When the DataPres field indicates that Response Data is present, it is encoded as shown in Table 9-9 and Table 9-10.

Table 9-9: Response Data Field

Byte\bit	7	6	5	4	3	2	1	0
0 to 2	Reserved							
3	Response Code							

Table 9-10: Response Codes

Status Code	Status
00h	Task Management Function Complete
02h	Invalid Frame
04h	Task Management Function Not Supported
05h	Task Management Function Failed
08h	Task Management Function Succeeded
09h	Invalid Logical Unit Number

The next frame type to consider is the XFER_RDY IU, shown in Table 9-11 and described in the following text.

Table 9-11: XFER_RDY IU

Byte	Field(s)
0 to 3	Requested Offset
4 to 7	Write Data Length
8 to 11	Reserved

- The **Requested Offset** indicates the offset from zero at which this data will be stored. The value will be zero for the first XFER_RDY in a series of them needed to transfer a data block, and each subsequent XFER_RDY frame for this command will have an offset value that reflects the combination of the last offset plus the size of the last transfer.
- The **Write Data Length** represents the number of bytes, in multiples of four, that the target is prepared to receive. The initiator must not send more than this.

Next is the Task IU, used for sending Task Management functions (commands) to a target, as shown in Table 9-12. The list of Task Management Functions is contained in Table 9-13.

Table 9-12: TASK Management IU

Byte	Field(s)
0 to 7	Logical Unit Number
8 to 9	Reserved
10	Task Management Function
11	Reserved
12 to 13	Tag of Task to be Managed
14 to 27	Reserved

Table 9-13: TASK Management Functions

Value	Task Management Function
01h	Abort Task - abort the task referenced by the tag of this task
02h	Abort Task Set - abort the task set (all the commands for this I_T_L nexus)
04h	Clear Task Set - clear all commands from all initiators to this target and logical unit
08h	Logical Unit Reset - reset target and logical unit

Table 9-13: TASK Management Functions

Value	Task Management Function (Continued)
40h	Clear ACA - clear the ACA for both target and logical unit, allowing access for other initiators
80h	Query Task - return status for the command referenced by the I_T_L nexus and tag

Frame Sequence Examples

Having looked at each of the frame types that can be sent over an SSP connection, we will now consider some example frame exchanges to better understand the sequence of frames. Note that for this example, as for all the others in this section, the sequence is simplified for illustration and does not include any Link Layer activity such as the ACK/NAK protocol that will be covered in "Frame Acknowledgement (ACK/NAK Handshake)" on page 349.

Example 1 - Non-Data Command

The first example demonstrates a non-data command sequence, as shown in Figure 9-6. Here, an Application Layer Send SCSI Command service request begins the process of creating an outgoing SCSI COMMAND frame.

Figure 9-6: SSP Non-Data Command Sequence

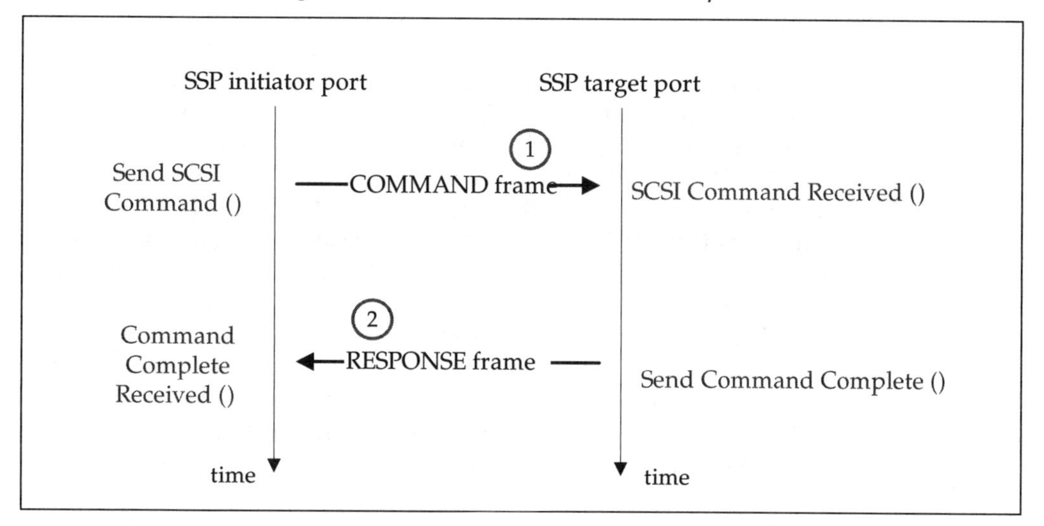

Frame Construction

The frame includes several arguments that were contained in the request and is passed to the lower layers, eventually making its way onto the link as a COMMAND frame. Some of the arguments have already been discussed and include:

- Connection rate - 1.5 Gb/s or 3.0 Gb/s
- Initiator connection tag - this is the third tag involved in SAS transactions (the other two are the transaction tag assigned by the initiator and the target port transfer tag assigned by the target). An initiator assigns a transaction tag to each command so it can associate the results with the original request when they are later returned. It also assigns a connection tag to the command that is only used when the target sends a connection request to return the response. If the target closes the connection and then wants to reopen it later to return the results, it will send a connection request to the initiator that includes the connection tag that was associated with the original request. That allows the initiator to quickly find the context for the frame coming from the target without having to wait on the arrival of the frame itself. The initiator could have waited and looked up the context based on destination address instead, but that would require more logic and more time because the address is so much bigger.
- Destination SAS address - used to select Phy for connection

- Transaction tag - used to track several outstanding requests
- Logical unit number - sub-unit within a target device
- Enable first burst value - This bit enables an initiator to bypass the normal flow control process for the first burst of a write command. This helps a long-latency architecture like iSCSI, where waiting on flow control would impact performance, but SAS connections will have very low latency, so this is not expected to be needed or even supported by many SAS devices.
- Task priority - assigns a relative priority to commands that have a SIMPLE task attribute. This is the same as legacy SCSI protocol.
- Task attribute - value can be SIMPLE, ORDERED, HEAD OF QUEUE, or ACA (Auto-Contingent Allegiance). This is the same as legacy SCSI protocol. The SIMPLE priority scheme usually yields the best performance, because it gives the target device the ability to optimally reorder the tasks. The ORDERED priority means the tasks must stay in the order assigned by the initiator, HEAD OF QUEUE means the task should become the very next one to be executed. The ACA attribute means the associated task can be executed even if an ACA condition has been created because of an error and other tasks will be aborted.
- Additional CDB length
- CDB - Command Descriptor Block
- Additional CDB bytes, if any

Target Response

When the target receives the frame, its Transport Layer sends the information to the Application Layer as a SCSI Command Received indication including the arguments that were passed with the command. Once the target has serviced the command, the Application Layer sends a Send Command Complete request back to the Transport Layer with arguments such as tag, status, and sense data. Based on that request, the Transport Layer of the target creates the RESPONSE frame and forwards it to the lower layers, where it eventually makes its way onto the link. When the RESPONSE frame is received by the initiator, the Transport Layer forwards a Command Complete Received confirmation to the Application Layer.

Example 2 - Write Command

Frame Construction

The next example is a write command sequence, shown in Figure 9-7. In this case, the initiator Application Layer sends a Send SCSI Command request for a write command, from which the Transport Layer creates a COMMAND frame with a CDB indicating a write of the requested size. The initiator then waits on an XFER_RDY frame from the target to grant permission to actually send the data, since SAS uses the SCSI model for data transfer that puts the target in control of the timing. The initiator is not allowed to "push" data to the receiver. Instead, the target "pulls" the data by sending the XFER_RDY frame. This simplifies the target design because data will never show up unexpectedly.

Figure 9-7: SSP Write Command Sequence

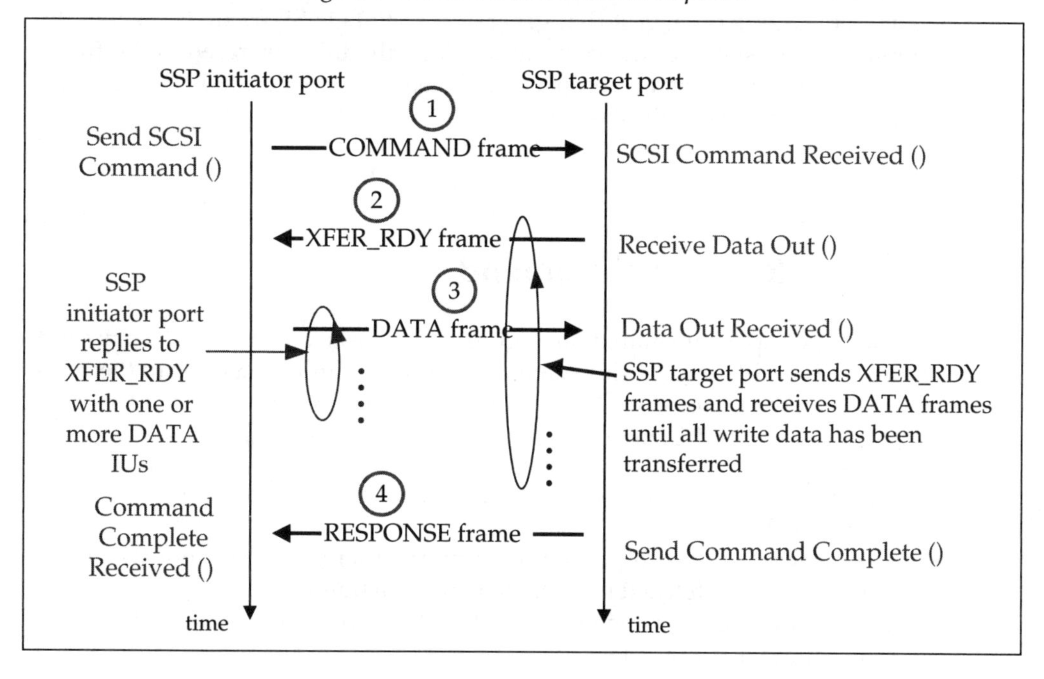

Target Response

When the receiver sees the COMMAND frame, its Application Layer services the command by sending a Receive Data Out request from which the Transport Layer constructs an XFER_RDY frame. Recall that for SCSI the data direction is always labeled from the initiator's point of view, so Data Out is write data from the initiator and Data In is read data that will be received by the initiator. Clearly, when the receiver sends an XFER_RDY it must be prepared to accept the write data immediately, since there is no way to know how soon it may arrive.

Data Frames

Once an XFER_RDY frame has been received, the initiator sends a DATA frame with a byte count that does not exceed the write data length specified by the XFER_RDY. Since the data length field is 32 bits, it could indicate that the receiver is ready for a transfer of as much as 4GB. A data frame cannot contain 1K bytes, so there could be many DATA frames for each XFER_RDY. The XFER_RDY and DATA frames alternate and repeat until all of the requested data has been sent. At that point the target's Application Layer sends a Send Command Complete request that generates a RESPONSE frame to convey the completion and status of the command. When the initiator receives the frame and generates a Command Complete Received confirmation to its Application Layer, the transaction is finished.

Example 3 - Read Command

The next example, illustrated in Figure 9-8, shows an SSP read command sequence. The difference in this example is how the target responds to the command. When the target's Application Layer receives and services the read command, it sends a Send Data In request with the following arguments:

- Nexus information (I_T_L_Q Nexus = Initiator address, Target address, LUN, and Tag),
- Device Server Buffer, a pointer to an internal target buffer from which the read data can be fetched for inclusion into the frame,
- Client Buffer Offset, which becomes the Data Offset field in the header, and
- Byte count for the transfer.

Figure 9-8: SSP Read Example

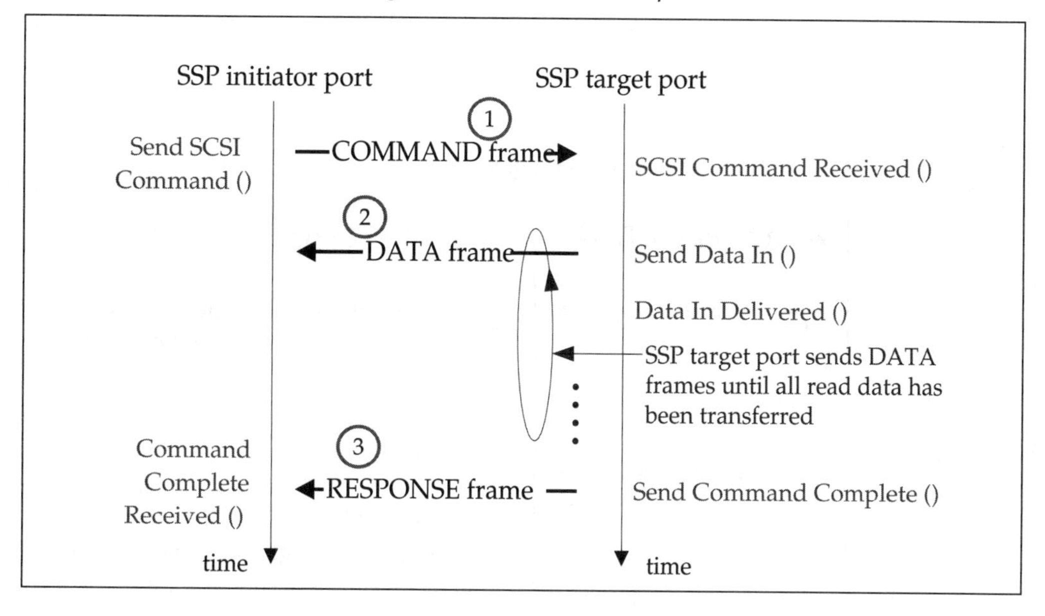

Those arguments are used to construct a DATA frame which is sent to the intiator. After all the requested data has been sent, or if there was an Application Layer problem that would prevent it, a Send Command Complete Application Layer response informs the Transport Layer to construct and send a RESPONSE frame with the status for the transaction. That frame makes its way across the link and eventually results in a Command Complete Received confirmation to the initiator's SCSI Application Layer.

Example 4 - Bi-Directional Command

The next example, illustrated in Figure 9-9, really just combines aspects of both read and write data commands. As before, it is the target device that controls the timing of data movement, for both the read and the write.

Figure 9-9: SSP Bidirectional Sequence

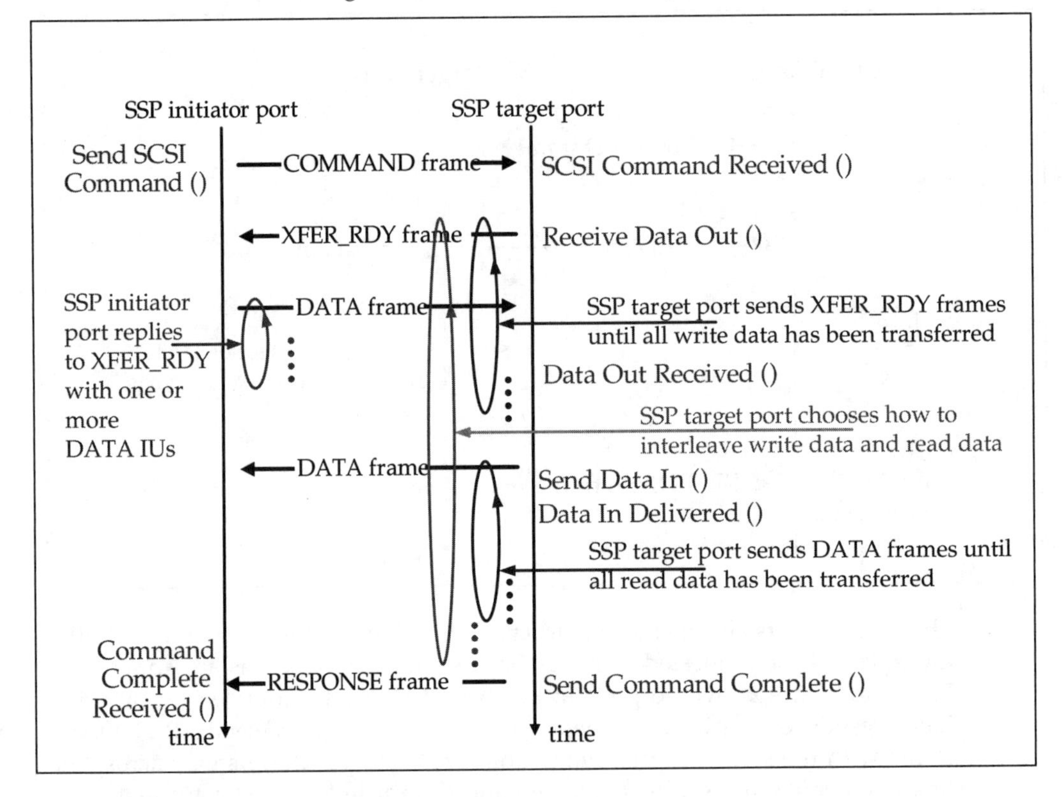

Example 5 - Task Management

The last example is the task management sequence, as shown in Figure 9-10. The protocol for this frame type is very simple and does not need much discussion here.

Figure 9-10: SSP Task Management Sequence

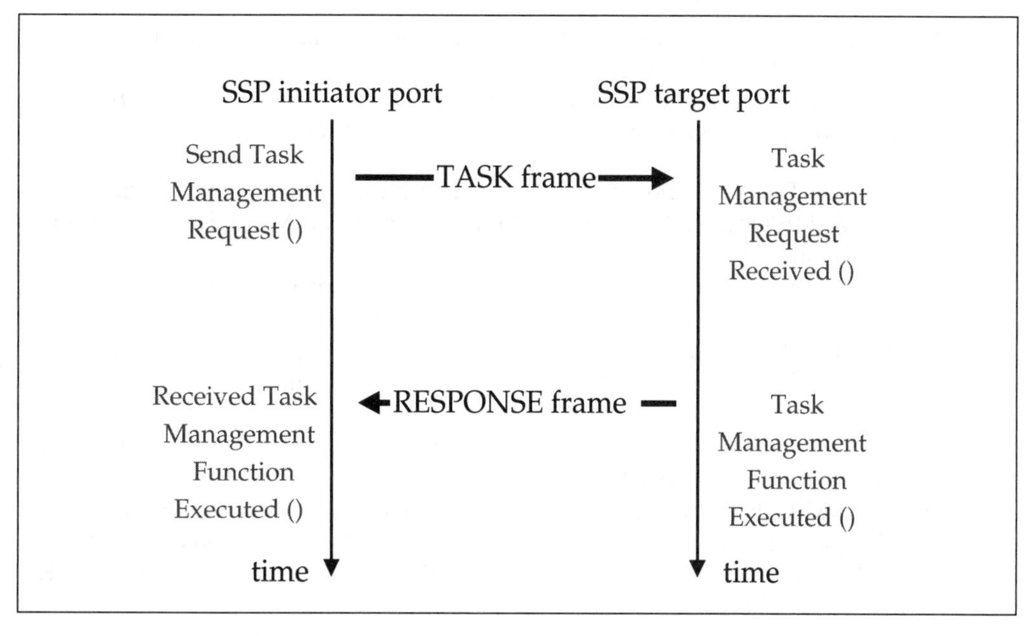

SSP Error Handling

Even a single bit error during serial transmission can cause a frame to be unrecognizable at the receiver. To handle this problem, some serial transports build in hardware protection against transmission errors, such as an automatic hardware retry mechanism. SAS didn't do that, opting instead to implement a link-layer mechanism for error detection, and define some error handling aspects for the Transport Layer. For this purpose, the Transport Layer maintains a copy of outgoing frames until the receiver confirms them so that they can be replayed if needed. At the time of this writing, it was not clear how designers were going to work with this function. That's because software error recovery mechanisms are already in place for SCSI, which did not have a hardware replay mechanism. Consequently, implementing a hardware-level retry was considered likely to be confusing to the system, at least in the early stages.

Transport Layer Errors

Consider first the Transport Layer errors, which are based on the device that sees them. It should be noted that there are some devices that are able to act as both initiator and target, but they are not allowed to do both within the same connection. Target errors include reception of the following:

- XFER_RDY or unknown frame type. Handling of these errors is simply to discard the frame. A target should never receive an XFER_RDY; those only go to initiators.
- COMMAND frame that is incomplete or badly formed, such as having no LUN or CDB, or Additional Length field indicates wrong length. This is handled by sending a RESPONSE frame with Response Code field set to Invalid Frame, informing the initiator that the command was invalid or misunderstood.
- TASK frame that is too short. For this case, send a RESPONSE frame with Response Code field set to Invalid Frame.
- COMMAND frame with a tag that is already in use. Reported by sending a RESPONSE frame with CHECK CONDITION status, sense key set to ABORTED COMMAND, and the additional sense code set to OVERLAPPED COMMANDS ATTEMPTED.
- DATA frame with unknown Tag value. This is handled by simply discarding the frame.
- DATA frame that arrives without permission; that is, it does not have First Burst set and there is no XFER_RDY outstanding for it. Again, the response is just to discard the frame.

Similarly, there are some frames that an initiator should not normally receive:

- COMMAND or TASK or unsupported frame - these should not arrive at an initiator, so discard the frame.
- DATA with an unknown tag - discard the frame and possibly abort the command with that tag. This situation might occur if a target is mistakenly sending data to the wrong initiator or sending data that is based on obsolete commands. To clear the problem, the initiator should send a TASK frame with ABORT TASK specifying the bad tag or, in increasing levels of severity, ABORT TASK SET, CLEAR TASK SET, or LOGICAL UNIT RESET.
- XFER_RDY that is not 12 bytes long - discard the frame and abort the command.

Link Layer Errors Affected by Transport Layer

The Transport Layer affects the handling of Link Layer errors because that handling often involves retransmission of frames. The response is defined for each of the five basic transactions: COMMAND, RESPONSE, TASK, XFER_RDY, and DATA. The Link Layer is described in more detail in Chapter 11, entitled "Link Layer Overview," on page 273, but one of its responsibilities is to acknowledge receipt of frames. If the frame is good at the Link Layer, an ACK primitive is sent, but if something is not right with it, a negative acknowledge, or NAK, is sent instead. For frames other than Data frames, an ACK must be received before the next frame can be sent.

Command Frames

If an initiator sends a command and sees a NAK in response to it, as illustrated in Figure 9-11, that means the frame was not seen correctly by the receiver and should simply be repeated. There is no question about the status of the command; even though it failed it is at least known that the target saw it as an error and is not attempting to execute it.

Figure 9-11: COMMAND Frame Corrupted, NAK Received

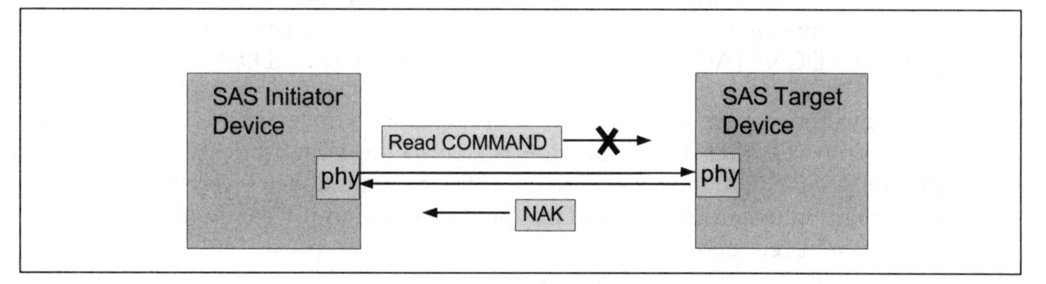

If, on the other hand, no ACK or NAK is received by the initiator, then one of two cases is possible. As shown in Figure 9-12 on page 236, it may be that the COMMAND frame itself was lost for some reason and never seen by the target, or it might have happened that the command was received without error, but the ACK/NAK indication was the part that failed. In either case, the initiators ACK/NAK timeout counter will expire after 1ms and it then must find out what happened.

Figure 9-12: COMMAND Does Not See an ACK

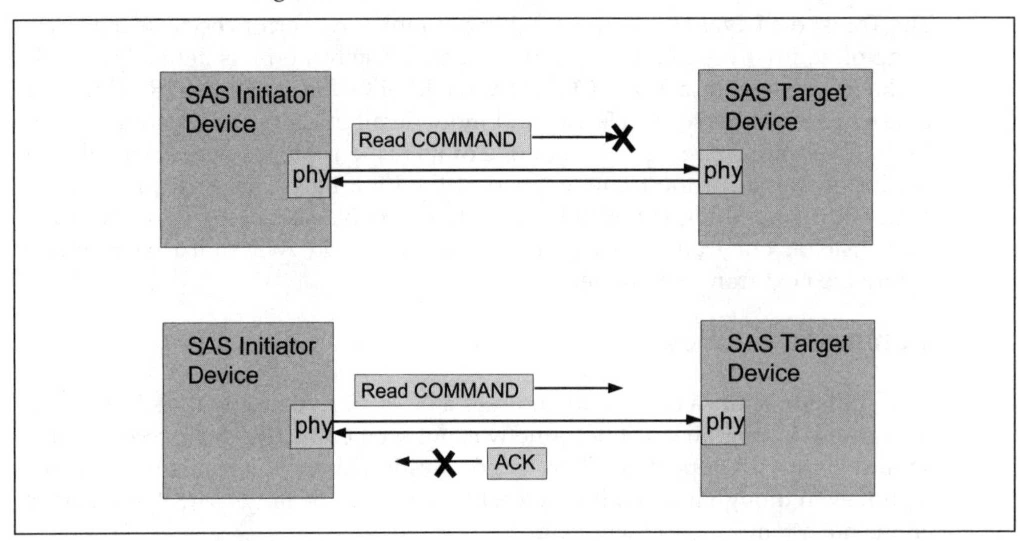

The only way to do this with certainty is to check to see whether the target received the command using a TASK QUERY command. Before doing that, the existing connection must be closed and a new one reopened. This is done by sending a DONE (ACK/NAK TIMEOUT) followed by a CLOSE.

Once the connection is closed, a new connection is opened and a TASK frame specifying a QUERY TASK function is sent to the target to learn whether the previous SSP command was received. If the command was received by the target, the initiator can simply wait for the response, but if was not, then the command can be reissued.

Inferred Response to Command Frame

If an ACK is not seen for a command, but an appropriate response arrives anyway, the missing ACK can be inferred from the response of the target. For example, in Figure 9-13 the ACK failed for some reason, but the read data with the appropriate tag starts to arrive at the initiator anyway. If the data arrives before the ACK/NAK timeout, the initiator can infer that the ACK must have been lost but that the command was received and serviced. In this case, there is clearly no need to query the target about the command.

Figure 9-13: COMMAND Missing ACK but Implicitly Good

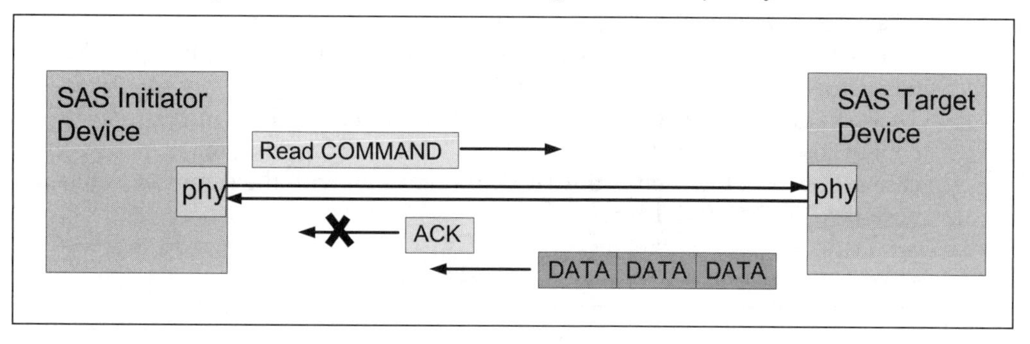

The same sort of event may be seen by a target, as well. Figure 9-14 shows a target sending a RESPONSE frame that does not see an ACK for some reason.

Figure 9-14: RESPONSE Missing ACK

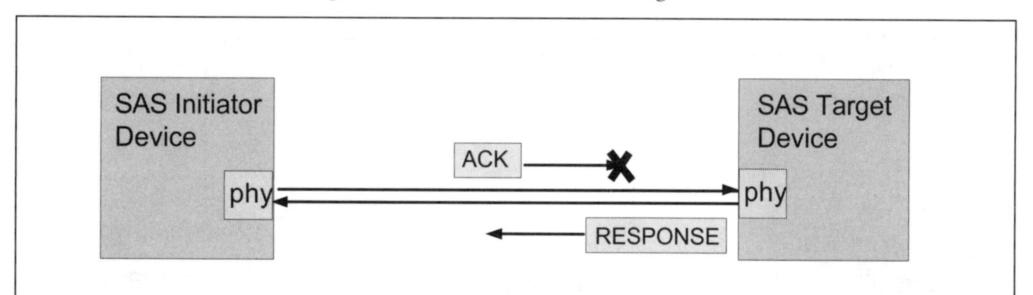

As before, the next step is to close the connection and reopen a new one, but this time there is no need to check for receipt of the previous frame, or method for doing so. Instead, the target resends the RESPONSE frame but this time with the RETRANSMIT bit set. Only three frame types can use this bit; two of them, RESPONSE and XFER_RDY, are target frames while the third is the TASK frame. If the initiator did see the earlier frame and now gets a repeat of it with the RETRANSMIT bit, it discards the new one. If the initiator did not see the earlier frame and instead just gets this one, the retransmitted frame will be treated as a valid response. If the target saw a NAK for the RESPONSE frame, the standard states that it should resend the frame at least once (up to a vendor-specific number of retries) without setting the RETRANSMIT bit.

Task Frames

Next consider a TASK frame sent from an initiator. If an ACK/NAK timeout is observed, as in Figure 9-15, the initiator is in the same situation as it was for the command case discussed earlier. It does not know which of the two possibilities has actually happened. Handling this condition is simpler, though, because a TASK frame is allowed to use the RETRANSMIT bit. The initiator closes the connection with a DONE (ACK/NAK TIMEOUT) primitive, reopens a new connection, and then sends the TASK frame again with the same tag value and with the RETRANSMIT bit set.

Figure 9-15: TASK Missing ACK

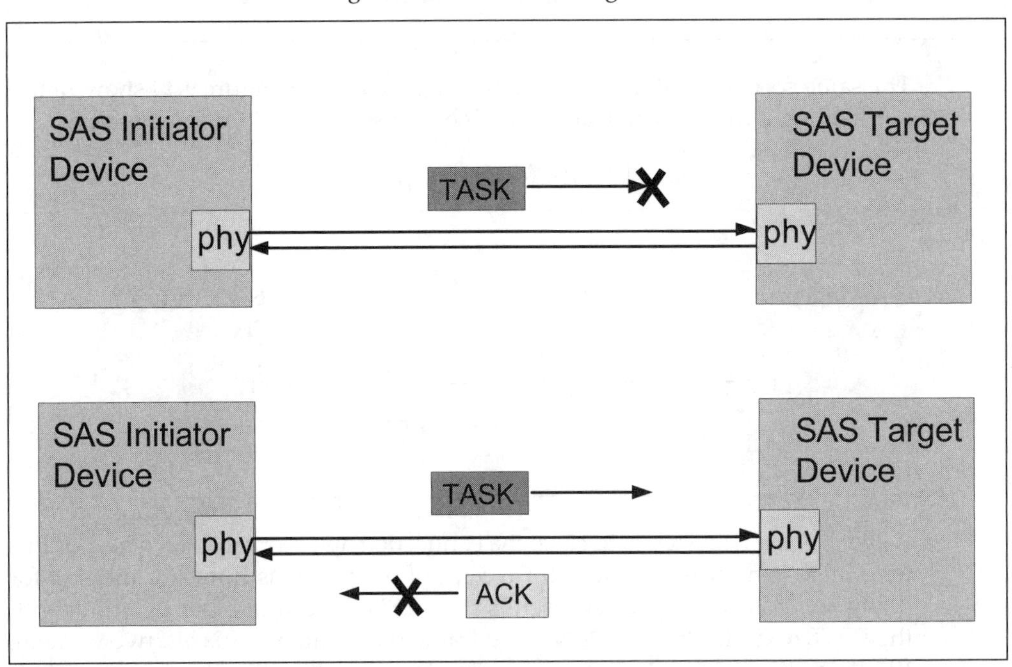

If no ACK arrived, but a RESPONSE frame was seen before the ACK/NAK timeout, as shown in Figure 9-16, the initiator can be assured that the TASK frame was received.

Figure 9-16: TASK Response Makes Up For Missing ACK

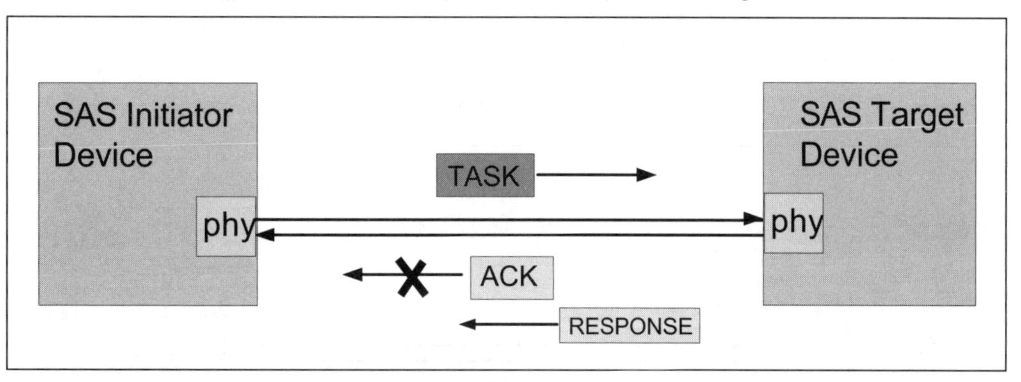

XFER_RDY and DATA Frames

When we move on the XFER_RDY and DATA frame error types, there is another aspect to consider. The question of whether these should be retried in the event of failure is determined by the setting of the TLR (Transport Layer Retries) bit in the Protocol-Specific Logical Unit Mode Page, as shown in bit 4 of byte 2 in Table 9-14.

Table 9-14: Frame Retry Policy

	Bit 7	**6**	**5**	**4**	**3**	**2**	**1**	**0**
Byte 0	PS	SPF =0	Page Code = 18h					
1	Page Length = 6							
2	Reserved			**TLR**	Protocol ID = 6			
3	Reserved							
4	Reserved							
7								

If a target port sees an ACK/NAK timeout for an XFER_RDY frame, as illustrated in Figure 9-17, it will close the connection with DONE (ACK/NAK TIMEOUT). If the vendor-specific number of retries has not been exceeded, it will then open a new connection and take the next step based on the setting of the TLR bit:

- If the TLR bit is set, resend the XFER_RDY using a different Target Port Transfer Tag and with the RETRANSMIT bit set.
- If TLR is not set, send a RESPONSE frame returning CHECK CONDITION, sense key of ABORTED COMMAND, and the additional sense code of ACK/NAK TIMEOUT.

Figure 9-17: XFER_RDY Missing ACK

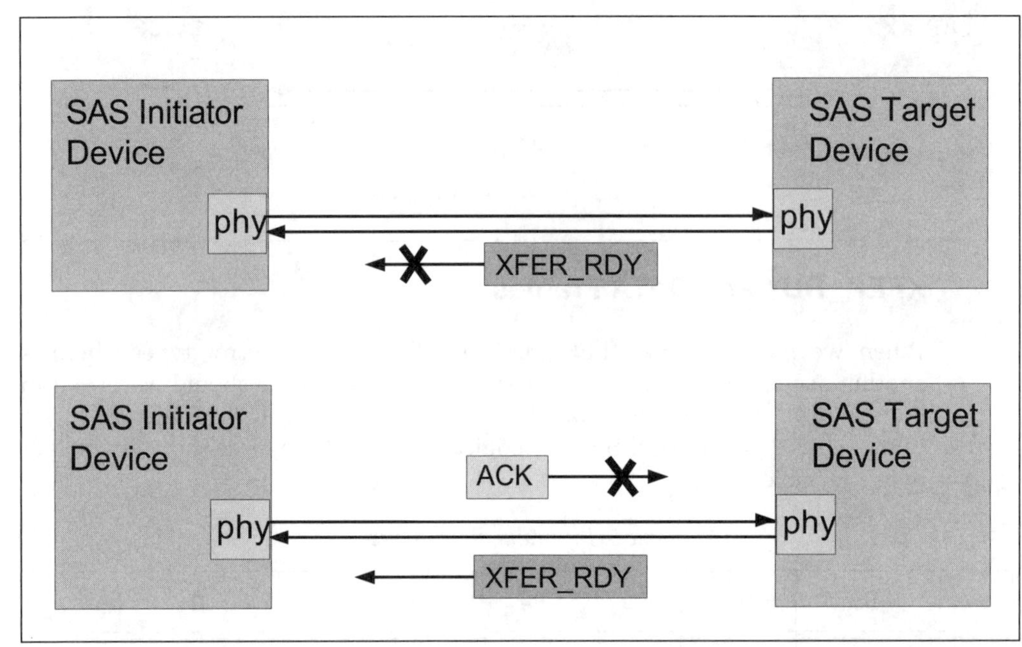

A target port that sees a NAK in response to an XFER_RDY (illustrated in Figure 9-18) will take the same actions as before, except that in this case it's not necessary to close the connection first.

Figure 9-18: XFER_RDY with NAK

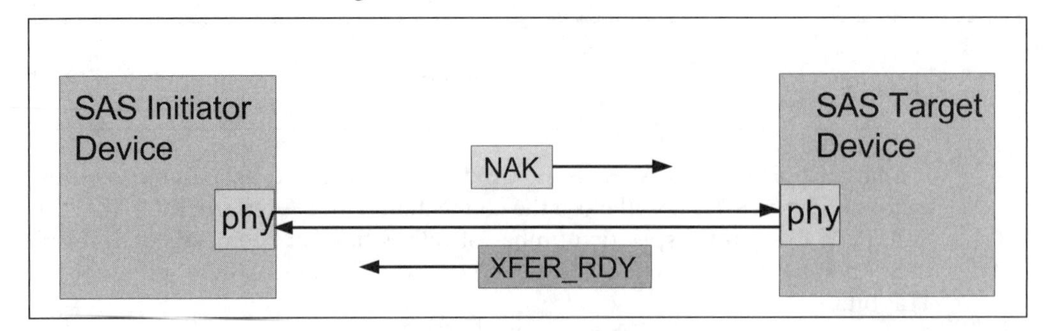

If an initiator sees a duplicate XFER_RDY with the RETRANSMIT bit set while it is servicing the previous XFER_RDY, it will stop processing the previous one and start servicing the new one. The expectation in this case is that the target has had some trouble with the first data and is probably discarding all the data from that transaction as it arrives, making it pointless to continue. To handle this situation, the initiator stops sending data for the first transaction and starts to send it for the subsequent one.

Handling Errors in Non-Interlocked DATA Frames

DATA frame errors are handled in a similar fashion, with one significant exception that requires a little more explanation of Link Layer behavior. SAS devices are required to wait for an ACK or NAK from the receiving device after every frame before they can send another one, with the exception of DATA frames. To improve performance, several DATA frames can be sent without waiting for an ACK/NAK handshake, provided the target has indicated sufficient room with XFER_RDY and permission for several frames by sending several RRDYs.

The ACK/NAKs do not contain an indication of which transaction they acknowledge. Normally, this doesn't matter because the next frame won't be sent until the ACK/NAK from the previous frame arrives. However, since DATA frames don't have to wait, the device sending the DATA frames is required to count the ACKs that are returned in order to ensure that one ACK is returned for every DATA frame that was sent. To do this, the initiator increments a counter when a DATA frame is sent, and decrements it when an ACK is received. When the counter reaches zero, all the frames sent have been acknowledged, referred to as achieving "ACK/NAK Balance".

If a target port detects an ACK/NAK timeout for read DATA frames, it will close the connection with DONE (ACK/NAK TIMEOUT) and open a new connection. An example is illustrated in Figure 9-19 on page 242. When this happens, then:

- if the TLR bit is set, it will retransmit all the DATA frames since the last time ACK/NAK Balance occurred.
- if TLR is not set, it will send a RESPONSE frame returning CHECK CONDITION, sense key of ABORTED COMMAND, and the additional sense code of ACK/NAK TIMEOUT.

Figure 9-19: Read DATA Missing ACK

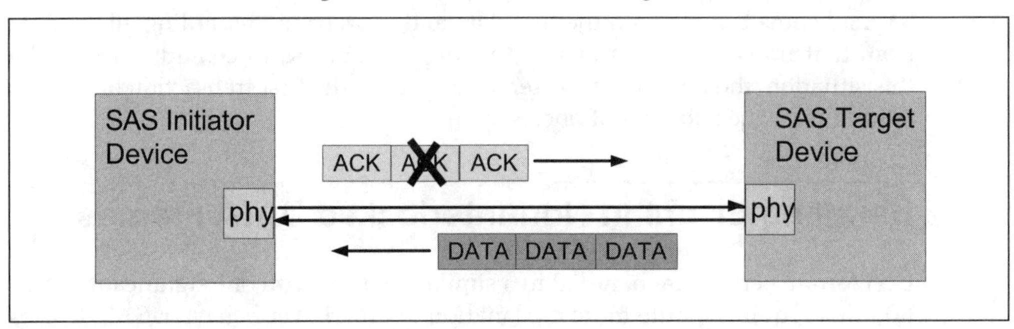

If a NAK is received, the target device will take the same actions, except that it is not required to close the connection and open a new one.

When an initiator device sees an ACK/NAK timeout for write DATA frames (see Figure 9-20), it will close the connection with DONE (ACK/NAK TIMEOUT) and open a new connection. Then:

- if the TLR bit is set, it will retransmit all the DATA frames for the previous XFER_RDY. If a new XFER_RDY or RESPONSE pertaining to that command arrives, it will stop retransmission and begin servicing the new frame.
- if the TLR bit is not set, it will abort the task by sending a TASK frame indicating (ABORT TASK).

Figure 9-20: Write DATA Missing ACK

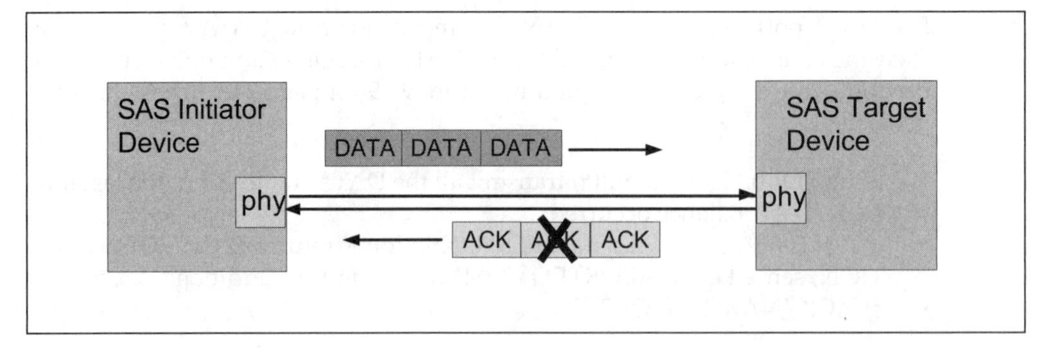

If an initiator receives a NAK for DATA frames it has sent, it is not required to close and reopen the connection, but:

- if the TLR bit is set, it simply retransmits all the data frames for the previous XFER_RDY.
- if the TLR bit is not set, it will abort the task by sending a TASK frame indicating (ABORT TASK).

Rules for Data Retries

If the TLR bit is set to enable retries of failed packets, there are a few rules that need to be observed for data retries:

1. For both reads and writes, the first retransmitted DATA frame has its CHANGING DATA POINTER bit set, and subsequent frames must have it cleared. This is a non-trivial event from the receiver's point of view as it almost certainly means that it will have to generate an interrupt to get processor help in resetting its scatter/gather list structure.
2. Each DATA frame that does not receive an ACK gets retried at least once, but exactly how many times is vendor specific.

STP (SATA Tunneled Protocol) Transport Layer

The material regarding STP is contained in Chapter 19, entitled "SATA Support," on page 455.

SMP (Serial Management Protocol) Transport Layer

As with the other protocols, the main responsibility of this layer is to construct outgoing frames and parse incoming ones. A simple view of the contents of an SMP request frame is shown in Table 9-15 on page 244, and the response frame is shown in Table 9-16 on the same page.

Table 9-15: SMP Request Frame

Byte	Field(s)
0	SMP Frame Type(40h)
1 to m	Request bytes
m to (n-3)	Fill bytes, if needed
(n-3) to n	CRC

Table 9-16: SMP Response Frame

Byte	Field(s)
0	SMP Frame Type(41h)
1 to m	Response bytes
m to (n-3)	Fill bytes, if needed
(n-3) to n	CRC

The SMP frame sequence is much simpler than the other two protocols, as illustrated in Figure 9-21. Only one request and one response can be sent within an SMP connection and then it must be closed. Because of this simple interaction, there is no need for flow control or permission to transmit, so no XFER_RDY, RRDY, or DATA will be sent. Both sides simply close the connection after the RESPONSE is transferred.

Figure 9-21: SMP Connection

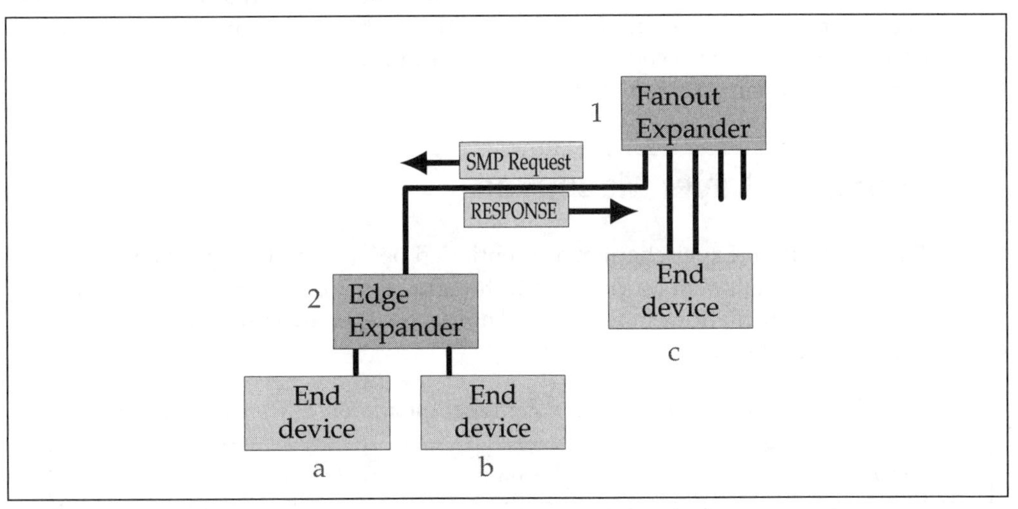

Transport Layer State Machines

For those interested in going deeper into the operation of this section, the state machines used in the standard to define Transport Layer behavior are discussed next and redrawn here for convenience. These drawings are intended to improve readability over what is offered in the standard by showing the reasons for state transitions and the messages that are sent to neighboring layers based on the state variables. They are not intended to be all inclusive and usually do not, for example, include interactions between state machines within the same layer. The casual reader may skip this section and still have a basic operational understanding of the material.

SSP State Machines

State machines are defined for SSP and SMP protocols and split into initiator and target parts. For SSP, one state machine called the Frame Router receives requests from the Application Layer and routes them to one of several independent transport server state machines for servicing. Received frames will cause data or status to be passed back up to the Application Layer. The description in the standard implies that there can be an infinite number of the transport server state machines available to accept new requests. In practice, though, all available state machines could be busy with previous commands, preventing a new one from being accepted. A target device can indicate such a condition by responding with BUSY or similar SCSI status. Initiators that are busy would need some vendor-specific feedback to inform the Application Layer that no new requests can be accepted temporarily, but the standard does not describe a particular implementation for this.

Transport Layer Messages

The Application Layer chapter, as mentioned before, sends requests in the form of procedure calls with arguments to the Transport Layer, and receives indications and confirmations in response. These messages are summarized for an initiator in Table 9-17.

Table 9-17: Initiator Communication Between Application & Transport Layers

From	Message	To
SCSI Application Layer - Requests	Send SCSI Command - COMMAND frame	SSP Initiator Port
	Send Task Management - TASK frame	
	Accept_Reject OPENs (Accept SSP)	
	Accept_Reject OPENs (Reject SSP)	
SSP Initiator Port - Indications and Confirmations	Command Complete Received - receipt of RESPONSE frame	SCSI Application Layer
	Received Task Management Function - Executed - receipt of RESPONSE frame	
	Nexus Loss	
	Transport Reset	

Requests

- The first two requests were described earlier in this chapter.
- **Accept_Reject OPENs** are simply a means for the Application Layer to indicate whether it wishes to accept new incoming connections. Any device is allowed to reject them temporarily for any reason. For example, a target

could run out of tags it can handle, in which case it can disable new connections until it has had a chance to clear the backlog. An initiator can also reject incoming connections but is not allowed to conditionally postpone accepting new connections until after it has gotten a frame out. A target can do that, but not an initiator, and the reason is that it could create a possible deadlock condition.

Indications and Confirmations

- The first two confirmations from the Transport Layer to the Application Layer simply indicate the completion of the desired action.
- **Nexus Loss** is an indication that the lower layers were unable to reconnect with a device with which communication had already been established, and have given up trying. When the timer expired, an indication was sent up to the Transport Layer that a nexus loss had occurred, and that report is forwarded to the Application Layer as a Nexus Loss indication. The nexus loss timer is maintained in the Port Layer and is discussed in more detail in Chapter 10, entitled "Port Layer," on page 259.
- The **Transport Reset** indicates that the Transport Layer has received a confirmation that a HARD_RESET was received on the link. The lower levels received a hard reset and that is propagated up to the higher layers.

A similar table for targets is presented in Table 9-18, and the corresponding interactions for the target are described in the text that follows.

Table 9-18: Target Communication Between Application & Transport Layers

From	Message	To
SCSI Application Layer - Responses	Send Command Complete - RESPONSE frame	SSP Target Port
	Task Management Function Executed - RESPONSE frame	
	Send Data_In - DATA frame	
	Receive Data_Out - XFER_RDY frame	
	Terminate Data Transfer	
	Accept_Reject OPENs (Accept SSP)	
	Accept_Reject OPENs (Reject SSP)	

Table 9-18: Target Communication Between Application & Transport Layers

From	Message (Continued)	To
SSP Target Port - Indications and Confirmations	SCSI Command Received - receipt of COMMAND frame	SCSI Application Layer
	Task Management Request Received - receipt of TASK frame	
	Data_In Delivered - receipt of ACKs for read DATA frames	
	Data_Out Received - receipt of write DATA frames	
	Data Transfer Terminated	
	Nexus Loss	
	Transport Reset	

Responses

- **Send Command Complete** causes a RESPONSE frame to be sent that indicates the status of a command (GOOD, CHECK CONDITION, etc.).
- A **Task Management Function Executed** response tells the target Transport Layer to send a RESPONSE frame that includes a Response Code describing the status of a Task Management request (see Table 9-10).
- A **Send Data_Out** response tells the Transport Layer to construct an outgoing DATA frame using a buffer specified in the message.
- Going the other way, a **Receive Data_Out** message indicates a readiness at the upper layer to receive the write data the initiator requested to send, and will result in an XFER_RDY frame back to the initiator.
- A **Terminate Data Transfer**, as the name implies, will cause the Transport Layer to terminate any Send Data_In or Receive Data_Out operations in progress for the specified nexus.
- **Accept_Reject OPENs** have the same meaning for targets that they do for initiators, allowing them to temporarily refuse to accept any incoming connection requests. Targets are allowed to make this conditional by refusing to accept incoming connections until they have succeeded in getting a frame out.

Indications and Confirmations

- The messages from the Transport Layer to the Application Layer are all fairly straightforward, indicating receipt of a command or a task management function or data. The SCSI Application Layer gets a confirmation when data has been sent out for a read request as well, which is the Data_In Delivered confirmation. Nexus Loss and Transport Reset have the same meaning for the target that they do for the initiator.

Initiator State Machines

To describe the initiator state machines, consider first the overall view shown in Figure 9-22 on page 250. For both initiator and target state machines, the notification of events that need action is received by a high-level state machine with only one state called a Frame Router, which in turn launches a Transport Server state machine to handle it. As mentioned before, there can be any number of Transport Server state machines in a design that process incoming or outgoing frames as requested by the Frame Router. The drawings are based on the state machine diagrams in the standard but are simplified to highlight the relationships between the states.

One thing illustrated by the block arrows in the diagram is that the IFR (Initiator Frame Router) state is in fact a single-state machine, so it has no state transitions at all, only messages sent to and from other state machines. An initiator has only one IFR state machine, but may have several ITS (Initiator Transport Server) state machines. The IFR acts as the launching point for outgoing frame requests coming from the Application Layer, and the target for the incoming frames which it then passes back to it. As an initiator, the outgoing requests create COMMAND, DATA, or TASK frames, and the incoming frames are XFER_RDY, DATA, or RESPONSE frames from a target device.

Figure 9-22: Transport Layer State Machines for SSP Initiator

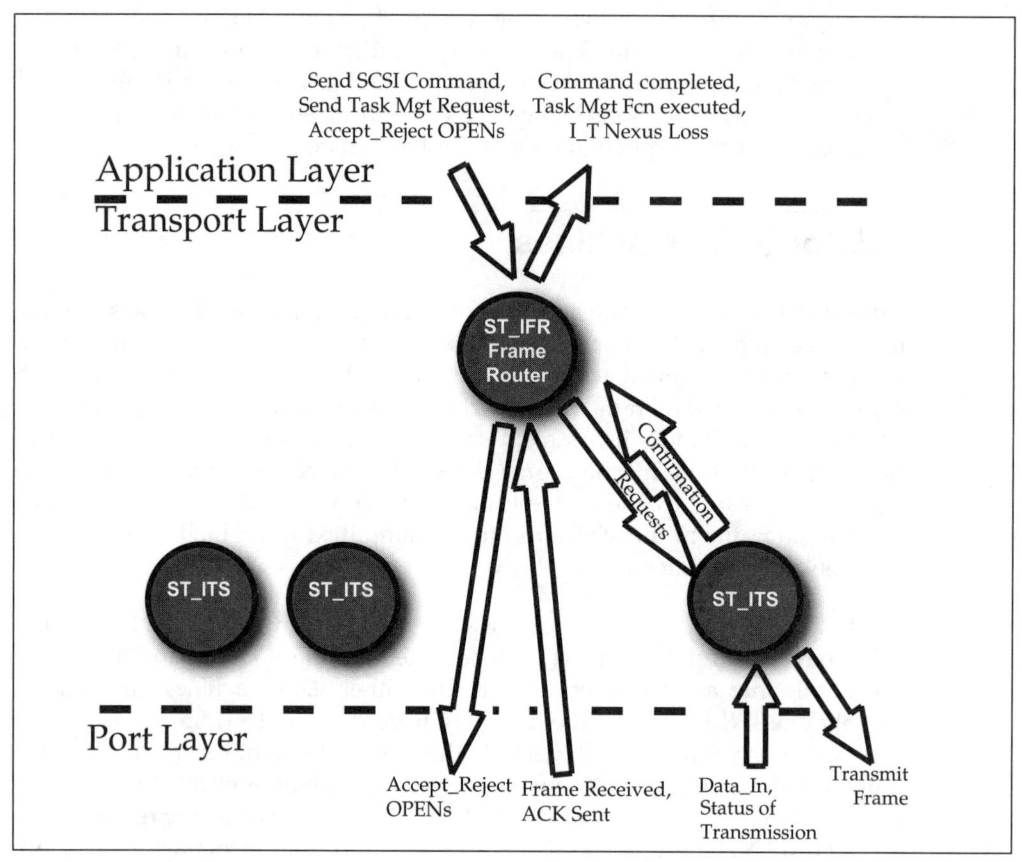

Outgoing Frames

When a request arrives from the Application Layer, the IFR selects an available ITS state machine and launches the request by forwarding it with the appropriate arguments. This relationship is illustrated in more detail in Figure 9-23 on page 251, where the selected ITS takes ownership of a new outgoing request by constructing the appropriate frame for it and forwarding a Transmit Frame Request to the Port Layer and waiting for a response. When it receives confirmation that the frame has been accepted for processing, it informs the IFR that the transmission completed, indicating that this ITS state machine is ready to accept another request.

Figure 9-23: Initiator State Machine

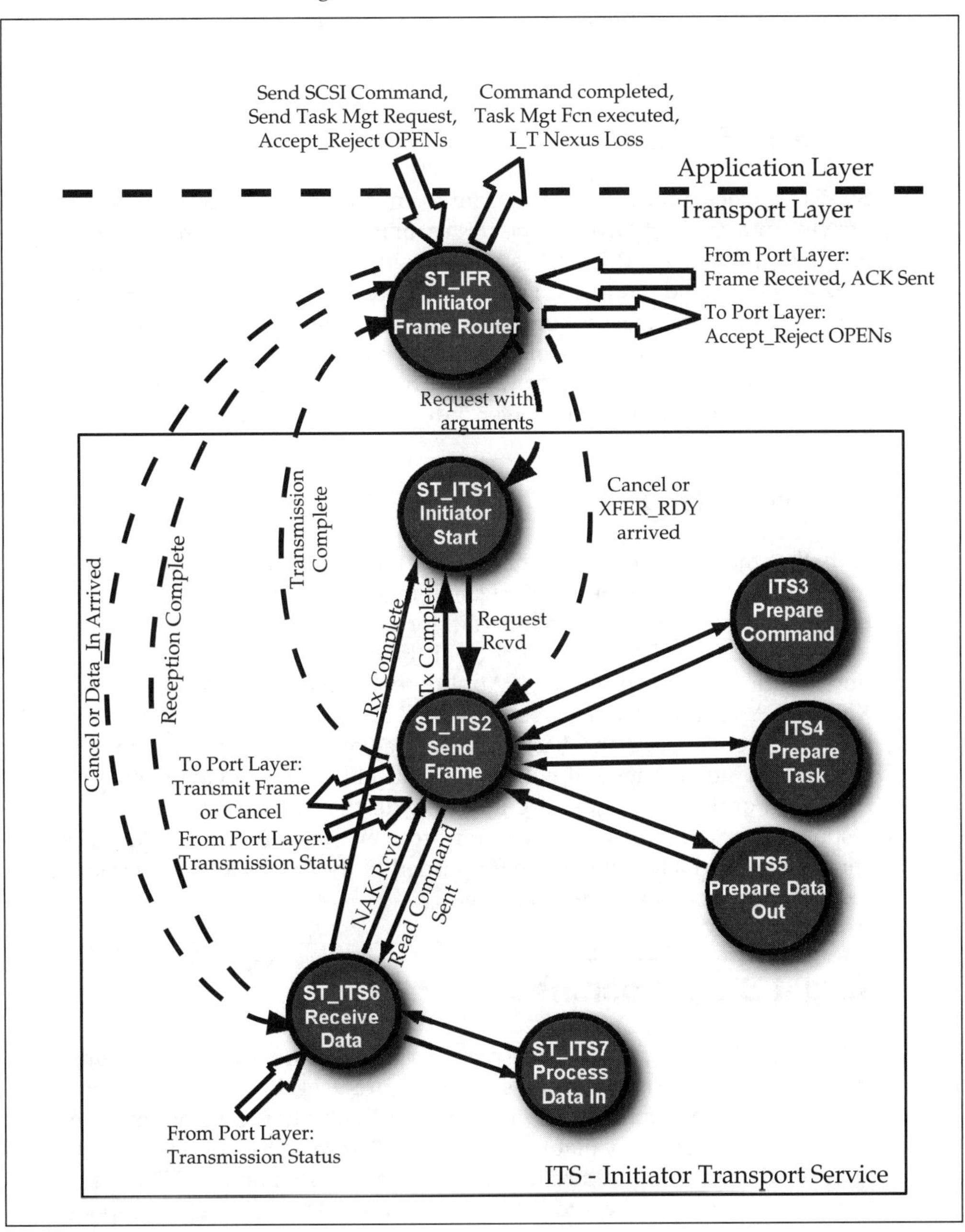

There are timeouts associated with the requests, such as an ACK/NAK Timeout if that response does not arrive in time, but the timers are not maintained in this layer. Instead, they reside in lower layers of the device. The ACK/NAK timeout timer, for example, resides in the Link Layer state machines. If this timer should expire, the Link Layer will inform the Transport Layer about it with a Transmission Status (ACK/NAK Timeout).

Incoming Frames

Similarly, when a request arrives from an incoming connection, the notification arrives from the Port Layer to the IFR as an indication. If the incoming frame is an XFER_RDY, the IFR launches an available ITS state machine, starting with ITS2:Initiator_Send_Frame. From there, the next transition is to ITS5:Prepare_Data_Out, where the DATA frame is constructed. When the frame is ready, the state machine switches back to ITS2 and sends a Transmit Frame request to the Port Layer with the frame. Eventually, a Transmission Status comes back from the Port Layer indicating whether the frame was successfully transmitted.

Cancelling Requests

Note that the diagram shows some paths that can be taken based on a Cancel request. It is possible that the SCSI client might decide to cancel all the remaining requests to a destination address if, for example, the device was reset or has gone off-line. The Cancel message from IFR to ITS can be generated by a vendor-specific means from the Application Layer, or by an unexpected XFER_RDY (one whose tag doesn't match any outstanding writes). If the ITS gets a Cancel message and hasn't received a confirmation for all the outstanding transmission requests, it will send a Cancel to the Port Layer, too. The Cancel to the Port Layer includes arguments of destination address and tag, and the response from the Port Layer is a Transmission Status (Cancel Acknowledged) confirmation, which will then be forwarded to the IFR as a Transmission Complete (Cancel Acknowledged) message.

Target State Machines

The state machines for the Transport Layer target device are very similar to those for the initiator, as can be seen in Figure 9-24. Responses from the SCSI server application arrive at the TFR (Target Frame Router) state machine and are used to launch an available TTS (Target Transport Server) state machine to generate the matching frames for outgoing traffic (see Figure 9-25 on page 254). Frames of that type would be DATA frames for a Data_In response, an

XFER_RDY frame for a Data_Out response, or a RESPONSE frame to return command status. An indication of arriving frames is received from the Port Layer and used to forward incoming commands or process incoming data for which a previously-sent XFER_RDY has been sent.

Figure 9-24: Transport Layer State Machines for SSP Target

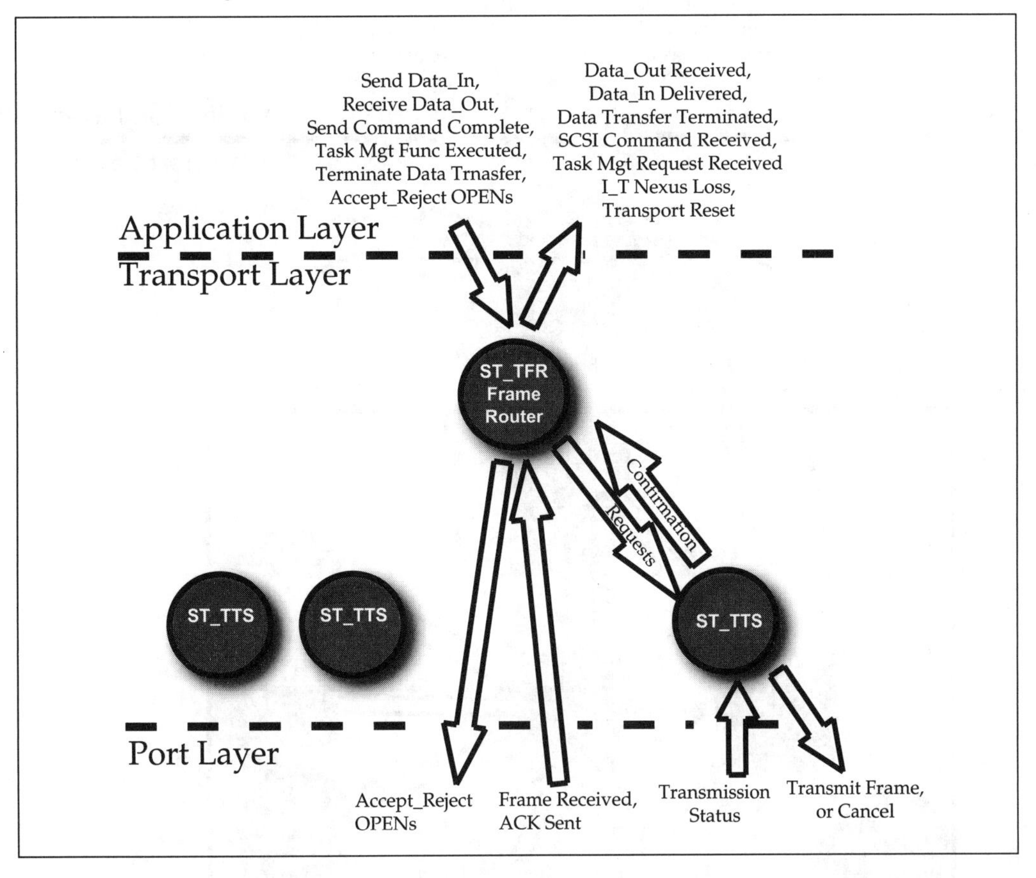

Figure 9-25: Target State Machine

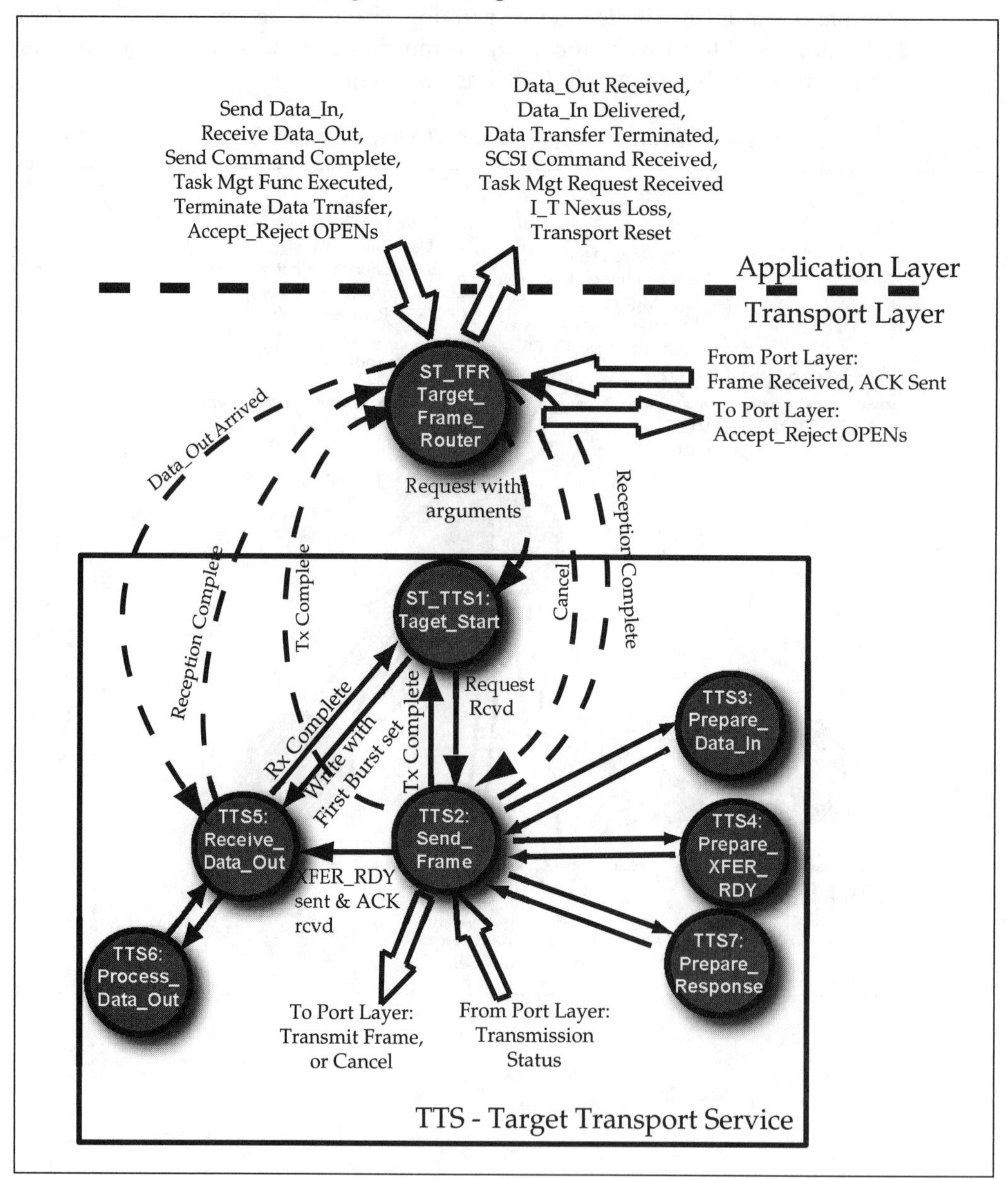

SMP State Machines

The SMP Transport Layer behavior is defined by two state machines, one for an initiator port labeled MT_IP (SMP Transport Layer for Initiator Ports) and one for a target port labeled MT_TP (SMP Transport Layer for Target Ports). The initiator port state machine, shown in Figure 9-26, receives the SMP request from the Application Layer while in state MT_IP1. That causes it to transition to MT_IP2, for which it attempts to open a connection to the destination address to send the request and waits for a response. If the connection succeeds and the frame is sent, the machine transitions to MT_IP3 where it waits to get the response frame returned from the target. When the response is detected the machine returns to its default state of MT_IP1.

Figure 9-26: MT_IP - SMP Transport Layer Initiator Port State Machine

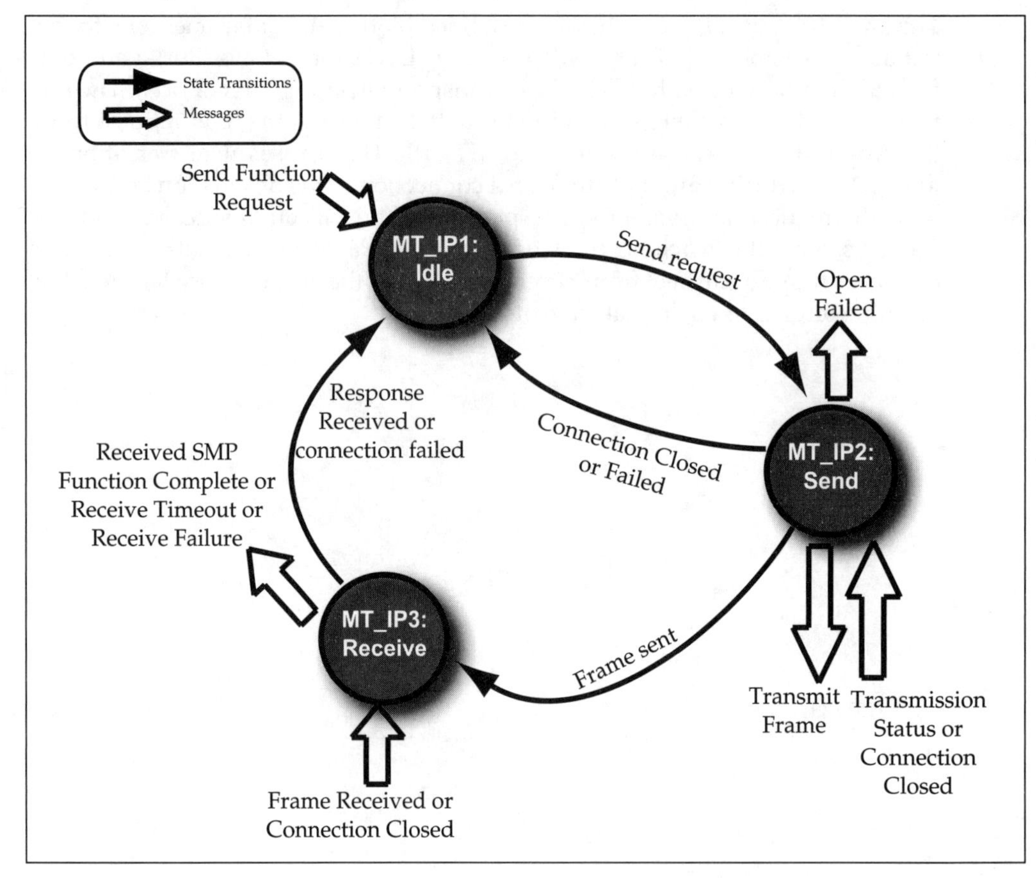

The target port state machine, shown in Figure 9-27, detects the arrival of an SMP request while in MT_TP1, transitions to MT_TP2 and forwards the received function up to the Application Layer. While in this state, it waits for a response from the Application Layer and then constructs a frame to forward that response back to the initiator. Once the response has been transmitted, the state machine returns to the default MT_TP1 state.

Figure 9-27: MT_TP - SMP Transport Layer Target Port State Machine

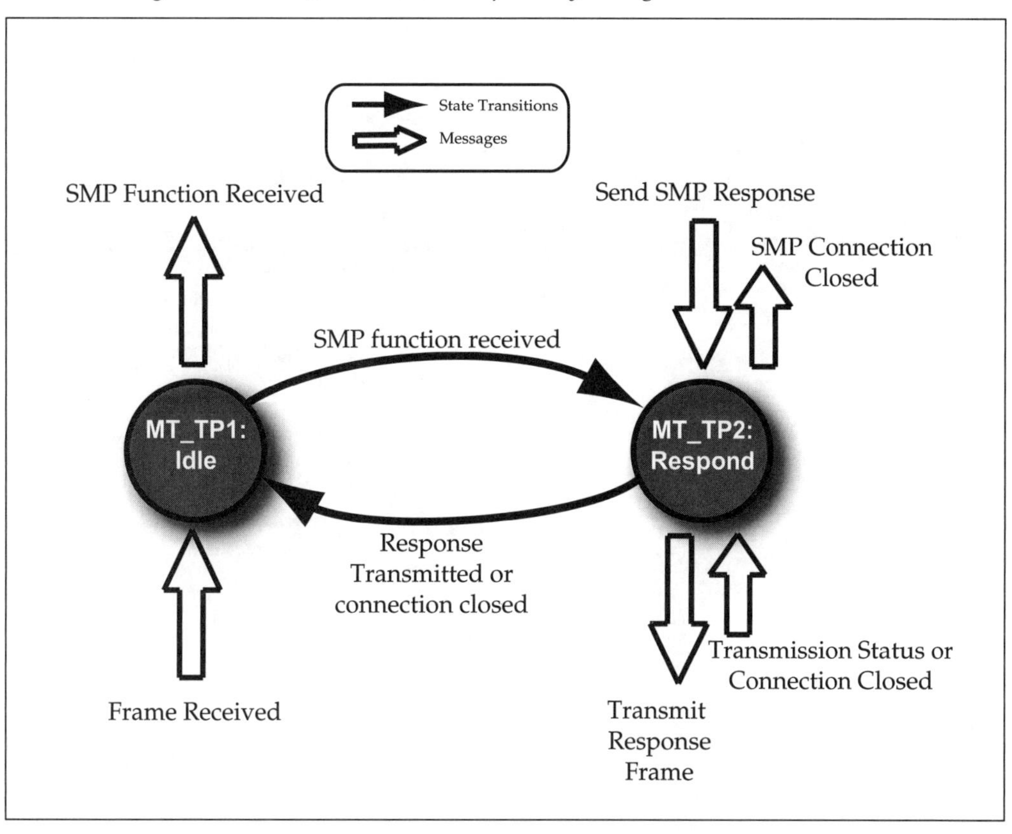

10 Port Layer

The Previous Chapter

The previous chapter described the function and responsibilities of the Transport Layer of the SAS hierarchy. This layer receives requests from the Application Layer modeled as function calls, creates frames to support the requested action and queues them until they are completed. The frames are then passed down to the next lower layer, which is the Port Layer.

This Chapter

This chapter describes the Port Layer of the SAS architecture along with the state machines used in the standard to explain its behavior, and the messages passed to and from it in support of the other layers. The function of this layer is primarily to select a Phy for an outgoing request from the phys which share the same address and are therefore grouped into the same port.

The Next Chapter

The next chapter introduces the Link Layer, which can rightly be considered the heart of the SAS architecture because the lion's share of the standard is devoted to describing its functions. There is so much to cover, in fact, that it is broken up into four blocks: Serial support, Connection management, Arbitration, and Protocol differences between the different types of connections.

Introduction

We begin our discussion of the Port Layer in an unusual way: by first pointing out where it is not used. Expanders do not implement a Port Layer, for example, because the expander function sorts out which Phy to use, making a Port Layer unnecessary. STP connections also have no need for a Port Layer because SATA devices do not implement wide ports and so have no need for a Port Layer to select between several outgoing phys. Consequently, the use of the Port Layer is limited to SAS devices using SSP or SMP protocol in their connections.

Port Layer Responsibilities

By way of review, Figure 10-1 illustrates the location of the Port Layer in the SAS layered architecture between the Transport Layer and the phy. The Transport Layer could have many threads in progress, and the frames get pooled together in the Port Layer according to destination address. Interestingly, the standard does not recommend a number of pools that should be implemented, or even the depth of the pools. Instead, only a conceptual model is presented that assumes infinite size. The Port Layer arranges for frame transmission on the link by either using an existing connection or selecting an available Phy (if more than one is available) and requesting that a connection be opened to the destination. When a connection is established, the pool of queued frames for that destination address is drained out to the selected phy. The process for incoming frames is much simpler; they are simply passed directly up to the Transport Layer.

Figure 10-1: Overview of Layered Architecture

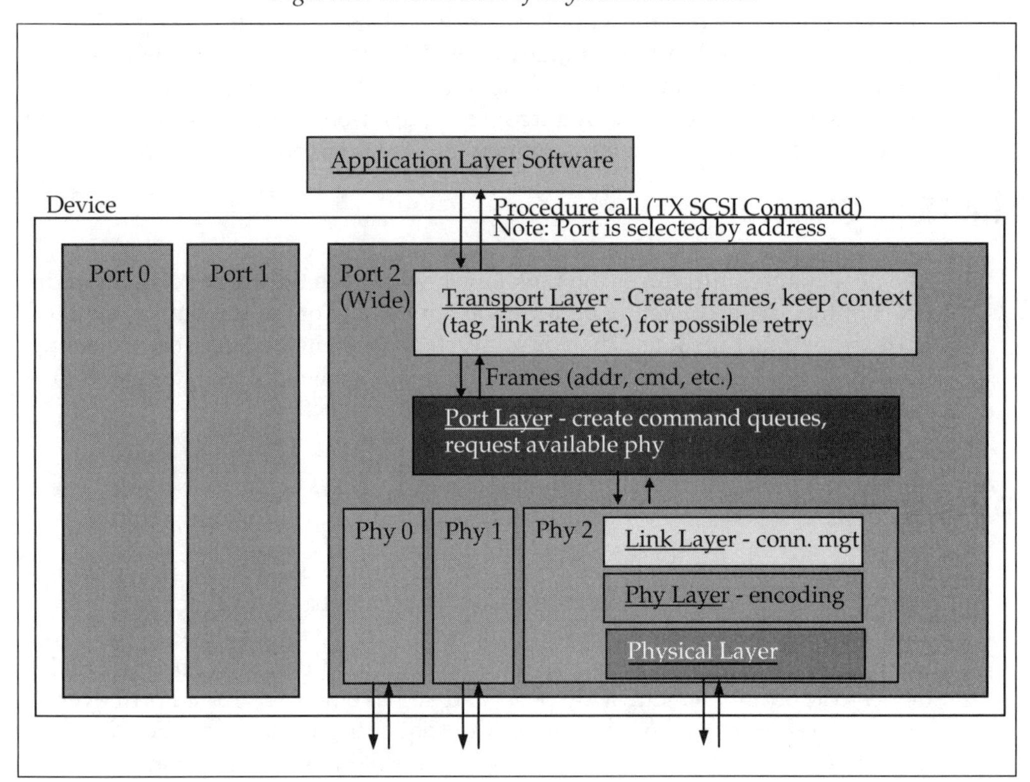

Port Layer State Machines

Unlike other sections, the Port Layer behavioral description is facilitated by including the state machines at the beginning of the discussion rather than putting them at the end. Before launching into the details of the state machines, though, it's helpful to give more context to show how they fit into the bigger picture. Figure 10-2 shows the Port Layer overall and the different parts within it.

Figure 10-2: Port Layer State Machine Overview

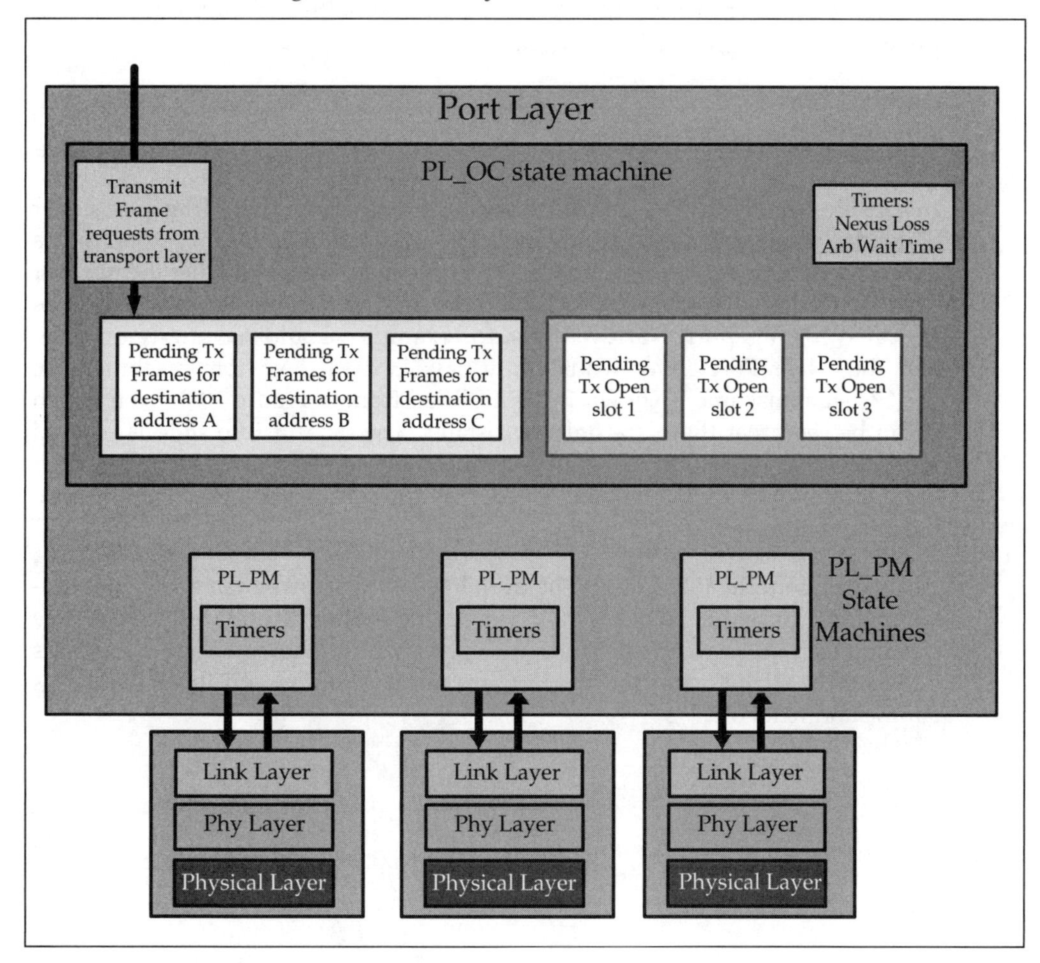

The Port Layer consists of two types of state machines: one PL_OC (Port Layer Overall Control) state machine and a separate PL_PM (Port Layer Phy Manager) state machine to support each Phy contained in the port. This layer also contains buffers to queue up outgoing transactions, and timers to verify that operations happen in a timely manner.

The PL_OC state machine accepts outgoing frames from the Transport Layer and pools them into groups that are all targeting the same address. The number of these groups available is vendor specific. When frames have been queued, the PL_OC sends a request to one of the PL_PM state machines to open a connection and drain out one of the pools to that phy. The PL_PM state machine receives requests from the PL_OC and interfaces with the Link Layer of that Phy to manage the needed connection.

PL_OC State Machine

In a fashion similar to the Transport Layer's frame router (see "Transport Layer State Machines" on page 245), the single PL_OC for a given port receives frames and parcels them out to one of the PL_PM state machines. Note that the number of available PL_PM state machines depends on the number of phys that were allocated for this port. Narrow ports, for example, would have only one Phy and thus their Port Layer would only have one PL_PM state machine. The PL_OC state machine is shown in a simplified form in Figure 10-3, from which it can be seen that there are only two states. The default Idle state is entered after reset and exits to the Overall_Control state as soon as at least one Phy for this port reports that it is enabled. As long as any phys remain enabled, the state machine will remain in this state.

As a note about the illustration, the dark lines with arrows represent state transitions and the white block arrows represent messages between layers. The communication between the state machines within the same layer, such as between the PL_OC and the PL_PM, are not shown to keep the illustrations simple and readable.

Figure 10-3: PL_OC State Machine

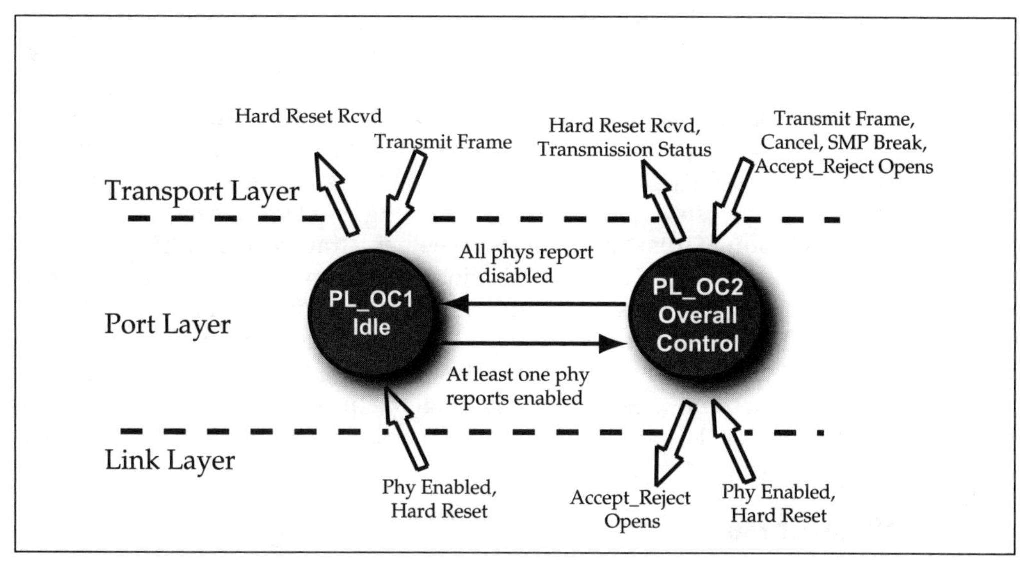

Transport Layer Messages

In the PL_OC2: Overall_Control state, requests arrive from the Transport Layer, and responses are returned to it, as listed below:

- **Transmit Frame:** This is a request to transmit a frame as described in the example of Figure 10-5 on page 267. A frame has been constructed in the Transport Layer and needs to be sent out.
- **Cancel:** The Transport Layer can determine that a previously queued transaction is no longer necessary and can be removed from the pool. All frames that match the destination address and tag of this request will be removed from the pool of pending transmit frames. If the frame has already been forwarded to a PL_PM, then a Cancel message will also be sent to that state machine with the tag of the transaction. If the connection has not yet been opened, the PL_PM will send a Stop Arb request to the Link Layer to abandon the open request. If the connection is already established, the PL_PM will discard any transmit frame requests for that tag, send a message confirming the transmission cancellation to the Transport Layer, and discard messages regarding previous transmit frame requests for that tag.
- **SMP Transmit Break:** If this message arrives from the Transport Layer, it will be forwarded to the PL_PM state machine associated with that SMP

connection. Break is sent to unconditionally close a connection that is currently open but has encountered a problem. If there is no such connection in progress, this message is ignored.

- **Accept/Reject OPENs:** This request is forwarded to all the phys in this port, telling them whether the Application Layer wishes to allow incoming transactions. Devices are permitted to disallow incoming requests temporarily for any reason, such as a transaction queue overflow condition that would preclude taking any more commands until some of those already present have been serviced. However, initiators must not make acceptance of incoming requests dependent on getting outgoing frames sent.
- **Transmission Status:** This indicates whether a transmission completed successfully or, if not, gives an indication of the problem. Possible problems include I_T Nexus Loss, Bad Destination, Rate or Protocol not supported.
- **HARD_RESET Received:** This indicates that a Phy in this port has received a HARD_RESET and will be reset. This will cause the machine to discard all the pending frame messages and reset all the times. The state will transition back to PL_OC1, and a HARD_RESET confirmation will be forwarded up to the Transport Layer.

Link Layer Messages

The list of messages passed between the PL_OC and the Link Layer is much smaller; in fact there are only three:

- **Accept/Reject OPENs:** This message is forwarded to the Link Layer to inform the connection management logic about whether to accept or reject incoming requests.
- **Phy Enabled:** This indicates that a Phy has successfully finished initialization and is ready for activity.
- **HARD_RESET Received:** This indicates that a Phy in this port has received a HARD_RESET and will be reset. This will cause the machine to discard all the pending frame messages and reset all the times. The state will transition back to PL_OC1, and a HARD_RESET confirmation will be forwarded up to the Transport Layer.

Port Layer Timers

The Port Layer maintains four timers for tracking bus activity. These give an indication of trouble, or enforce connection policies. The I_T Nexus Loss timer is maintained by the PL_OC state machine for the port, while the other three timers exist and are maintained within the individual PL_PM state machine that is discussed in the next section.

1. **I_T Nexus Loss Time:** This is the amount of time the device is willing to wait while trying to re-establish a connection with an existing nexus. This was intended for targets when attempting to reconnect with an initiator that sent a command earlier, because the expectation is that a storage device might go offline for some reason, but the initiator should not. Still, initiators are also allowed to use this timer. If the timer expires, give up on sending the current frame and notify the upper layers of the problem. The value of the timer for SSP target ports is set by the I_T NEXUS LOSS field in the Protocol-Specific Port mode page. Used only for STP or SMP connections, this value is vendor specific.
2. **Arbitration Wait Time:** This timer indicates how long this Phy has been waiting for a connection request to be accepted or rejected. The value is set to zero the first time an open request is sent, but if the open does not succeed (for example, because an incoming OPEN overrides the outgoing request), then the AWT is updated and included when the next OPEN address frame is sent. The value continues to increase while the connection is waiting until it reaches the maximum value and then stops. The reason this value is tracked is that it's used for arbitration: a higher AWT value gives a request a higher priority. (For more on arbitration, see "Link Layer - Arbitration" on page 333.)
3. **Bus Inactivity Time Limit:** This value measures the time between frames that are sent within a connection. For an SSP connection, this time limit is specified in the Disconnect-Reconnect mode page, while for other protocols the time is vendor-specific. If the initial value is set to zero, it means that there is no limit on bus inactivity. This timer measures time during which the connection is open but no frames are being sent. It will be reinitialized whenever a new Tx Frame request is received. If it expires, a Close Connection request will be sent to the Link Layer. It is important for SAS overall operation that connections are short-lived, so leaving a connection open but idle is undesirable.
4. **Maximum Connect Time Limit:** This timer measures the time that a connection has been open, regardless of whether there has been activity on it, and does not allow it to exceed a set value. A value of zero indicates that there is no maximum connect time limit to be enforced, but any other value indicates a limit. When the timer expires, the connection will need to be closed. If an SSP target port has a frame in progress when this timer expires, it will complete the frame before preparing to close the connection.

PL_PM State Machine

Each Phy has an associated PL_PM state machine that implements the state diagram shown in Figure 10-4, and the PL_OC exchanges requests and responses with it. The messages passed between state machines within the same layer are not shown, but what is shown are the messages exchanged with the layers above and below the Port Layer. Rather than go through all the messages and their meanings, which are summarized in Annex K of the standard, let's consider an example and describe the messages in the context of them.

Figure 10-4: PL_PM State Machine

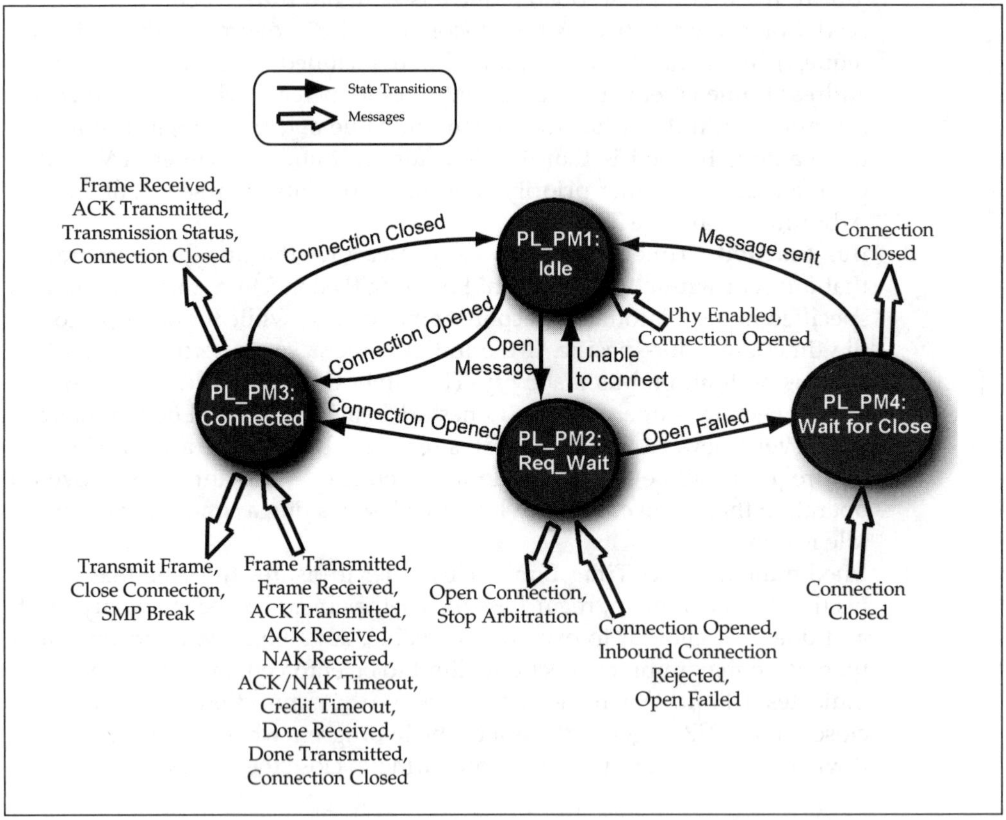

Example Operation

To bring these pieces together into a comprehensive picture, consider the example of Figure 10-5, showing a port containing three phys. To start, let the PL_OC receive an outgoing frame, which is placed into a pool of frames based on the destination address in the step labeled "b".

Figure 10-5: Port Layer Example

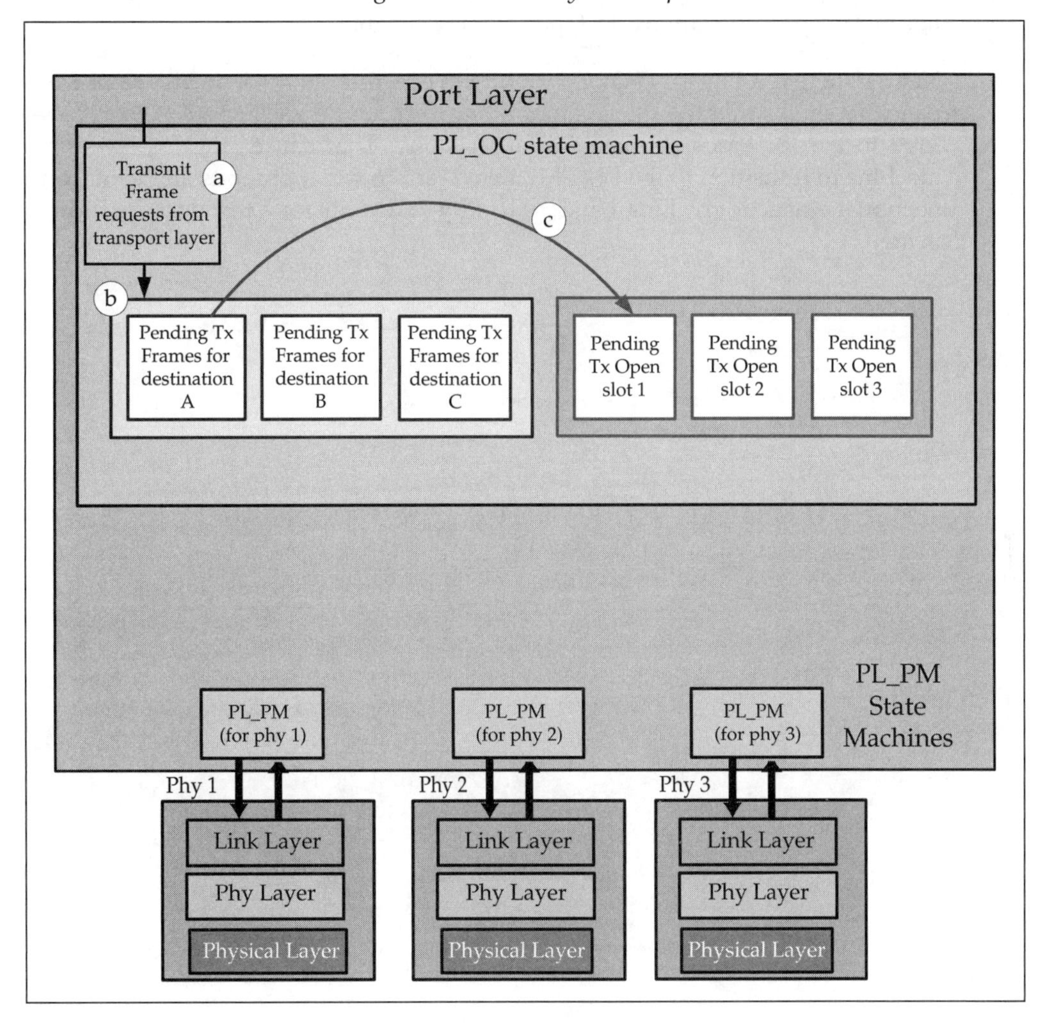

Forwarding the frame to the destination address requires a connection to that destination and the first step would be to see whether a connection to it is already open, which means the PL_OC will need to be aware of existing connections. If such a connection does not already exist, it will need to be opened and, provided there is an available slot, that process is started by creating a Pending Tx Open message as shown as step "c" in the drawing. There can be as many of these pending open slots as there are phys available to the port, but they are not dedicated to any particular phy. In this example, if there were already three pending opens the request for the new frame's connection would have to wait. For our purposes, assume a Tx Open slot is available.

Next, if there is a Phy that is not currently in use, then step "d" in Figure 10-6 on page 269 shows that the PL_OC forwards the Open Request as a Tx Open message to the PL_PM state machine of that phy. That causes the PL_PM state machine to transition to the PL_PM2:Req_Wait, in which it sends an Open Connection message to the Link Layer of its Phy and waits for a response, as shown in step "e".

Figure 10-6: Port Example Part 2

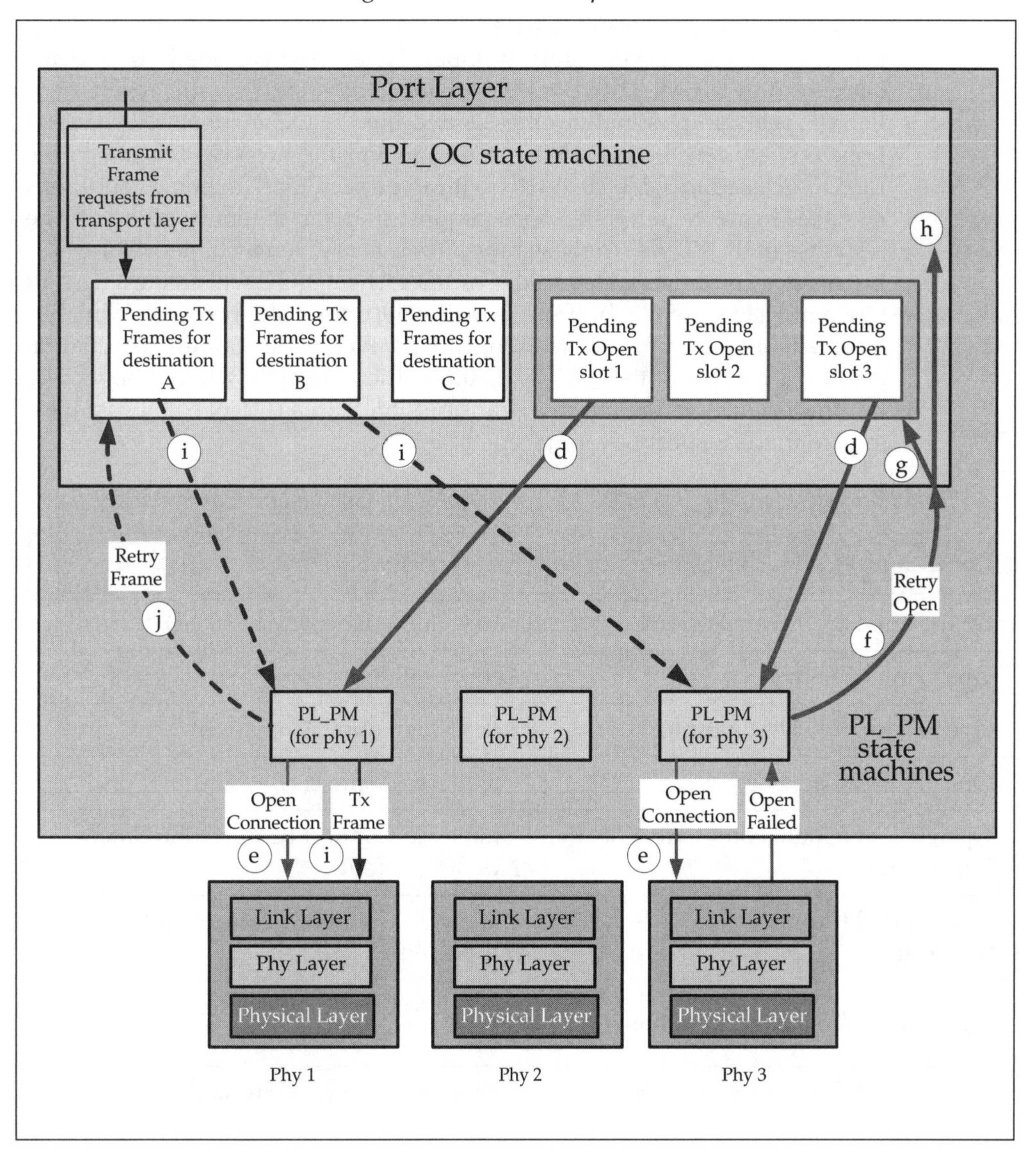

For its part, the Link Layer sends an OPEN address frame and waits for a response. At this point there are a two possible outcomes:

- Using Phy 3 as our example, assume the Phy is unable to establish a connection and the Link Layer sends an Open Failed (No Destination) message back to the PL_PM. That does not change the state, but still results in a Retry Open (No Destination) message to the PL_OC in step "f". The relationship between the Link Layer message and the message relayed to the PL_OC is listed in Table 10-1, where it can be seen that, for some conditions it makes sense to retry the open request and for others it doesn't. (The response of the PL_OC to those messages is also given in Table 10-2.)
- If there is a Pending Tx Open slot available, the PL_OC will create a new Tx Open message (step "g"). If not, it will wait until a slot becomes available. In either case, the process will repeat. However, if this failure is accompanied by a timeout of the I_T Nexus timer, then the open will not be retried, but this will instead result in a Transmission Status (I_T Nexus Loss) message to the Transport Layer in step "h".

Table 10-1: Messages PL_PM to PL_OC in Response to Open Failed Confirmations

Confirmation from Link Layer	Message sent to PL_OC
Open Failed (Pathway Blocked)	Retry Open (Pathway Blocked)
Open Failed (Retry)	Retry Open (Retry)
Open Failed (No Destination)	Retry Open (No Destination)
Open Failed (Bad Destination)	Unable To Connect (Bad Destination)
Open Failed (Connection Rate Not Supported)	Unable To Connect (Connection Rate Not Supported)
Open Failed (Protocol Not Supported)	Unable To Connect (Protocol Not Supported)
Open Failed (STP Resources Busy)	Unable To Connect (STP Resources Busy)
Open Failed (Wrong Destination)	Unable To Connect (Wrong Destination)

Table 10-2: Confirmations from PL_OC to Transport Layer

Message received by PL_OC	Confirmation to be sent to Transport Layer
Retry Open (No Destination)	Transmission Status (I_T Nexus Loss) if the I_T Nexus Loss timer for the SAS address has expired, or Transmission Status (No Destination) if it has not
Retry Open (Open Timeout Occurred)	Transmission Status (I_T Nexus Loss) if the I_T Nexus Loss timer for the SAS address has expired, or Transmission Status (Open Timeout Occurred) if it has not
Retry Open (Pathway Blocked)	Transmission Status (I_T Nexus Loss) if the I_T Nexus Loss timer for the SAS address has expired
Unable to Connect (Bad Destination)	Transmission Status (Bad Destination)
Unable To Connect (Break Received)	Transmission Status (Break Received)
Unable To Connect (Connection Rate Not Supported)	Transmission Status (Connection Rate Not Supported)
Unable To Connect (Port Layer Request)	Transmission Status (Cancel Acknowledge)
Unable To Connect (Protocol Not Supported)	Transmission Status (Protocol Not Supported)
Unable To Connect (STP Resources Busy)	Transmission Status (STP Resources Busy)
Unable To Connect (Wrong Destination)	Transmission Status (Wrong Destination)

- Using Phy 1 as the next example, the same process takes place, but this time the Link Layer is successful in creating the connection. It reports that success with a Connection Opened message to the PL_PM, causing its state to change to PL_PM3:Connected. This state forwards the Connection Opened message to the PL_OC, which sends a Transmit Open message back to the PL_PM and begins draining the pool of Tx Frame messages for that address by sending a Transmit Frame message and forwarding the first of those frames (step "i"). That message is passed to the Link Layer as a Transmit Frame request along with the frame to be sent. For SSP ports, the information also includes another indicator, Balance Required or Balance Not Required, to tell the Link Layer whether this frame is interlocked and must wait for an ACK before the next frame can be sent.

- If the frame succeeds on the link, the PL_PM machine sends a Transmission Status to the Transport Layer that includes the source address, destination address, and tag, so that frame can be removed from its queue. If the frame does not succeed on the link for some reason, the PL_PM will send a Retry Frame message to the PL_OC, as in step "j", essentially reloading that frame into the pool of frames. If the frame does succeed in going out on the link, the PL_PM informs the PL_OC with a Transmission Status message and sends a confirmation to the Transport Layer as a Transmission Status (Frame Transmitted) message.

Assuming the connection is accepted by the destination and an OPEN ACCEPT is returned, a Connection Opened status is relayed back to the PL_PM. The PL_PM forwards this confirmation to the PL_OC which, in step 4, begins to forward the frames in the pool for that destination address.

Once all the frames for that address have been sent, the PL_OC sends a request to the PL_PM that the connection be closed. The PL_PM forwards that request to the Phy and the Link Layer handles the logistics of closing out the connection. When the connection is closed, the Phy informs the PL_PM with a Connection Closed message, and that is relayed to the PL_OC. It is not relayed to the Transport Layer, which does not need to know connection status unless there was a problem that will need attention.

11 Link Layer Overview

The Previous Chapter

The previous chapter described the Port Layer of the SAS architecture along with the state machines used in the standard to explain its behavior, and the messages passed to and from it in support of the other layers. The function of this layer is primarily to select a Phy for an outgoing request from the phys which share the same address and are therefore grouped into the same port.

This Chapter

This chapter introduces the Link Layer, which can rightly be considered the heart of the SAS architecture because the lion's share of the standard is devoted to describing its functions. There is so much to cover, in fact, that it is broken up into four blocks: Serial support, Connection management, Arbitration, and Protocol differences between the different types of connections.

The Next Chapter

The next chapter is the first of the Link Layer sub-blocks and describes the functions carried out by the Link Layer in support of serial transmission. All serial transports have the same basic tasks that must be accomplished to prepare the information for serial transmission or to reverse that process for received packets, and in SAS, most of these steps take place in the Link Layer.

Introduction

The Link Layer comprises the biggest part of the SAS standard and is thus perhaps the heart of the SAS architecture. As shown in Figure 11-1, it resides hierarchically between the Port Layer and Phy Layer.

Figure 11-1: SAS Layers in Hardware

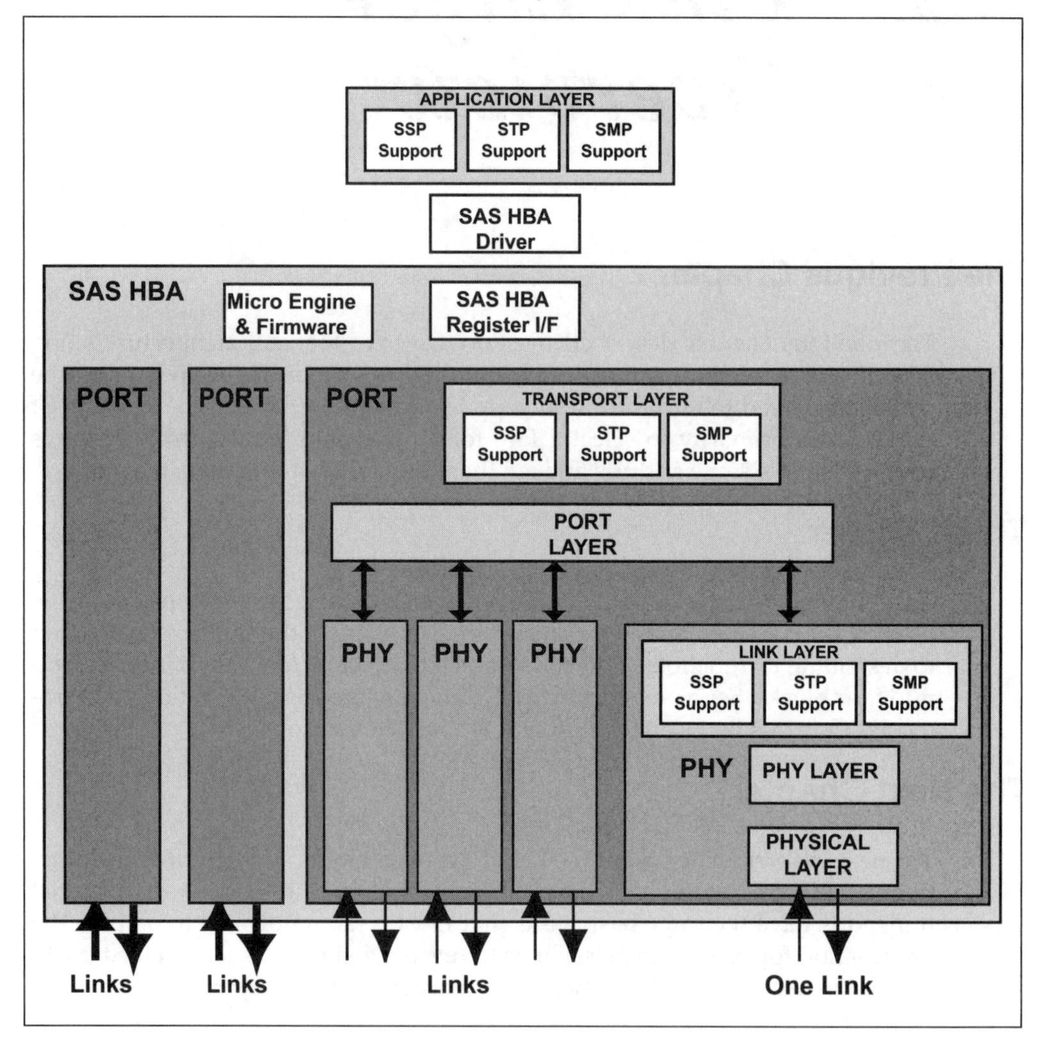

The responsibilities of this layer include the following:

- Sending and receiving Address Frames
- Sending and receiving the Identification Sequence
- Management of Primitives
- Clock Compensation
- CRC Generation and Checking

- Scrambling
- Connection Management
- Generation of Idle cycles
- Byte Ordering

In an effort to make this long section of the standard more manageable, these topics are broken into four chapters. The first three responsibilities are described in this chapter, and most of the rest are covered in the chapter on Serial Support. Connection management merits a chapter of its own to discuss the means for establishing and maintaining connections across a SAS fabric. Finally, some of the Link Layer responsibilities are protocol specific and these differences are discussed in the last of the Link Layer chapters.

To better illustrate the logical blocks within the Link Layer, consider the diagram shown in Figure 11-2. Here it can be seen that there are some parts common to all devices, such as the SL (SAS Link) transmitter that receives transmission requests from the general state machines and responds with the status of the transmission. There are also some parts that are not common, like the XL state machine that is present in expander ports but not elsewhere.

To give some motivation for what follows, we'll first explore the process of opening a connection and using it for frame transmission. Then we'll be ready to look at the sequence of transmission for each protocol.

Figure 11-2: Link Layer Block Diagram

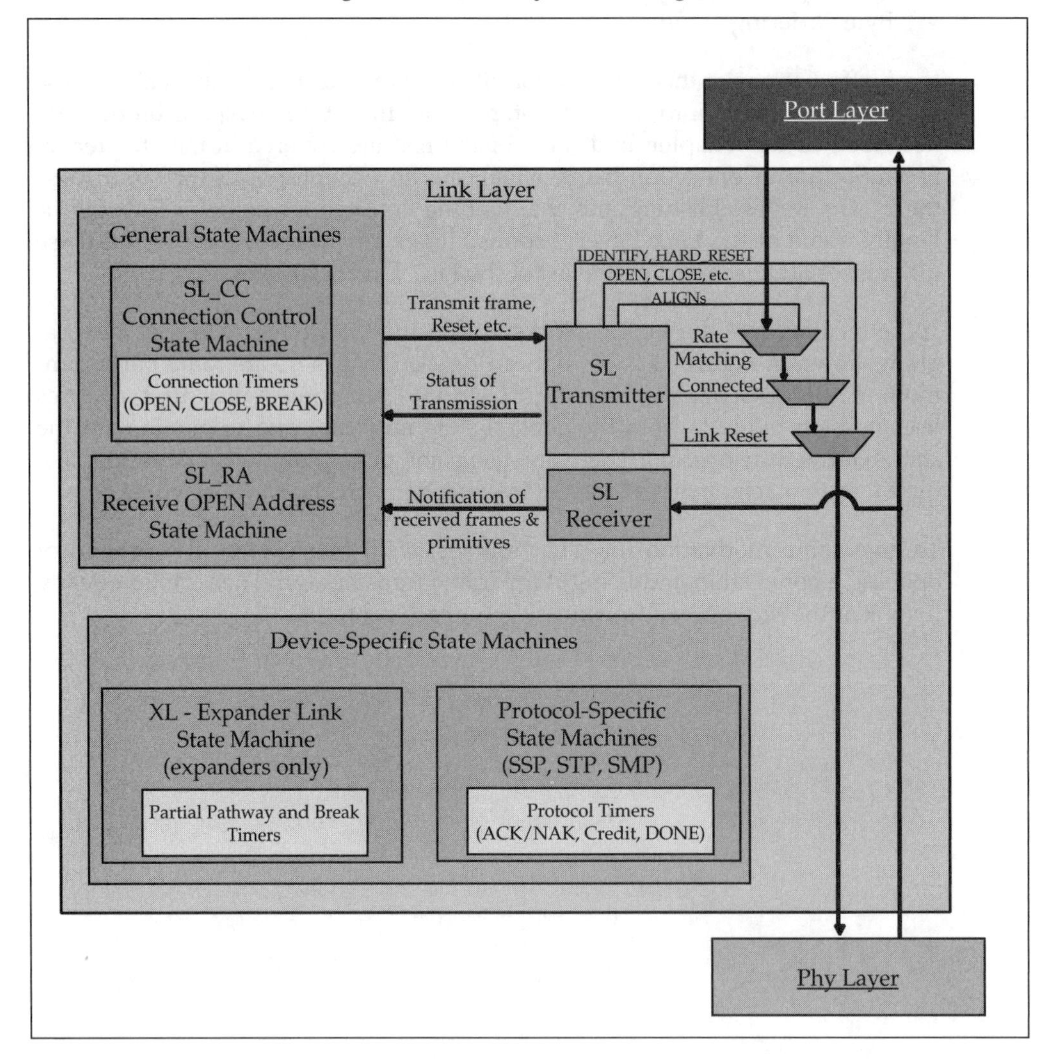

Address Frames

Figure 11-3 shows a ladder diagram that illustrates the beginning of a connection. Every connection begins with an OPEN address frame, which is bounded by SOAF (Start of Address Frame) and EOAF (End of Address Frame) primitives. In the example shown, an AIP primitive (Arbitration In Progress) is received in response to the OPEN request, indicating that an expander is routing the request toward it's destination. The expander continues to send this response periodically until it's able to route the request to the destination Phy. Later, an OPEN_ACCEPT or OPEN_REJECT primitive is returned to inform the requester regarding the final status of this connection request.

Figure 11-3: Opening a Connection

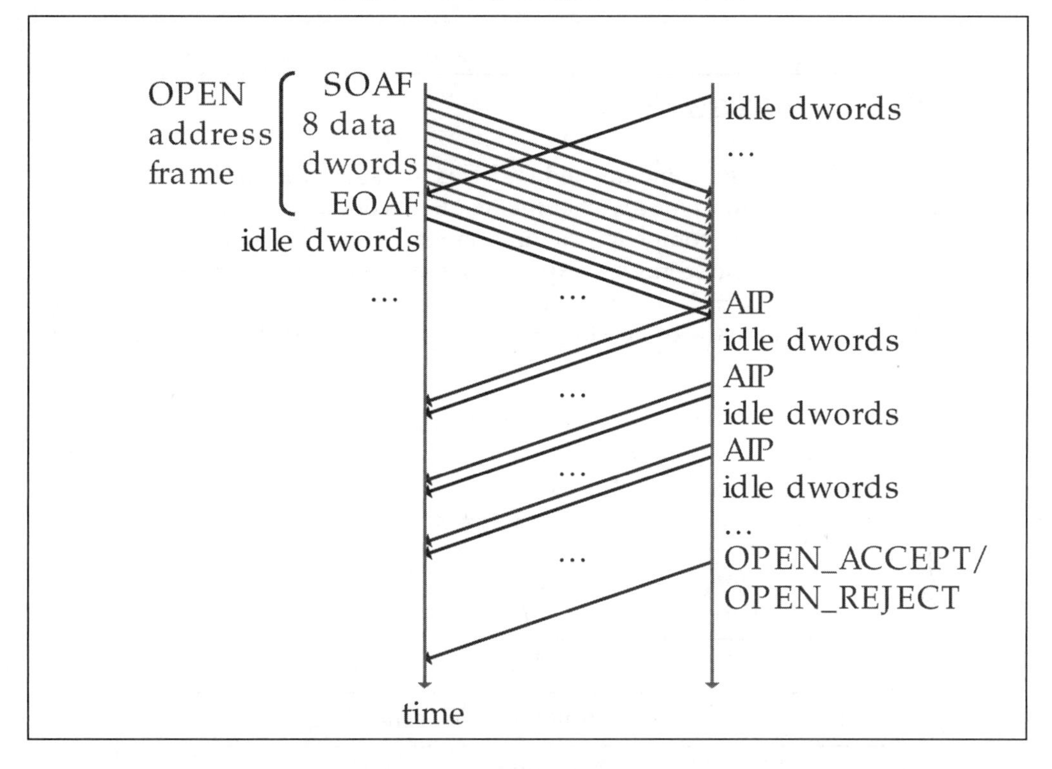

The contents of an address frame are as shown in Figure 11-4 on page 278. The frame begins with an SOAF primitive, followed by the frame-dependent bytes containing the request and destination address. Next is the CRC, used to verify transmission integrity, and then an EOAF primitive that indicates the end of the frame There are two types of these frames: the OPEN address frame and the IDENTIFY address frame.

Figure 11-4: Address Frame

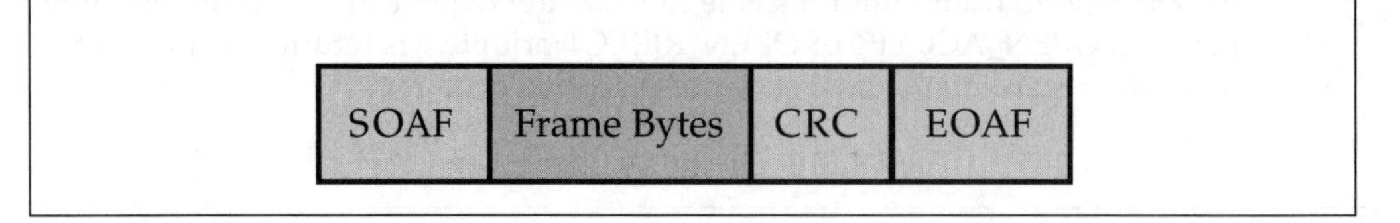

OPEN Address Frame

The OPEN address frame-dependent bytes are shown in Table 11-1, and the fields are described in the text that follows. Some of this information, relating to arbitration between competing connection requests in expanders, is covered in in more detail in the section on expanders (see Appendix A, entitled "Expander Devices," on page 505). For more on how these fields are specifically used for arbitration, refer to the discussion in the section called “Arbitration Fairness” on page 512.

Table 11-1: OPEN Address Frame

Byte	Bit 7	Bits 6 - 4	Bits 3 - 0
0	Initi-ator Port	Protocol	Address Frame Type = 1
1	Features (= 0 for now)		Connection Rate
2 to 3	Initiator Connection Tag		
4 to 11	Destination SAS Address		
12 to 19	Source SAS Address		
20	Compatible Features (= 0 for now)		
21	Pathway Blocked Count		
22 to 23	Arbitration Wait Time		
24 to 27	More Compatible Features (= 0 for now)		
28 to 31	CRC		

Initiator Port Bit: When set to one, this indicates that the source of this request is an initiator port; if set to zero the source is a target port. When a device that is capable of acting as both initiator and target accepts a request, it will operate as the opposite of the requesting device. In other words, if the requesting device was not an initiator, then the receiving device will need to act as the initiator. If a device can only act as an initiator, then it would not expect to receive a connection request from another initiator; such a request would be seen as incorrect.

Protocol: Similarly, a SAS device would expect to get requests for SSP connections, but not for STP connections. The expander Phy would be aware of target device expectations like these, because the supported protocols and initiator status were reported in the Identification Sequence (see Table 11-2). Note that it is not possible to open a connection using one protocol and then switch to another protocol without closing the connection. The connection is only allowed to use the protocol that was specified in the OPEN frame.

Table 11-2: Protocol Field

Value	Description
000b	SMP
001b	SSP
010b	STP
All others	Reserved

Address Frame Type: This value is set to one for OPEN address frames. Address frames with an unknown address frame type are ignored by the recipient.

Features: Available for future use, but set to zero for now, this is ignored by the receiver of this frame.

Connection Rate: For requests that are competing for access to the same outgoing expander port, this is the third-level term to evaluate, as shown in Table 11-

3. At the time of this writing there were only 2 valid rate values (see Table 11-4).

Table 11-3: Arbitration Priority for Competing Requests, Retry Status: Normal

Bits 83-68 (83 is MSB)	Bits 67-4 (67 is MSB)	Bits 3-0 (0 is LSB)
Arbitration Wait Time	Source SAS Address	Connection Rate

Table 11-4: Connection Rate

Value	Description
8h	1.5 Gb/s
9h	3.0 Gb/s
All others	Reserved

Initiator Connection Tag: This optional value in SSP and STP connection requests is assigned by an initiator to facilitate quickly looking up the context when the reply returns from the target at some later time. Of course, this context could also be derived from the source address of the request, which is also contained in the OPEN address frame, but that 64-bit value would take more logic and time to look up than a 16-bit tag. Initiators are expected to use the same Initiator Connection Tag for all connection requests to the same target and only change it when there are no longer any outstanding requests to that target. However, targets are not required to check for consistency on this.

Destination SAS Address: This uniquely identifies the intended recipient of this connection request. Expanders will use it for port selection, and check the other arguments to verify that the matching port will actually support the request. The recipient verifies that the address matches its own SAS address.

Source SAS Address: The second-highest priority term for arbitration in expanders is the SAS address of the originating device (see Table 11-5). For requests that are passing each other on the same link (one outgoing and one incoming), only the AWT and source address are compared to see which will win access to that link.

Table 11-5: Arbitration Priority for Passing Requests

Bits 79-64 (79 is MSB)	Bits 63-0 (0 is LSB)
Arbitration Wait Time	Source SAS Address

Compatible Features: Available for future use, but set to zero for now, this is ignored by the receiver of this frame.

Pathway Blocked Count: This value indicates the number of times this request has been forced to retry because it received an OPEN_REJECT (PATHWAY BLOCKED) response. This happens when an expander's Partial Pathway Time-out timer expires, indicating a potential deadlock condition, and the expander must reject one of the competing requests. The goal of this field is to ensure that a request which has previously been retried will have a higher priority next time and thus be less likely to be retried again.

Arbitration Wait Time (AWT): This tracks how long a request has been waiting to receive an accept or reject response and is used to assign arbitration priority to competing requests. This value has two parts, one that counts microseconds from 0 to 32,768, and another that counts milliseconds from 0 to 32,768.

A counter is started by the initiating device when a request is sent and is normally initialized to zero, but can be set to a non-zero value as high as 32,768 µs by setting the AWT field in the OPEN address frame to as high as 8000h. This makes the arbitration unfair, of course, but gives system administrators a means of assigning relative priorities among various devices. The counter continues to run until an accept or reject response arrives or until it reaches its maximum value, at which point it holds that value rather than wrapping around to zero.

When the request is received by an expander phy, the counter for that Phy is initialized to the value given in the OPEN address frame and the timer is started. When the OPEN address frame is transmitted by the expander, the AWT value is assigned based on the current value of the internal timer. Consequently, the AWT is constantly updated as the OPEN address frame makes it way through the fabric. This is important because AWT is the most significant consideration in determining which requests have priority in an expander: requests that have been waiting longer are deemed to have higher priority.

More Compatible Features: Available for future use, but set to zero for now, this is ignored by the receiver of this frame.

CRC: Cyclic Redundancy Code Address frames with unknown address frame types, incorrect lengths, or CRC errors are ignored by the recipient.

IDENTIFY Address Frame

The IDENTIFY frame, shown in Table 11-6, is the information that a SAS Phy passes to its neighbor over the link during a link reset.The frame-dependent bytes are also shown in the table, and its fields are described in the text that follows.

Table 11-6: Identify Address Frame

	Bit 7	6	5	4	3	2	1	0
Byte 0	Restricted	Device Type			Address Frame Type = 0			
1	Restricted							
2	Reserved				SSP Initiator	STP Initiator	SMP Initiator	Restricted
3	Reserved				SSP Target	STP Target	SMP Target	Restricted
4 - 11	Restricted							
12 -19	SAS Address							
20	PHY Identifier							
21 - 27	Reserved							
28 - 31	CRC							

- **Device Type:** There are three possibilities, as listed in Table 11-7.

Table 11-7: Device Type

Value	Device type
001b	End device

Table 11-7: Device Type

Value	Device type
010b	Edge expander
011b	Fanout expander
111b - 100b	Reserved

- **Address Frame Type:** For an IDENTIFY address frame, this value is zero.
- **Protocols supported:** The six protocol-specific bits indicate what type of device this is, such as an SSP Initiator or SSP Target, or both. Note that an expander is restricted in this regard, and has only two possible settings: SMP Initiator is optional, while SMP target is mandatory. None of the other settings are allowed for expanders.
- **SAS Address:** The 64-bit SAS address assigned to this phy. This will be used when sending or receiving connection requests.
- **Phy Identifier:** The identifier for this Phy within this device. This can be used to clarify which topology has actually been implemented when more than one is possible.

Identification Sequence

The identification sequence is the overall process by which the two devices on either end of a link exchange IDENTIFY frames with each other. For SAS ports, this sequence occurs after a Phy reset on the link, as shown in Figure 11-5.

Figure 11-5: SAS Link Reset Sequence

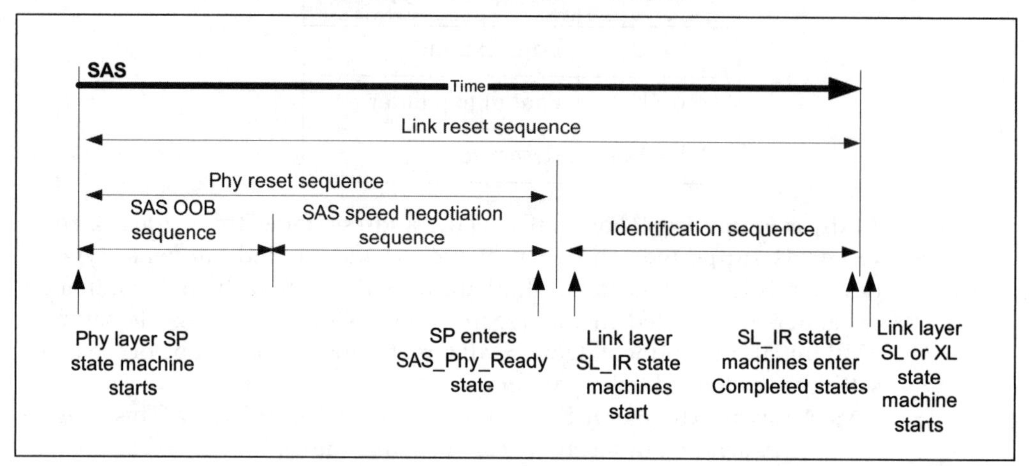

Note that SATA devices also implement a Phy reset, but they don't use addresses and so don't perform the identification sequence. For a SAS port the reset sequence is a Phy reset followed by an identification sequence. If a hard reset is requested, the sequence becomes a Phy reset followed by a hard reset, followed by another Phy reset and then the identification sequence. The difference between a Phy reset and a hard reset is the level of layers that are affected by the reset. For an SSP port, a hard reset causes a Transport Reset event notification to the Application Layer and results in a SCSI device reset. For an STP port, it is the equivalent of a power-on hardware reset. A Phy reset, on the other hand, will only reset the affected Phy and will not affect the port, transport, or Application Layers of the device.

A SAS Phy reset consists of an OOB sequence followed by speed negotiation, as was shown in Figure 11-5 on the previous page. The combination of Phy reset and the Identification sequence is referred to as a SAS link reset sequence.

For more on the reset process, see "Reset Sequences" on page 127. For more on the OOB and speed negotiation process, refer to Chapter 16, entitled "Phy Layer," on page 365.

Primitives

Primitives are dwords that have special meaning to the system. They are readily recognized because they are the only dwords that include a control character, which must be in the first position of the dword, as shown in Figure 11-6 on page 285. For reference, recall that in SAS an 8-bit byte is encoded into a 10-bit character by the 8b/10b encoder, and that a group of four bytes or four characters is referred to as a dword. As mentioned earlier, the first character for SAS primitives must be K28.5, and it must be K28.3 for SATA primitives. There is also a special primitive that begins with K28.6, used when an expander acts as a bridge to a SATA device and receives an error in the flow of traffic to the SATA target. In order to convey an error with certainty, this primitive is used because it is not legal in SATA and will therefore be certain to be seen as an error. This approach is preferable to passing along a SAS error that could be misunderstood by the SATA target.

Figure 11-6: Primitive Dword Format

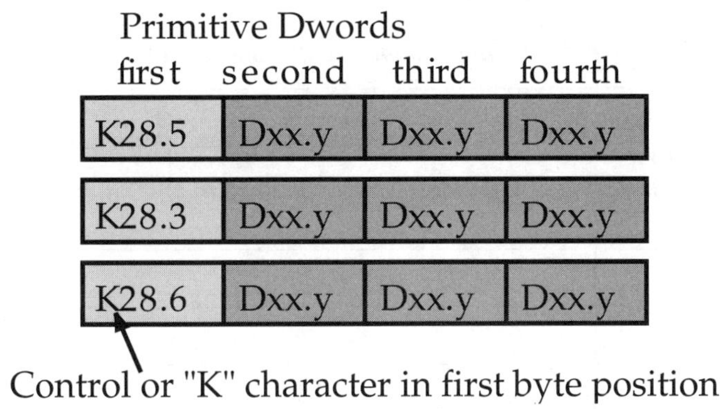

Primitive Dwords

first	second	third	fourth
K28.5	Dxx.y	Dxx.y	Dxx.y
K28.3	Dxx.y	Dxx.y	Dxx.y
K28.6	Dxx.y	Dxx.y	Dxx.y

Control or "K" character in first byte position

Endian Notation in Primitives

Endian ordering is an issue for devices that must support both SAS and SATA, because SAS uses big-endian ordering of bytes, sending the highest-order byte first, while SATA is little-endian and sends the lowest-order byte first. As a result, their bytes appear in backward order relative to each other. Fortunately, this is not a factor for primitives, because both SAS and SATA send the control character first on the wire.

Error Protection in Primitives

Primitives are self-contained units that are not placed within the context of a frame. Because they are intended to be small (just one dword) they do not include CRC protection. Errors can still occur in transmission, of course, so another means of protecting against them was needed. The approach chosen was to select characters for the primitives that would make it very difficult for corruption of a valid primitive to change it into a different valid primitive. To do that, the standard writers chose combinations of characters that would maximize the Hamming distance between any two valid primitives. As can be seen in Table 11-8, which lists the possible Hamming distance between characters based on the number of bits in the frame, several 40-bit values could be chosen that would have a Hamming distance as high as 9 between them. The calculations for coding indicate that, to detect *n* errors, a coding scheme needs to use values with a Hamming distance of $n+1$. As a result, forcing a Hamming distance of 9 between values means it would take an 9-bit error to change one valid primitive into another valid primitive, while any difference of 8 or less would be detected. Needless to say, the probability of an 9-bit error is quite small.

Table 11-8: Hamming Distance with respect to Frame Size

Hamming distance	Number of bits in the frame
15	8 to 10
14	-
13	-
12	11 to 12
11	13 to 21
10	22 to 34
9	35 to 57
8	58 to 91
7	92 to 171
6	172 to 268
5	269 to 2974
4	2975 to 91,607
3	91,608 to more than 131,072

Use of Primitives

Primitives uses include indicating address frames for connections and identification, starting and ending frames, ensuring proper clock compensation, and performing flow control. Two SATA primitives are shown in Table 11-9 and two SAS primitives are shown in Table 11-10. Note that the SATA ALIGN and the SAS ALIGN(0) are the same. They appear in reverse byte order because of the endianess of the different designs, but when they are transmitted on the wire they look the same because SATA begins with byte 0 and counts up while SAS begins with the byte 3 and counts down.

Table 11-9: SATA Primitive Encoding Examples

Primitive name	Byte 3	Byte 2	Byte 1	Byte 0
ALIGN	D27.3	D10.2	D10.2	K28.5
CONT	D25.4	D25.4	D10.5	K28.3

Table 11-10: SAS Primitive Encoding Examples

Primitive	1st	2nd	3rd	4th (last)
ALIGN(0)	K28.5	D10.2	D10.2	D27.3
SATA_CONT	K28.3	D10.5	D25.4	D25.4

Primitive Contexts

Non Protocol Specific

Primitives are used in three different contexts, depending on the protocol being used. The first group consists of those which are not protocol specific. For example, several are only used outside of a connection, as listed below:

- **AIP** - Arbitration in Progress, used by expanders to report that the arbitration process for a connection request is underway and not yet resolved. As is the case for other primitives, this one has several versions that each communicate some additional information.
- **BREAK** - Used to terminate a connection without going through the normal

close handshake process (emergency close).

- **CLOSE** - Used to close out a connection and free the resources for other connections.
- **OPEN_ACCEPT** - Sent by the recipient of a connection request to indicate that it will accept the connection and participate in the transaction.
- **OPEN_REJECT** - Sent by the recipient of a connection request to indicate that a problem of some kind is preventing the acceptance of a connection request.
- **SOAF, EOAF** - Sent to indicate the boundaries of an IDENTIFY address frame or an OPEN address frame.

There are also some general primitives that are not protocol-specific but which might still appear within a connection anyway. These include the following:

- **ALIGN** - Used for clock skew management, both inside and outside a connection, as well as for rate matching within a connection.
- **NOTIFY** - This is a version of ALIGN that may contain additional information. There are 4 versions of this in the standard, but 3 are reserved, leaving only one currently defined for use: NOTIFY (ENABLE SPINUP) that informs a drive to spin up the media.
- **BROADCAST** - Sent out on all expander ports except the one that experienced the change to tell initiators in the system that they need to take steps to discover the change.
- **ERROR** - Sent by expanders when forwarding dwords that have been detected on the incoming Phy as invalid dwords.
- **HARD_RESET** - Used to force a device-level reset.

Within SSP and SMP Connections

Secondly, there is a group of primitives that are used within SSP and SMP connections to manage aspects of the Link Layer protocol such as flow control and ACK/NAK handshakes.

- **SOF** and **EOF** - These indicate the beginning and ending of a frame.
- **DONE** - Indicates that the connection is being prepared for closing.
- **ACK, NAK** - These are positive and negative frame acknowledgements used to indicate status of SSP frame reception.
- **RRDY** - Used in SSP to indicate readiness to receive a frame.
- **CREDIT_BLOCKED** - This indicates that no more RRDYs will be sent in this connection. This is helpful in cases where the receiver will not have any more credits to give for 1ms or longer, because the transmitter would time out waiting for credit after 1ms anyway and when this primitive is received it does not have to wait for the timeout.

Most primitives only need to be sent once for each event they are indicating, but to reduce the possibility of misunderstandings, some of them are required to be sent and received as a sequence. The different types are listed in Table 11-11 and described in the text that follows.

Table 11-11: Primitive sequences

Type	Transmit	Receive
Single	1	1
Repeated	1 or more	1
Continued	2 followed by SATA_CONT	1
Triple	3	3
Redundant	6	3

Single primitives

These require only one instance of the primitive to be sent and only one needs to be detected to achieve a valid result. These primitives occur frequently and do not have a high cost if they fail. For example, if an SOAF or EOAF is missed, the result may be a loss of the frame with which they were associated, but that can be recovered. All primitives that are used exclusively within SSP and SMP connections are single type.

Repeated primitives

These primitives must be repeated several times by the sender and detected several times in a row by the receiver to be valid. They are currently only used in STP connections when responding to power management requests. Since SAS devices do not respond to STP power management requests, this is not interesting for our discussion.

Continued primitives

Only used in SATA connections, these provide a means of allowing primitives to repeat indefinitely.

It's possible that an SSP or SMP connection might also encounter a situation in which a primitive needs to be sent for some time, but SAS handles this case differently. Rather than define a Continue mechanism, the writers of the standard created different versions of some primitives. For example, the ALIGN primitive has four versions: ALIGN(0), ALIGN(1), ALIGN(2), and ALIGN(3). They all have the same meaning during normal operation, but they are encoded differently. If a transmitter needs to send several ALIGN primitives together, it avoids repetition by cycling through them in order. The symbols that go onto the wire are not all identically the same, so the EMI problem is avoided, but the receiver understands that they all have the same meaning.

Triple primitives

This type must be both sent three times by the transmitter and seen three times in a row at the receiver, although ALIGN and NOTIFY primitives can be mixed into the sequence with no loss of continuity in this regard. The only triple primitives specified in the standard are the four versions of the CLOSE primitive. Closing unexpectedly would cause trouble if a device mistakenly saw it, and so requiring that three instances be seen together at the receiver guards against the possibility of an "accidental" closure. Figure 11-7 shows several triple primitive sequences. The first of them suffers an error during transmission of the primitives and so fails to be recognized by the receiver. The second sequence has ALIGNs mixed in with the primitives, but these are transparent to the receiver, so it does detect three in a row. The last example shows the three primitives arriving consecutively and without error, so they are correctly detected as a triple primitive sequence.

Figure 11-7: Triple Primitive Example

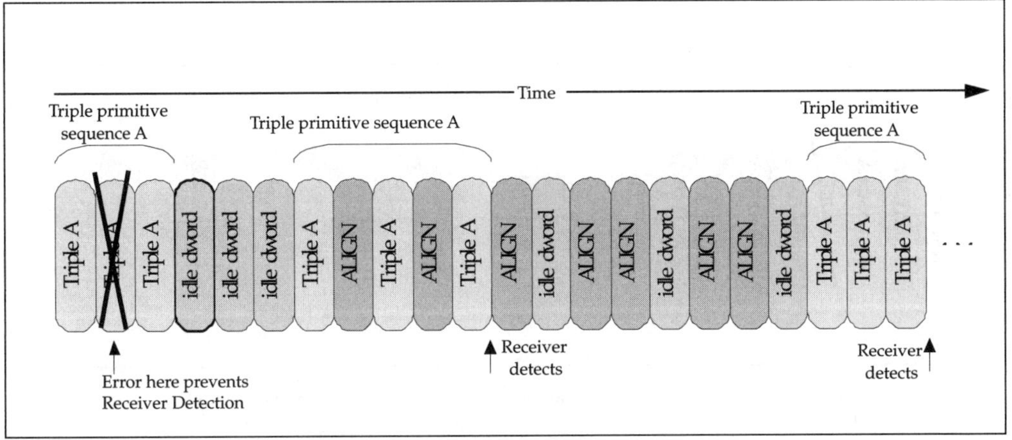

Redundant primitives

These must be sent 6 times in a row and at least 3 of those must be seen consecutively by the receiver to recognize the primitive. Since redundant primitives only need to be seen 3 times at the receiver, this allows for the loss of some of the primitives without loss of the intended meaning. There are two primitives listed with this characteristic: the 8 versions of BROADCAST, and the HARD_RESET primitive.

Figure 11-8 illustrates some examples of redundant primitives being received. At the top left, the primitive is recognized after 3 consecutive primitives are seen, and it does not matter that the next primitive has an error.

Figure 11-8: Redundant Primitive Example

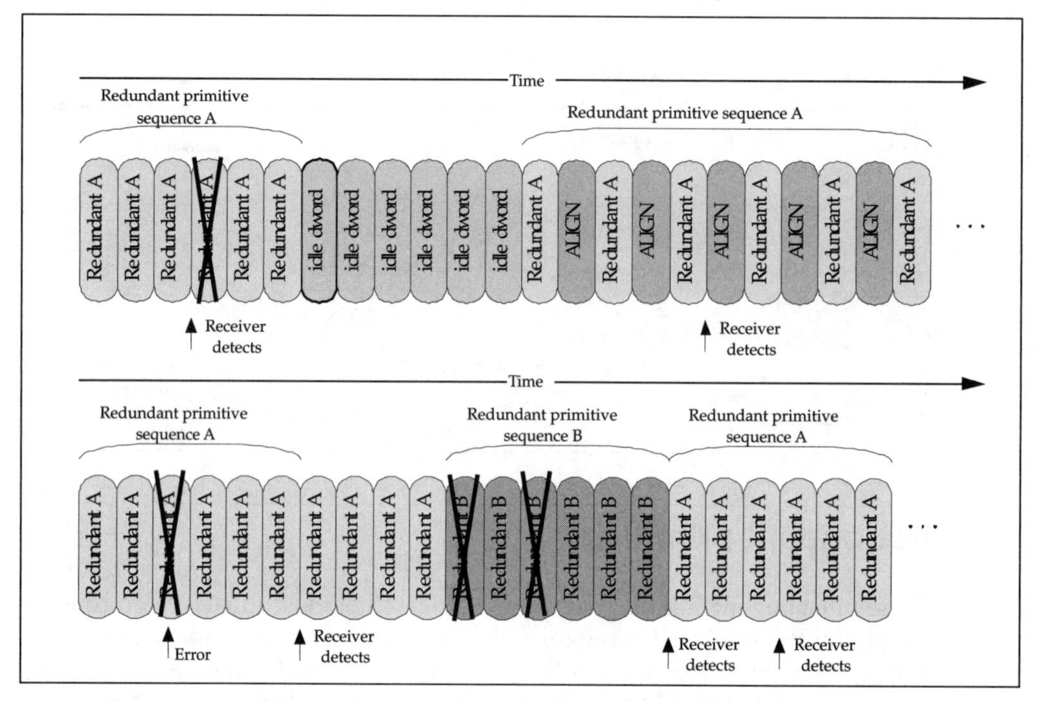

On the top right, a redundant primitive is received with ALIGNs inserted between every dword, as might be the case if rate matching was necessary. As before, the ALIGNs are ignored for purposes of primitive detection, so the third primitive appears to be consecutive and will be sufficient for the receiver to recognize it. In the bottom left part of the figure, one of the primitives has an error before three in a row have been seen. In this case, the receiver starts over on the process of looking for three consecutive primitives, and still successfully finds them. Note that in this case, the transmitter actually sent more than the required 6 primitives in a row, which is legal. In sequence B at the bottom in the middle, a redundant sequence sustains two errors in the transmission but is still recognized because three consecutive primitives were seen. Finally, at the bottom right, sequence A has no errors and is recognized after 3 contiguous primitives.

State Machines - Link Layer Identification and Reset

For those interested in going deeper into the detailed operation of this section, the state machines used in the standard to define its behavior are discussed next and redrawn here for convenience. These state machine drawings are intended to improve readability over what is offered in the standard by showing the reasons for state transitions and the messages that are sent to neighboring layers based on the state variables. They are not intended to be all inclusive and usually do not, for example, include interactions between state machines within the same layer. The casual reader may skip this section and still have a basic operational understanding of the material.

The Link Layer defines state machines that control the generation and receipt of the identification sequence. This functionality is described by three separate machines (the SL_IR abbreviation stands for **S**AS **L**ink Layer **I**dentify and **R**eset):

- SL_IR_TIR (Transmit Identify and Reset) for transmission of the Identify frame or Hard Reset on the link,
- SL_IR_RIF (Receive Identify Frame) for receipt of the Identify frame from the neighbor on the link, and
- SL_IR_IRC (Identify and Reset Control) for the overall control of the Identify and Reset process.

Together, these state machines ensure that an IDENTIFY address frame is both sent and received before this Phy is considered ready for operation.

Transmitter and Receiver

As is the case for many of the state machine definitions in the standard, there are two more blocks that are not part of the machines themselves, but service requests from them. These are called the state machine's transmitter and receiver. For this set of state machines, these are called the SL_IR transmitter and the SL_IR receiver. These logical blocks do just as their name suggests, acting on requests from the machines to send an Identify or Reset sequence, or reporting that one has been received. The interaction between these machines is simple. The transmitter can be told to send the Identify frame, or a Hard Reset, or Idle dwords. For the first two, it also reports when it has sent them. The receiver reports receipt of the components of the Identify or Reset sequence: SOAF, data dwords, EOAF, ERROR, invalid dword, and Hard Reset. Verifying the receipt of these components in the proper order informs the state machines that a valid sequence has been received, as described in the following sections.

SL_IR_TIR (Transmit IDENTIFY or HARD_RESET)

State Machine

The function of this state machine is to send one IDENTIFY address frame or Hard Reset after the Phy Layer enables the Link Layer. Starting in SL_IR_TIR1:Idle, this Link Layer state sends idle dwords until the Phy Layer reports ready. The upper layers also see this notification and then, if this state receives a Tx IDENTIFY request from the Application Layer to send an IDENTIFY address frame, the machine will transition to SL_IR_TIR2:Transmit Identify and send a Transmit Identify message to the SL_IR transmitter. When this state receives an IDENTIFY Address Frame Transmitted confirmation, it forwards a similar confirmation to the SL_IR_IRC state machine and transitions to SL_IR_TIR4:Completed.

If, on the other hand, the TIR1:Idle state receives a Tx HARD_RESET message from the Application Layer, it will transition to the TIR3:Transmit_Hard_Reset state and send a Transmit Hard Reset message to the SL_IR transmitter. When it gets confirmation that the hard reset was sent, it forwards confirmation of that event to the Application Layer and changes to TIR4:Completed.

Figure 11-9: SL_IR_TIR: Transmit Identify or Hard Reset State Machine

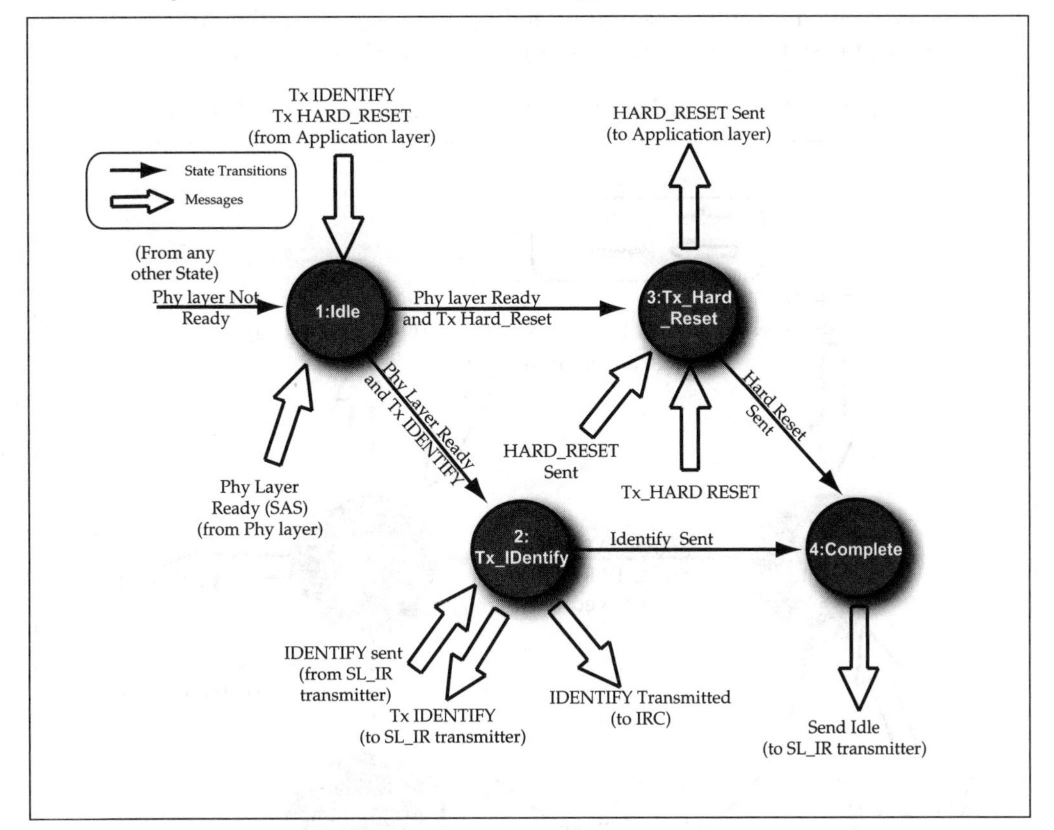

SL_IR_RIF (Receive IDENTIFY address Frame) State Machine

This state machine, shown in Figure 11-10 on page 296, verifies receipt of a valid IDENTIFY address frame. It transitions from SL_IR_RIF1 to SL_IR_RIF2 when the Start SL_IR Receiver confirmation from the Phy Layer has been received, indicating that dword synchronization has been achieved, and an SOAF received confirmation has been received, indicating that an address frame has arrived. In this state, the frame is checked to confirm that it has 8 data dwords followed by an EOAF primitive and a valid CRC value. If the Frame Type field shows this to be an IDENTIFY address frame and all the conditions are good, this state will send an Identify Received message to the SL_IR_IRC state machine. If there is a problem of some kind, an Address Frame Failed confirmation is sent to the Application Layer to indicate that an invalid IDENTIFY frame was received. In either case, after sending a message regarding the status of the frame, the state machine transitions to SL_IR_RIF3:Completed.

Figure 11-10: SL_IR_RIF: Receive Identify or Hard Reset State Machine

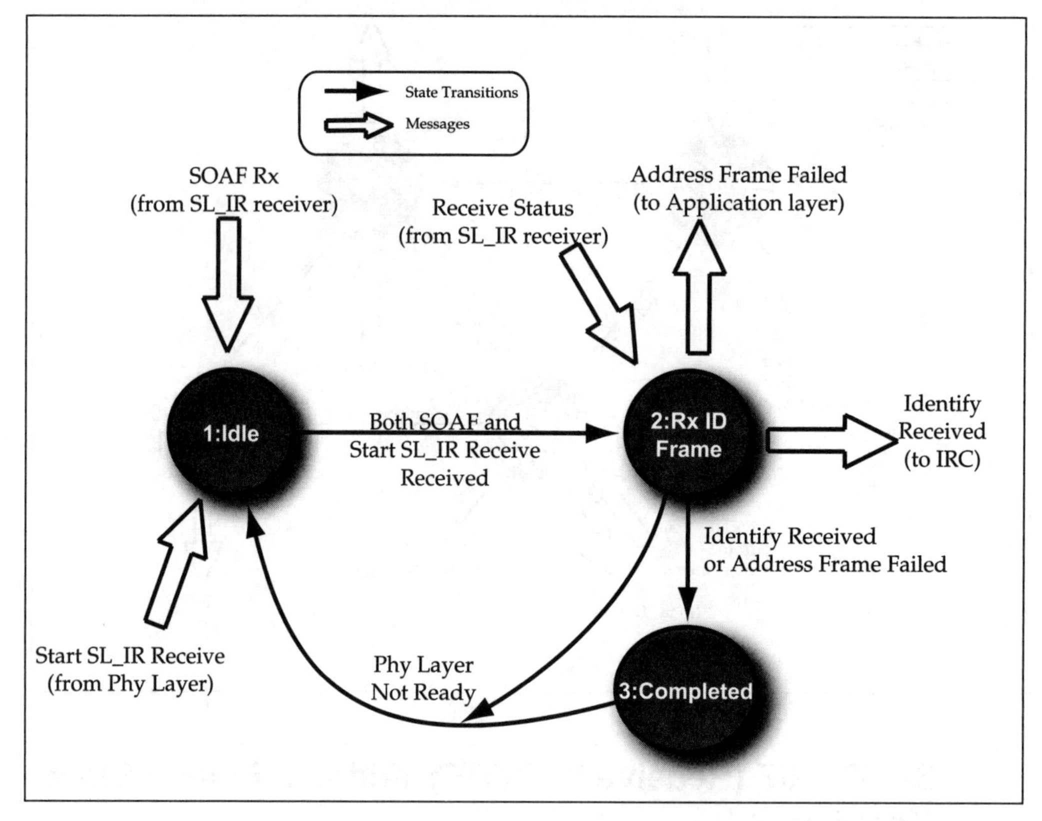

SL_IR_IRC (Identification and hard Reset Control) State Machine

From the initial state or SL_IR_IRC1:Idle, this state machine, shown in Figure 11-11 on page 297, sends an Enable Disable SAS Link (Disable) to halt any Link Layer activity and sends a Phy Disabled confirmation to the port and Application Layer to indicate that the Phy is not ready for use. When this state receives a Start SL_IR Receiver confirmation from the Phy Layer, it transitions to

IRC2:Wait, where it waits for confirmation that an IDENTIFY frame has been both sent and received before enabling the rest of the Link Layer. These can occur in any order, but if it is sent first, a timer is started to verify receipt of a corresponding IDENTIFY frame. If the timer times out, an Identify Timeout message is sent to the Application Layer.

If an Identify Received message arrives before the timer expires, an Identification Sequence Complete confirmation is sent to the Application Layer with arguments that include the contents of the incoming IDENTIFY frame. In addition, an Enable Disable SAS Link (Enable) message informs the Link Layer state machines that they may start operation, while a Phy Enabled confirmation tells the port and Application Layers that the Phy is ready for use.

Figure 11-11: SL_IR_IRC: Identify and Hard Reset Control State Machine

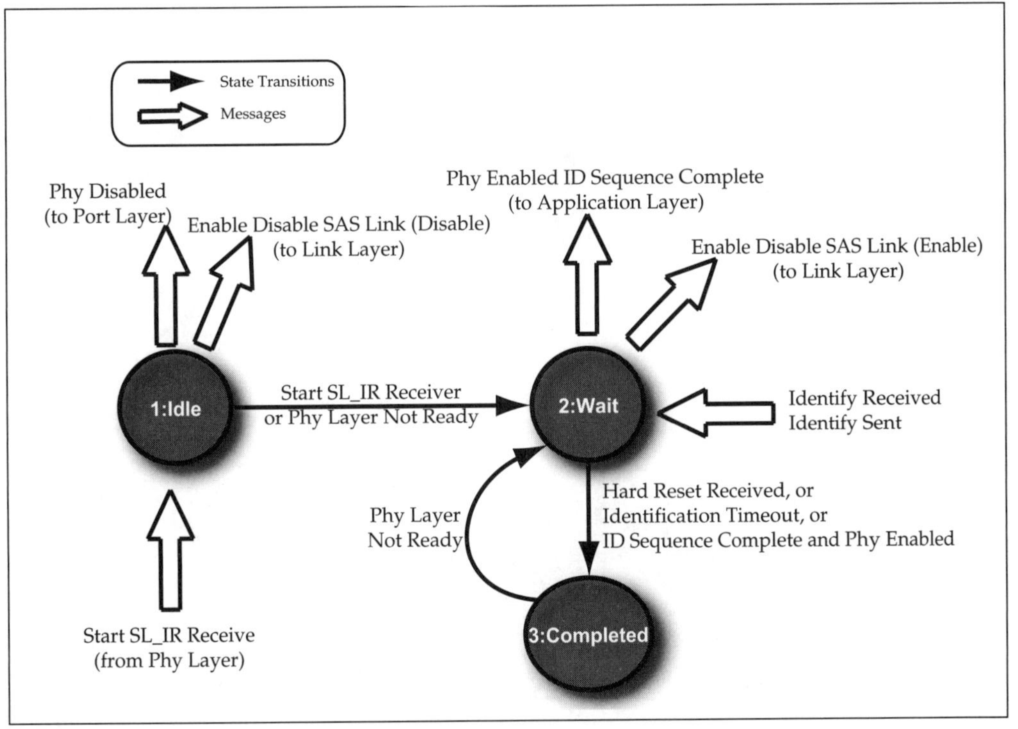

12 Link Layer - Serial Support

The Previous Chapter

The previous chapter introduced the Link Layer responsibilities from a high level and described the four logical sub-blocks of this layer.

This Chapter

This chapter is the first of the four Link Layer sub-blocks. It describes the steps that are taken to prepare frames for serial transmission and then how those steps are undone at the receiver to recover the original information.

The Next Chapter

The next chapter describes the second sub-block of the Link Layer - connection management. This involves the steps for opening a new connection across a SAS topology, maintaining that connection with flow control and ACK/NAK protocol, and then closing the connection when it's no longer needed or has timed out.

Introduction

There are several functions needed in support of any serial transport that are defined as Link Layer responsibilities in SAS. Three functions are described in this chapter:

- Clock Compensation,
- CRC Generation and Checking, and
- Scrambling.

Clock Compensation

All serial interfaces embed the clock into the data at the transmitter and recover it at the receiver, eliminating the need for a common reference clock and allowing much higher frequencies. However, this also means the transmitter and receiver clocks are essentially asynchronous to each other. When data is latched into the receiver it crosses from the transmitter's clock domain into the receiver's clock domain. To compensate for the slight differences between the transmitter and receiver clock frequencies a receive buffer called an elastic buffer is employed. It is in this buffer that bits actually cross from one clock domain to the other, by latching the data into the buffer with one clock and latching it out with the other clock.

Elastic Buffer

Figure 12-1 shows several parts of the Phy Layer and Physical Layer that we'll come back to later, and highlights the elastic buffer, which is the first item in the receive path for the Link Layer. The elastic buffer clocks data in with the clock that was recovered by the receiver, and then clocks data out with the local clock of the device.

The Link Layer receives the data stream from the Phy Layer after it has been properly grouped into dwords. Recall that a dword is four bytes, each of which is encoded into 10 bits for transmission, meaning 40 bits on the wire represents one dword. The receiver recovers the transmit clock and latches the bits into a 40-bit buffer, then clocks them out in parallel at one-fortieth of that rate. (To learn more about embedding and recovering the clock refer to Chapter 16, entitled "Phy Layer," on page 365.) The 10-bit characters then go through a 10b/8b decoder to recover the original 8-bit bytes plus an indication of whether each byte is a control character. Recall that a control character in the first byte would mean a dword is actually a primitive. Finally the 1/40 receiver clock is also used to clock the dwords into the elastic buffer.

The local clock of the receiver clocks the dwords out of the elastic buffer. Even though the local clock is very close to the same frequency from the receiver's recovered clock, they are still technically asynchronous to each other because the difference in their timing cannot be perfectly predicted. This is where the data crosses from one clock domain into the other.

Figure 12-1: Link Layer Receiver: Elastic Buffer

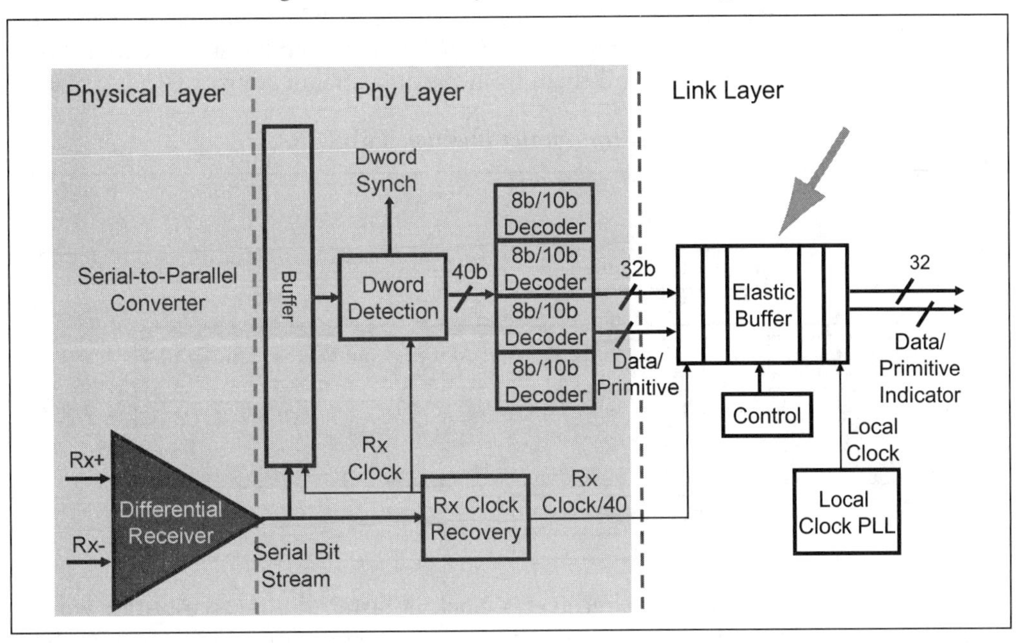

Crossing Clock Domains

Crossing clock domains, which happens in the elastic buffer, involves latching incoming data with one clock that was generated by a system using a different clock. For a SAS environment, there are a couple of considerations in this regard.

Frequency Difference Can Change

First, the frequency difference between the transmit and receive clocks is specified to remain within a legal range but can change dynamically within that range according to temperature or voltage changes. At any given time the transmitter's clock may be slightly faster or slightly slower than the receiver's clock. If the transmitter's clock is running faster, the receiver's buffer will begin to approach an overflow condition as the dwords come in to the elastic buffer faster than they are taken out. To compensate, the transmitter is required to inject ALIGN characters that can be discarded at the receiver as needed. This is shown in Figure 12-2, where it can be seen that the injection of the ALIGN primitives is done in the Phy Layer. We can also see that the injection of these primitives is a very high priority, since no Link Layer traffic can override their transmission. When the elastic buffer approaches an overflow condition the monitoring logic can remove one or more of the ALIGNs and empty the buffer that way. It doesn't matter that the ALIGNs are removed because the logic after the elastic buffer will discard them from the data stream anyway.

Figure 12-2: Transmitter Injection of ALIGNs

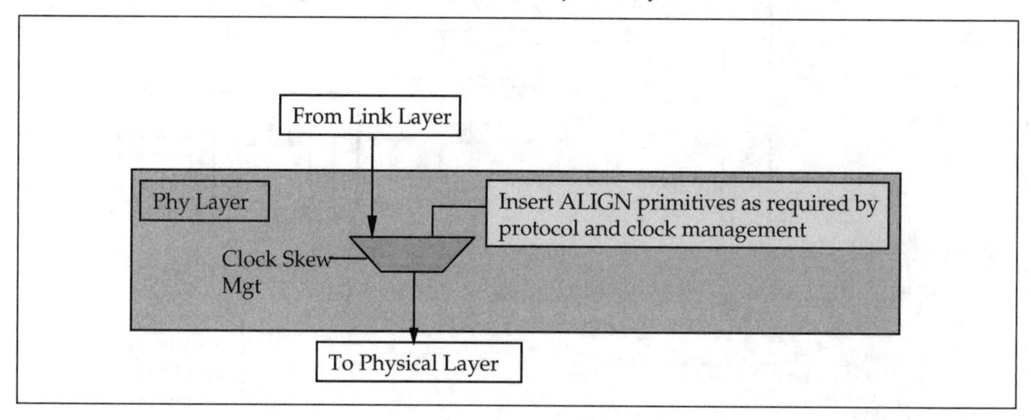

If, on the other hand, the receiver's clock is faster, the receive buffer would eventually underflow because the dwords are being removed faster than they are being inserted. The solution in this case is for the logic that evaluates the status of the elastic buffer to inject more ALIGNs into the buffer as needed. The size of the elastic buffer is not specified in the standard, but will need to have a few entries to be able to compensate for the possible differences in the clock.

Metastability Risk

Second, whenever signals arrive asynchronously at the receiver there is a risk of metastability at the input register. This happens because the register that samples the input has timing parameters, such as setup and hold times, that must be met for reliable operation. However, when the input is asynchronous to the clock this timing cannot be guaranteed. If those times are violated, the output of that register can end up at a value that is neither one nor zero, but an intermediate state. How long the output will stay in this state before finally resolving to one or zero is design-dependent, but it can be long enough to cause trouble for subsequent logic that is using it. The common method for robustly guarding against this problem is to implement a multi-stage register that acts as a synchronizer. In the example shown in Figure 12-3, the first register feeds a second one without any intervening combinatorial logic, giving the output of the first stage more time to settle out from a possible metastable state before the last stage is clocked. While there is no method that can completely eliminate the possibility of metastability, adding more input register stages results in a large reduction in MTBF (Mean Time Between Failures) and is consequently a common design technique. The actual number of registers implemented represents a trade-off between cost and improved MTBF.

Figure 12-3: Metastability Synchronizer (Elastic Buffer Stages)

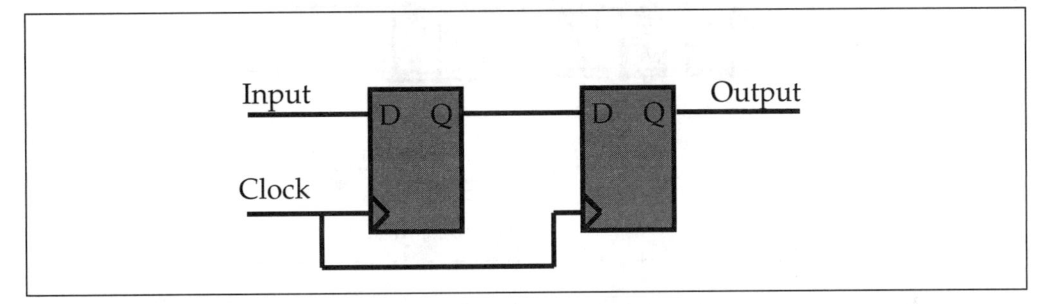

The place where the risk of metastability exists in a SAS receiver is in the Elastic Buffer, because that's where the incoming data is clocked with the receiver's local clock. Designers may wish to implement another register stage in the elastic buffer to protect against this problem. Discussions with SAS designers at the time of this writing indicated that they expected the typical size of a SAS elastic buffer to be around 4 entries deep.

Elastic Buffer Design

The standard does not give design details regarding the size and design of the elastic buffer, leaving it as a vendor-specific implementation. An illustration of how this might be implemented is shown in Figure 12-4, where the goal is to always keep the buffer half full using the incoming data stream. If the local clock is running faster, after a certain time the last entry in the buffer will get clocked out before another dword arrives at the receiver. If the next local clock arrives before incoming data arrives, the buffer will have no data to give and an underflow condition results. The solution is simply to recognize this condition and insert an ALIGN primitive into the dword stream instead of the expected data. As mentioned earlier, ALIGNs are ignored by the rest of the receiver logic, so there is no harm in adding them to the incoming stream.

Figure 12-4: Elastic Buffer Example

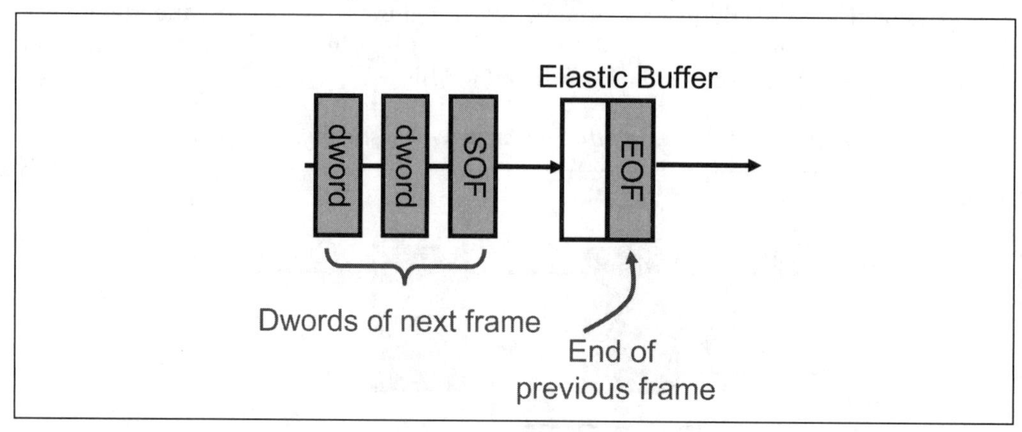

If the local clock were instead running slower, then the buffer might become full and have another dword come in before one is clocked out to make space for it, resulting in an overflow condition. The solution for this case is for the sender to include the throw-away ALIGN primitives that can be discarded when needed at the receiver to reduce the incoming dword flow.

An example of this situation is shown in Figure 12-5. Here, dwords are clocked into the elastic buffer with the Recovered Rx Clock, whose edges are represented by down arrows on the top row. The same data is then clocked out of the buffer with the Local Rx Clock, whose edges are shown by the arrows on the bottom row.

Figure 12-5: Clock Skew Example

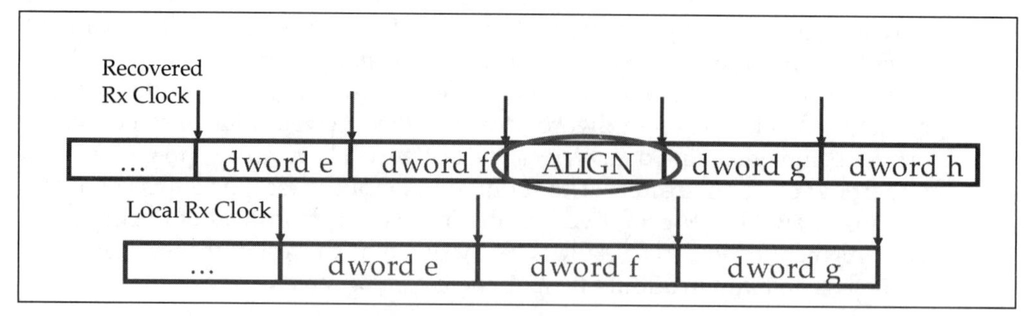

In the example, after "dword f" is clocked in and then out, the clocks happen to line up so that the next dword gets clocked in but does not get clocked out before the next incoming dword arrives, as highlighted by the circled area. The buffer in Figure 12-4 can tolerate this happening once, but not more than that, so if were to happen repeatedly, the buffer will overflow. To guard against this, a control block needs to observe that the second stage of the buffer has been filled and search for the next ALIGN primitive to remove. Removing a primitive from the buffer immediately frees up a register and the buffer is once more back to a half-full condition.

One thing that makes elastic buffer design both simpler and smaller in SAS as compared to some other serial transports is that the ALIGN primitives can be injected at any point in the stream. Transmitters are not required to wait for frame boundaries, for example, and can inject ALIGNs within data blocks or at any time. That means the time between instances of sending ALIGNs can be consistent because it doesn't depend on the sequence of dwords in a frame. That mean the elastic buffer can be made smaller, because the time between ALIGNs is relatively small.

Justification for an Elastic Buffer

A question might arise as to whether SAS receivers need a sophisticated elastic buffer design if the standard requires that the ALIGN primitives be injected by the transmitter at a high enough rate. The standard does not give any real guidelines about elastic buffer design, so designers have complete freedom in their implementations to do whatever works best for a particular design. For discussion, though, consider that SAS has a maximum allowed clock variation of +/- 100ppm (literally 100 parts out of a million or 0.01%). The worst-case separation between neighboring devices is thus 200ppm, if they both vary by the maximum amount in opposite directions. That amount corresponds to a gain or loss of one clock every 5000 clocks (1/0.0002). For the lower clock rate of 1.5 Gb/s the standard requires that ALIGN primitives be injected at a rate of 1 out of every 2048 dwords. Since the internal logic latches one dword on every clock edge, there would be more than twice the number needed to avoid gaining or losing a clock.

However, at the higher rate of 3.0 Gb/s the rate of ALIGNs is 2 out of 4096, which could legally be 2 ALIGNs followed by 4094 other dwords. That would still leave some margin to maintain proper operation, but not as much. However, since the ALIGN characters themselves could suffer corruption in flight and not be recognized at the receiver, there could be more than 5000 dwords between ALIGNs at the receiver, even if they were properly injected at the transmitter. In general then, it makes sense that SAS receivers should implement an elastic buffer with the capability for handling both overflow and underflow to provide for robust operation. For more on clock management, refer to the discussion in the Phy Layer called "Clock Management Primitives" on page 367.

CRC Generation and Checking

In a serial transport, even a single-bit failure can cause an entire frame to be misinterpreted, possibly resulting in a system destabilizing event. To guard against this possibility, a means of robustly checking for errors in serial transmission is required. While many error-checking schemes exist, by far the most popular option is referred to as CRC (Cyclic Redundancy Check or Cyclic Redundancy Code). CRCs are hash functions that are popular because they are simple to implement, easy to analyze mathematically, and are good at detecting common errors caused by noise in transmission. Using this method, the transmitter performs a mathematical operation on the outgoing dwords to create a 32-bit result which is appended at the end of the frame. This calculation, which uses a well understood mathematical algorithm and is clearly delineated in the standard, creates many bit changes in the CRC value in response to small changes in the payload. Adding this information to the frame helps ensure that any changes from the original pattern will be easily detected at the receiver. Note that primitives are not considered part of the payload and are therefore not involved in CRC calculations.

Figure 12-6 on page 307 illustrates a few interesting aspects about the generation of the CRC. First, note that primitives are muxed into the data stream at the end, so they are not included in the CRC calculation (and are not scrambled). All the other dwords are both sampled for CRC generation and scrambled to reduce repetitive patterns. Also note that, for SSP and SMP frames, the bit order of each byte in every dword is transposed going into the CRC generator and then the result has the bits transposed back to the original bit order afterwards, and then the whole result is inverted. The standard is careful to point this out because STP handles it differently, foregoing the bit transposing step and the inversion of the CRC result (see Chapter 19, entitled "SATA Support," on page 429). In addition, since SAS devices operate on dwords in big-endian order, STP connections require that the byte order be transposed at the end to make the dwords byte-wise little-endian the way SATA expects them to be.

Figure 12-6: SSP and SMP Transmitter CRC Generation

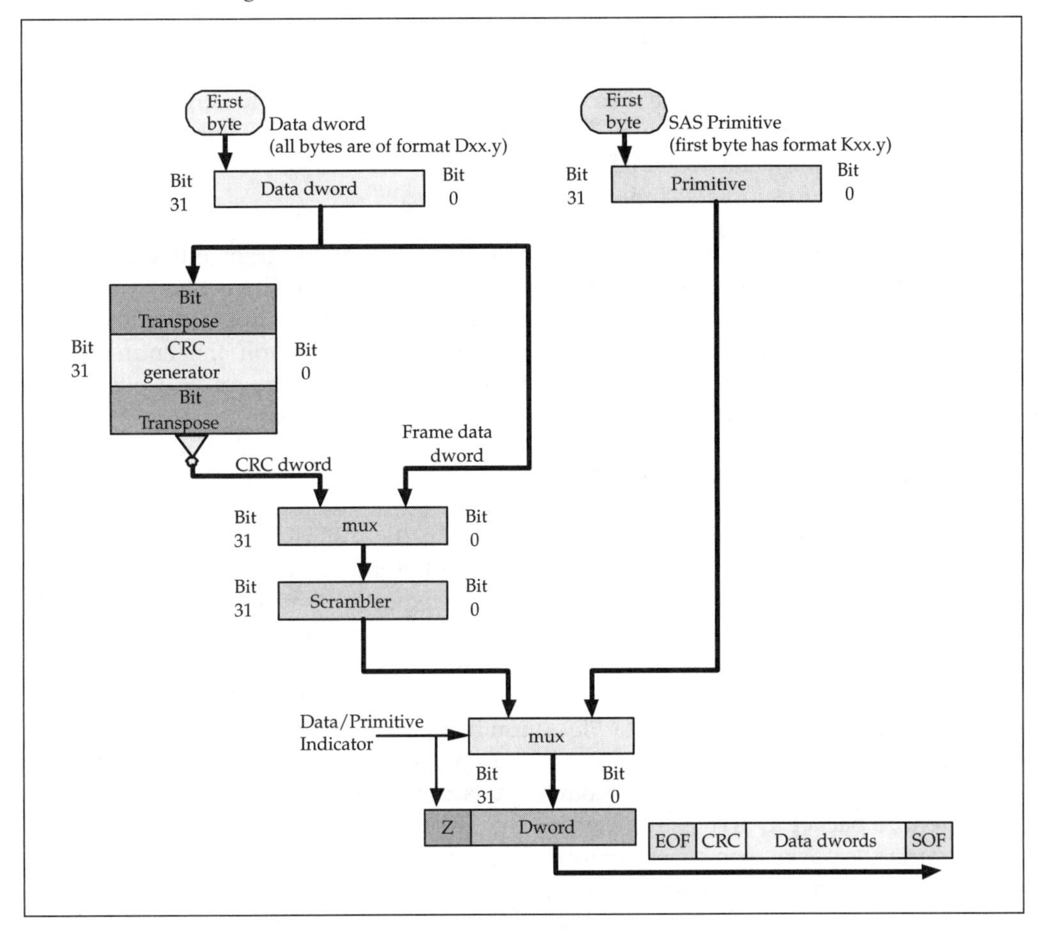

Finally, note that an indicator bit (labeled with the letter Z in the standard and used the same way here) is also appended to each dword at the end to signify whether or not the outgoing dword is a primitive. The reason is that control characters have a different 8b/10b encoding than data bytes with the same bit pattern, so the 8b/10b logic in the Phy Layer needs to know which it is. Any character could be a control character, which would mean we'd need an indicator bit for each character separately, but it's sufficient to just mark the dword overall because the only place control characters can legally appear in SAS is at the beginning of a primitive. The standard doesn't explicitly state the meaning of the Z bit, but infers that a dword is a primitive when it's set (like the K indicator for a control character) and a data dword when it's not set.

Incoming Frames

For incoming frames, the receiver evaluates the attached CRC and verifies that it correctly matches the expected value for this frame. The standard does not specify a particular scheme, so implementation will be vendor specific, but there are two simple techniques for doing this:

1. The receiver simply duplicates the process that the transmitter used and regenerates the CRC based on the frame without the CRC value, then compares the received CRC with the locally generated version.
2. The receiver performs the mathematical operation on the entire frame including the received CRC and then confirms that the result is always an expected constant value.

Implementation Methods

This provides an opportunity for discussing the differences between the way the CRC checking may be handled for different devices. For example, SSP frames cannot be larger than 1KB, and it's expected that SAS hard drives will choose to buffer up the entire frame and verify the CRC before taking action, such as committing the data to the media. This requires a large input buffer space and adds cost to the design, but provides better reliability. In contrast, STP data frames (called data FISes) can be up to 8KB in size. SATA drives, ever cost conscious, are not expected to implement receive buffers of that size. Instead, they may choose to commit data to the media without waiting on the entire packet to arrive. That means they won't be able to verify the CRC until after the packet has been largely written to the disk, which could make for less robust operation, but will enable lower cost.

Robust Error Detection

For any of the protocols, if a CRC error is detected, the entire frame is discarded by the recipient because the CRC does not include sufficient information to correct the error or resolve which bits were changed. Since the error cannot be corrected at the receiver, any recovery attempt will require that the frame be replayed, and that requires that notification be returned to the sender. For SSP frames, a NAK (CRC ERROR) response from the receiver provides that error indication. For an SMP request or response frame received with a CRC error, a BREAK primitive is sent to begin closing the connection. Since an SMP connection only consists of one request and one response, a BREAK indicates that there was trouble with the transmission. When the sender learns that an error has occurred, the decision about what to do in response is made at higher levels, such as the Transport and Application Layers.

Error Coverage

The error coverage provided by the CRC is based on the number of dwords that are transmitted in a given frame. The reason is that the Hamming distance, defined as the number of bits that would have to change to convert one valid value into another valid value, is a function of the number of bits that are being sent, as shown in Table 12-1. Consequently, smaller frames will have a larger Hamming distance while larger frames will have a smaller Hamming distance. For the worst case STP frame, with 8KB of data, the best Hamming distance is 4. That means that all 2-bit and 3-bit errors will be detected, but a 4-bit error could convert one valid frame into another. There are slightly more than 1 out of 2^{32} possible 4-bit errors that would be undetectable.

Table 12-1: CRC Coverage

Hamming distance	Number of bits in the frame
15	8 to 10
14	-
13	-
12	11 to 12
11	13 to 21
10	22 to 34
9	35 to 57
8	58 to 91
7	92 to 171
6	172 to 268
5	269 to 2974
4	**2975 to 91,607**
3	91,608 to more than 131,072

To learn more about CRC coverage and implementations, useful references include 32-Bit Cyclic Redundancy Codes for Internet Applications, by Philip Koopman, and the corresponding website at http://www.ece.cmu.edu/~koopman/networks/dsn02/dsn02_koopman.pdf.

Scrambling

The next aspect to consider in preparing data for serial transmission is the scrambling of outgoing dwords. This is another common technique in serial transports and its purpose is simply to reduce the EMI that could otherwise be caused by repetitive patterns on the link. SAS currently has no mechanism that would allow a transmitter to be turned off so, when SAS links are not being actively used for a connection, the transmitters just send idle dwords. These dwords are always the same and there is nothing to prevent them from being repeated over a long period of time, which could result in unacceptable noise being generated on the link.

To avoid this problem, scrambling imposes a pseudo-random pattern onto the outgoing data stream at the transmitter, and the receiver uses the same algorithm to unscramble the data at the other end. All data dwords for both SAS and SATA are scrambled, while primitives are not. The astute reader may then ask, "If primitives are not scrambled, couldn't the same situation come up in which a long string of primitives is being transmitted?" The answer is that it could. For SSP and SMP connections, this is handled by using slightly different versions of primitives to mean the same thing, thereby allowing a mix of primitives to be understood as though they were a single continued primitive. The primitive used for this purpose is ALIGN, and to allow it to be sent continuously without actually repeating, there are four versions of it: ALIGN(0), ALIGN(1), ALIGN(2), and ALIGN(3). When the bus is idle the transmitter can cycle through these versions, which have different encodings but all mean the same thing. (SATA uses a different scheme, which is described in the section titled "Continued primitives" on page 470.)

At the receiver, all the scrambled dwords have to be unscrambled to make sense of them. This is actually easier than it sounds, because the pattern imposed on the data is known and does not involve any feedback in transmission, which means that misinterpreting a character will not foul up the descrambling for all the following characters. In addition, rather than let the scrambler run continuously, it gets reset to its initial value every time an SOF or SOAF primitive appears. Consequently, even if an error causes the descrambling to get out of sync, the next SOF or SOAF will restore it. Primitives are not scrambled so there is no danger of a mix-up causing the SOF or SOAF to be unrecognized.

Scrambler Implementation

The implementation of the scrambler is described in the standard as a 16-bit linear feedback shift register (LFSR) that is initialized to FFFFh and which implements the following polynomial: $G(x) = X^{16} + X^{15} + X^{13} + X^4 + 1$. After initialization, every subsequent dword will generate the next pseudo-random output that is then XORed with the data to scramble it. Since the scrambler polynomial is only 16 bits, the first output is applied to the lower 16 bits of the dword, and then the next output is applied to the upper 16 bits of the dword. To make implementation of this design easier, Annex F of the SAS standard shows a scrambler implementation example that uses two 16-bit multipliers, as repeated here in Figure 12-7 for convenience. Annex F also provides a C program that can be used to generate the scrambled data dwords for transmission.

Figure 12-7: Scrambler Implementation Example

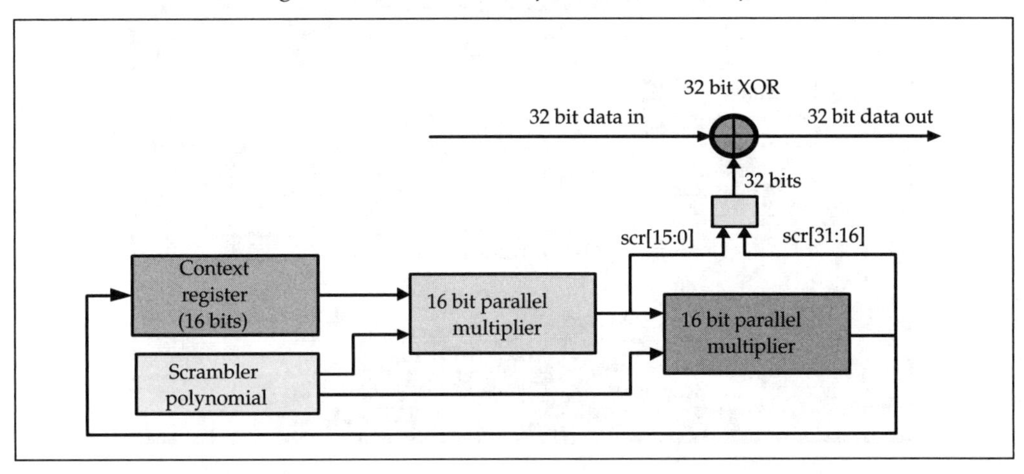

A hypothetical receiver implementation is shown in Figure 12-8 on page 312. As a reminder, the standard does not tightly define layer boundaries or responsibilities. That gives freedom for designers to create proprietary solutions in the SAS design, but also means there is no specific recommended implementation. In the example here, the input to the Link Layer passes first through the descrambler and then into one of several buffers. Multiple buffers are shown because a SAS frame can contain only 1KB at most, but a receiver could have several of them available for incoming frames. The availability of each buffer space is communicated with RRDY primitives sent to the transmitter.

The CRC is evaluated at the end of each frame, and a failure would cause a NAK to be sent to the transmitter to indicate the status. When the frame arrives into the buffers of the Link Layer, the Transport Layer is informed that the frame needs to be fetched.

Figure 12-8: Example Receiver Implementation

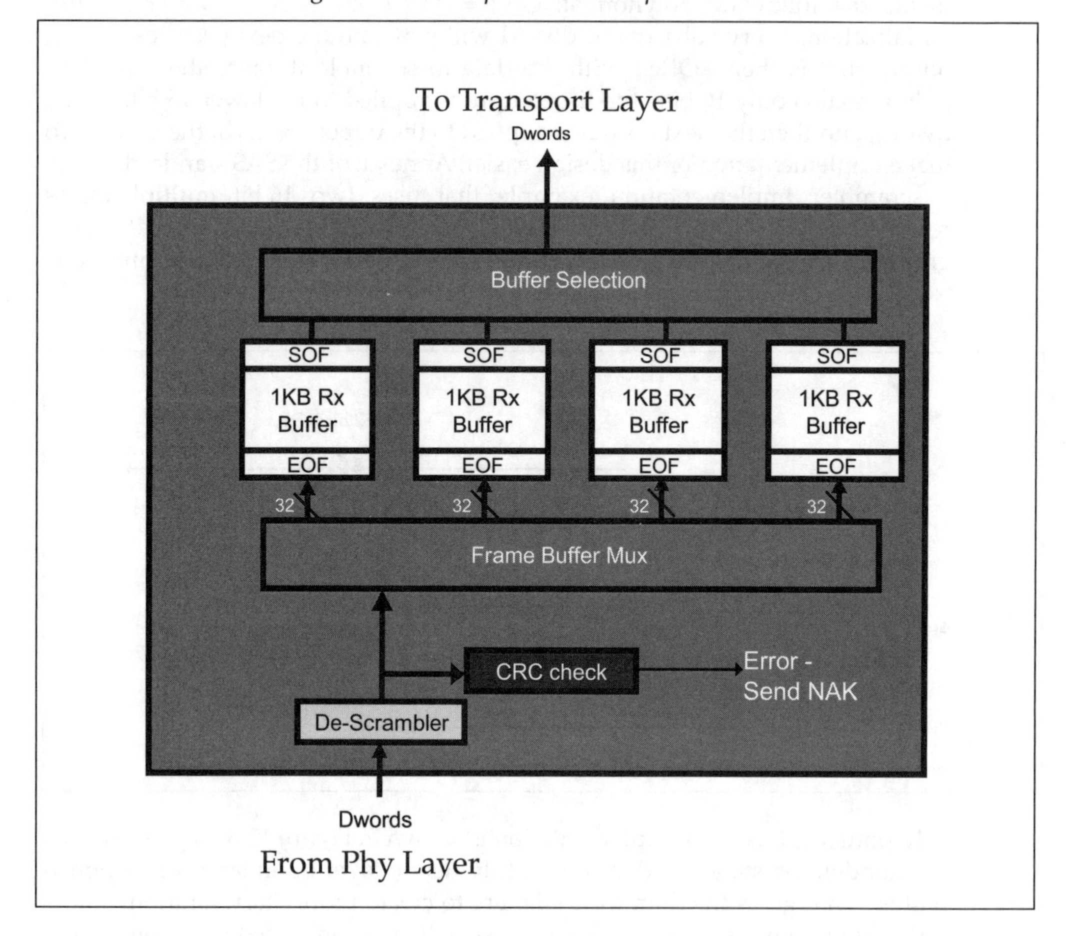

13 Link Layer - Connection Management

The Previous Chapter

The previous chapter covered Link Layer Serial Support, and described the various aspects of preparing dwords for serial transmission. These include the generation and checking of the CRC to verify data integrity, scrambling and descrambling to prevent repeated patterns on the link, and compensation for the slight frequency variations between transmitter and receiver clocks.

This Chapter

This chapter describes the second sub-block of the Link Layer - connection management. This involves the steps for opening a new connection across a SAS topology, maintaining that connection with flow control and ACK/NAK protocol, and then closing the connection when it's no longer needed or has timed out.

The Next Chapter

The third of the specific Link Layer chapters explores how competing connection requests are arbitrated within expanders. This includes deciding between requests competing for the same resources and handling deadlock or livelock conditions in a non-trivial system.

Introduction

To communicate, devices on a SAS network must establish connections that permit them to temporarily take control of a path through the network in order to exchange frames. The frames themselves are requested and constructed at higher levels, but the protocol on the link used to send and receive them is a Link Layer responsibility. The Link Layer tasks involved in meeting these responsibilities include management of the following:

- Opening and Closing a Connection
- SSP ACK/NAK Protocol
- SSP Flow Control
- STP OK/ERR Protocol
- STP Flow Control
- STP Affiliations
- SMP Protocol

This chapter focuses on the opening and closing of connections. Because they are specific to the protocol being used for the connection, the rest of these topics are described in Chapter 15, entitled "Link Layer - Protocol Differences," on page 345.

Opening a Connection

For this discussion, recall that a connection is a temporary association between two SAS device Phys. Transactions are sent to specific addresses, but a connection is actually established between two available Phys. Consequently, a wide port with more than one Phy can establish more than one connection at the same time.

Frames for all three protocols supported by SAS are managed at the Link Layer, which coordinates the process of sending or receiving them on the link. When the Port Layer queues up a transmission request, it checks to see whether a connection to the destination address is already active. If not, a connection request is sent to the Link Layer of an available phy. The Link Layer then begins the process of opening the connection, and that starts with the construction of the OPEN address frame. The details of this frame were discussed in an earlier chapter, but the frame format is repeated here in Table 13-1 on page 316 for convenience (refer to Table 11-1 on page 278 for a description of each field in this frame). An example of the basic protocol is shown in the trace capture of Figure 13-1 on page 315, using an HBA connected directly to a SAS drive. The capture shows an OPEN frame with the parameters it used and an OPEN_ACCEPT returned by the target drive.

Figure 13-1: Simple OPEN Address Frame and Response

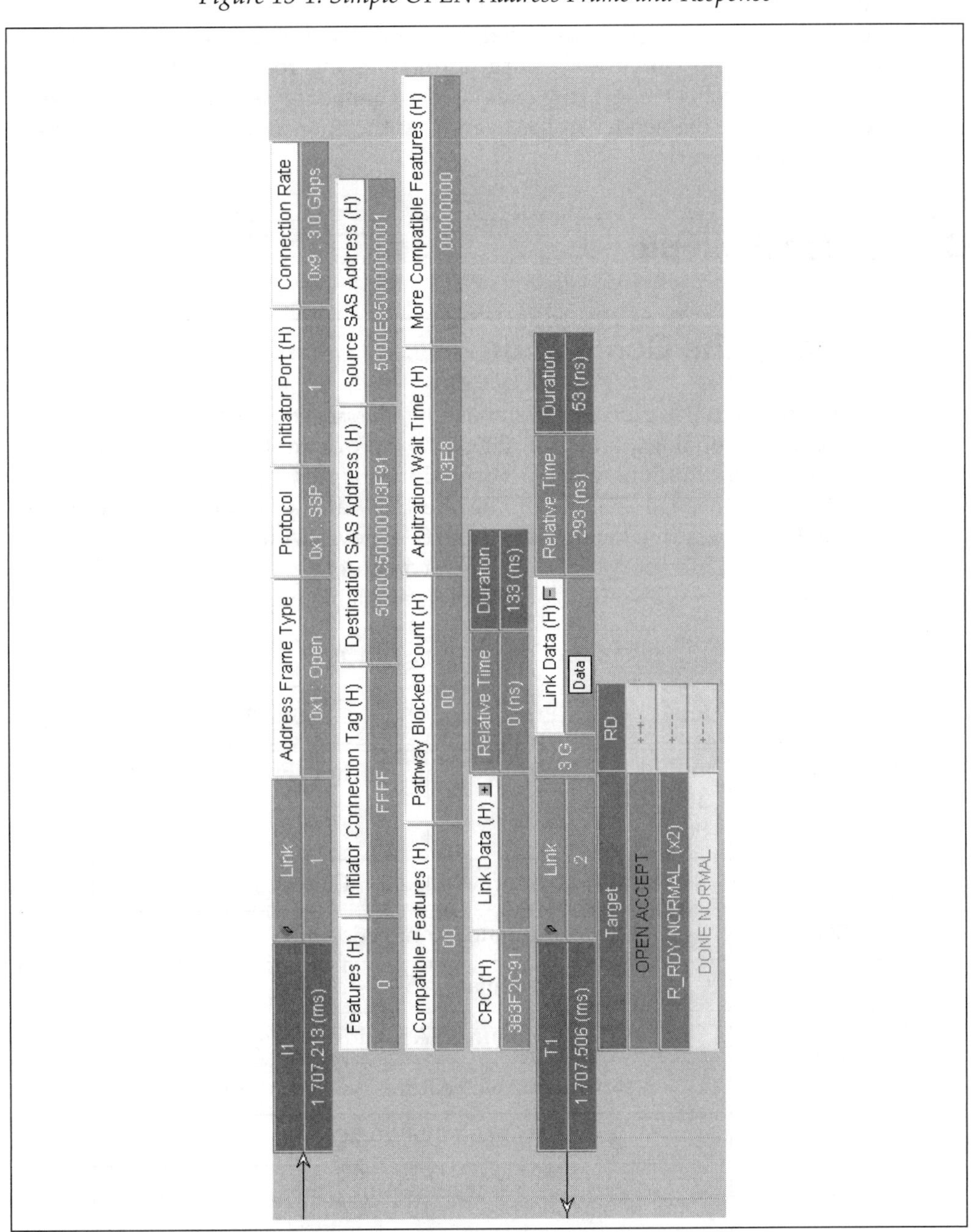

The OPEN address frame, which can only be sent when the link is idle, specifies the destination address for the connection and provides several fields, such as Arbitration Wait Time, that are used to resolve any arbitration issues. The sender's source address is included, too, both as another factor in arbitration decisions and to provide a return address to the receiver. That allows the receiver to establish the I_T Nexus of the connection and thus to be able to reconnect with the sender in the event that the connection needs to be closed and reopened later.

Connection Example

Opening the Connection

To step through the process of establishing a connection, consider an example based on the topology shown in Figure 13-2. For simplicity, this example will not consider arbitration, which is covered in Chapter 14, entitled "Link Layer - Arbitration," on page 333. Assuming the HBA at the bottom of the drawing wishes to send a frame to fetch data from SAS device A in the network, the Link Layer in the HBA port will begin by constructing and sending an OPEN address frame (see Table 13-1) on one of its available phys.

Table 13-1: OPEN Address Frame

Byte	Bit 7	Bits 6 - 4	Bits 3 - 0
0	Initi-ator Port	Protocol	Address Frame Type = 1
1	Features (= 0 for now)		Connection Rate
2 to 3	Initiator Connection Tag		
4 to 11	Destination SAS Address		
12 to 19	Source SAS Address		
20	Compatible Features (= 0 for now)		
21	Pathway Blocked Count		
22 to 23	Arbitration Wait Time		

Table 13-1: OPEN Address Frame

Byte	Bit 7	Bits 6 - 4	Bits 3 - 0
24 to 27	More Compatible Features (= 0 for now)		
28 to 31	CRC		

Figure 13-2: Connection Example Topology

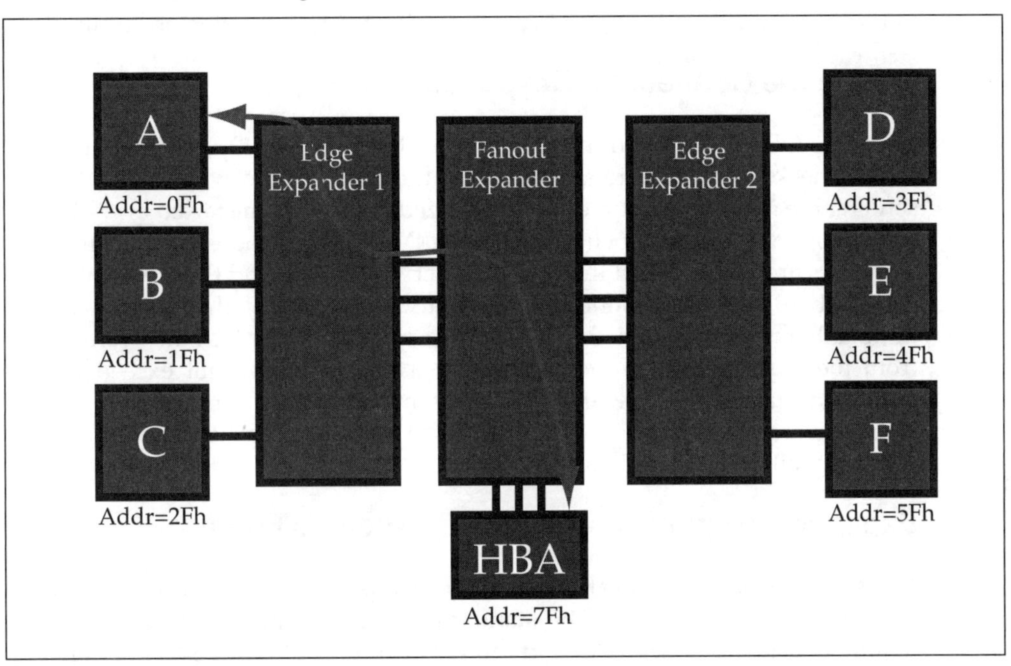

The fields for the OPEN frame used to establish this connection are described in the text that follows.

Initiator Port: Set to one because the HBA port is acting as an initiator.

Protocol: Set to SSP (001b) because a SAS device is being targeted.

Address Frame Type: Set to one to indicate that this is an OPEN address frame.

Connection Rate: Assuming the device is 3.0GHz capable, this is set to 9h.

Initiator Connection Tag: This optional value is used for quick lookup of the transaction context in the event the connection is closed and reopened later by the destination. The target device should memorize this value for that purpose.

Destination SAS Address: The 64-bit SAS address for device A is shown, for simplicity, as 0Fh, and that will be the destination address for the OPEN address frame.

Source SAS Address: This is shown in the example as 7Fh.

Pathway Blocked Count and **Arbitration Wait Time** will be set to zero. The use of these fields will be described in more detail later in the section on Arbitration.

Timing the Connection Response

Once this OPEN address frame is sent, the HBA starts an Open Timeout timer, which checks to make sure a response to the OPEN is received within 1ms of sending the request. This timer is reinitialized to zero and restarted every time a valid response is seen, such as AIP (NORMAL) from the expander. If valid responses are not seen within 1ms, the timer will expire, and the HBA will send a BREAK to abort the connection request. Another timer that the HBA may optionally implement is the I_T Nexus Loss timer to verify that the overall time from the request until the connection is established does not exceed a programmed maximum. This timer has more meaning for a target device that is trying to reconnect with an initiator to return data for an earlier request, but initiators are allowed to implement it, too.

Expander Responses to an OPEN Address Frame

The fanout expander indicates that it has accepted the connection request by returning AIP (NORMAL). The standard mentions that future versions may require expanders to send AIPs in groups of three, but doing so is optional at this point. Until the expander forwards the connection request out on the selected Phy, it must keep sending AIP (NORMAL) periodically to keep the requester from timing out. (at least one AIP out of every 128 dwords on the link). When the request has been forwarded on the selected Phy, the expander returns AIP (WAITING ON DEVICE) just one time. After that, the expander no longer sends AIPs but just passively forwards responses from the next level of devices. The full list of responses that an expander can send is given in Table 13-2 below. Note that all of the AIPs may be sent multiple times except for AIP (WAITING ON DEVICE), which is only sent once. The AIPs are sent until the request has been routed to the destination, at which point the expanders simply pass the response from the destination device back to the original requester.

As can be seen in Table 13-2, there are also several reasons why an expander might reject a connection request. In general, there are two categories of OPEN_REJECT: problems that are temporary and for which the request can be retried, and those that cannot be retried and must be abandoned. For expanders, all of the reject cases except Bad Destination can be retried.

Table 13-2: List of Expander Responses to a Connection Request

Response	Description
AIP (NORMAL)	Expander has accepted the connection request (the request is making progress).
AIP (Reserved 0)	Reserved, but processed the same as AIP (Normal).
AIP (Reserved 1)	Reserved, but processed the same as AIP (Normal).
AIP (Reserved 2)	Reserved, but processed the same as AIP (Normal).
AIP (WAITING ON CONNECTION)	Expander has determined the routing, but either the destination phys are all in use, or there are insufficient resources to complete the request.
AIP (WAITING ON DEVICE)	Expander has determined the routing and forwarded the request to the output phy. This is only sent once.
AIP (WAITING ON PARTIAL)	Expander has determined the routing, but the destination phys are all busy with other partial pathways (connection requests that have not yet reached the destination phy). This may indicate a deadlock condition; see the Link Layer chapter on Arbitration for more information about resolving potential deadlock conditions.
AIP (Reserved WAITING ON PARTIAL)	Reserved, but processed the same as AIP (Waiting on Partial).
OPEN_REJECT (BAD DESTINATION)	If the request would have to be routed back to the same expander port on which it arrived, and the expander has not chosen to return OPEN_REJECT (No Destination), then this would be the response. This is the only OPEN_REJECT by an expander that conveys the meaning that this request should be abandoned rather than retried.

Table 13-2: List of Expander Responses to a Connection Request

Response (Continued)	Description (Continued)
OPEN_REJECT (NO DESTINATION)	Either: a) No such destination Phy exists, or b) The request would have to be routed back to the same expander port on which it arrived, and the expander has not chosen to return OPEN_REJECT (Bad Destination), or c) An STP device is targeted, but it's initial Register - Device to Host FIS has not yet been received.
OPEN_REJECT (CONNECTION RATE NOT SUPPORTED)	If none of the destination phys support the rate requested, an expander reports it with this response.
OPEN_REJECT (PATHWAY BLOCKED)	The expander reports that the pathway was blocked by higher-priority requests.
OPEN_REJECT (WAITING FOR BREAK)	Indicates the expander is waiting to receive a BREAK response from the requesting Phy and will not accept a new request until then.

While the fanout expander returns AIP (NORMAL) periodically, it sorts out the routing of the request to the destination address. Fanout expanders have a table that contains every address in the network, and in this case it finds that the request should be routed to the port which is attached to edge expander 1 (see Figure 13-3 on page 321).

Figure 13-3: Edge Expander Returns AIP

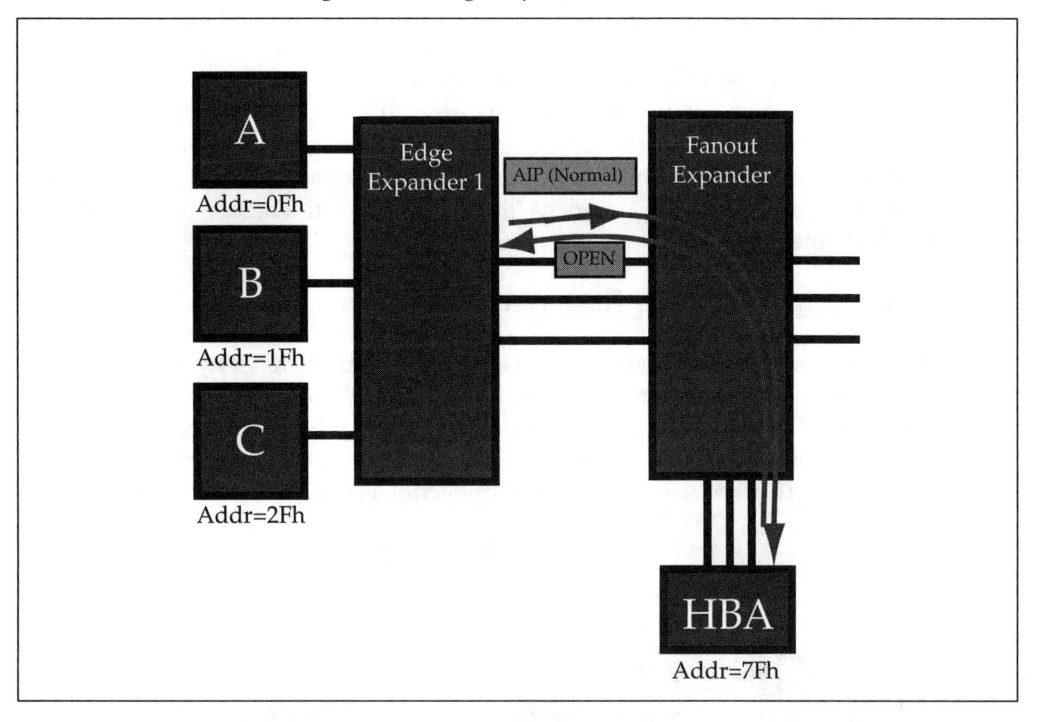

To accomplish this, an OPEN address frame with the same information as the original is sent over one of the available links to that expander. When that happens, the fanout expander switches from regularly sending AIP (NORMAL) and sends AIP (WAITING ON DEVICE) just one time to indicate that it has forwarded the request and is now just passively forwarding responses that come back to it. At that point, the connection is tentatively established over the pathway from the HBA through the fanout expander, and the responses that now arrive at the HBA will be those that are sent by the next device.

Edge expander 1 receives the request and indicates acceptance of it by repeatedly sending AIP (NORMAL), which the fanout expander passively forwards back to the HBA. Recall that edge expanders have three methods for finding an address: it may be directly connected, or the address may be found in the address lookup table, or there may be a subtractive port that is the destination if the address is not found by either of the other two methods. For this example it's not important which method is used, but the destination address is determined to be device A. The Phy attached to device A is not currently busy, so the request is forwarded to that Phy by sending the same OPEN address frame to it. When the request has been forwarded, Edge Expander 1 returns AIP (WAITING ON DEVICE) once and the connection is now tentatively established through this device as well.

When device A receives the connection request, it first verifies that all aspects of the request are supported. For example, since it is a target device, it is acceptable to receive a request from an initiator. Another qualifier might be the source address, since some devices may be programmed to accept requests only from certain initiators and not others. A third parameter to check would be that it supports the requested connection rate.

Accepting the OPEN Request

Assuming all the qualifiers are acceptable and that this Phy has not been instructed to reject incoming connection requests, the device would respond with an OPEN_ACCEPT primitive to complete the connection (see Figure 13-4). That response is forwarded through Edge Expander 1 and the fanout expander back to the HBA, confirming that this connection is valid and will remain active.

Figure 13-4: OPEN_ACCEPT Returned by Target Device

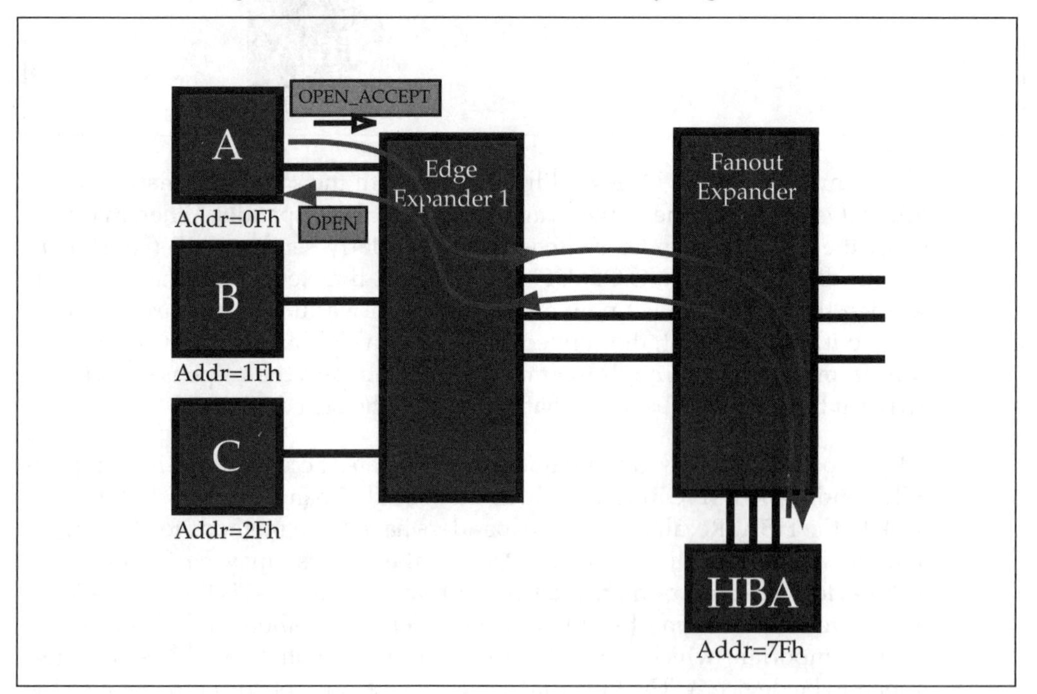

The HBA now knows that the connection to the target device is working and will serve as a dedicated transmission medium between the two devices. At this point frames can be sent in both directions at the same time as needed. There are a number of possible responses from the target device, of course, and the full list appears in Table 13-3 below.

Table 13-3: List of Destination Phy Responses to a Connection Request

Response	Description
OPEN_ACCEPT	Phy supports and accepts the requested connection.
OPEN_REJECT (CONNECTION RATE NOT SUPPORTED)	Phy doesn't support the requested rate.
OPEN_REJECT (PROTOCOL NOT SUPPORTED)	Phy doesn't support the requested initiator/target role, protocol, initiator connection tag, or features specified in the request.
OPEN_REJECT (WRONG DESTINATION)	The destination address in the OPEN address frame doesn't match the SAS address of the port that received the request.
OPEN_REJECT (STP RESOURCES BUSY)	This STP target port has an affiliation with another initiator, or all the task file registers have been allocated to other STP initiator ports. If this request was routed to an STP device by mistake, this response will be understood by the requester as OPEN_REJECT (Wrong Destination).
OPEN_REJECT (RETRY)	Either: a) The Phy is unable to accept connections, or b) The Phy is currently waiting on a response to a BREAK. Note that this is the only reject from a destination Phy that can be retried. All of the other rejections mean the request is to be abandoned.

Sending Frames

Our example connection is now ready to transmit frames, but before that can happen the devices must indicate their readiness to receive them by sending an RRDY primitive. This indicates that the device can accept one frame with up to 1KB of data. The target device must send at least one RRDY; in fact, it must not accept the connection at all unless it is able to receive at least one frame. For initiators, sending RRDY is optional, but it's often done when the connection is opened because the target may have data frames to return from an earlier command or some other communication. The RRDYs are counted as they are received, so it is possible to indicate a readiness to receive several frames and thus a large amount of data, even though it will be in 1KB increments.

Closing the Connection

Assume now that the HBA sends a SCSI Read command to device A, and that it will take device A some time to fetch the data. Rather than leave the connection open and tie up system resources while there is nothing to send, device A may choose to close the connection and reopen it later when the data is ready. To begin the process of closing down the connection, device A sends a DONE (NORMAL) primitive, indicating that it will not send any more frames, and starts the DONE Timeout counter to check for a DONE coming back within 1ms. The expanders forward the DONE to the HBA, which recognizes that device A is not going to send any more frames, although it will still send ACK/NAK, RRDY, and CREDIT_BLOCKED primitives. If the HBA still has frames to send, it is allowed to do so, and the DONE Timeout counter will be reinitialized every time a frame is received, but device A will not send any more frames. Interestingly, if the state machine that controls this process (SSP_D) receives notification that the receive credit has been exhausted, the timer is stopped. The reason for waiting is to give the other device in the connection a chance to respond with DONE (CREDIT TIMEOUT).

The standard describes a potential race condition regarding the DONE timeout. In our example, suppose device A had sent a DONE (NORMAL) and then the HBA sent a series of non-interlocked frames. If one of those frames had a corrupted SOF, then device A would not recognize it as a frame and would consequently not return the number of ACK/NAKs that the HBA was expecting. The result would be that A stopped sending frames while waiting on DONE, while the HBA stopped sending frames while waiting for another ACK/NAK. Both events have a counter running that has a 1ms timeout, so the counters might expire at the same time. As a result, device A would send a BREAK at the same time the HBA sends a DONE (ACK/NAK TIMEOUT). Fortunately, both of these Link Layer errors are handled the same way, as described in the section titled "Link Layer Errors Affected by Transport Layer" on page 235.

When the HBA is ready to close the connection, it will return a DONE back to device A through the expanders. When device A receives the DONE, it sends a CLOSE (NORMAL) and starts the Close Timeout Timer to verify that a CLOSE is received in response within 1ms. Once a device has both received and sent DONE, it is not required to wait for the CLOSE from the other device before sending CLOSE. Whenever a device has both sent and received the CLOSE primitive, the connection has been completely broken down.

Within the expanders, the arrival of a CLOSE causes a CLOSE to be sent out to the destination phy, and also causes the expander to break down the path in that direction. Nothing more can be sent in that direction on that connection. When the corresponding CLOSE is returned, it has the same effect going the other way, finishing the release of all the resources for this connection within the expander.

Rate Matching

When a connection is established in a system has a mix of rates, some steps will have to be taken to accommodate that. Earlier versions of the SAS standard allowed for a 1.5 Gb/s link rate, but when SATA debuted at 1.5 Gb/s, the designers of SAS were motivated to move to a higher speed. Since SAS was targeting the higher end servers, the focus has moved to the 3.0 Gb/s rate. Higher rates in the future will increase the possibility that a SAS system could end up with a mix of rates. The process used to accommodate different rates in the same system is called rate matching.

To accomplish rate matching, transmitters operating at the 3.0 Gb/s rate must add one ALIGN or NOTIFY primitive, which are logically equivalent for this purpose, for every dword they send. The result is that half of their bandwidth is consumed with primitives. Consider the example shown in Figure 13-5 on page 326. The slower receivers remove the extra primitives, as shown in Figure 13-6 on page 326. For this example, the transmitter for C will add the extra primitives, and Expander 1 will remove them and send the data at the slower rate on the link between the expanders. When the fanout expander forwards the dwords to the HBA it must insert the extra primitives again to compensate for the fact that this outgoing link is running at twice the rate of the incoming data. When the frame finally reaches the HBA, the extra primitives are ignored, just as they would normally be when used for things like clock compensation. This results in reduced performance on the links that were capable of faster operation, but allows mixing older and newer parts in the same system.

Figure 13-5: Rate Matching Scenario

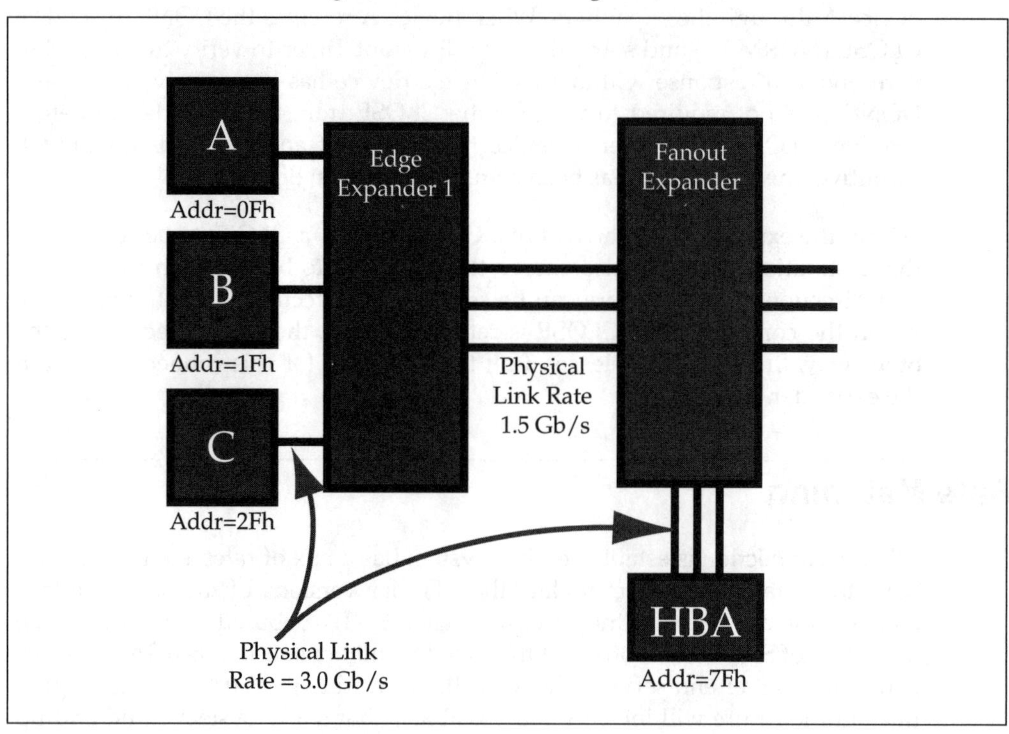

Figure 13-6: Rate Matching Dwords

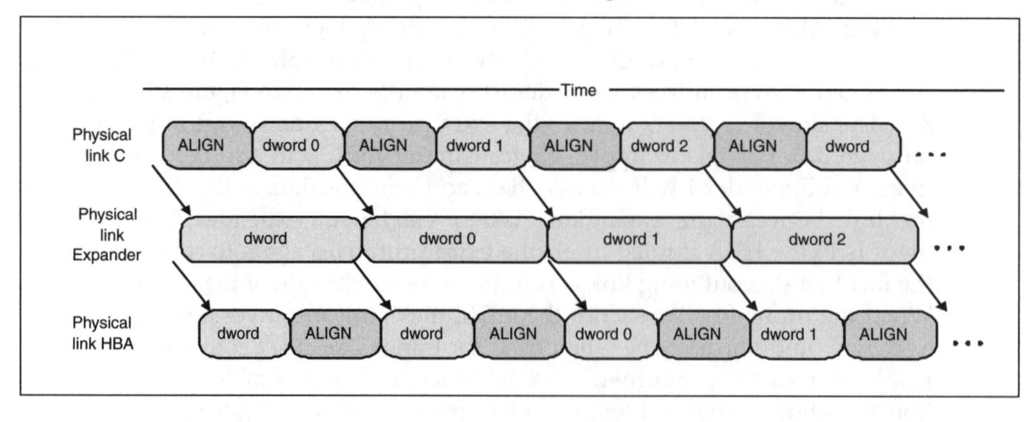

Link Layer State Machines

Having looked at the broad view of how an SSP example works, let's now consider the underlying details by exploring the state machines by which the standard defines the Link Layer behavior. There are several state machines defined, as listed below:

- XL (eXpander Link Layer)
- SL_IR (SAS Link Identification and Reset)
- SL_RA (SAS Link Receive open Address frame)
- SL_CC (SAS Link Connection Control)
- SSP_TF (Transmit Frame control)
- SSP Receive - there are 5 state machines associated with frame reception:
  1. SSP_RF (Receive Frame control)
  2. SSP_RCM (Receive frame Credit Monitor)
  3. SSP_RIM (Receive Interlocked frame Monitor)
  4. SSP_TC (Transmit Credit control)
  5. SSP_TAN (Transmit ACK/NAK control)
- SMP_IP (SMP Initiator Port)
- SMP_TP (SMP Target Port)

Rather than discuss all of them in one place, it seems more intuitive to cover them in the context where they apply. For example, the SL_IR state machines are described in the section on Identification frames called "Link Layer Overview" on page 273, and the XL state machine is covered in the appendix on "Expander Devices" on page 505. Of the remaining state machines, all but one are protocol-specific and will be described in Chapter 15, entitled "Link Layer - Protocol Differences," on page 345, leaving the SL_RA and SL_CC state machines to be covered here.

All the SL state machines begin operating when they receive an Enable Disable SAS Link (Enable) message from the SL_IR state machine indicating that the link completed the Identification sequence and is ready for use. That process is covered in the section titled, "SL_IR_IRC (Identification and hard Reset Control) State Machine" on page 296.

SL Transmitter and Receiver

The Link Layer state machines exchange messages with two blocks of logic that are called the SL transmitter and SL receiver. These logic blocks actually send or receive the information on the link, but are not described as state machines even though they exchange messages like state machines do.

SL Transmitter

The SL Transmitter receives instructions about what needs to be transmitted in the form of messages from the SL state machines, as listed here:

- Transmit Idle Dword - no frames or primitives are pending
- Transmit SOAF/Data Dwords/EOAF - Address frame
- Transmit OPEN_ACCEPT
- Transmit OPEN_REJECT with an argument that gives the type, such as OPEN_REJECT (RETRY)
- Transmit BREAK
- Transmit BROADCAST
- Transmit CLOSE with an argument that gives the type, such as CLOSE (NORMAL)

If no requests are pending, the transmitter simply sends Idle dwords, but if multiple requests are queued up, they must be handled in a certain priority order, as indicated by the following list, starting with the highest priority:

1. BREAK - a problem has caused this connection to need to be shut down immediately
2. CLOSE - connection is being closed in the ordinary manner
3. OPEN_ACCEPT or REJECT
4. SOAF, or data dword, or EOAF
5. Idle dword

After sending an address frame, the SL transmitter responds with the message: "SOAF/Data dword/EOAF Transmitted".

SL Receiver

The SL Receiver simply takes in the incoming dword stream and passes one of the following messages to the SL state machines about the status of what has been received. Dwords received that somehow don't fall into one of these categories are ignored by the SL Receiver. The messages are:

- SOAF Received
- Data dword Received
- EOAF Received
- BROADCAST Received, with an argument specifying the type, such as BROADCAST Received (CHANGE)

- BREAK Received
- OPEN_ACCEPT Received
- OPEN_REJECT Received, with an argument specifying the type, such as OPEN_REJECT Received (No Destination)
- AIP Received
- CLOSE Received - including an argument specifying the type, such as CLOSE Received (NORMAL)
- ERROR Received
- Invalid Dword Received

SL_RA (Receive open Address frame) State Machine

Like some of the other SAS state machines, this one has the odd quality for a state machine in that it consists of only one state. As such, there are no state transitions, and the behavior is defined solely by the messages it sends and receives. Its function in life is simply to detect incoming OPEN address frames and evaluate them for correctness. To do this, it receives three messages from the SL Receiver:

- SOAF Received
- Data Dword Received
- EOAF Received

After receiving the SOAF Received message, the machine will accept the incoming dwords until it sees an EOAF Received message. At that point, it can evaluate the data dwords to ensure that:

- Exactly 8 data dwords were received between SOAF and EOAF
- The destination address matches the address for this device
- The CRC evaluates correctly

If all the conditions are correctly met, then this machine will send an OPEN Address Frame Received message to the Connection Control state machine (SL_CC0:Idle state and SL_CC1:ArbSel state) and the message will include an argument that contains all the data dwords.

If there is a problem, such as the wrong number of dwords, or another SOAF arrives before an expected EOAF, or an invalid dword, then the address frame is simply discarded and no message is sent.

SL_CC (Connection Control) State Machine

For initiators and targets, the Connection Control state machine acts as the highest level control in the Link Layer and the other state machines exchange messages with it. In the standard, the illustration for this machine takes two pages: one that shows the state transitions and another that highlights the messages sent and received by each state. The state machine is redrawn in Figure 13-7 on page 331 in an effort to make it easier to see the events that cause the transitions between the states. There is clearly too much information to place it all legibly on one page, so this diagram reduces some details to improve readability. It is intended to serve as an aid to understanding the overall operation of the state machine rather than including all the details.

Example: OPEN Request

For example, when an outgoing connection request is received while the machine is in Idle, it results in a transition to the ArbSel state, in which the OPEN address frame is transmitted. If an OPEN_ACCEPT is received to show that the request is accepted by the target, a message is sent to the Port Layer to report that and the next state will be the Connected state. If the request was rejected instead, this state will inform the Port Layer about the reason for the failure, and the next state will be Idle again.

Example: Competing Requests

Another possibility is that, after the OPEN has been sent and the machine is in the ArbSel state, an incoming OPEN is received. If the incoming OPEN has a higher priority than the outgoing one, it will override the outgoing request and the next state becomes the SL_CC2:Selected state. This state will evaluate whether permission has been given to accept incoming requests for the protocol indicated in the request. If it has, and the address, connection rate, and other fields are all acceptable, this state will send an OPEN_ACCEPT and the next state is SL_CC3:Connected. If anything does not match properly or if this protocol has not been given permission, then an OPEN_REJECT is sent and the next state is SL_CC0:Idle.

Figure 13-7: SL_CC - Link Layer Connection Control State Machine

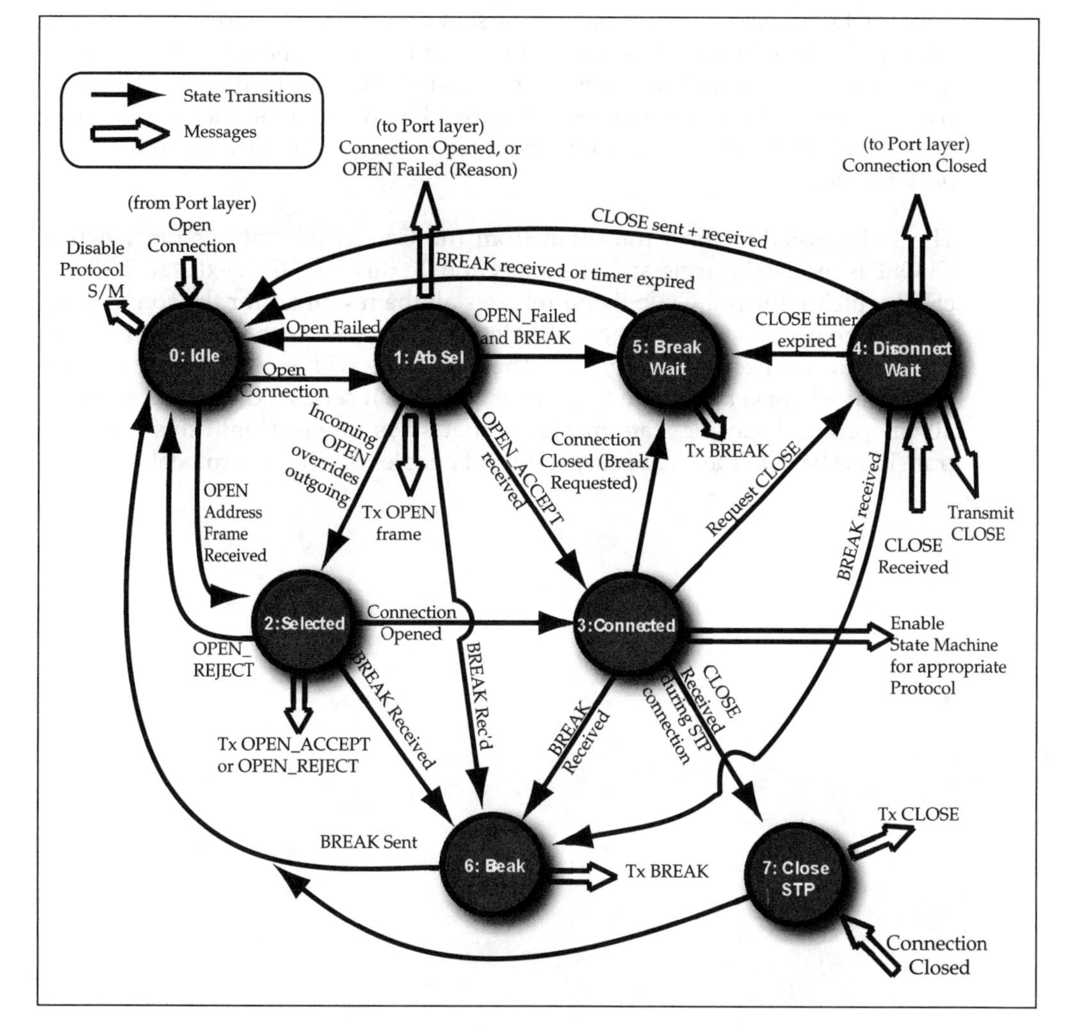

Connected

Once the machine gets to the Connected state, it will send an Enable message to the protocol-specific state machine selected by the OPEN address frame. That enables the appropriate state machines to transmit and receive dwords during a connection, and monitor flow control, ACK/NAK handshakes, and so on. This state continues until something happens to close the connection, such as the receipt of a CLOSE or BREAK primitive. Receipt of a BREAK causes a transition to the Break state, which requests that a BREAK be sent and then transitions to Idle. Receipt of a CLOSE results in a transition to the DisconnectWait state and, once a CLOSE primitive has been both sent and received, a transition to Idle takes place. If something has gone wrong and the device needs to do an emergency close, it transitions this machine from Connected to BreakWait, which requests that a BREAK be sent and waits for a BREAK to come back in response. If a BREAK is received, or if the timeout for it expires, the machine transitions back to Idle.

The last possibility for a transition from the Connected state occurs when a CLOSE is received during an STP connection. In this case, the next state is CloseSTP, which returns a CLOSE and releases all the resources for the connection. There is no need to wait for the SATA device to respond with CLOSE, since it is unaware of connections altogether. The next state will again be back to Idle. Note that whenever the state machine enters Idle it sends a disable message to all the protocol-specific state machines that stays in effect until this machine transitions back to the Connected state and enables one of the protocols.

14 Link Layer - Arbitration

The Previous Chapter

The previous chapter described the process of opening and managing connections for SAS. That includes sending an address frame to request a connection and receiving a response from the target device. Managing the connection includes acknowledging the arrival of frames and handling flow control to guarantee buffer space at the receiver.

This Chapter

This third link-layer-specific chapter explores how competing connection requests are arbitrated within expanders. This includes deciding between requests competing for the same resources and handling deadlock or livelock conditions in a non-trivial system.

The Next Chapter

The last Link Layer chapter explores the differences in Link Layer responsibilities for each protocol, including how they each handle flow control and acknowledgement of frame transmission.

Introduction

When more than one device in a SAS network attempts to establish a connection using the same path resources, there must be a mechanism for arbitrating which device will win. In non-trivial networks there is also the possibility of a deadlock or livelock condition if competing requests end up blocking each other, and the system must have a way to prevent or resolve these as well.

Arbitration Fairness

The factors that are used to determine arbitration fairness are shown in Table 14-1, reproduced from the section on "Arbitration Fairness" on page 512. Rather than repeat parts of that discussion here, let's consider some illustrative examples. First, consider the topology shown in Figure 14-1 on page 335, and assume that the system is idle and then devices A, B, and D all initiate connection requests at the same time. The first thing to happen is that all three will receive AIP (NORMAL) from their nearby expander.

Table 14-1: Expander Phy to ECM Request

Message	Description
Request Path	Request for a connection.
Arguments presented with Request Path	Arguments used for arbitration: **Arbitration Wait Time (AWT)** - how long the request has been waiting to be accepted or rejected **Source SAS Address** - address of initiating device **Connection Rate** - 1.5 Gb/s or 3.0 Gb/s **Retry Priority Status** - set to Ignore AWT when AWT should not be considered for arbitration **Partial Pathway Timeout Status** - maintained by the expander phy, this tracks how long the request has been waiting when all expander phys at the destination port are blocked waiting on partial pathways **Pathway Blocked Count** - number of times this connection has been retried by the originating device due to being rejected with a pathway blocked status

Figure 14-1: Arbitration Example

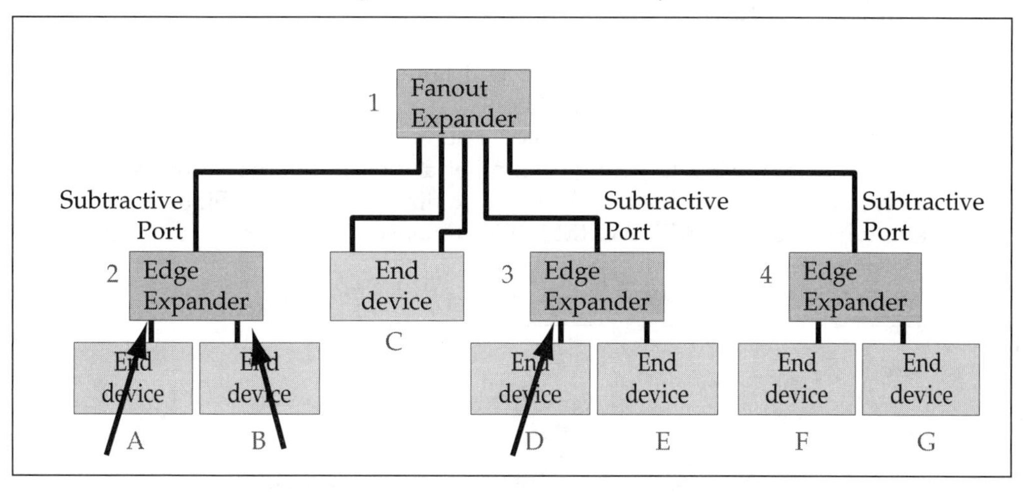

Arbitration Example

Competition for Narrow Port

Assume expander 2 cannot find the destination address for the request from A or the request from B, meaning they should both be routed to its subtractive port. Since that is not a wide port, only one request will be allowed to proceed and arbitration is necessary. The two requests are evaluated based on the contents of the OPEN address frame: first, the AWT (Arbitration Wait Time), then the PBC (Pathway Blocked Count), then the Source SAS address, and finally, the connection rate. Based on this comparison, assume the request from A wins the arbitration and receives AIP (WAITING ON DEVICE) to indicate that the request is making forward progress. Device B will continue to receive AIP (NORMAL) as long as the request that has blocked it is still making progress.

Partial Pathway Timer

If expander 2, after forwarding the request to the fanout expander, receives AIP (WAITING ON PARTIAL) in return, then the Phy handling the request from device B would start the Partial Pathway Timeout counter. If the timer expired, that would cause device B to receive an OPEN_REJECT (PATHWAY BLOCKED). In that case device B would increment its PBC to give it a higher priority for the next time. This process is the resolution to a possible deadlock scenario and is discussed in more detail in the next section, "Deadlock and Livelock" on page 338.

Backoff-Reverse Path

Continuing with this example, we will now consider three possible cases: a Backoff-Reverse Path, Crossing Requests, and a Backoff-Retry case. Starting with the Backoff-Reverse Path case, assume the OPEN address frames from devices A and D are targeting each other as the destination address and both arrive at the fanout expander at the same time, as shown in Figure 14-2 below, and both receive an AIP (NORMAL) in response.

Figure 14-2: Backoff-Reverse Path Example

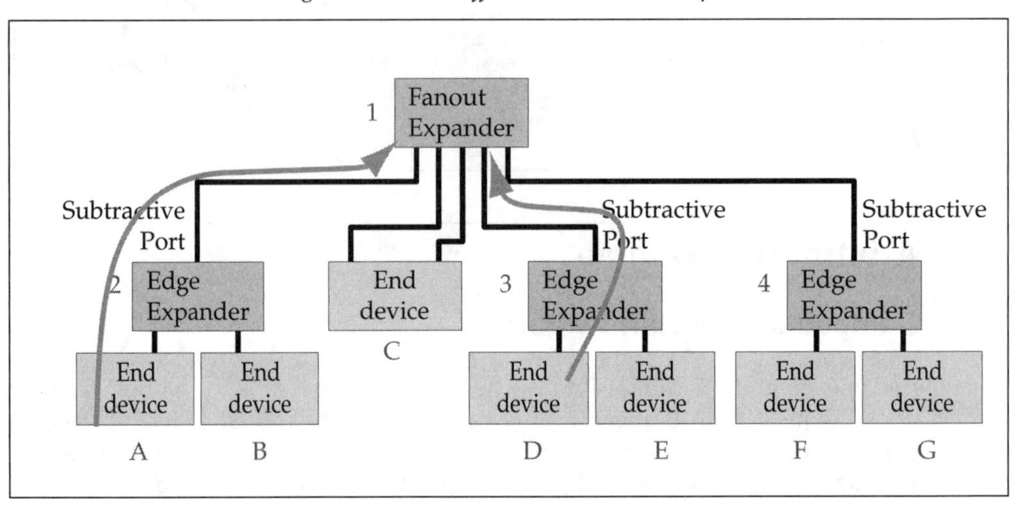

The expander ECM evaluates the requests based on AWT and source address and determines that the request from device A wins the arbitration. The next step is to forward the connection request from A on the port that connects to device D. When edge expander 3 sees an OPEN address frame arrive after having already seen an AIP (NORMAL), that means it's outgoing connection request lost the arbitration in another expander. Since this incoming request has a source address that matches the destination address of the outgoing request, this is the reverse-path case. The request is guaranteed to succeed in connecting to device D because the outgoing request from D had already made it this far.

Next, expander 3 forwards the OPEN address frame to device D, which also recognizes that an incoming OPEN after already receiving an AIP (NORMAL) means that it's outgoing request has lost arbitration. Device D now has a happy ending to its rejected request because the device that has connected to it is in fact the device it was trying to reach with it's own request. In response to receiving the request, device D returns an OPEN_ACCEPT.

Crossing Requests

For the second example, assume devices A and D are again trying to send an OPEN to each other, but this time we'll change the timing of the connection requests. Instead of arriving at the fanout expander together, assume the request from device A is being forwarded to expander 3 at the same time the request from device D is being forwarded to the fanout expander. In this case, the requests cross on the wire, as shown in Figure 14-3. This time both expanders 1 and 3 will compare the contents of the OPEN frames to determine an arbitration winner. If the request from A wins again, both expanders will recognize it and expander 3 will forward the request to device D, which recognizes as before that it's OPEN request has lost the arbitration and it will need to evaluate the incoming OPEN instead.

Figure 14-3: Crossing-On-the-Wire Example

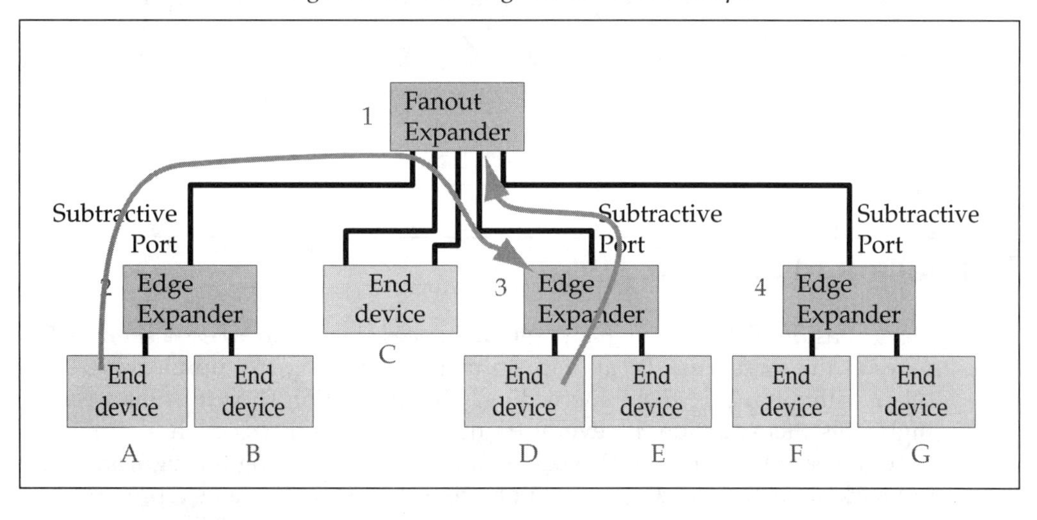

Backoff-Retry

Finally, for the third example, consider the case in which the requests from A and D both arrive at the fanout expander at the same time as before, but this time let the request from A be targeting device E instead, as shown in Figure 14-4. Assuming the request from A wins as usual, the difference now is that there is no guarantee that the request will win the arbitration in expander 3 because, unlike the backoff-reverse path case, the request that lost the arbitration in expander 1 was not the destination device. It could happen, for example, that when this request is forwarded to expander 3 there will be a request there that has come in from device E. If that request has a higher priority than the one from A, then that OPEN address frame will be forwarded back up to the fanout expander instead. The request from A lost the arbitration and was essentially backed-off to try again later. How far back the request gets pushed depends on which destination address the connection request from E was targeting.

Figure 14-4: Backoff-Retry Example

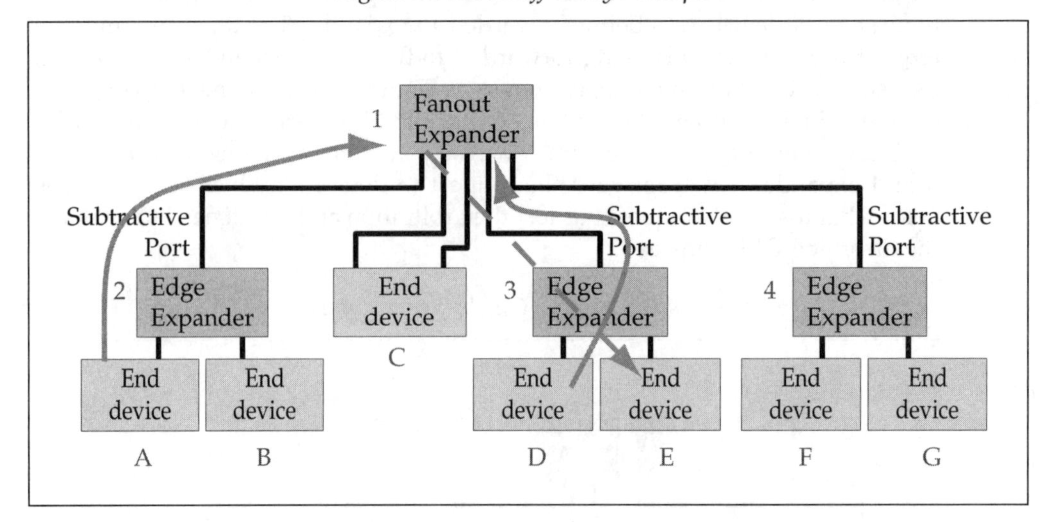

Deadlock and Livelock

Next, consider the case in which several devices attempt to access a set of pathways at the same time. It can happen that the requests end up blocking each other without any of them succeeding. The illustration shown in Figure 14-5 highlights this situation. If several trains arrive at an intersection at the same time, are each long enough to block another train from going through, and cannot back up, then a deadlock condition arises. For SAS, the trains represent connection requests and resulting connections occupying physical links in a group of expanders. A variation on this theme is a "livelock". Using the same illustration, assume now that the trains can detect that they have been blocked, and when that happens they will back up and try again in an effort to clear the intersection. However, if they all arrive at the same time, back up by the same amount at the same time and then try again, there will be more activity but still no progress on clearing the jam.

Figure 14-5: Deadlock Illustration

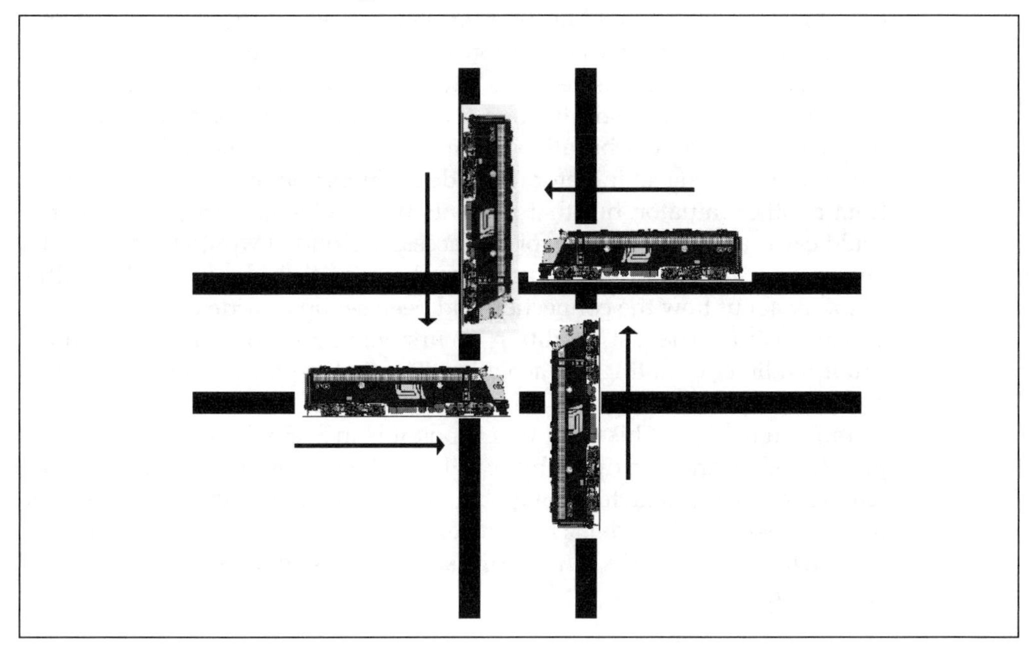

Conditions for Deadlock

There are two approaches to resolving this possibility. The first is to prevent or avoid the conditions that give rise to a deadlock. As it turns out, there are four conditions that must be simultaneously true for a deadlock to exist. To prevent the possibility of a deadlock condition, it's only necessary to ensure that all four conditions can't all be true at the same time, so let's examine whether that can be done in a SAS environment. The four conditions are:

1. **Mutual Exclusion** - This means a resource is not shareable by two requesters. For SAS, this is the case for a physical link. Avoiding this condition would require sharing of resources, but a SAS link can only allow one connection at a time, so that's not a possibility.
2. **Hold and Wait** - This condition means a requester holds one resource while requesting use of another. In SAS this happens when the link between an initiator and expander is kept busy while the expander requests access to another link to get to the target. Preventing this condition would require

that requesters hold and release all their resources at the same time. This won't work in SAS because a connection request only arbitrates for one link at a time and must hold all the previous ones. Waiting for all the physical links to be available would hurt performance and be difficult to implement.

3. **No Preemption** - The third condition arises when one requester has no way to override another requester. SAS allows for arbitration between competing requests but it can still happen that a circular wait condition can arise that would prevent arbitration from working. To avoid this condition would mean letting an initiator override a connection or connection request from another initiator, but that presents two problems. First, one initiator could cause another to starve for bus access. Second, it would be difficult to take over resources in other expanders because there would still be little visibility about how the connection had been set up outside of it.
4. **Circular Wait** - The last condition occurs when a set of requesters can all end up indirectly waiting on each other. The first requester is waiting on the second, which is waiting on a third, which completes the circle because it is waiting on the first. This condition is possible in SAS when there are multiple expanders and multiple physical links. Preventing this problem would require imposing some form of global ordering to ensure that all requesters request resources in order. The problem with this is that it can still starve ports with lower priority SAS addresses, and it is counter to the notion of arbitration fairness.

Deadlock Recovery

Given the difficulties or undesirable consequences inherent in preventing deadlocks in SAS, the standard writers chose the second option: to detect situations that might indicate that a deadlock has occurred and recover from it. The method for detecting this is to track how long a partially-completed connection waits when it is waiting on another partial connection. This is measured by the Partial Pathway Timeout timer, which is used to detect this suspicious condition and force one of the connection requests to back off.

When a connection request has been accepted by an expander, there are two conditions that might cause it to have to wait. The first situation occurs if the resources it needs are currently in use and blocked by an active connection. For this case the request can legally wait forever because connections are assumed to be short-lived; if a SAS port left a connection open for a long time it would cause problems. The second case arises if the connection can't proceed because it is blocked by another connection that can't proceed. For this case, the Partial

Pathway Timeout timer is initialized and started because this is the possible deadlock scenario. Note that the default value of this timer is recommended in the standard as 7µs, but it can be programmed using the PHY CONTROL function. As the standard points out, this value should be selected based on the size of the topology. Setting it to a small value for devices in a large topology could result in OPEN_REJECT (PATHWAY BLOCKED) being sent too quickly, when a longer wait might have allowed the condition to resolve without intervention. On the other hand, setting a high value in a small topology could result in connection requests that wait a long time only to be backed off anyway.

By way of review, recall that expanders inform the requester about the status of a connection request by means of the AIP primitives they return, as show in Table 14-2 below.

Table 14-2: AIP Primitives Returned by Expanders

Primitive	Description
AIP (NORMAL)	The expander has accepted the OPEN request and started internal arbitration for an output phy
AIP (WAITING ON DEVICE)	The expander has routed the request to an output Phy and the connection is tentatively complete, waiting for the target device's reply for confirmation.
AIP (WAITING ON CONNECTION)	The expander has routed the request to a destination Phy that is currently in use by an active connection. That connection must eventually close, so this request can continue to wait for it's turn.
AIP (WAITING ON PARTIAL)	The expander has routed the request to a destination Phy that is currently busy with another request that has

To see how this would work, consider the example based on the discussion in section I.17 of the standard. In Figure 14-6 on page 342, three devices are connected by two expanders with a wide port between them. The example begins when both device A and device B initiate connection requests to each other at the same time. Each device will receive AIP (NORMAL) repeatedly after the nearby expander accepts the connection request, and then AIP (WAITING ON DEVICE) just once when the request is forwarded to the next expander. At that point, however, we encounter the problem that the ports to the targeted devices are only narrow ports, so there cannot be two connections in progress at the same time. When expander 1 realizes that the request from B coming in on Phy 5 is targeting Phy 1, which is already in use but only partially connected, it will send an AIP (WAITING ON PARTIAL). When that response is sent, expander 1 initializes and starts the Partial Pathway Timeout counter for Phy 5. The same thing happens with the request from device A when it reaches expander 2, and the partial pathway timer for Phy 9 is also started. Assuming nothing else happens to break this logjam, the timer in each expander eventually expires and the expanders now have to sort out which of the requests has higher priority. It doesn't matter if the timers expire at different times, because both expanders will make the same evaluation and reach the same conclusion.

Figure 14-6: Pathway Recovery Example

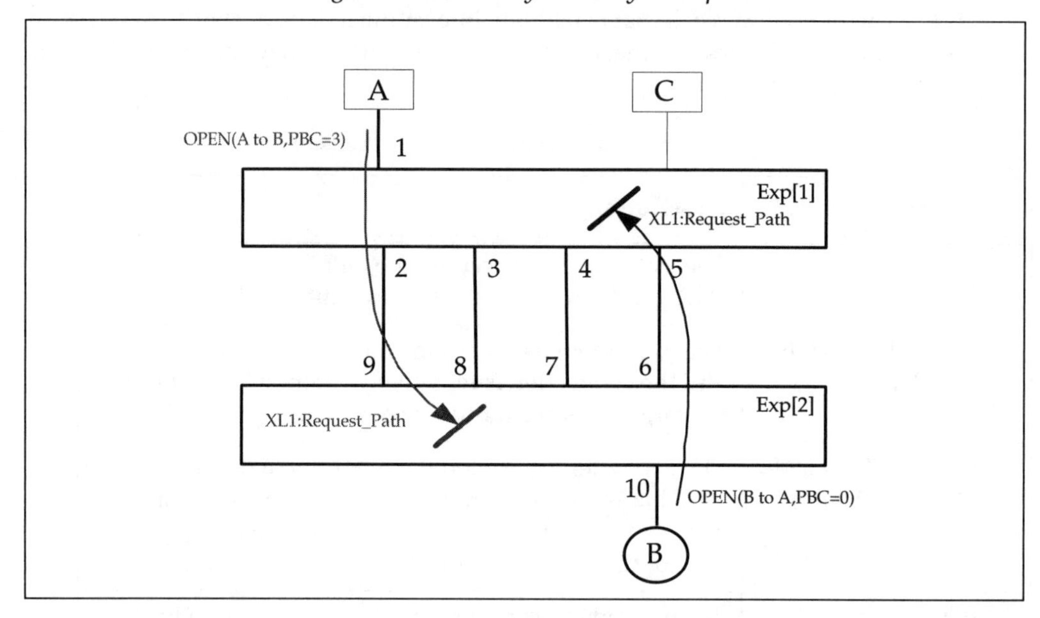

Their evaluation is based on the pathway recovery priority as shown in Table 14-3 below. As can be seen, the most significant consideration is the pathway blocked count (PBC), representing the number of times this request has been backed off before.

Table 14-3: Pathway Recovery Priority

Bits 71-64 (71 is MSB)	Bits 63-0 (0 is LSB)
Pathway Blocked Count	Source SAS Address

In the example, the PBC value is three for the request from device A and zero for the request from device B, meaning the request from A wins the arbitration.

If the PBC values had been equal, the next step would have been to compare the source SAS addresses, which should always be different. Since the request from B lost, expander 1 Phy 5 will send back an OPEN_REJECT (PATHWAY BLOCKED) which will break down the connection in expanders 1 and 2, and tell device B to retry the request again later. When that rejection frees up Phy 10 in expander 2, the request from device A is allowed to proceed (see Figure 14-7) and so expander 2 will forward an AIP (WAITING ON DEVICE) back to device A.

Figure 14-7: Partial Pathway Recovery Result

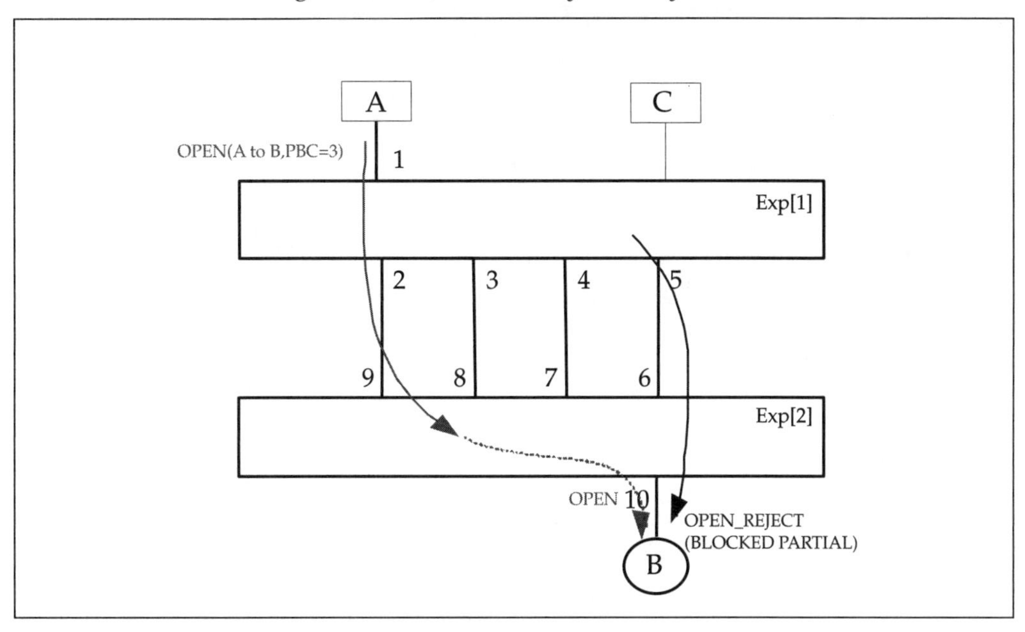

15 Link Layer - Protocol Differences

The Previous Chapter

The previous chapter explored how competing connection requests are arbitrated within expanders. This includes deciding between requests competing for the same resources and handling deadlock or livelock conditions in a non-trivial system.

This Chapter

This chapter describes the Link Layer responsibilities that are unique to each of the supported protocols, such as the mechanisms for flow control and acknowledgement of received frames. This discussion includes a description of the protocol-specific state machines.

The Next Chapter

The next chapter describes the responsibilities of the Phy Layer, which prepares the packets forwarded from the upper layers for serial transmission. These responsibilities include encoding and decoding of bytes into 10-bit symbols, managing clock skew between devices, and handling the OOB (out of band) signaling used for link initialization.

Introduction

Link Layer responsibilities within connections for the possible protocols are similar, but the way they are carried out varies. For example, flow control is handled quite differently between SSP and STP connections, and is not a factor at all in SMP connections.

The Link Layer tasks involved in meeting these responsibilities include the following:

- SSP: ACK/NAK Protocol and Flow Control
- SMP: Single Response

Flow Control

To start, assume an SSP connection has already been established using the same topology and devices as the example covered in the previous chapter and illustrated here in Figure 15-1. The connection is ready to transmit frames but SSP flow control rules ordinarily require that no frames arrive before the receiver explicitly indicates readiness to receive them.

Figure 15-1: SSP Connection Example

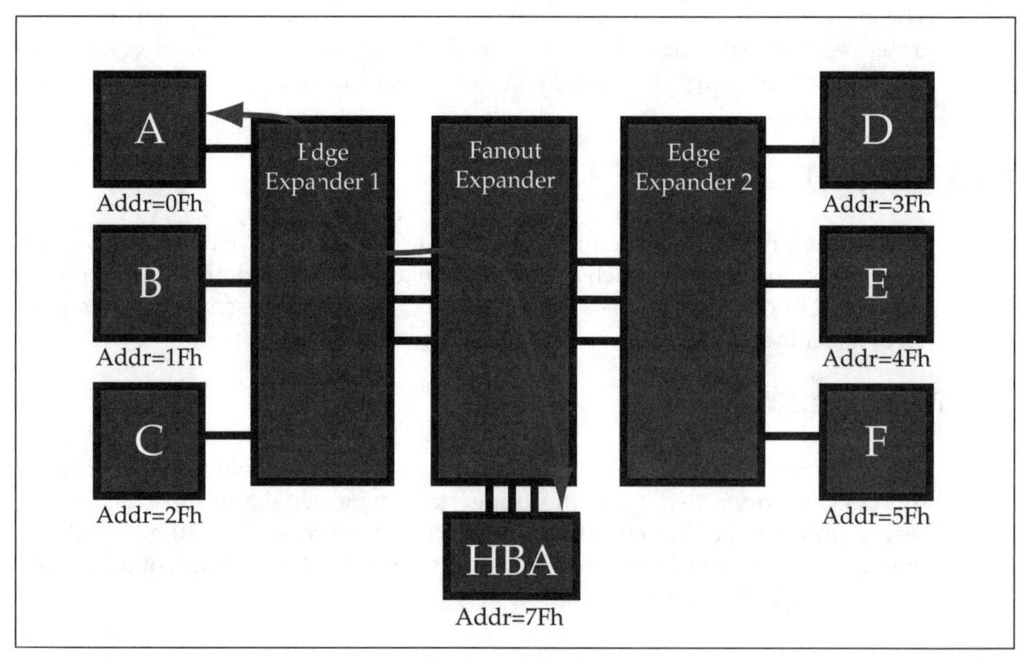

Exception Case

There is an exception to this case called the First Burst mechanism that gives an initiator permission to send one burst of a certain data size without waiting for an XFER_RDY frame from the target. This exception is carried over from other transports and is more useful in high-latency environments. Since SAS was designed to expect short latencies and, in fact, may have trouble operating correctly if latencies become excessive, it is not expected that this case will find much use in SAS. Experts with whom the author spoke regarding this went so far as to say that they encouraged designers not to use it for SAS topologies.

Normal Case

Normally, therefore, before any frames can be sent the devices must indicate their readiness by sending an RRDY primitive. To avoid any confusion at this point, recall that RRDYs are primitives and therefore do not count as frames themselves. No flow control permission is needed to send primitives.

One RRDY indicates that the device can accept one frame with up to 1KB of data. A target device is required to send at least one RRDY if it accepts the connection request; if it cannot send an RRDY for some reason (e.g.: buffers are full), then it is not allowed to accept the connection. For initiators, sending RRDY is optional, but is commonly done when the connection is opened because the target may have data frames to return or because it will need to send XFER_RDY for a write command. Note that only SSP supports full-duplex traffic. STP connections are only half-duplex even though confirmation of link activity is returned during a FIS. SMP connections are also half duplex because they send only one request and one response before closing. SSP frames can be sent in both directions at the same time, but the devices must give RRDYs to make that possible. Each RRDY primitive is counted as it is received, so a device can send several RRDYs to indicate a readiness to receive several frames and thus a larger amount of data, even though each frame is limited to 1KB.

Setting Up a Write Command

If the command from the initiator is a write, the next step is for the target to indicate when it is ready to accept the write data. This is accomplished by sending an XFER_RDY frame that specifies how much buffer space is available. In the example illustrated in Figure 15-2, assume that the HBA sends a SCSI Write command to device A, desiring to send a 4KB batch of data to the target.

Figure 15-2: SSP Flow Control Example

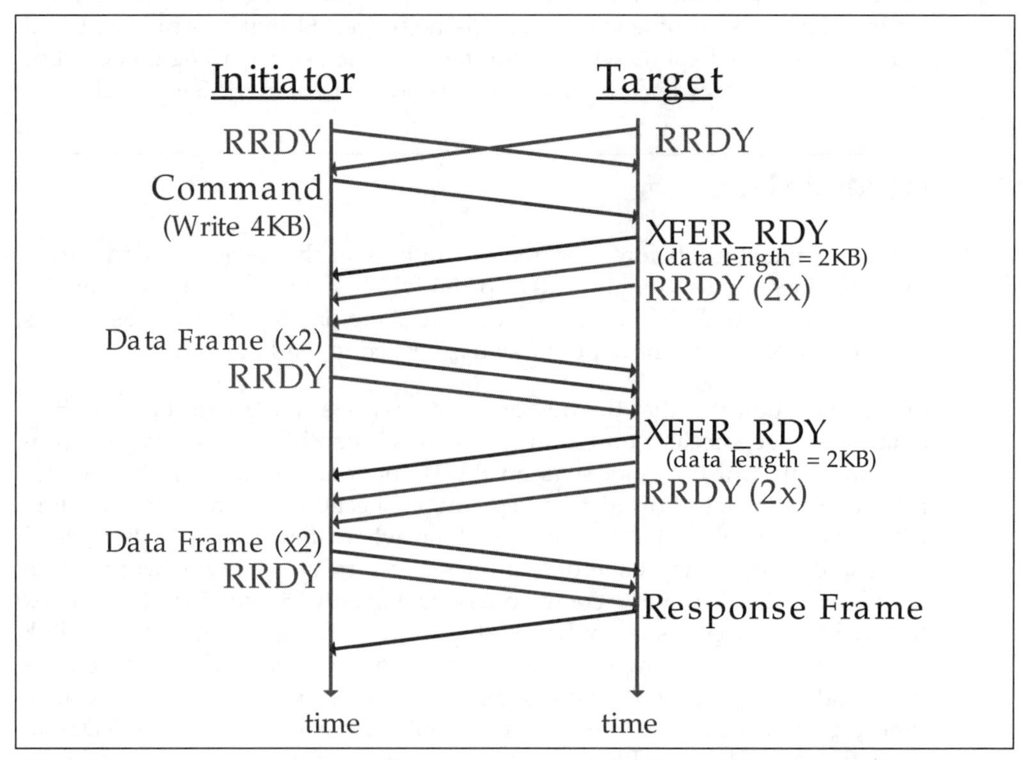

The SCSI protocol puts the target in control of data transfers on the bus, which means the initiator must wait for permission from the target before sending the data. This simplifies target design because the initiator is not allowed to "push" data at the target, and the target does not have to be designed to accept unsolicited data. Instead, when the target has prepared buffer space it then returns an XFER_RDY frame to the initiator specifying both the amount of data that can be accepted and the offset that is associated with it in memory space. The offset is normally zero on the first XFER_RDY and set to the sum of previously sent data for subsequent XFER_RDYs. The offset serves primarily as a confirmation that both devices are in sync about where this data should go. If the offset doesn't match what the initiator expects to see, the initiator discards the frame and aborts the command because it means the target has lost track of where the data should go, perhaps because it has lost data or had some other serious problem, making it pointless to continue.

In the example, the target indicates an XFER_RDY with data length of 2KB and offset of zero. At this point, all of the frame transfer credits in both directions have been consumed and the flow of frames is stopped until more RRDYs are sent to give permission for them. If the target now returns two RRDY primitives, the meaning to the initiator is that the target is ready for half of the data and can only accept two frames.

Finishing the Write Command

Continuing this example, if the initiator sends two data frames it must then wait for permission from the target to send any more frames. If the frames each contain the maximum 1KB of data, then those two will consume all the available buffer space. That means the initiator will need to receive another XFER_RDY frame from the target before it can send more data. Since the XFER_RDY is itself a frame, the initiator will first need to send another RRDY to the target to indicate readiness to accept that frame. After the HBA sends one RRDY, the target responds with the XFER_RDY frame of data length 2KB and offset of 2KB and follows that with two more RRDYs, giving the HBA the same permission it had previously. The HBA responds by again sending two data frames with 1KB each to finish the write transfer, and one more RRDY to the target to give permission for a response frame. The Response frame is then sent by the target to give the status of the just-executed command and the write command is now completed. However, the connection is not automatically closed. It remains open and available for new commands or responses to previously queued commands until the devices decide to close it.

Frame Acknowledgement (ACK/NAK Handshake)

In the flow control example above, the interactions between devices were simplified to make it easier to see the flow control handshakes. One important aspect of SSP communications that was not shown is the acknowledgement, positively or negatively, of every frame that is sent across the link. This handshake is actually very simple, and there are two versions of it: interlocked and non-interlocked.

Interlocked Frames

All frames except data frames are interlocked, which means that another frame cannot be sent until receipt of the previous frame has been acknowledged with ACK or NAK. ACK affirms the good receipt of a frame while NAK, or negative acknowledge, indicates that there was a problem with the frame. As shown in Table 15-1, there is currently only one reason that can be reported for a NAK, and that is a CRC error or its equivalent. There are three reserved versions of NAK for future use, but in the current revision of the standard they are all interpreted as a NAK (CRC ERROR) by the recipient. The length of time that the sender will wait for an ACK or NAK is specified by the ACK/NAK Timeout timer as 1 ms. If the timer expires, the device waiting for ACK/NAK sends a DONE (ACK/NAK TIMEOUT) to begin the process of closing down the connection.

Table 15-1: NAK Primitives

NAK Primitive	Description
NAK (CRC ERROR)	The frame encountered a bad CRC, or an invalid dword, or an ERROR was received during frame reception.
NAK (RESERVED 0)	Reserved - processed same as NAK (CRC ERROR).
NAK (RESERVED 1)	Reserved - processed same as NAK (CRC ERROR).
NAK (RESERVED 2)	Reserved - processed same as NAK (CRC ERROR).

The ACK and NAK primitives contain no information that could be used to associate them with a particular frame, so it's not possible to distinguish which frames have been acknowledged. Instead, the next frame waits until the previous one has been acknowledged before it can proceed. While a device is waiting for an ACK or NAK before sending the next frame, frames can still be received from the other direction. For example, an initiator could be awaiting an ACK for a COMMAND frame while a DATA frame is coming in from an earlier read command. Also, even though a device cannot send more frames while waiting, it can still send primitives in response to incoming traffic, such as ACKs or NAKs to acknowledge incoming frames.

Non-Interlocked Frames

The only non-interlocked frames are DATA frames, and they are not constrained as much as all the other frames. Several non-interlocked data frames may be sent consecutively without waiting on an ACK/NAK response. Instead, the sender counts how many frames have been sent and how many ACK/NAKs have been returned. This is permitted as long as all the frames are part of the same transaction and carry the same tag information. If the transmitter wants to start sending data frames for another transaction, then the previous transaction must finish before the new one can start. The transmitter detects that the transaction is finished when ACK/NAK balance is achieved, meaning that the number of frames sent is equal to the number of ACKs received, and there are no more frames with that tag to be sent. This task is made easier for the Link Layer because when the Port Layer sends a Tx Frame message it includes an argument that says Balance Required or Balance Not Required. The Balance Not Required argument can only be included if the transmission is for a DATA frame that uses the same logical unit and the same tag value as the previous Tx Frame message.

ACK/NAK Example 1

If we now go back to our previous example of the write command and add the ACKs and NAKs, the result is as shown in Figure 15-3 on page 352. Notice that the non-interlocked frames like COMMAND and XFER_RDY must wait for an ACK before the transmitter can send anything else, whereas the data frames are not so constrained. The first data frame must wait until the ACK for the COMMAND frame is returned, but after that two of them are sent without waiting for ACKs. There are still more DATA frames to send, and the sender doesn't have to wait for ACK/NAK in this case, but now we encounter the flow control issue again. Once permission is given by receiving XFER_RDY and RRDYs, the remaining two DATA frames are immediately sent without waiting for the ACKs for the previous frames.

Counting ACKs and NAKs

Since four non-interlocked frames are sent overall, the sender will need to see four ACKs returned before moving on to the next step. If the frame sent count did not match the ACK received count for some reason, the device has no way to know which of the frames had trouble. If recovery will be attempted, some or all of the transaction will need to be replayed, and the Transport Layer controls this. In this example all four ACKs are received. The last step is to receive the Response frame from the target. The initiator sends an RRDY to indicate readiness to receive a frame, and the Response frame is sent to complete the transfer.

Figure 15-3: Write Command with ACK/NAKs

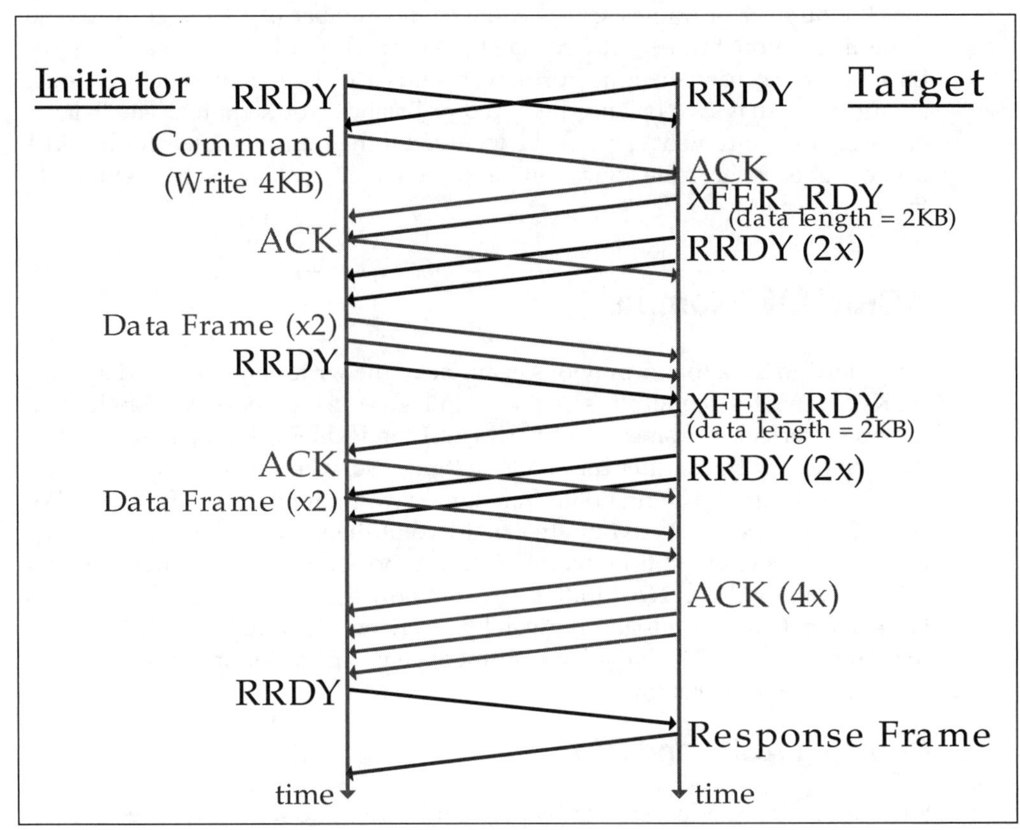

Transaction Retries

If Transport Layer retries are enabled, the Transport Layer stores a copy of the data offset for the last time a DATA frame was sent and ACK/NAK Balance was achieved. Then, if trouble is encountered during a data transaction, the Transport Layer considers the transaction to have been successful up to the point where ACK/NAK Balance was seen, and can restart the transaction again from that point by reverting to the stored data offset and setting the CHANGING DATA POINTER bit in the frame. The number of times a failed transmission will be retried is vendor specific.

ACK/NAK Example 2

Another example is shown in Figure 15-4, and illustrates how non-interlocked frames using different tag values are handled. Note that subsequent DATA frames using Tag A do not have to wait for ACK/NAK confirmation before the next one is sent. However, when a data frame that uses another tag is ready to send, its transmission request will have the argument ACK/NAK Balance Required. Consequently, it's transmission will have to wait until ACK/NAK balance is again achieved. When that happens, the frame with tag B can be sent. The next frame is still non-interlocked, but once more uses a different tag value. As a result, the first frame using tag C will also specify ACK/NAK Balance Required and will have to wait until ACK or NAK for the frame with tag B is returned. Subsequent frames using tag C will not require ACK/NAK Balance, so they do not need to wait on the previous frame's ACK/NAK before they can proceed.

Figure 15-4: Non-Interlocked Frames with Different Tags

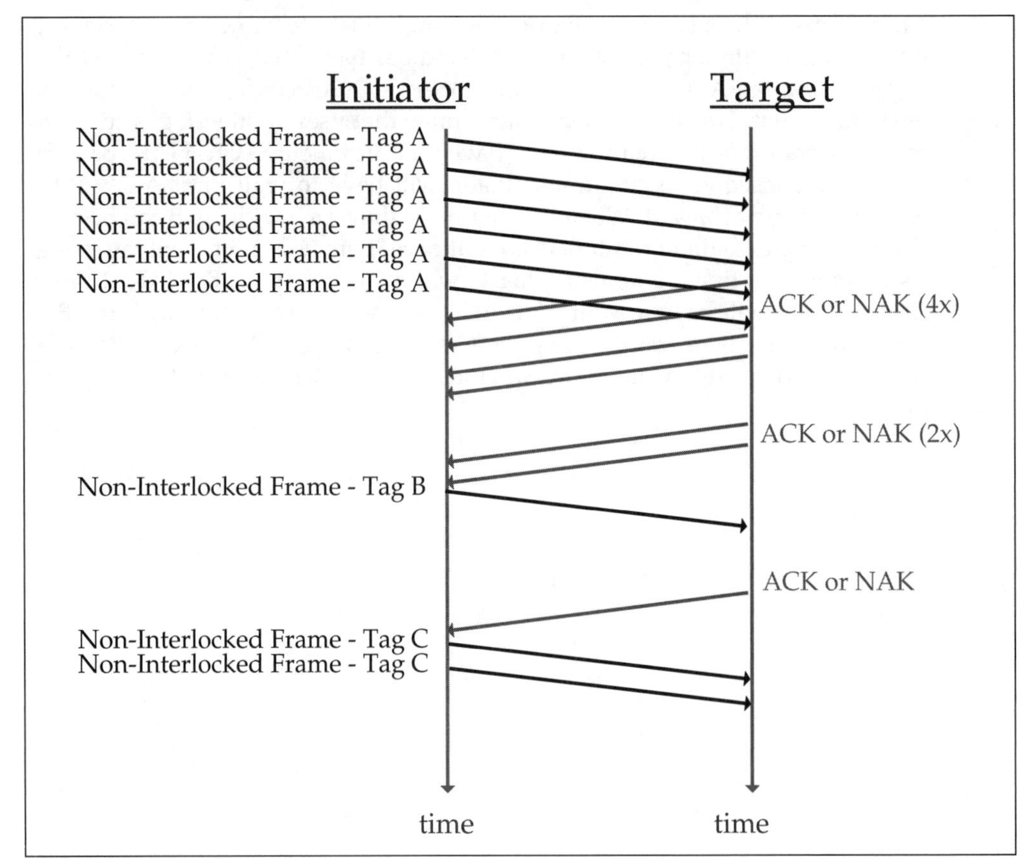

SSP Connections

State Machines

There are four SSP-specific state machines for frame transmission and five for frame reception given in the standard to define Link Layer behavior. In addition to the state machines, there is also a block of logic referred to as the SSP transmitter that receives messages from the SSP state machines about primitives and frames that need to be sent. When the requested item has been transmitted, this logic returns a message to the state machines to confirm it. Similarly, another logic block is defined as the SSP receiver, which sends messages to the state machines to inform them about what has been received, such as ACK, NAK, SOF, data, or EOF.

Transient Nature of the State Machines

These state machines do not run all the time and don't even have a transition back to the Idle state. Instead, all the SSP state machines start when an Enable Disable SSP (Enable) message is received from the SL state machines to indicate that an SSP connection is in progress. Similarly, they all terminate when one of the following occurs:

- An Enable Disable SSP (Disable) message is received from the SL state machines, or
- The SSP_D state machine indicates the connection is closed by sending a Request Close message, or
- The SSP_D state machine indicates that a BREAK has been sent by sending a Request BREAK message.

In contrast to the SL_CC state machine covered in the previous chapter that was large and complex, the state machines that follow are small and simple. As before, they are redrawn here in an effort to make them more readable and the flow between states more understandable. The first set represents the state machines used for transmission of SSP frames. In the drawing, the dotted-line box highlights the Transmit Frame Control state machine containing four states. The other three state machines are all single-state and have no state transitions but send messages based on events detected.

Transmit State Machines

All four SSP transmit state machines are listed below and illustrated in Figure 15-5 on page 358.

TIM (Transmit Interlocked Frame Monitor)

This machine counts the number of frames sent and the number of ACK/NAKs received in response to make sure that an ACK or NAK is received for every frame. Based on these counts, it sends a Tx Balance Status message to the SSP_TF2:Tx_Wait state with the argument *Balanced* if the sum of ACKs and NAKs received equals the number of frames sent, or *Not Balanced* if the counts are not equal. The counts will automatically be set equal to each other whenever a Request Close or Request Break or SSP Enable Disable (Enable) message is received. In the event that ACK/NAKs are received but the frame count is already equal to the ACK/NAK count, they are ignored. Any time the count is not balanced, the ACK/NAK Timeout counter is started and reinitialized every time an ACK or NAK is counted. If no ACK/NAKs are seen within 1ms, the timer expires and the state sends an ACK/NAK Timeout message to the Port Layer and the SSP_TF1 and SSP_TF2 states.

TF (Transmit Frame control)

This machine controls the transmission of the SSP frame components: SOF, DATA, EOF, and DONE. To transmit a frame, the Port Layer would sent a Tx Frame request with arguments including whether Balance was required for it, indicating whether it was to be an interlocked frame. In response, the state transitions to SSP_TF2:Tx_Wait, where it checks to see whether credit is available for sending this frame. If the Transmit Credit Monitor state machine indicates there is no credit available, the Credit Timeout timer is initialized and started, checking to ensure that credit does arrive within 1ms. If credit is available, and if the Tx Balance Status shows the proper status for the requested frame, the machine transitions to the SSP_TF3:Indicate_FrameTx state and sends a Tx Credit Used message to the SSP_TCM state machine. From there, a Transmit Frame message is sent to the SSP Transmitter, which sends one frame in response and then replies with a message reporting that the frame has been sent. After that, the machine transitions back to SSP_TF1:Connected_Idle.

If, while in the SSP_TF2:Tx_Wait state, the original request from the Port Layer had been for a Close, or if the Credit Timeout timer expired, or if the ACK/NAK Timeout timer expired, this machine will transition to the SSP_TF4:Indicate_DONE_Tx state. That state will request that a DONE be transmitted, get a confirmation that it was, and then stop. Since there can be no more frames transmitted after sending DONE, the state machine at that point is just waiting for the machine to be terminated.

TCM (Transmit frame Credit Monitor)

This machine tracks the number of frame credits available to make sure that there is credit before a frame is transmitted. It adds one credit for every RRDY received and subtracts one for every Tx Credit Used message it receives. The status that is passed to the SSP_TF2:Tx_Wait state will be *Available* if transmit credit is available, or *Not Available* if there is no more credit, or *Blocked* if a CREDIT_BLOCKED message was received. In the case of blocked credit, the machine may ignore RRDYs that arrive after that until it gets a Request Close or Request Break message. The CREDIT_BLOCKED primitive indicates that the other device is not going to send any more credit during this connection, and in fact will not be allowed to send any more RRDYs. The reason for doing this is to tell the receiver that no credit will be coming so it does not have to wait for the 1ms timeout before sending DONE.

D (Done control)

The purpose of this machine is to make sure a DONE has been both sent and received before disabling the SSP state machines. If a DONE has been sent but not received, the DONE Timeout counter is started and expires after 1ms. If the timer expires, a DONE Timeout message is sent to the Port Layer. If a DONE is received before one is sent, then that confirmation is sent to the Port Layer. Recall that the DONE primitive does report something about the reason it was sent, as shown in Table 15-2 below.

Table 15-2: DONE Primitives

Primitive	Description
DONE (NORMAL)	Device is ready to close the connection.
DONE (ACK/NAK TIMEOUT)	ACK/NAK was not received before the timer expired.
DONE (CREDIT BLOCKED)	A CREDIT_BLOCKED primitive was received and, since nothing more can be sent, the connection is being prepared for closing.

Since we've described the DONE timeout timer, this also seems like a good place to mention all of the Link layer timers, and these are listed in Table 15-3. The first one times the arrival of ACK or NAK for a frame, while the last one times the arrival of credits from the receiver to enable the sender to transmit frames.

Table 15-3: SSP Link Layer Timers

Timer	Initial Value
ACK/NAK Timeout	1ms
DONE Timeout	1ms
Credit Timeout	1ms

Figure 15-5: SSP Transmit State Machines

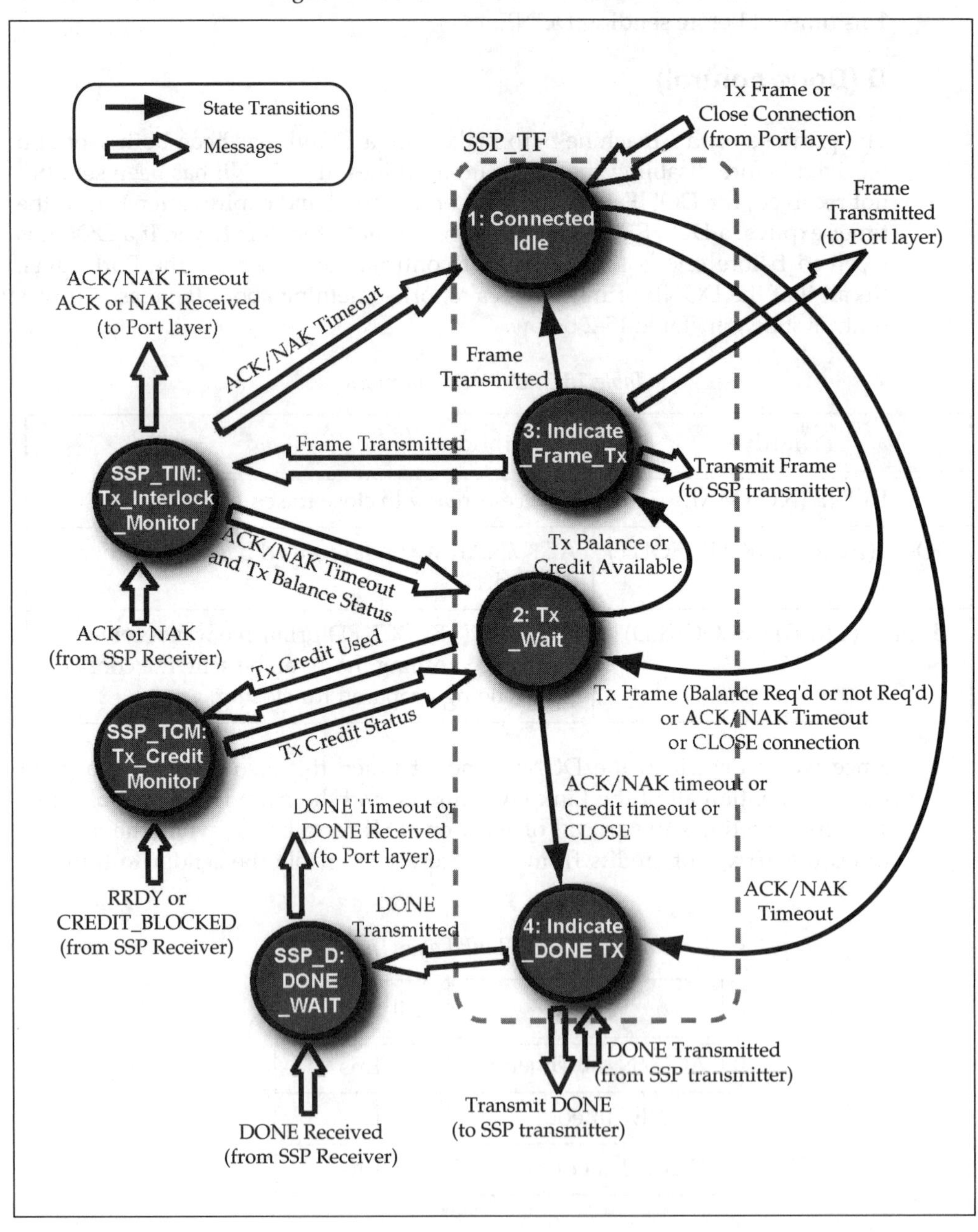

Receive State Machines

The state machines for the SSP receive logic are illustrated in Figure 15-6 below, and described in the text that follows it.

Figure 15-6: SSP Receive State Machines

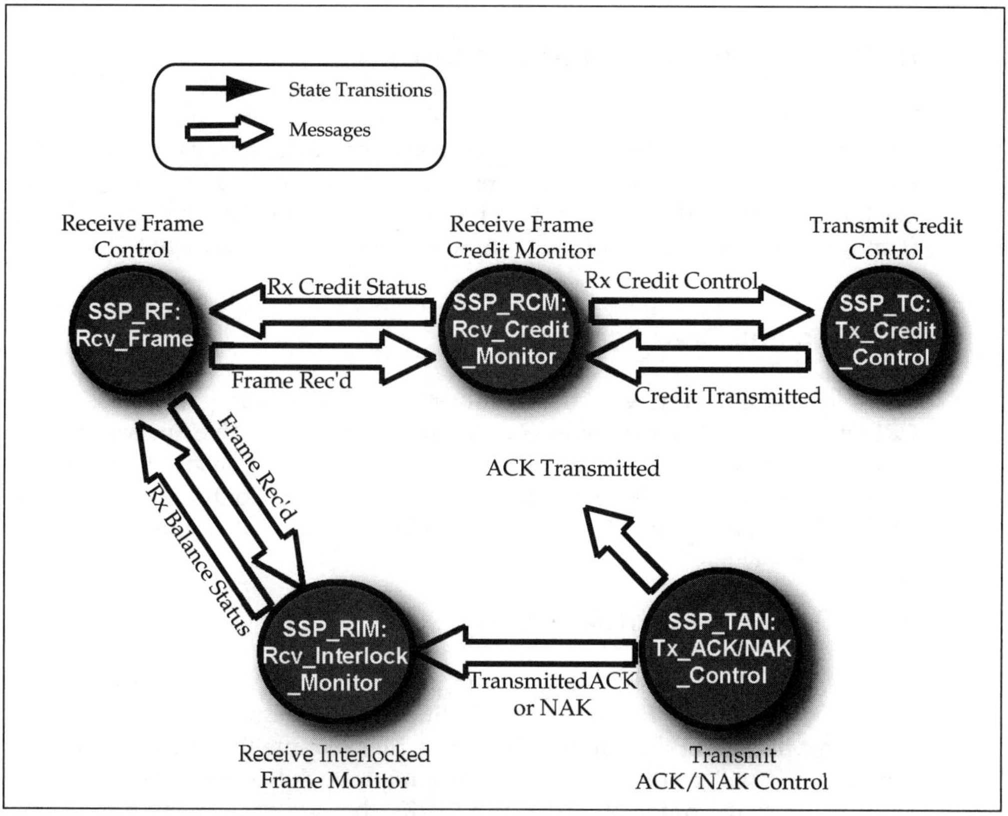

RF (Receive Frame control)

This machine checks incoming frames to verify that they are legal and should be accepted. For example, an SOF should be followed by data and then an EOF. If another SOF is seen before an EOF for the previous frame, that previous frame will be discarded. Other illegal cases include: frame too short or too long, insufficient credits were granted to allow the frame, or a DONE has already been received for this connection. Another possibility is that the SSP receiver might indicate an invalid dword or ERROR, and that would also cause the frame to be discarded.

If the frame is alright, this state sends a Frame Received message to the SSP_RIM and SSP_RCM machines. If the CRC then turns out to be bad, it sends a Frame Received (Unsuccessful) message to the SSP_TAN1:Idle state. If the CRC is good, a Frame Received (Successful) message is sent instead, and then a Frame Received (ACK/NAK Balanced/Not Balanced) confirmation is sent to the Port Layer.

RCM (Receive frame Credit Monitor)

This machine tracks the number of RRDYs sent versus the number of frames received. Any time more RRDYs have been sent than frames received, this machine sends an Rx Credit Status (Extended) to the SSP_RF and SSP_D state machines. Anytime the number of frames received equals the number of RRDYs sent, this machine sends an Rx Credit Status (Exhausted) message to the same machines.

TC (Transmit Credit control)

This machine oversees the requests to transmit an RRDY or CREDIT_BLOCKED. It receives Rx Credit Control (Available) messages that specify how many RRDYs may be sent, and then sends Transmit RRDY (Normal) requests to the SSP transmitter. When it receives confirmation that the RRDYs have been sent, it also sends a Credit Transmitted message to the SSP_RCM machine.

TAN (Transmit ACK/NAK control)

The TAN machine controls the sending of ACKs or NAKs in response to received frames. If a Frame Received (Successful) message is received, this machine will request that an ACK be sent, while a Frame Received (Unsuccessful) message will result in a NAK being requested. If several messages are received, then the order of ACKs and NAKs that are sent must be the same order in which the frames were received. The sending of ACKs and NAKs is also reported to the SSP_RIM state machine as well.

RIM (Receive Interlocked frame Monitor)

This machine tracks the ACK/NAK balance at the receiver and reports that status with an Rx Balance Status (Balanced/Not Balanced) message. To do that operation, it tracks the number of frames received versus the number of ACKs and NAKs that have been sent.

SMP Connections

SMP connections are very simple compared to the other two protocols. One device acts as the initiator and opens the connection to the target based on the destination address and specifying SMP protocol. If the destination contains an SMP target, it will accept the connection request. What follows next is just one command from the initiator and one response from the target, after which the connection is closed. Because there can only be one frame in each direction, SMP connections do not have to bother with flow control or ACK/NAK protocols. When the target accepts the OPEN request, it agrees to accept the one request frame from the initiator, and when the initiator sends the SMP_REQUEST frame it must be prepared to accept the SMP_RESPONSE frame that will be returned. After sending the SMP_RESPONSE frame, the target will then send CLOSE (NORMAL), and when the initiator sees that response, it will also send CLOSE (NORMAL).

SMP State Machines

Because the protocol is so simple, only two state machines are needed to define the device's behavior. The SMP_IP (SMP Initiator Port) defines the initiator's behavior, and the SMP_TP (SMP Target Port) defines it for the target. The standard also defines an SMP transmitter that receives requests to send either idle dwords or a frame, and an SMP receiver that detects the arrival of the frame components SOF, data, and EOF, or else ERROR or invalid dword. Like the SSP state machines, the SMP state machines don't run all the time. They start when an Enable Disable SMP (Enable) message is received from the SL state machines to indicate that an SMP connection is in progress, and terminate when an Enable Disable SMP (Disable) message is received.

SMP_IP (Initiator Port)

Shown in Figure 15-7, this state machine stays in SMP_IP1:Idle and requests that idle dwords be sent until a Tx Frame request is received. That will transition the state to SMP_IP2:Transmit_Frame, where the request is sent to the SMP transmitter logic to send the frame. When the transmitter confirms that the frame has been sent, it sends a Frame Transmitted confirmation to the Port Layer. The machine then transitions to SMP_IP3:Receive_Frame, where it waits for the response frame from the target. If a frame is received, but is not legal because it has too many or too few bytes, or an invalid dword or ERROR, a BREAK will be requested. If the frame looks OK but has a CRC error, a CLOSE will be requested. In any of these error cases, the frame will be discarded and a Frame Received (SMP Failure) confirmation will be sent to the Port Layer. If the response frame is received without error, a Frame Received confirmation is passed to the Port Layer, and a Request Close is sent to the SL state machines.

Figure 15-7: SMP_IP State Machine

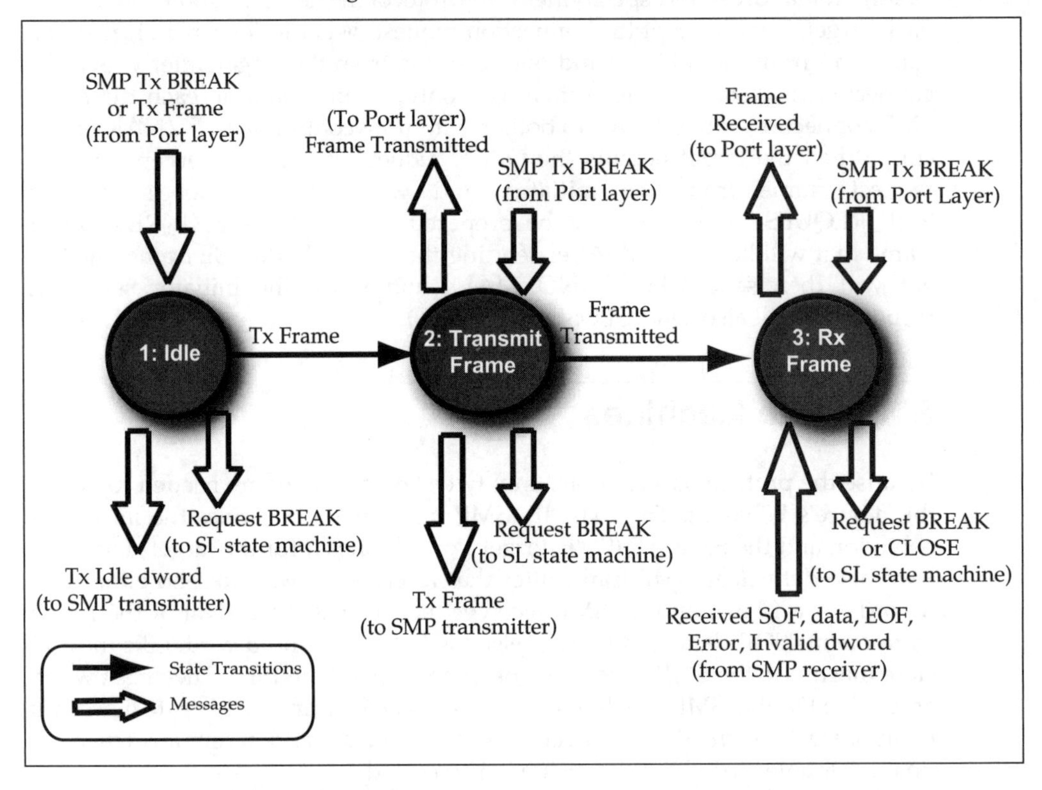

SMP_TP (Target Port)

This machine, shown in Figure 15-8 on page 363, waits in SMP_TP1:Receive_Frame until the incoming frame components are seen. In the same fashion as the initiator state machine, this state checks to see that the frame is not too long or too short and doesn't contain an invalid dword or ERROR or CRC error. If any of those problems occur, the state requests that a BREAK be sent and terminates the state machine. If the frame arrives in good shape, this state sends a Frame Received confirmation to the Port Layer and changes to SMP_TP2:Transmit_Frame, where it waits for a Tx Frame request. When that request arrives, it sends a transmit frame message to the SMP transmitter and waits for confirmation that the frame was sent. When that confirmation is returned, the state sends a Frame Transmitted message to the Port Layer, which sends a Request Close message to the SL state machines and terminates.

Figure 15-8: SMP_TP State Machines

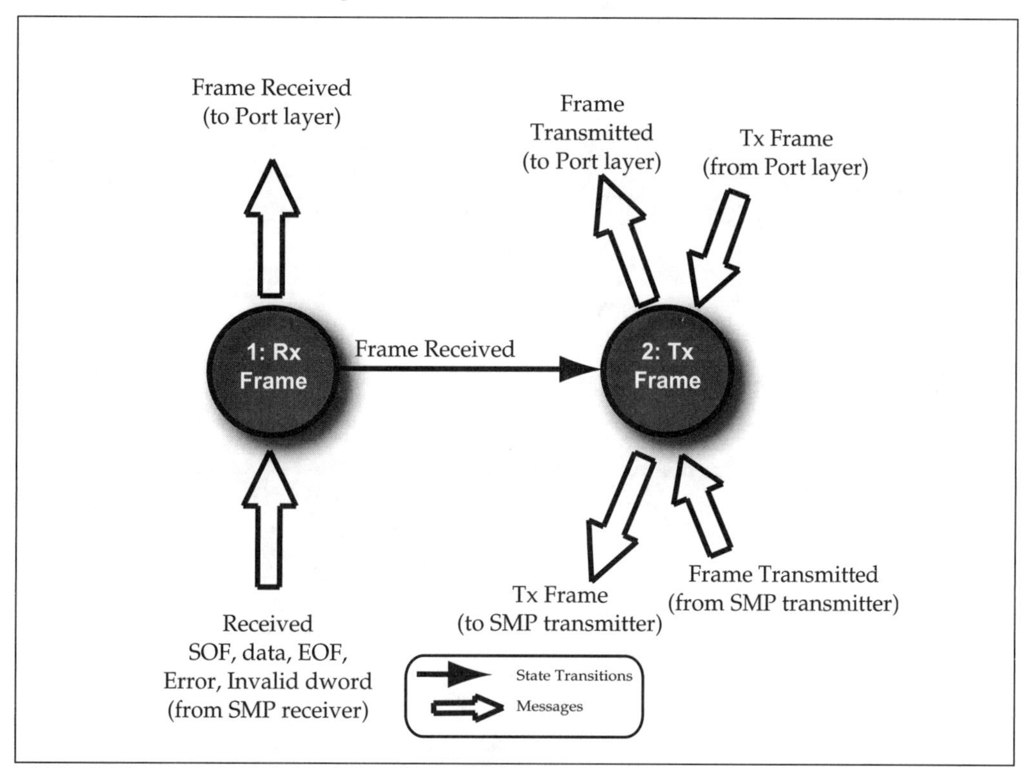

16 Phy Layer

The Previous Chapter

The previous chapter described the Link Layer responsibilities that are unique to each of the supported protocols, such as the mechanisms for flow control and acknowledgement of received frames. This discussion included a description of the protocol-specific state machines.

This Chapter

This chapter describes the responsibilities of the Phy Layer, which prepares the packets forwarded from the upper layers for serial transmission on the wire. These responsibilities include encoding and decoding of bytes into 10-bit symbols, managing clock skew between devices, and handling the OOB (out of band) signaling used for link initialization.

The Next Chapter

The next chapter covers the Physical Layer, which describes the electrical characteristics of the differential transmitter and receiver used to transmit the bits across the wire, and includes a discussion of the four interface environments defined for use with SAS. Apart from the discussion about the analog transmitter and receiver sections, the Physical Layer is largely concerned with the passive interface that includes backplanes, cables, and connectors.

Introduction

After all the work that has been done to create a frame or primitive for transmission, it is the Phy Layer that the final piece of logic that it will pass through before it reaches the differential output driver. As shown in Figure 16-1 on page 366, this layer resides hierarchically between the Link Layer and Physical Layer.

Figure 16-1: SAS Block Diagram

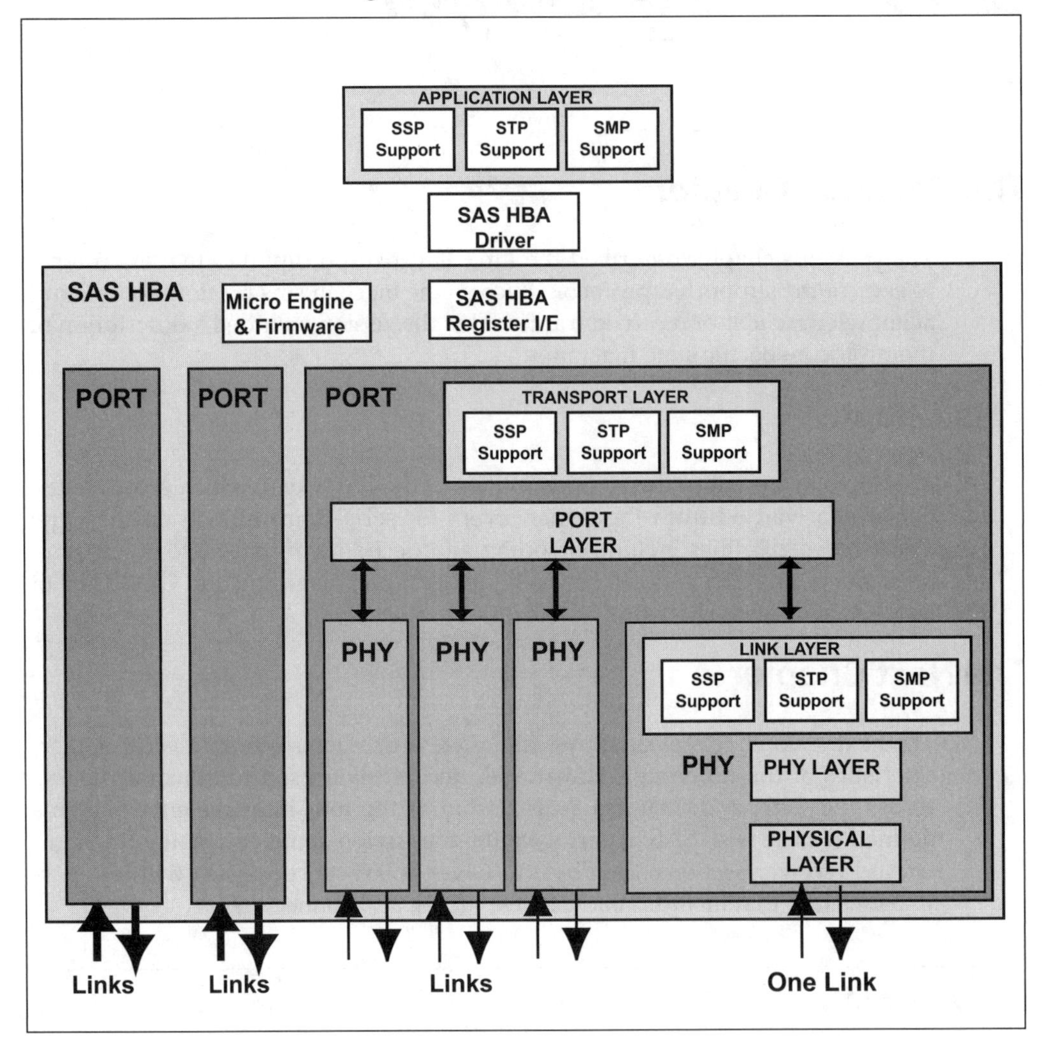

The responsibilities of this layer on the transmit side include:

- Insertion of primitives for Clock skew management
- 8b/10b encoding of outgoing bytes
- Generation of the Phy reset sequence
- Generation of the OOB (Out of Band) signaling, and primitives for speed negotiation, that are used during initialization

The responsibilities on the receive side are:

- 8b/10b decode of received bytes
- Clock recovery and establishing dword synchronization
- Detection of Phy reset sequences
- Detection of OOB signals and speed negotiation primitives

Clock Management Primitives

Figure 16-2 below helps illustrate the overall transmit data path from the Link Layer through the Phy Layer. One thing this shows is the relative priority of injection of primitives. For example, the insertion of ALIGN primitives for clock compensation is a much higher priority than ALIGN primitives inserted in the Link Layer for rate matching. They cannot be delayed by any other inputs except the OOB signals and ALIGNs used in the Phy reset sequence.

Figure 16-2: Phy Transmit Data Path

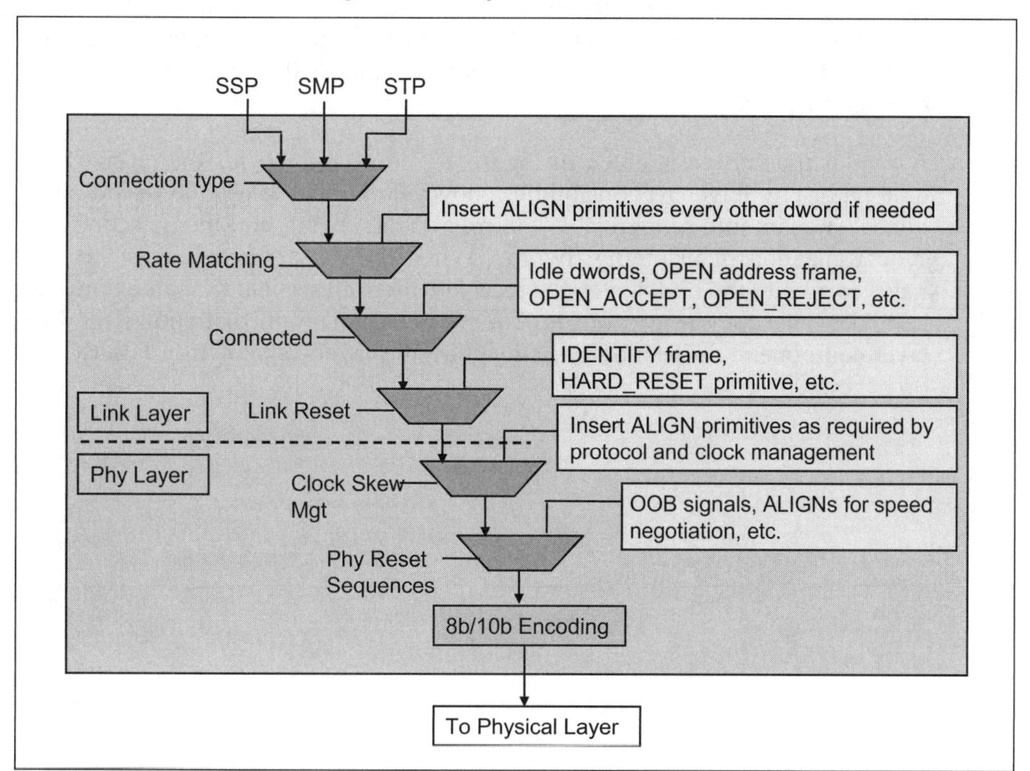

Primitive Injection Rate

The rate of this injection is frequency dependent: at 1.5 Gb/s, the required rate is one ALIGN or NOTIFY within every 2048 dwords; at 3.0 Gb/s, the required rate is two ALIGNs or NOTIFYs within every 4096 dwords. At the higher rate, there is no requirement for the ALIGNs to be distributed, so they can legally be sent back-to-back. Expanders have a little more to manage, because the clock domains on two different phys which are internally connected will not be the same. Consequently, expanders aren't required to pass through the same number of ALIGNs or NOTIFYs that they see on a source phy, but are allowed to change the number as needed to satisfy the destination phy. One simple approach that the standard mentions in this regard, but does not require, is that an expander can remove all the ALIGNs and NOTIFYs from an incoming path and then simply insert them at the outgoing Phy as needed.

Figure 16-2 on page 367 clarifies this somewhat, but it's worth mentioning here that the insertion of primitives for clock management is unrelated to the insertion of other primitives for things like rate matching, for example. An ALIGN inserted for one purpose cannot be counted against the number needed for another purpose.

A similar illustration is given in Figure 16-3 on page 369 for the receive side data path. Phy Layer responsibilities shown here include 8b/10b decoding of the data stream into recognizable control and data bytes, and the detection and synchronization of incoming dwords. When the data stream leaves the Phy Layer to go into the Link Layer, the receivers there all see it at the same time and just take what they need from it. Another block diagram that shows the Phy layer components in relation to its neighboring layers is shown in Figure 16-4 on page 370.

Figure 16-3: Phy Receive Data Path

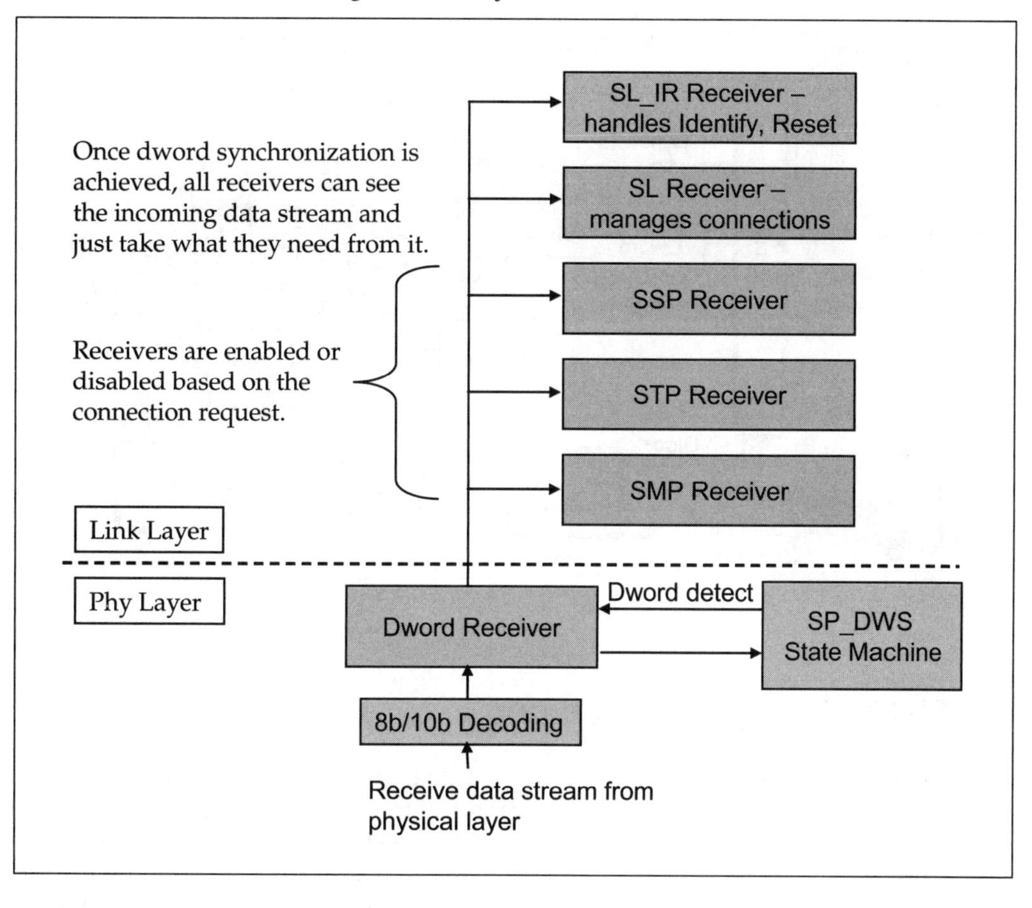

Figure 16-4: Phy Layer Receive Block Diagram

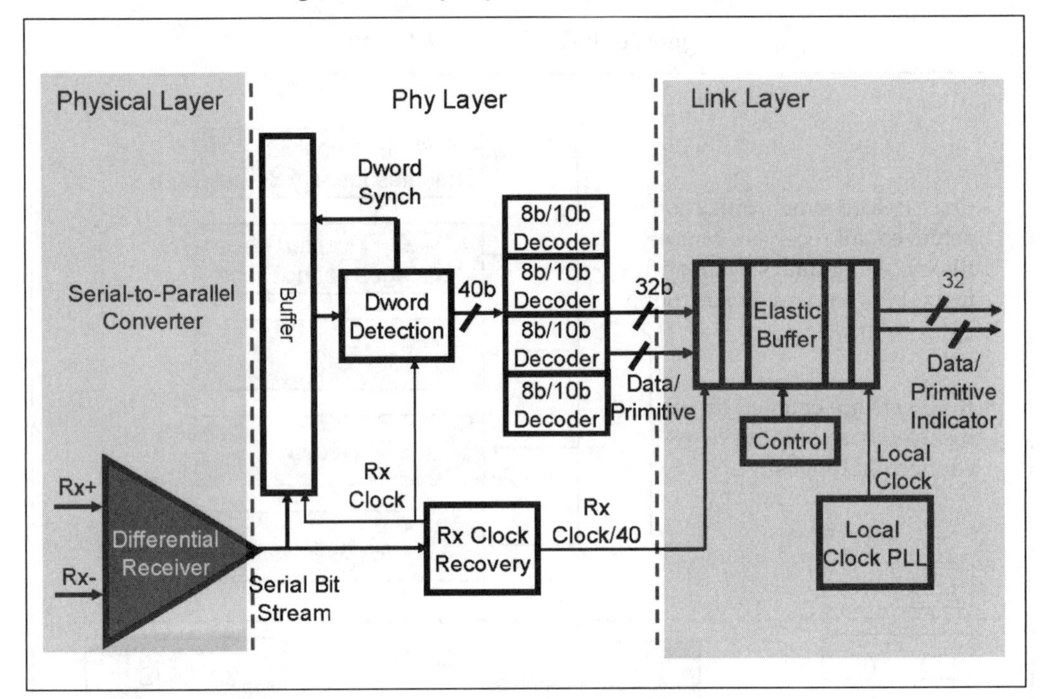

8b/10b Encoding and Decoding

The first responsibility of the Phy Layer is to encode the data stream as it arrives from the Link Layer in preparation for serial transmission using 8b/10b encoding (see Figure 16-5 on page 371). For those new to serial transports, encoding provides several benefits and perhaps the most important is that it embeds a clock into the data stream. The receiver recovers that embedded clock for use in latching the data as it arrives, which serves to remove the timing problems inherent in common-clock designs. The data stream appears to the receiver as an imperfect but predictable clock reference which allows it to recover the transmitter's clock frequency with acceptable accuracy. To make this work, the encoding scheme needs to ensure sufficient transitions in the data so that it looks enough like a clock at the receiver that it can be used to lock a PLL or other clock recovery circuit to the incoming frequency.

Figure 16-5: 8b/10b Encoder

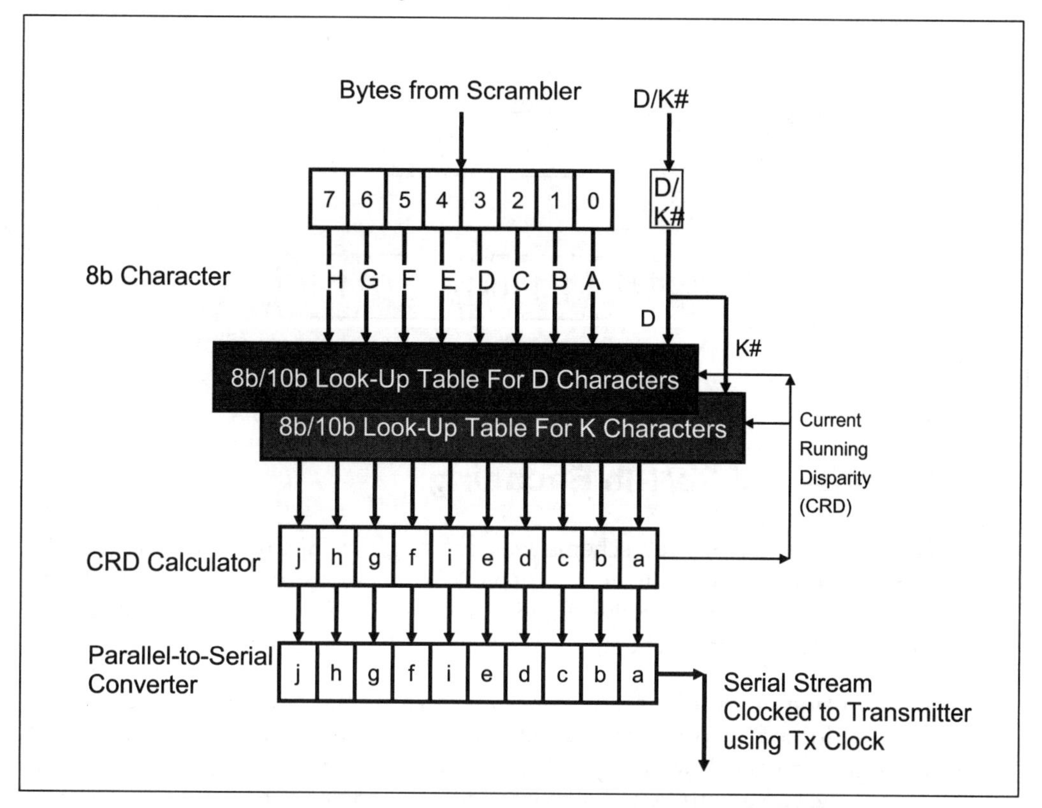

There are other serial encoding schemes available. For example a 64b/66b encoding is used in 10Gb Ethernet and by the SONET interface. Still, the method chosen for SAS was 8b/10b, presumably because it is simple, and because it has been used successfully in other serial interconnect designs like PCI Express, InfiniBand, and Fibre Channel. Figure 16-6 shows an example of 8b/10b encoding, where a data zero byte is encoded into a 10-bit value that meets the requirements.

Figure 16-6: 8b/10b Example Encoding

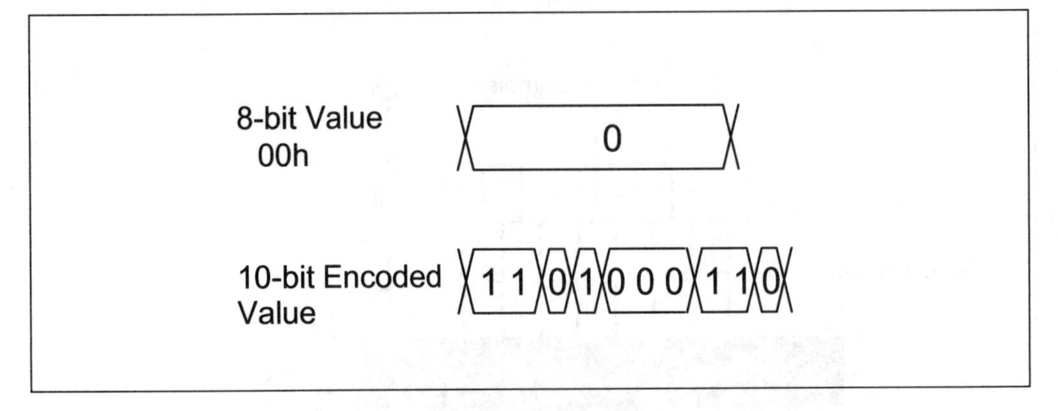

Purposes of 8b/10b Encoding

For reference, the 8b/10b scheme was patented by IBM back in 1984 (see the U.S. Patent Office web site at http://patft.uspto.gov for more details on Patent number 4486739). Among the stated purposes for this transmission design are the four items described here:

1. **Limiting the run length** is important because the receiver won't be able to stay locked onto the embedded clock if there are long periods where the signal remains low or high. Minimizing this problem is referred to as limiting the run length (length of a contiguous string of 1s or 0s), and represents one way to improve transition density for clock recovery. The maximum run length for 8b/10b is five. Each character will have a mix of zeros and ones, and no combination of characters would ever be able to create more than 5 ones or zeros in a row.
2. **DC balance** simply means keeping an even mix of ones and zeros going across the wire to prevent the line from becoming charged up. This is needed in applications where the transmitter and receiver are AC-coupled by means of capacitors. Only the AC component of the signal is of interest and the DC or common-mode voltage at the transmitter can be different from that of the receiver, meaning they do not need the same ground reference. To accomplish this with encoding requires the logic to observe the number of ones and zeros in the previous character and use that information in generating the next one. This is also referred to as maintaining disparity balance. A character with more ones than zeros is labeled as having a

positive disparity, while one with more zeros is said to have a negative disparity and one with 5 zeros and 5 ones is said to have neutral disparity. When a character with positive disparity is generated, that changes the Current Running Disparity (CRD) to positive. The CRD is fed back to the encoder and the next character will be generated with something other than a positive disparity (either negative or neutral), resulting in a DC balance on the wire.

As an example of how this works, consider Table 16-1, in which a simple character stream is transmitted onto the wire. To start with, the CRD for this transmission line is negative and the character that is to be sent is the K28.5 character. Looking up that combination of CRD and character in Table 16-2 yields a 10-bit value to be transmitted of 001111 1010, and that is shown in the bitstream. Because this value contains more ones than zeros, it is said to have positive disparity. Based on that, the Current Running Disparity changes to become positive, and that's a legal transition: going from negative to positive or positive to negative is legal, but it's not legal to have a positive CRD and send a character with a positive disparity. That case would be seen as an error at the receiver.

Table 16-1: Example Transmission Sequence

	CRD	Character	CRD		CRD		CRD
Character to be transmitted	-	K28.5	+	K28.5	-	D10.3	-
Bit stream sent		10-bit Symbol 001111 1010 (Disparity is positive)		10-bit Symbol 110000 0101 (Disparity is negative)		10-bit Symbol 010101 1100 (Disparity is neutral)	

Table 16-2: Example 8b/10b Encodings

D or K Character	Binary Bits	Byte Name	CRD - abcdei fghj	CRD + abcdei fghj
Data (D)	011 01010	D10.3	010101 1100	010101 0011
Control (K)	101 11100	K28.5	001111 1010	110000 0101

The next character to be sent is again the K28.5, but this time the CRD is positive, so when the logic computes or looks up the 10-bit value for it, the number ends up being 110000 0101. This value has more zeros than ones, so it has a negative disparity and changes the CRD from positive to negative. The last character to be sent is D10.3, and since the CRD is now negative, that generates a 10-bit value of 010101 1100. For this character, the number of ones and zeros is equal, so it is said to have neutral disparity. When a neutral character goes through the logic, the CRD remains unchanged from the value it had, and so in this case it remains negative.

3. **Special characters:** Since the encoding adds 2 more bits to each byte, there are 4 possible encodings for each data byte. However, many would create violations of the run length or DC balance rules, and only two variations are needed at most to provide each character an option based on the CRD. Some characters that already have neutral disparity actually use the same character regardless of the CRD so, in the end, not even half of the possible characters are actually used. Some of the unused characters are reserved for use as control characters and don't appear as data but instead have special meaning at the receiver. These characters were chosen to be easily recognized as different from the data characters, as described in the next point.
4. **Minimizing complexity** of the encoder/decoder was accomplished in part by splitting the problem into two pieces. Rather than the more complex straight 8-to-10 conversion, encoding is done by splitting the 8-bit input into 5b/6b and 3b/4b bit sub-blocks. One benefit of this approach is to help with recognition of special characters. For example, in the 5b/6b piece of the character, the last 4 of those 6 bits will never all be the same unless the character is a control character.

8b/10 Nomenclature

It makes sense at this point to describe the nomenclature that results from the encoding process. The bytes are split into a 5-bit sub-block and a 3-bit sub-block for conversion. A shorthand is used to describe the bytes based on this split, as illustrated in Figure 16-7 on page 375. One factor that needs to be known for the encoding is whether the byte is a data byte or one of the special control bytes. This is included with the byte to be encoded and shown in the diagram by the D/K# bit, which indicates (D)ata or (K)ontrol. SAS only uses the control characters for generation of primitives, which always start with a control character. The example in Figure 16-7 shows a Data byte with bits 01101010, which is referred to as a D10.3 character (usually pronounced as, "dee-ten-dot-three").

Figure 16-7: Nomenclature for 8-bit Encoding

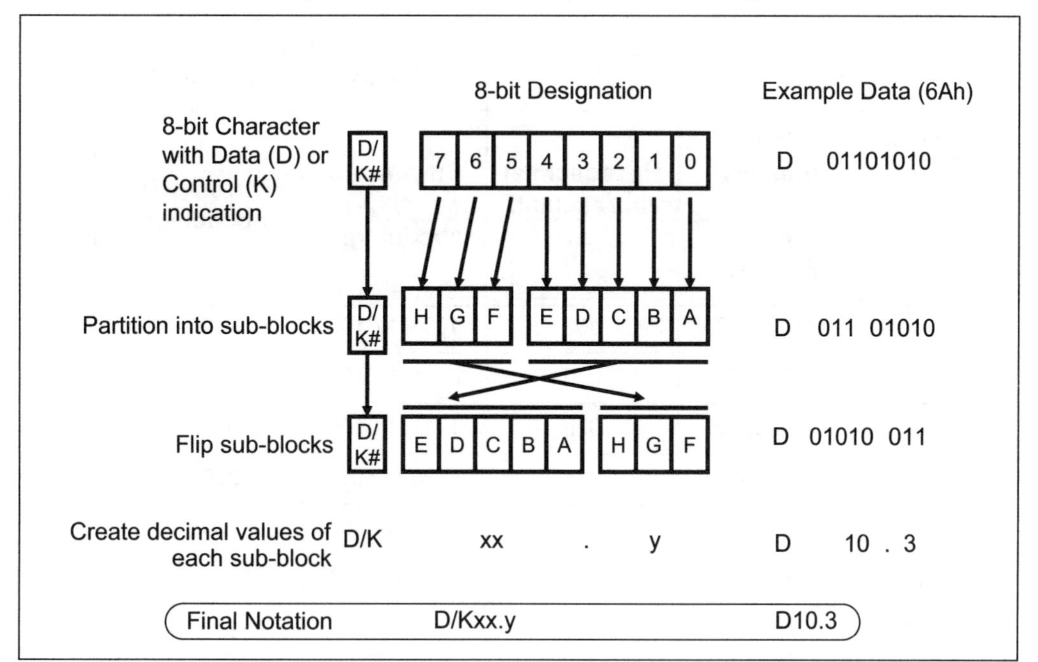

8b/10b Encoding Table

The full list of all the data characters and their encodings is given in section 6.3 of the SAS standard and is repeated here for convenience in Table 16-3 on the following page.

Table 16-3: Data characters (Sheet 1 of 13)

Name	Data byte		Data character (binary representation)	
	Binary representation (HGF EDCBA)	Hexadecimal representation	Current RD - abcdei fghj	Current RD + abcdei fghj
D00.0	000 00000	00h	100111 0100	011000 1011
D01.0	000 00001	01h	011101 0100	100010 1011
D02.0	000 00010	02h	101101 0100	010010 1011
D03.0	000 00011	03h	110001 1011	110001 0100
D04.0	000 00100	04h	110101 0100	001010 1011
D05.0	000 00101	05h	101001 1011	101001 0100
D06.0	000 00110	06h	011001 1011	011001 0100
D07.0	000 00111	07h	111000 1011	000111 0100
D08.0	000 01000	08h	111001 0100	000110 1011
D09.0	000 01001	09h	100101 1011	100101 0100
D10.0	000 01010	0Ah	010101 1011	010101 0100
D11.0	000 01011	0Bh	110100 1011	110100 0100
D12.0	000 01100	0Ch	001101 1011	001101 0100
D13.0	000 01101	0Dh	101100 1011	101100 0100
D14.0	000 01110	0Eh	011100 1011	011100 0100
D15.0	000 01111	0Fh	010111 0100	101000 1011
D16.0	000 10000	10h	011011 0100	100100 1011
D17.0	000 10001	11h	100011 1011	100011 0100
D18.0	000 10010	12h	010011 1011	010011 0100

Table 16-3: Data characters (Sheet 2 of 13)

Name	Data byte		Data character (binary representation)	
	Binary representation (HGF EDCBA)	Hexadecimal representation	Current RD - abcdei fghj	Current RD + abcdei fghj
D19.0	000 10011	13h	110010 1011	110010 0100
D20.0	000 10100	14h	001011 1011	001011 0100
D21.0	000 10101	15h	101010 1011	101010 0100
D22.0	000 10110	16h	011010 1011	011010 0100
D23.0	000 10111	17h	111010 0100	000101 1011
D24.0	000 11000	18h	110011 0100	001100 1011
D25.0	000 11001	19h	100110 1011	100110 0100
D26.0	000 11010	1Ah	010110 1011	010110 0100
D27.0	000 11011	1Bh	110110 0100	001001 1011
D28.0	000 11100	1Ch	001110 1011	001110 0100
D29.0	000 11101	1Dh	101110 0100	010001 1011
D30.0	000 11110	1Eh	011110 0100	100001 1011
D31.0	000 11111	1Fh	101011 0100	010100 1011
D00.1	001 00000	20h	100111 1001	011000 1001
D01.1	001 00001	21h	011101 1001	100010 1001
D02.1	001 00010	22h	101101 1001	010010 1001
D03.1	001 00011	23h	110001 1001	110001 1001
D04.1	001 00100	24h	110101 1001	001010 1001
D05.1	001 00101	25h	101001 1001	101001 1001
D06.1	001 00110	26h	011001 1001	011001 1001

Table 16-3: Data characters (Sheet 3 of 13)

Name	Data byte		Data character (binary representation)	
	Binary representation (HGF EDCBA)	Hexadecimal representation	Current RD - abcdei fghj	Current RD + abcdei fghj
D07.1	001 00111	27h	111000 1001	000111 1001
D08.1	001 01000	28h	111001 1001	000110 1001
D09.1	001 01001	29h	100101 1001	100101 1001
D10.1	001 01010	2Ah	010101 1001	010101 1001
D11.1	001 01011	2Bh	110100 1001	110100 1001
D12.1	001 01100	2Ch	001101 1001	001101 1001
D13.1	001 01101	2Dh	101100 1001	101100 1001
D14.1	001 01110	2Eh	011100 1001	011100 1001
D15.1	001 01111	2Fh	010111 1001	101000 1001
D16.1	001 10000	30h	011011 1001	100100 1001
D17.1	001 10001	31h	100011 1001	100011 1001
D18.1	001 10010	32h	010011 1001	010011 1001
D19.1	001 10011	33h	110010 1001	110010 1001
D20.1	001 10100	34h	001011 1001	001011 1001
D21.1	001 10101	35h	101010 1001	101010 1001
D22.1	001 10110	36h	011010 1001	011010 1001
D23.1	001 10111	37h	111010 1001	000101 1001
D24.1	001 11000	38h	110011 1001	001100 1001
D25.1	001 11001	39h	100110 1001	100110 1001
D26.1	001 11010	3Ah	010110 1001	010110 1001

Table 16-3: Data characters (Sheet 4 of 13)

Name	Data byte		Data character (binary representation)	
	Binary representation (HGF EDCBA)	Hexadecimal representation	Current RD - abcdei fghj	Current RD + abcdei fghj
D27.1	001 11011	3Bh	110110 1001	001001 1001
D28.1	001 11100	3Ch	001110 1001	001110 1001
D29.1	001 11101	3Dh	101110 1001	010001 1001
D30.1	001 11110	3Eh	011110 1001	100001 1001
D31.1	001 11111	3Fh	101011 1001	010100 1001
D00.2	010 00000	40h	100111 0101	011000 0101
D01.2	010 00001	41h	011101 0101	100010 0101
D02.2	010 00010	42h	101101 0101	010010 0101
D03.2	010 00011	43h	110001 0101	110001 0101
D04.2	010 00100	44h	110101 0101	001010 0101
D05.2	010 00101	45h	101001 0101	101001 0101
D06.2	010 00110	46h	011001 0101	011001 0101
D07.2	010 00111	47h	111000 0101	000111 0101
D08.2	010 01000	48h	111001 0101	000110 0101
D09.2	010 01001	49h	100101 0101	100101 0101
D10.2	010 01010	4Ah	010101 0101	010101 0101
D11.2	010 01011	4Bh	110100 0101	110100 0101
D12.2	010 01100	4Ch	001101 0101	001101 0101
D13.2	010 01101	4Dh	101100 0101	101100 0101
D14.2	010 01110	4Eh	011100 0101	011100 0101

Table 16-3: Data characters (Sheet 5 of 13)

Name	Data byte		Data character (binary representation)	
	Binary representation (HGF EDCBA)	Hexadecimal representation	Current RD - abcdei fghj	Current RD + abcdei fghj
D15.2	010 01111	4Fh	010111 0101	101000 0101
D16.2	010 10000	50h	011011 0101	100100 0101
D17.2	010 10001	51h	100011 0101	100011 0101
D18.2	010 10010	52h	010011 0101	010011 0101
D19.2	010 10011	53h	110010 0101	110010 0101
D20.2	010 10100	54h	001011 0101	001011 0101
D21.2	010 10101	55h	101010 0101	101010 0101
D22.2	010 10110	56h	011010 0101	011010 0101
D23.2	010 10111	57h	111010 0101	000101 0101
D24.2	010 11000	58h	110011 0101	001100 0101
D25.2	010 11001	59h	100110 0101	100110 0101
D26.2	010 11010	5Ah	010110 0101	010110 0101
D27.2	010 11011	5Bh	110110 0101	001001 0101
D28.2	010 11100	5Ch	001110 0101	001110 0101
D29.2	010 11101	5Dh	101110 0101	010001 0101
D30.2	010 11110	5Eh	011110 0101	100001 0101
D31.2	010 11111	5Fh	101011 0101	010100 0101
D00.3	011 00000	60h	100111 0011	011000 1100
D01.3	011 00001	61h	011101 0011	100010 1100
D02.3	011 00010	62h	101101 0011	010010 1100

Table 16-3: Data characters (Sheet 6 of 13)

Name	Data byte		Data character (binary representation)	
	Binary representation (HGF EDCBA)	Hexadecimal representation	Current RD - abcdei fghj	Current RD + abcdei fghj
D03.3	011 00011	63h	110001 1100	110001 0011
D04.3	011 00100	64h	110101 0011	001010 1100
D05.3	011 00101	65h	101001 1100	101001 0011
D06.3	011 00110	66h	011001 1100	011001 0011
D07.3	011 00111	67h	111000 1100	000111 0011
D08.3	011 01000	68h	111001 0011	000110 1100
D09.3	011 01001	69h	100101 1100	100101 0011
D10.3	011 01010	6Ah	010101 1100	010101 0011
D11.3	011 01011	6Bh	110100 1100	110100 0011
D12.3	011 01100	6Ch	001101 1100	001101 0011
D13.3	011 01101	6Dh	101100 1100	101100 0011
D14.3	011 01110	6Eh	011100 1100	011100 0011
D15.3	011 01111	6Fh	010111 0011	101000 1100
D16.3	011 10000	70h	011011 0011	100100 1100
D17.3	011 10001	71h	100011 1100	100011 0011
D18.3	011 10010	72h	010011 1100	010011 0011
D19.3	011 10011	73h	110010 1100	110010 0011
D20.3	011 10100	74h	001011 1100	001011 0011
D21.3	011 10101	75h	101010 1100	101010 0011
D22.3	011 10110	76h	011010 1100	011010 0011

Table 16-3: Data characters (Sheet 7 of 13)

Name	Data byte		Data character (binary representation)	
	Binary representation (HGF EDCBA)	Hexadecimal representation	Current RD - abcdei fghj	Current RD + abcdei fghj
D23.3	011 10111	77h	111010 0011	000101 1100
D24.3	011 11000	78h	110011 0011	001100 1100
D25.3	011 11001	79h	100110 1100	100110 0011
D26.3	011 11010	7Ah	010110 1100	010110 0011
D27.3	011 11011	7Bh	110110 0011	001001 1100
D28.3	011 11100	7Ch	001110 1100	001110 0011
D29.3	011 11101	7Dh	101110 0011	010001 1100
D30.3	011 11110	7Eh	011110 0011	100001 1100
D31.3	011 11111	7Fh	101011 0011	010100 1100
D00.4	100 00000	80h	100111 0010	011000 1101
D01.4	100 00001	81h	011101 0010	100010 1101
D02.4	100 00010	82h	101101 0010	010010 1101
D03.4	100 00011	83h	110001 1101	110001 0010
D04.4	100 00100	84h	110101 0010	001010 1101
D05.4	100 00101	85h	101001 1101	101001 0010
D06.4	100 00110	86h	011001 1101	011001 0010
D07.4	100 00111	87h	111000 1101	000111 0010
D08.4	100 01000	88h	111001 0010	000110 1101
D09.4	100 01001	89h	100101 1101	100101 0010
D10.4	100 01010	8Ah	010101 1101	010101 0010

Table 16-3: Data characters (Sheet 8 of 13)

Name	Data byte		Data character (binary representation)	
	Binary representation (HGF EDCBA)	Hexadecimal representation	Current RD - abcdei fghj	Current RD + abcdei fghj
D11.4	100 01011	8Bh	110100 1101	110100 0010
D12.4	100 01100	8Ch	001101 1101	001101 0010
D13.4	100 01101	8Dh	101100 1101	101100 0010
D14.4	100 01110	8Eh	011100 1101	011100 0010
D15.4	100 01111	8Fh	010111 0010	101000 1101
D16.4	100 10000	90h	011011 0010	100100 1101
D17.4	100 10001	91h	100011 1101	100011 0010
D18.4	100 10010	92h	010011 1101	010011 0010
D19.4	100 10011	93h	110010 1101	110010 0010
D20.4	100 10100	94h	001011 1101	001011 0010
D21.4	100 10101	95h	101010 1101	101010 0010
D22.4	100 10110	96h	011010 1101	011010 0010
D23.4	100 10111	97h	111010 0010	000101 1101
D24.4	100 11000	98h	110011 0010	001100 1101
D25.4	100 11001	99h	100110 1101	100110 0010
D26.4	100 11010	9Ah	010110 1101	010110 0010
D27.4	100 11011	9Bh	110110 0010	001001 1101
D28.4	100 11100	9Ch	001110 1101	001110 0010
D29.4	100 11101	9Dh	101110 0010	010001 1101
D30.4	100 11110	9Eh	011110 0010	100001 1101

Table 16-3: Data characters (Sheet 9 of 13)

Name	Data byte		Data character (binary representation)	
	Binary representation (HGF EDCBA)	Hexadecimal representation	Current RD - abcdei fghj	Current RD + abcdei fghj
D31.4	100 11111	9Fh	101011 0010	010100 1101
D00.5	101 00000	A0h	100111 1010	011000 1010
D01.5	101 00001	A1h	011101 1010	100010 1010
D02.5	101 00010	A2h	101101 1010	010010 1010
D03.5	101 00011	A3h	110001 1010	110001 1010
D04.5	101 00100	A4h	110101 1010	001010 1010
D05.5	101 00101	A5h	101001 1010	101001 1010
D06.5	101 00110	A6h	011001 1010	011001 1010
D07.5	101 00111	A7h	111000 1010	000111 1010
D08.5	101 01000	A8h	111001 1010	000110 1010
D09.5	101 01001	A9h	100101 1010	100101 1010
D10.5	101 01010	AAh	010101 1010	010101 1010
D11.5	101 01011	ABh	110100 1010	110100 1010
D12.5	101 01100	ACh	001101 1010	001101 1010
D13.5	101 01101	ADh	101100 1010	101100 1010
D14.5	101 01110	AEh	011100 1010	011100 1010
D15.5	101 01111	AFh	010111 1010	101000 1010
D16.5	101 10000	B0h	011011 1010	100100 1010
D17.5	101 10001	B1h	100011 1010	100011 1010
D18.5	101 10010	B2h	010011 1010	010011 1010

Table 16-3: Data characters (Sheet 10 of 13)

Name	Data byte		Data character (binary representation)	
	Binary representation (HGF EDCBA)	Hexadecimal representation	Current RD - abcdei fghj	Current RD + abcdei fghj
D19.5	101 10011	B3h	110010 1010	110010 1010
D20.5	101 10100	B4h	001011 1010	001011 1010
D21.5	101 10101	B5h	101010 1010	101010 1010
D22.5	101 10110	B6h	011010 1010	011010 1010
D23.5	101 10111	B7h	111010 1010	000101 1010
D24.5	101 11000	B8h	110011 1010	001100 1010
D25.5	101 11001	B9h	100110 1010	100110 1010
D26.5	101 11010	BAh	010110 1010	010110 1010
D27.5	101 11011	BBh	110110 1010	001001 1010
D28.5	101 11100	BCh	001110 1010	001110 1010
D29.5	101 11101	BDh	101110 1010	010001 1010
D30.5	101 11110	BEh	011110 1010	100001 1010
D31.5	101 11111	BFh	101011 1010	010100 1010
D00.6	110 00000	C0h	100111 0110	011000 0110
D01.6	110 00001	C1h	011101 0110	100010 0110
D02.6	110 00010	C2h	101101 0110	010010 0110
D03.6	110 00011	C3h	110001 0110	110001 0110
D04.6	110 00100	C4h	110101 0110	001010 0110
D05.6	110 00101	C5h	101001 0110	101001 0110
D06.6	110 00110	C6h	011001 0110	011001 0110

Table 16-3: Data characters (Sheet 11 of 13)

Name	Data byte		Data character (binary representation)	
	Binary representation (HGF EDCBA)	Hexadecimal representation	Current RD - abcdei fghj	Current RD + abcdei fghj
D07.6	110 00111	C7h	111000 0110	000111 0110
D08.6	110 01000	C8h	111001 0110	000110 0110
D09.6	110 01001	C9h	100101 0110	100101 0110
D10.6	110 01010	CAh	010101 0110	010101 0110
D11.6	110 01011	CBh	110100 0110	110100 0110
D12.6	110 01100	CCh	001101 0110	001101 0110
D13.6	110 01101	CDh	101100 0110	101100 0110
D14.6	110 01110	CEh	011100 0110	011100 0110
D15.6	110 01111	CFh	010111 0110	101000 0110
D16.6	110 10000	D0h	011011 0110	100100 0110
D17.6	110 10001	D1h	100011 0110	100011 0110
D18.6	110 10010	D2h	010011 0110	010011 0110
D19.6	110 10011	D3h	110010 0110	110010 0110
D20.6	110 10100	D4h	001011 0110	001011 0110
D21.6	110 10101	D5h	101010 0110	101010 0110
D22.6	110 10110	D6h	011010 0110	011010 0110
D23.6	110 10111	D7h	111010 0110	000101 0110
D24.6	110 11000	D8h	110011 0110	001100 0110
D25.6	110 11001	D9h	100110 0110	100110 0110
D26.6	110 11010	DAh	010110 0110	010110 0110

Table 16-3: Data characters (Sheet 12 of 13)

Name	Data byte		Data character (binary representation)	
	Binary representation (HGF EDCBA)	Hexadecimal representation	Current RD - abcdei fghj	Current RD + abcdei fghj
D27.6	110 11011	DBh	110110 0110	001001 0110
D28.6	110 11100	DCh	001110 0110	001110 0110
D29.6	110 11101	DDh	101110 0110	010001 0110
D30.6	110 11110	DEh	011110 0110	100001 0110
D31.6	110 11111	DFh	101011 0110	010100 0110
D00.7	111 00000	E0h	100111 0001	011000 1110
D01.7	111 00001	E1h	011101 0001	100010 1110
D02.7	111 00010	E2h	101101 0001	010010 1110
D03.7	111 00011	E3h	110001 1110	110001 0001
D04.7	111 00100	E4h	110101 0001	001010 1110
D05.7	111 00101	E5h	101001 1110	101001 0001
D06.7	111 00110	E6h	011001 1110	011001 0001
D07.7	111 00111	E7h	111000 1110	000111 0001
D08.7	111 01000	E8h	111001 0001	000110 1110
D09.7	111 01001	E9h	100101 1110	100101 0001
D10.7	111 01010	EAh	010101 1110	010101 0001
D11.7	111 01011	EBh	110100 1110	110100 1000
D12.7	111 01100	ECh	001101 1110	001101 0001
D13.7	111 01101	EDh	101100 1110	101100 1000
D14.7	111 01110	EEh	011100 1110	011100 1000

Table 16-3: Data characters (Sheet 13 of 13)

Name	Data byte		Data character (binary representation)	
	Binary representation (HGF EDCBA)	Hexadecimal representation	Current RD - abcdei fghj	Current RD + abcdei fghj
D15.7	111 01111	EFh	010111 0001	101000 1110
D16.7	111 10000	F0h	011011 0001	100100 1110
D17.7	111 10001	F1h	100011 0111	100011 0001
D18.7	111 10010	F2h	010011 0111	010011 0001
D19.7	111 10011	F3h	110010 1110	110010 0001
D20.7	111 10100	F4h	001011 0111	001011 0001
D21.7	111 10101	F5h	101010 1110	101010 0001
D22.7	111 10110	F6h	011010 1110	011010 0001
D23.7	111 10111	F7h	111010 0001	000101 1110
D24.7	111 11000	F8h	110011 0001	001100 1110
D25.7	111 11001	F9h	100110 1110	100110 0001
D26.7	111 11010	FAh	010110 1110	010110 0001
D27.7	111 11011	FBh	110110 0001	001001 1110
D28.7	111 11100	FCh	001110 1110	001110 0001
D29.7	111 11101	FDh	101110 0001	010001 1110
D30.7	111 11110	FEh	011110 0001	100001 1110
D31.7	111 11111	FFh	101011 0001	010100 1110

Control Characters and the Comma Pattern

The full list of control characters is also repeated here in Table 16-4. Three of these characters, highlighted in the table, have an easily recognizable pattern that does not occur in any other characters or even at the boundary between any two characters: they begin with 2 bits of one polarity followed by 5 bits of the other polarity. This is sometimes referred to as a "comma" pattern and is a useful feature for establishing SAS dword synchronization, as will be seen later. Not all of the available control characters are used in the SAS standard; in fact, only three of them are actually used, as shown in Table 16-5. The K28.5 character, which does contain the comma pattern, is the only control character used in SAS transactions, while K28.3 is used in STP connections and K28.6 only appears on SATA physical links. In fact, K28.6 is the SATA_ERROR indicator and is only sent by expanders that receive a frame during an STP connection that has an invalid dword or other error.

Table 16-4: Control Characters

Name	Control byte		Control character (binary representation)	
	Binary Representation (HGF EDCBA)	Hexadecimal Representation	CRD - abcdei fghj	CRD + abcdei fghj
K28.0	000 11100	1Ch	001111 0100	110000 1011
K28.1	001 11100	3Ch	**001111 1001**	**110000 0110**
K28.2	010 11100	5Ch	001111 0101	110000 1010
K28.3	011 11100	7Ch	001111 0011	110000 1100
K28.4	100 11100	9Ch	001111 0010	110000 1101
K28.5	101 11100	BCh	**001111 1010**	**110000 0101**
K28.6	110 11100	DCh	001111 0110	110000 1001
K28.7	111 11100	FCh	**001111 1000**	**110000 0111**
K23.7	111 10111	F7h	111010 1000	000101 0111
K27.7	111 11011	FBh	110110 1000	001001 0111
K29.7	111 11101	FDh	101110 1000	010001 0111
K30.7	111 11110	FEh	011110 1000	100001 0111

Table 16-5: Control Character Usage in SAS

First Character of a dword	Use in SAS physical links	Use in SATA physical links
K28.3	Primitives that are only used inside STP connections	All primitives except ALIGN
K28.5	ALIGN and most primitives defined within the standard	ALIGN
K28.6	Not used	SATA_ERROR

Properties of 10b characters

Some characteristics of the 10-bit characters that result from 8b/10b encoding help facilitate detection of errors in transmission, as listed below. Any character without these properties is invalid by definition and will be discarded at the receiver.

- Using disparity forces an equal number of ones and zeros over time.
- The longest continuous string of either ones or zeros is five.
- A 10-bit character must have: 5 ones and 5 zeros, or 4 ones and 6 zeros, or 6 zeros and 4 ones. No other combination is legal.
- The 6-bit sub-block cannot contain more than 4 ones or 4 zeros.
- The 4-bit sub-block cannot contain more than 3 ones or 3 zeros.

Bytes, Characters, and Dwords

For clarity, it is helpful to remember that, before encoding, information moves through the device in 8-bit bytes that are grouped into groups of four bytes called dwords. After encoding, the 10-bit result is called a character, and these are also gathered into groups of 4 called dwords. A dword before encoding is 32 bits, and after encoding it is 40 bits. Characters can be either data or control characters, while dwords can be data or primitives.

A primitive is a dword that begins with a control character and is followed by three data characters that define the meaning of the primitive. For SAS primitives, the first character will always be K28.5, while for SATA primitives it will be K28.5 or K28.3. A SATA target could also see a K28.6 character as part of the special error primitive, coming from a SAS expander that received an invalid dword or other error. (Using K28.6, which is not recognized by SATA and will be considered an error, is a way for expanders to robustly communicate errors in the path from SAS to SATA.) Primitives are always sent out on the wire in this order: first the control character, followed by three data characters. It is important to mention this because the endianess of SAS and SATA are normally different, but for primitives the endianness of both is the same.

Initialization

While this topic is a Phy Layer responsibility, the discussion about it has been moved to Chapter 6, entitled "SAS Initialization," on page 125 in an effort to create a more logical flow as the concepts are introduced.

The pieces involved in initialization are the generation of the Phy reset sequence, generation of the OOB (Out of Band) signaling, and primitives for speed negotiation. All of these tasks are handled by the Phy Layer.

Implementation Examples

Having described the Phy Layer in some detail, let's consider some implementation examples. The standard is careful not to specify any particular implementations, but for instructional purposes the block diagrams and description that follow should nevertheless help clarify the various tasks that must be accomplished for transmission and reception of frames.

Transmit Block

On the transmit side, as shown in Figure 16-8, the Phy Layer generates and injects the ALIGN(0) primitives for the OOB sequence. This is done automatically when the device is reset or the link is reset.

For normal transmission, the Phy Layer receives a scrambled output from the Link Layer along with an indication of whether the dword is a primitive or data. It is expected, though not required, that many vendors will implement the transmit path as four bytes wide, as shown here, to simplify the design. This would also mean that the internal clock would only need to be 1/40th of the transmit clock, so if the serial data rate is 3.0 Gb/s, then the internal dword rate would be 75 MHz.

Figure 16-8: Phy Layer Transmit Block Diagram

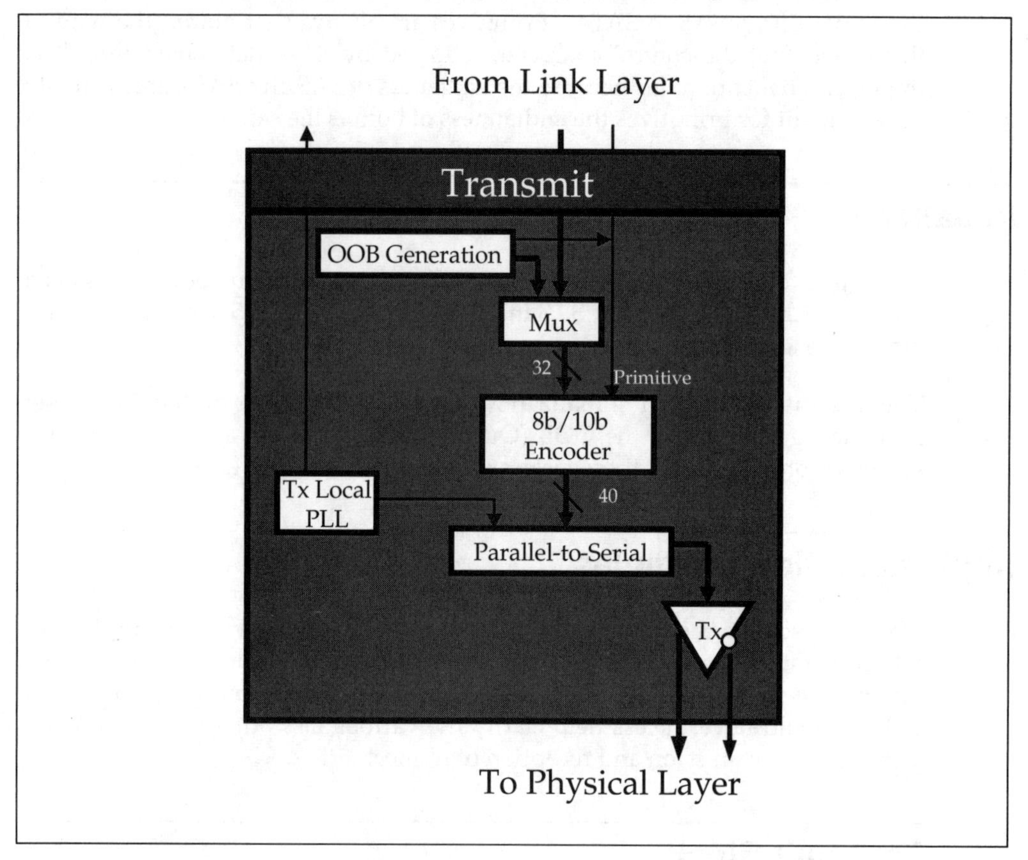

Selecting Frames or OOB Primitives

As shown, the first step is to select whether the scrambled data stream from the Link Layer or the OOB primitive stream generated by the Phy Layer will be forwarded to the encoder. This selection is based on the status of the link. The OOB primitives could be generated and injected before the encoder, or the encoded versions injected after the encoder, and the designer can choose what seems best. The next step is to pass the data stream from the mux through the 8b/10b encoder. Since 8b/10b is only defined for one byte at a time, and the result depends on the CRD generated by the previous byte, the four bytes coming in cannot be directly converted in parallel. Instead, the CRD of the first byte conversion is needed as an input to the second, and so on. The logic to perform the encoding can still be set up to do a full dword in one clock period, though, in much the same way that a wide arithmetic adder can be designed to pass the carry bit from the previous section of the operand to the next. In the diagram of Table 16-9, the 40-bit output of the encoder next passes to the serializer, which takes in a dword and shifts the bits out serially to the differential transmitter based on the transmit clock frequency that was selected during speed negotiation on the link.

Figure 16-9: Parallel CRD Generation

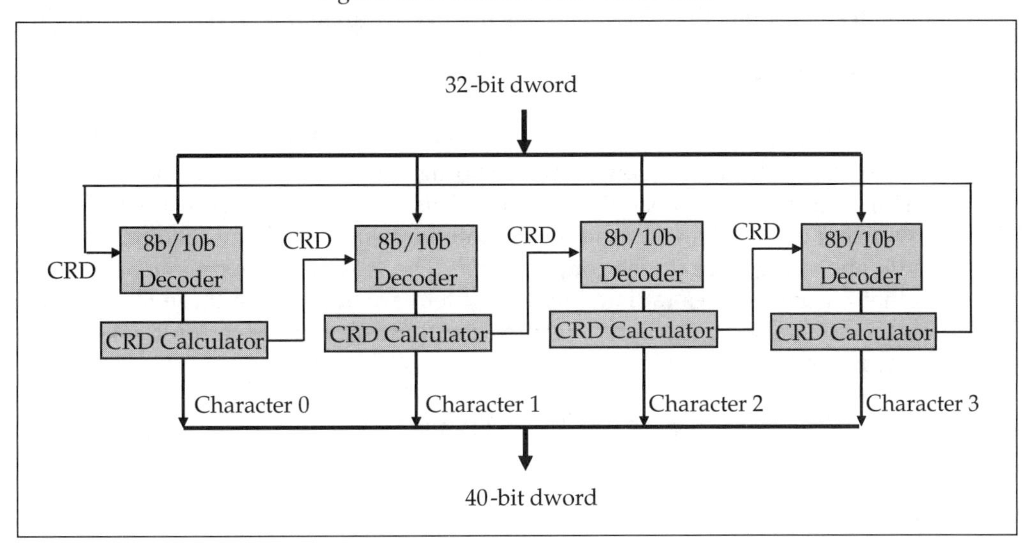

Reducing EMI by Using SSC

The data is clocked out of the serializer using the internal transmit clock running at either 1.5 GHz or 3.0 GHz. This clock must be accurate to within +/- 100 ppm (parts per million; 100 ppm translates to 0.01%) of the center frequency for SAS, resulting in a maximum possible difference between two devices of 200 ppm. The range is much wider for SATA, at 5,700 ppm, because the clock accuracy is not as tight to start with at +/- 350 ppm, and it permits the use of SSC (Spread Spectrum Clocking). SSC varies the clock over a range of frequencies rather than keeping it fixed as a pure reference clock, for the purpose of reducing EMI (electro-magnetic interference). For that reason, it is commonly used in devices that operate in consumer environments where stricter EMI requirements must be met. While varying the operating frequency does not reduce the overall radiated energy of the device, it spreads that energy across a wider range of frequencies and therefore reduces how much is seen at any one given frequency. Since emissions tests like those used by the FCC in the U.S. test for energy thresholds at certain frequencies, the goal is to ensure that none of the frequencies has so much radiated energy that it would fail the threshold test. SATA is designed for use in such environments and so SSC is optional for SATA transmitters, and required for SATA receivers. SAS, on the other hand, is designed for the server market where such strict EMI standards are not required, so SAS does not use SSC at all. Still, SAS ports that will support SATA devices must be capable of handling this frequency range without error. This means that the PLL or other clock-generation logic must be designed with that in mind. A digital PLL that will support SATA, for example, will likely need more feedback bits to cover the wider frequency range than it otherwise would.

Bit Frequency

An interesting observation regarding frequency is that the frequency of the signals seen on the wire using NRZ encoding must necessarily be less than or equal to half of the transmit frequency. This is shown in Figure 16-10, where two rising edges of the internally-generated transmit clock are required to generate one rising edge on the output signal. The reason for mentioning this here is that the frequencies radiated by the system are likely to be those that appear on the transmission medium, meaning the frequency of concern for a 3.0 Gb/s system would be 1.5 GHz.

Figure 16-10: Output Frequency

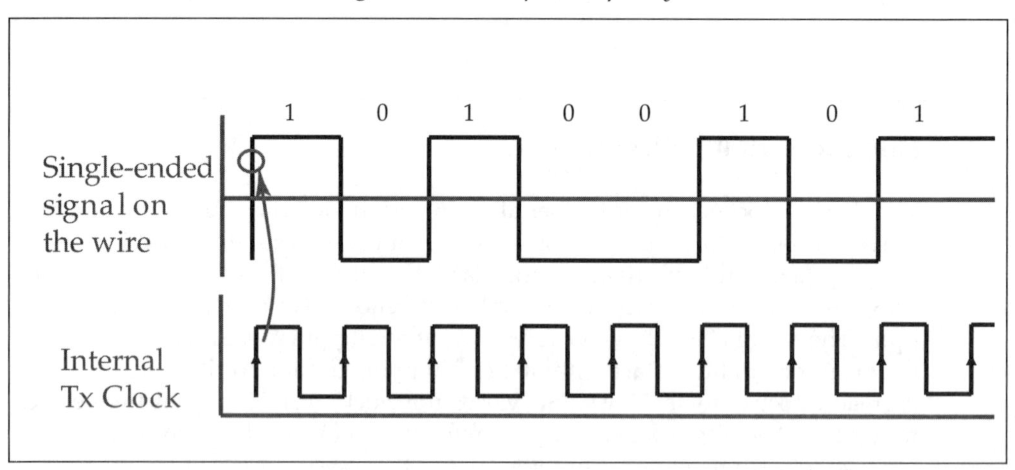

Receive Block

On the receive side (see Table 16-11), the data stream passes through the differential receiver and is converted back into the stream of bits that was sent by the transmitter. After a reset or power-up event, the receiver must learn what type of device is attached, and that is the purpose of the OOB detection logic. Since no synchronization has been achieved yet during OOB, it is not required for the logic to be able to recognize primitives or other structures. Instead, the logic only needs to behave as a squelch-detect circuit, observing whether the incoming stream is above or below a voltage threshold. When transitions above the threshold are seen, the circuit then measures the idle time between bursts of activity to determine the OOB pattern from the transmitter.

Figure 16-11: Receive Block Diagram

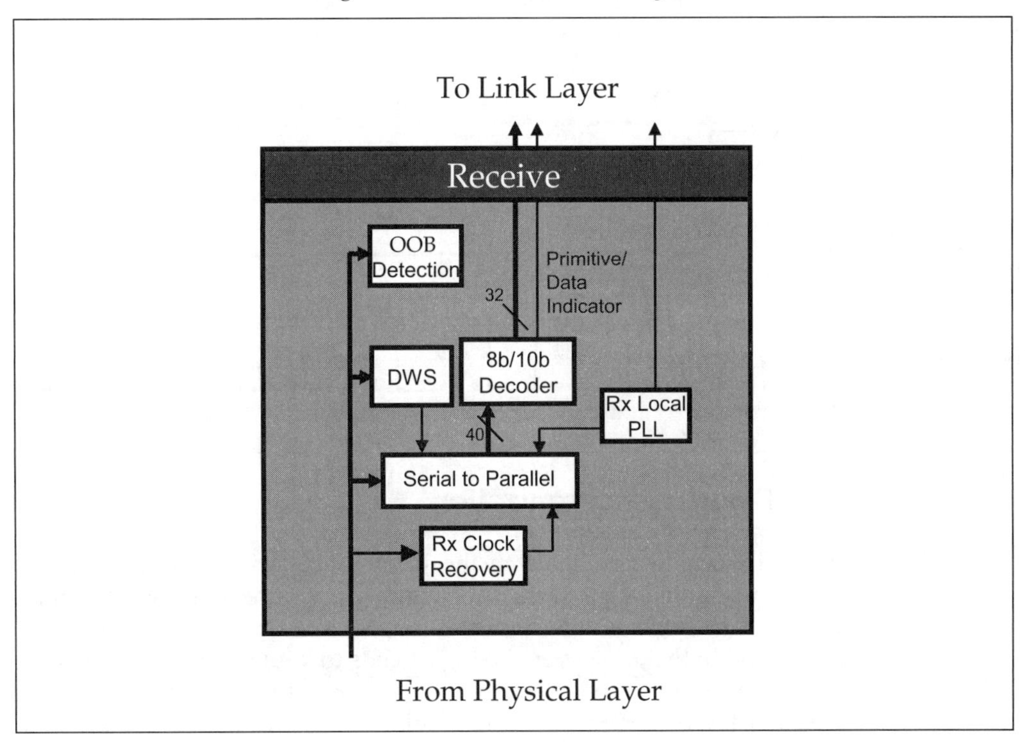

Recovering the Clock

Once OOB and speed negotiation are complete, the receiver knows the operational frequency and uses a local PLL or oversampling circuit to lock onto that frequency in the incoming bit stream. Locking onto the clock is a straight-forward process that involves adjusting the phase of the recovered clock relative to the bit stream. Doing so moves the clock edges away from transitions in the data, as shown in Figure 16-12 on page 396, allowing it to reliably latch the incoming data. The illustration is purposely drawn with the longest legal run length of 5 bits of the same polarity to show the trouble that the receiver needs to avoid. The longer the run length, the longer the clock is running without any reference and the more opportunity it has to drift from the actual frequency. That makes the later bit positions more and more a matter of guesswork. Trouble is avoided by ensuring a maximum run length of only 5 bits.

Figure 16-12: Recovering Receiver Clock

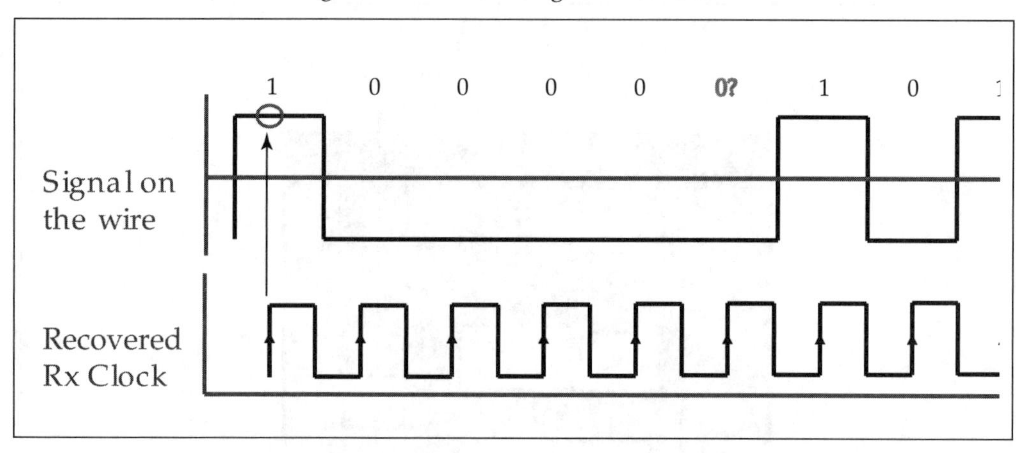

Achieving Dword Synchronization

This recovered clock is used to latch the incoming bits into a de-serializing buffer at the negotiated data rate. The buffer groups the bits together into groups of 40 bits to create a dword output for the next stage in the process. In order to correctly do that, however, the logic needs to know where the previous dword ended and the next one begins, and that task is handled by a block of logic called the DWS (DWord Synchronization) state machine. As described earlier, when it has been instructed to find a dword, this logic watches the incoming bit stream and searches for the recognizable comma pattern. The detection of the pattern establishes both the bit position for the incoming bytes, and the byte position for grouping them into dwords, since K28.5 is required to be in the first byte position of a primitive dword. The DWS forces that byte pattern into the first byte position and fills in from there. Although it continues to watch the incoming stream to verify that every dword is valid, the DWS state machine will not go through this dword synchronizing search routine again unless instructed to do so.

8b/10b Decoding

After the bits are gathered into dwords, the next step is to decode them from 8b/10b characters back into bytes. As shown in Figure 16-13, this can be modeled with a look-up table, although it is more likely to be implemented as combinatorial logic in hardware. As can be seen, for each 10-bit character, the CRD from the previous character must be computed and fed into the decode process.

Figure 16-13: 8b/10b Decoding

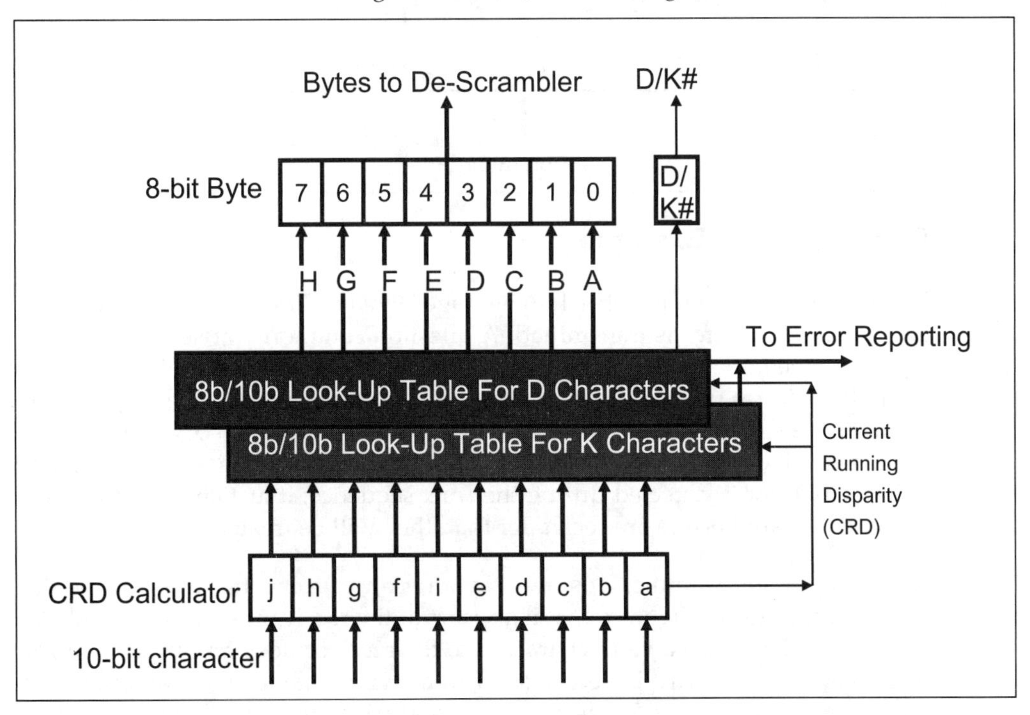

For a single-byte stream this is simple, but as with the transmitter, working with a dword stream means another step is involved, as shown in Figure 16-14 on page 398. The CRD results must be routed to the appropriate decoder so that each one sees the results for the byte that appeared just before the one it is evaluating. The CRD is included in the bit stream to maintain the disparity or D.C.

balance of the transmission, but disparity mismatches can also detect errors earlier than might otherwise happen, as described in the following example.

Figure 16-14: 40-bit Version of 8b/10b Decoder

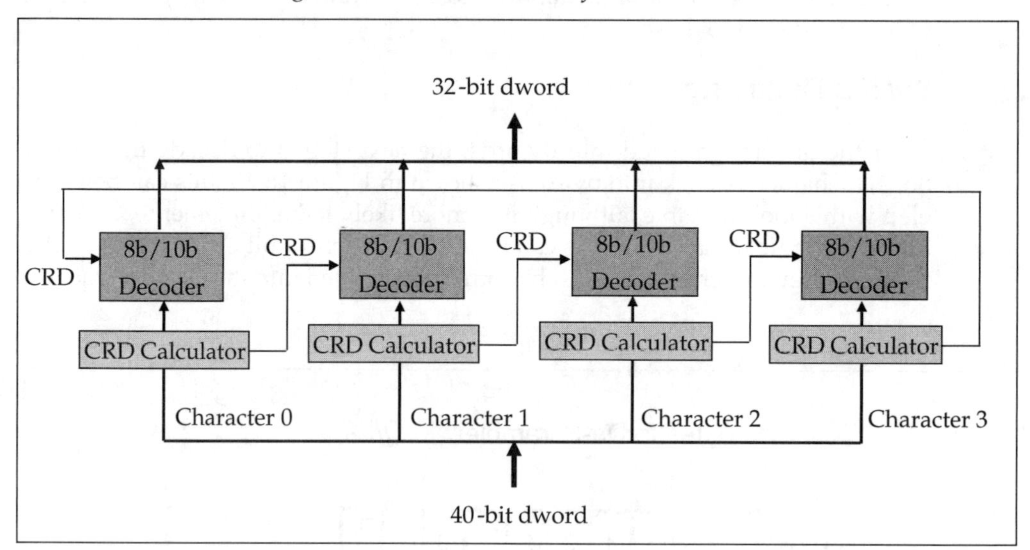

Disparity Error Example

In the example shown in Table 16-6 on page 399, the CRD is currently negative and a D21.1 character is transmitted. A question commonly arises at this point regarding the initial value of the CRD at the receiver since it cannot know what the initial CRD at the transmitter will be. Basically, a receiver will set the initial value of the CRD based on the first non-neutral character it sees after a reset. That means it doesn't matter what CRD value the receiver chooses after reset: if a disparity error is detected during the reset sequence, it just changes the CRD value. If disparity errors are seen after that, they will be treated as errors.

Returning to our example, let's now say an error causes a bit to flip while the D21.1 character is in flight, so that it appears at the receiver as D21.0 instead. As it happens, this is still a valid character, so the receiver does not detect an error there, and the disparity is also legal. The arriving character is valid and has more ones than zeros, so it has a positive disparity. Since the CRD is negative, the only legal disparity values that can be received are neutral disparity, which leaves the CRD as it was, and positive disparity, which changes the CRD to positive. As a result, the receiver does not see an error.

Table 16-6: Disparity Error Example

	CRD	Character	CRD	Character	CRD	Character	CRD
Transmitted Character Stream	-	D21.1	-	D10.2	-	D23.5	+
Transmitted Bit Stream	-	101010 1001	-	010101 0101	-	111010 1010	+
Bit Stream After Error	-	101010 1011	+	010101 0101	+	111010 1010	+
Decoded Character Stream	-	D21.0	+	D10.2	+	Invalid	+

Error occurs here

Error detected here

The next character sent is D10.2. Since the transmitter sees the CRD as negative, it arrives at the 10-bit value shown, which has a neutral disparity (5 ones and 5 zeros) and leaves the CRD unchanged. The character is transmitted across the link without error, so the receiver sees that the character is valid and has a neutral disparity. The receivers CRD was positive, so a neutral disparity leaves it unchanged. Finally, a D23.5 character is sent, which looks up to a value that has positive disparity. Since the transmitter CRD was negative, this is valid and changes the CRD to positive. When it arrives without trouble at the receiver, the problem finally is visible. The receiver's CRD was positive and the incoming character also has a positive CRD. This disparity error tells the receiver that there has been a problem in transmission, but unfortunately not which byte or dword had the trouble.

Disparity errors are recognized as invalid dwords and may cause loss of dword synchronization. A count of how often this has happened is maintained in the protocol-specific log page for SAS, and is also readable with an SMP REPORT PHY ERROR LOG request. This count is maintained separately from the count of invalid dwords such as 8b/10b code violations, or dwords inconsistent with dword construction rules.

Power Management

Unlike SATA, SAS does not include any power management features, except in support of SAS ports acting as SATA host devices. Even then, "support" is a euphemistic term, since the host is not allowed to initiate any power management activity, and denies target requests for it with SATA_PMNAK.

Resets

There are several reset sequences defined for the SAS link. The Phy Layer is only responsible for generating the Phy Reset, but this is a good place to review them all. A Phy reset, consisting of an OOB sequence followed by a speed negotiation sequence, resets only the Phy of the receiving device, not the port containing the Phy or other ports or Phys of the device. It has no affect on upper levels so queued commands are still available, making this an option for clearing transmission errors. A hard reset, by comparison, is interpreted as an upper-level reset that causes the device to abort everything it is working on. The link reset and hard reset can be requested by an SMP PHY CONTROL request using the appropriate bits of the Phy Operation field. Keeping in mind that a Phy reset is the first part of both a link reset and hard reset as seen in the following diagrams, the reasons for requesting a Phy reset are:

- Power on
- Receiving a Hard Reset OOB pattern
- Receiving a management Application Layer request to reset
- Losing dword synchronization and not attempting to re-acquire it
- Timeout of Receive Identify timer
- For expander phys, after a hot-plug timeout (500ms)

Hard Reset

The hard reset sequence and identification sequence (see Figure 16-15 on the following page) are controlled by the Link Layer, as described in the section called "Primitives" on page 284. If a SAS Phy receives a hard reset it initiates a reset of that port, but not any other ports of the device. If the port is an SSP port, this results in a Transport Reset event notification to the SCSI Application Layer and the SCSI device will perform a hard reset. For an STP port, all the resets are effectively the same, and the SATA device will take steps associated with a hardware or power-on reset. Expander ports do not forward OOB patterns or hard reset, and they do not reset their internal settings, such as routing tables. However, a hard reset to a wide port does cause all the phys of that port to reset.

Figure 16-15: SAS Hard Reset Sequence

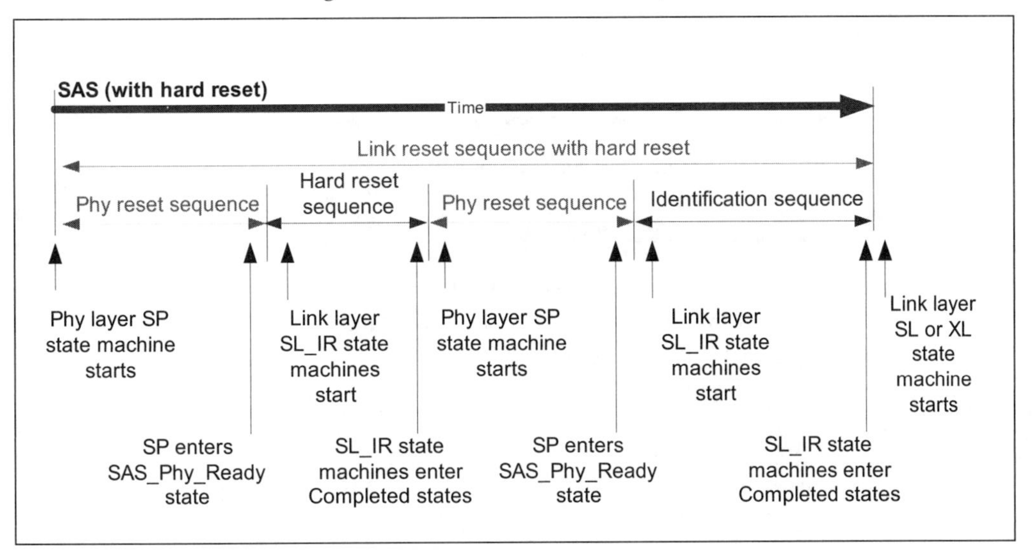

Link Reset

For SATA, a link reset and Phy reset are the same thing (see Figure 16-16 on page 402) and both have the effect of a hard reset. A soft reset is under consideration for a future version of SATA. For SAS (see Figure 16-17 on page 402), an IDENTIFY frame is expected from the attached device after a link reset or hard reset, and the Receive Identify Timeout timer is maintained by the SL_IR state machine to ensure that this frame arrives within 1ms. If the timer expires before an IDENTIFY is received, the state machine will send a message confirming that event to the Management Application Layer, which may then send a Management Reset request to reset the Phy again.

Figure 16-16: SATA Reset Sequence

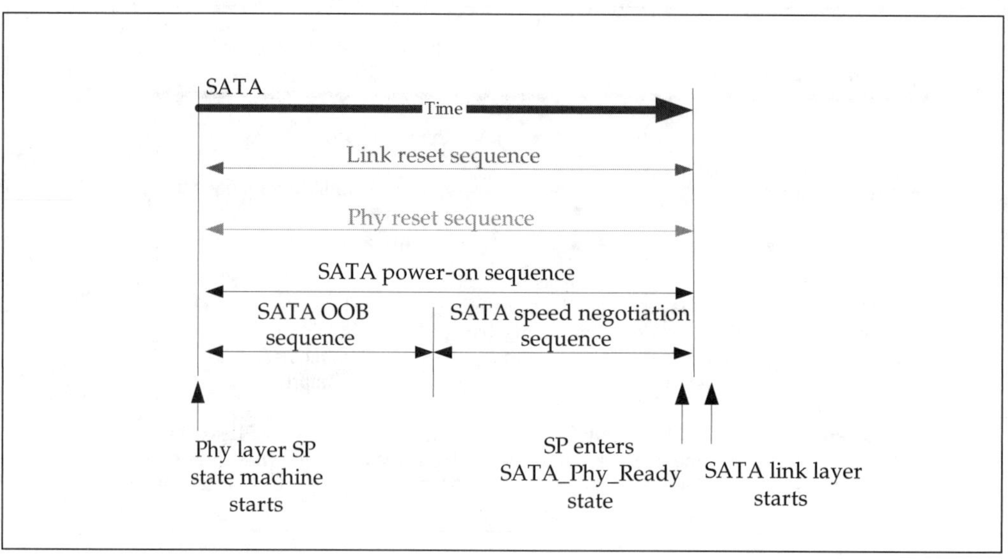

Figure 16-17: SAS Link Reset Sequence

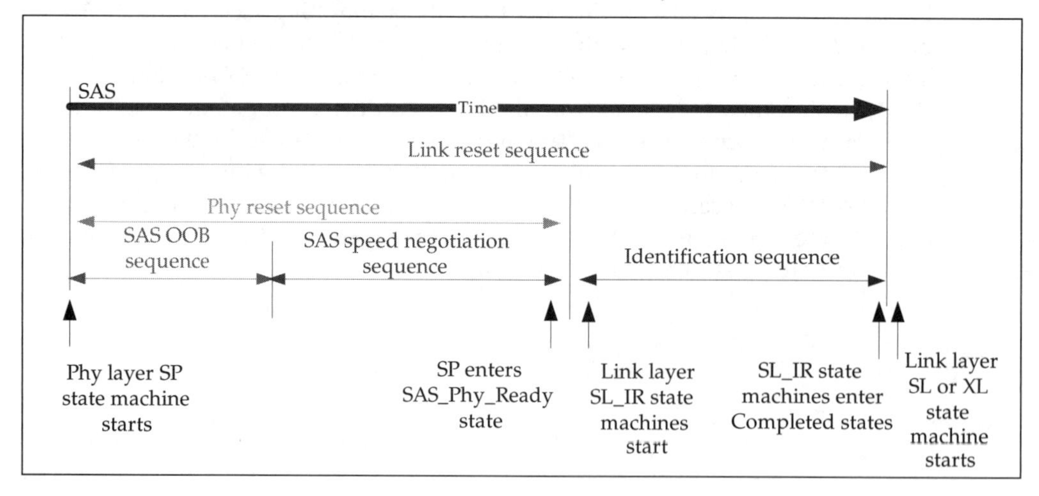

Phy Reset

The Phy reset looks like the SAS link reset sequence but doesn't include the Identification sequence. It consists of the OOB sequence followed by a speed negotiation sequence. There is an opportunity for some confusion here about the difference between a Phy reset and a link reset. It is clear from the drawings that they are communicated as two parts, but the Phy reset is not shown separate from the link reset. The reason for this is that, at the time of this writing, there was no option for a separate Phy reset. However, the Phy Reset Problem is an example of an event that uses that term since if a Phy reset fails it is reported this way. There is not currently a similar Link Reset problem, but if it is defined in the future it will have a different meaning.

Phy State Machines

For those interested in going deeper into the detailed operation of this section, the state machines used in the standard to define its behavior are discussed next and redrawn here for convenience. These state machine drawings are intended to improve readability over what is offered in the standard by showing the reasons for state transitions and the messages that are sent to neighboring layers based on the state variables. They are not intended to be all inclusive and usually do not, for example, include interactions between state machines within the same layer. The casual reader may skip this section and still have a basic operational understanding of the material.

The Phy Layer behavior is defined in two state machines. The first state machine is the SAS Phy (SP) machine, which has 27 states and is partitioned into three sections, one each for OOB Sequencing, SAS Speed Negotiation, and SATA Speed Negotiation. The second state machine is the SAS Phy DWord Synchronization (SP_DWS) machine, which has 10 states and serves to establish and monitor dword synchronization for the phy. The full state diagrams in the standard show every possible state transition and relevant messages, which makes them useful for finding answers to specific questions but difficult to read for general behavioral understanding. The diagrams shown here have been simplified by reducing the amount of information displayed but including the reasons for the state transitions in an effort to make it easier to see the overall flow.

SAS Phy State Machine

OOB Sequencing Section

The behavior of the OOB Sequencing section of the SP state machine, shown in Figure 16-18, shows the flow of events that was described earlier for OOB. Here it can be seen that the SAS Phy is simply looking for COMINIT sent and received, and then COMSAS sent and received. After that, the state machine will transition to the "SP8: SAS_Start" state.

Speed Negotiation Section

The SAS Speed Negotiation section of the state machine is shown in Figure 16-19 on page 406. One aspect that was not described earlier is that, once the speed negotiation is completed, the state machine will remain in SP15: SAS_PHY_READY until dword synchronization is lost again for some reason. This status is conveyed to the Link Layer state machine as the confirmation "Phy Layer Ready (SAS)" meaning that COMSAS was received and the neighbor is therefore a SAS device. If COMSAS was not received but the device supported SATA host emulation, the state machine would transition to SP16: COMWAKE and finish the OOB as a SATA device. When that process is completed, indicated in Figure 16-20 by arriving at state SP22:PHY Ready, this information is conveyed to the Link Layer with a "Phy Layer Ready (SATA)" confirmation. For more on the process for SATA, refer to Chapter 20, entitled "SATA Initialization," on page 489.

Figure 16-18: SP-OOB Sequence State Machine

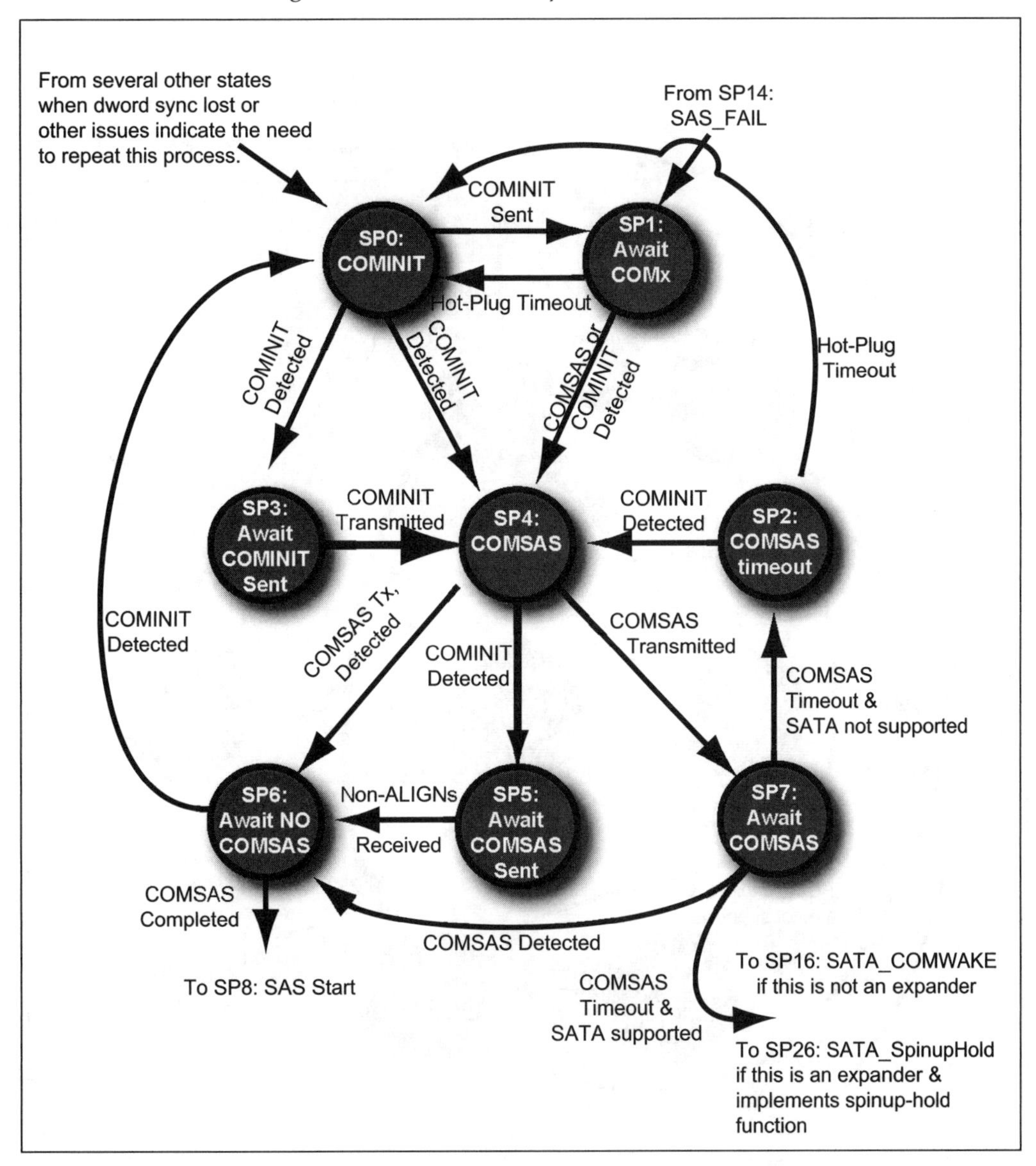

Figure 16-19: SAS Speed Negotiation State Machine

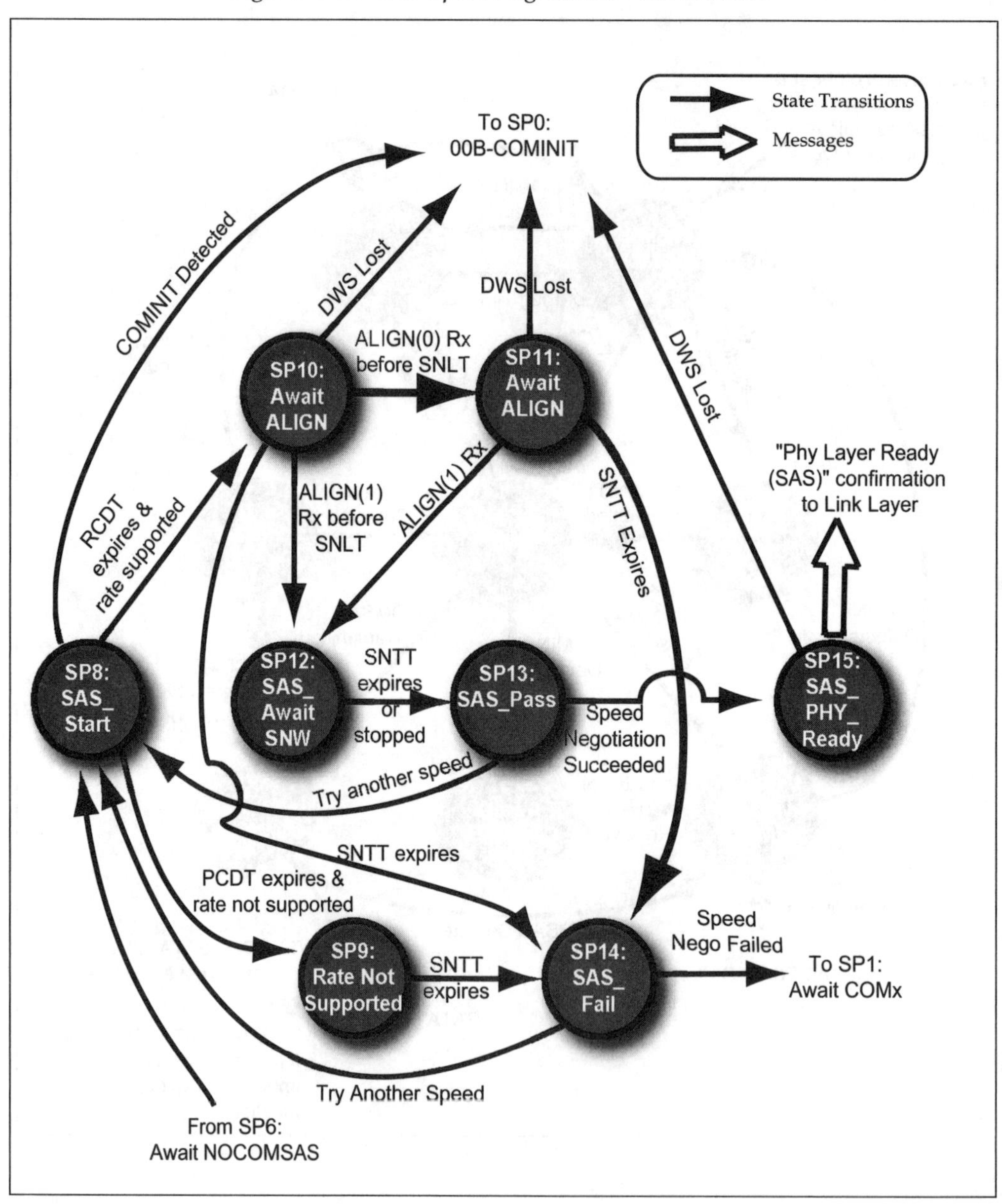

Figure 16-20: SATA Host Emulation

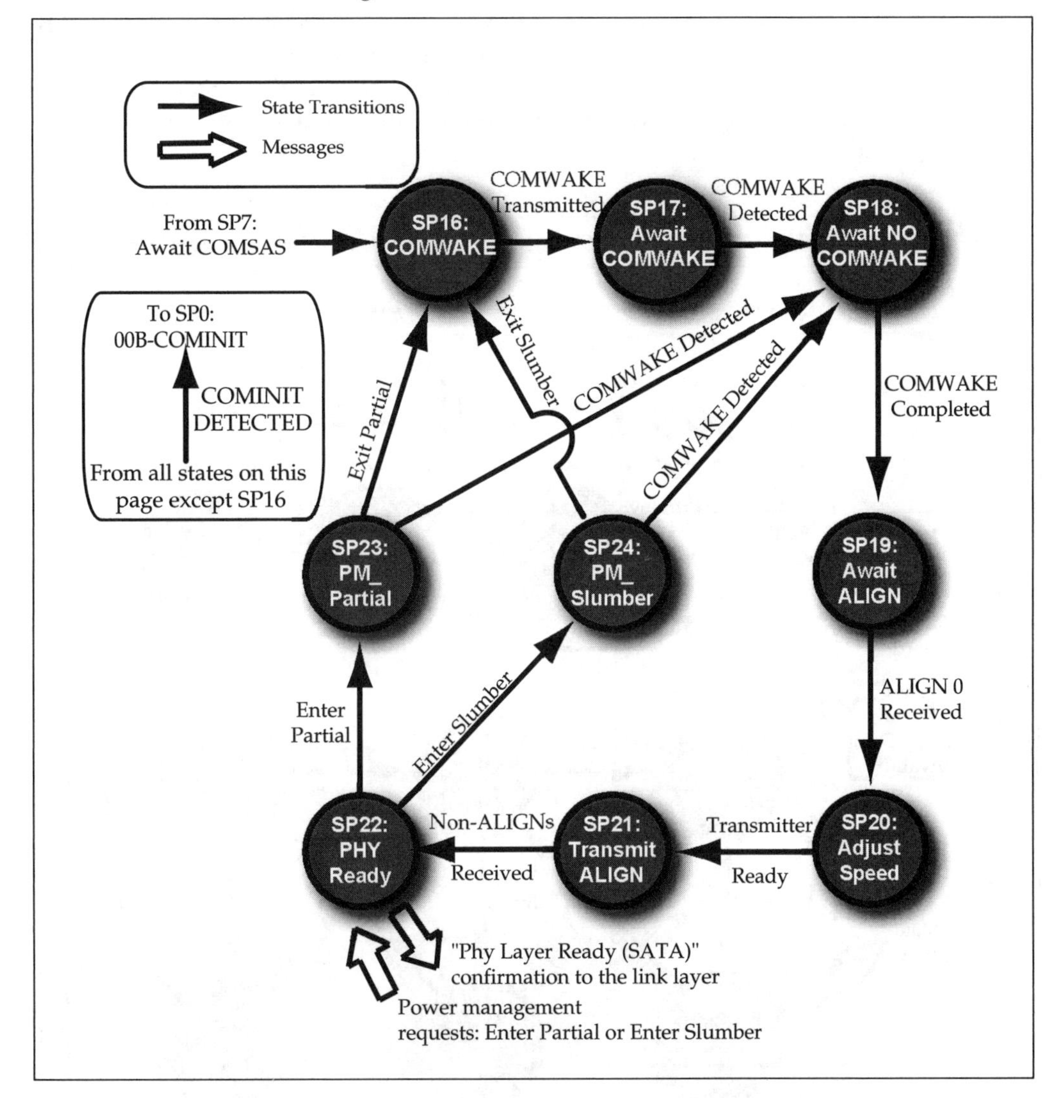

DWS (Double-Word Synchronization) State Machine

The DWS state machine, shown in Figure 16-21, is small enough that it made sense to include more of its message interactions with the SP state machine as well as with the DWS Receiver logic. From the illustration, it can be seen that the process of establishing dword synchronization begins from the initial state DWS0 whenever the SP state machine sends a Start DWS message. When the DWS0 state receives the message, it sends a Find Dword message to the DWS Receiver and starts a DWS Reset Timeout timer. Similarly, the state also reinitializes to DWS0 whenever the SP state machine tells it with a Stop DWS message to stop trying to synchronize because the OOB process needs to be repeated.

Figure 16-21: DWS State Machine

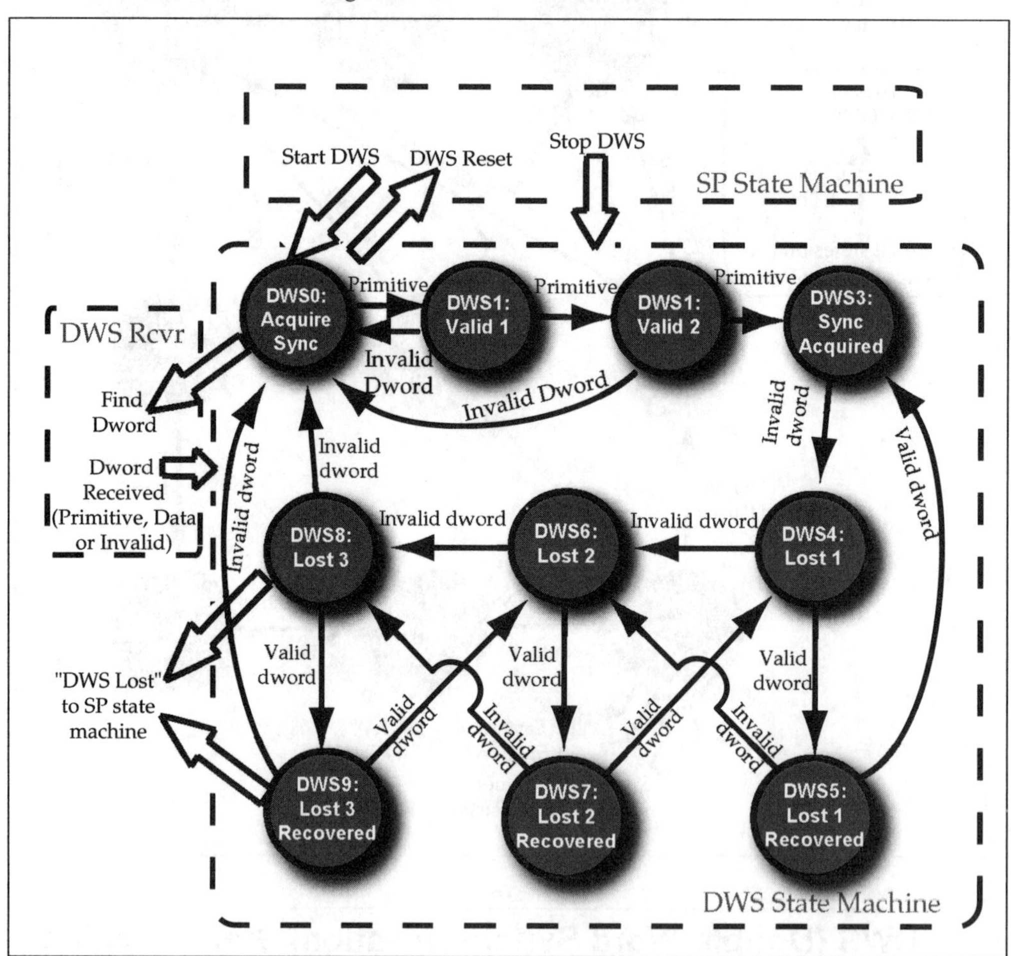

Starting Synchronization

When instructed to start DWS, the machine sends a Find Dword message to the DWS Receiver. This receiver is not defined as a state machine itself, but is a block of logic that simply begins watching the incoming data stream, searching for a K28.5 character. The method for doing this is to search for the comma sequence that identifies the first 7 bits of the K28.5 character, as shown in Figure 16-22. When that is received then the next 3 bits should complete the 10-bit symbol, and that identifies the character (sometimes referred to as "symbol") boundary for the incoming bitstream. Since the K28.5 symbol is required to be the first in the group of 4 symbols that make up a dword, this also identifies the dword boundaries. Placing it in the first position and then checking the next 3 characters allows the machine to verify the arrival of a valid primitive dword. Once that has been done, the DWS receiver simply reports the status of every subsequent received dword as Primitive, Data, or Invalid.

Figure 16-22: Dword Detection

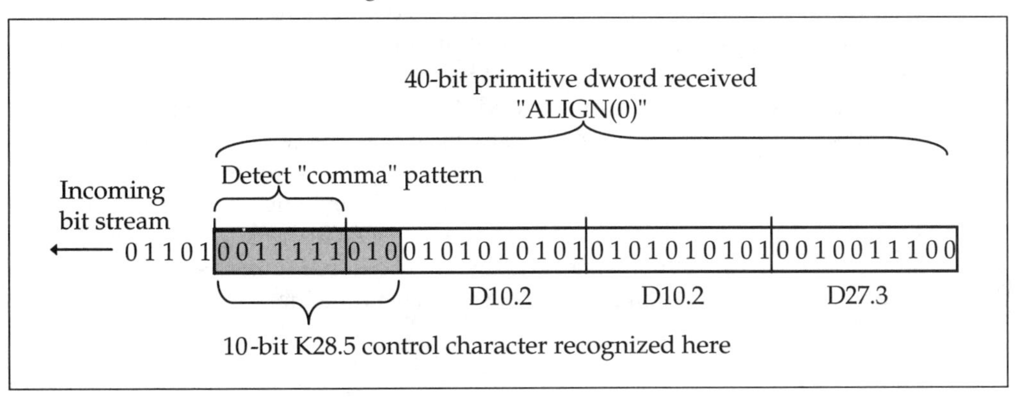

Synchronization Timing

As mentioned earlier, when the DWS0 state sends a Find Dword request to the DWS Receiver, it starts the 1ms DWS Reset Timeout timer and leaves it running until the machine reaches the DWS3: SyncAcquired state. The function of the timer is to ensure that synchronization is achieved within a reasonable time. When the DWS Receiver reports Dword Received (Primitive), the state changes to DWS1, where it waits for another valid primitive and leaves the timer running. The next primitive moves the state from DWS1 to DWS2, and the third one finally moves it to DWS3. In other words, the machine is waiting until it has received three valid primitive dwords, which should be arriving regularly during the Phy reset sequence. If the reset timer expires before the state reaches

DWS3, the machine will transition back to DWS0 and optionally send a DWS Reset message to the SP state machine. For the SP machine, this acts as a reset to reinitialize it and cause it to begin OOB again. Sending this message is controlled by the DWS, and might include other vendor-specific considerations.

Once the DWS state machine reaches the SP_DWS3: SyncAcquired state, the incoming dwords are forwarded to the Link Layer for processing. It doesn't make sense to forward them otherwise, of course, because if the machine is in any of the other states it means that dword synchronization is incomplete or is having difficulty.

Recovering Synchronization

After reaching the DWS3 state, the machine continues to forward received dwords unless an invalid dword is received. As can be seen in Figure 16-21, for each invalid dword received, two valid ones must be seen in a row before the bad one has been nullified and confidence is restored in the dword flow. While waiting for invalid dwords to be nullified, no dwords are forwarded to the Link Layer until the process is completed. If invalid dwords persist, the DWS state machine will eventually reach the DWS8: Lost3 or the DWS9: Lost3Recovered states. At that point, one more invalid dword will cause it to transition to the initial state and send a "DWS Lost" message to the SP state machine. In response, the SP machine may simply send the Start DWS message again to begin the process of re-acquiring dword synchronization without running a link reset sequence. If it does not send the Start DWS, the SP machine will transition back to the initial state and begin OOB. For many states in the SP machine, DWS Lost automatically causes such a transition.

17 Physical Layer

The Previous Chapter

The previous chapter described the Phy Layer, which prepares the packets forwarded from the upper layers for serial transmission. That includes encoding 8-bit bytes into 10-bit symbols, managing clock skew between devices, and handling the OOB (out of band) signaling used for link initialization.

This Chapter

This chapter describes the electrical characteristics of the differential transmitter and receiver used to transmit the bits across the wire, and includes a discussion of the four interface environments defined for use with SAS. Apart from the discussion about the analog transmitter and receiver, the Physical Layer is largely concerned with the passive interface that includes backplanes, cables, and connectors.

The Next Chapter

The next chapter gives the second part of the Physical Layer definition in the standard, discussing the passive cables and connectors that are used to connect devices to each other.

Introduction

The SAS Physical Layer defines the lowest-level details of the interconnect in two parts: the transmitter/receiver electrical characteristics, and the passive interconnect (i.e., cables and connectors). This chapter will focus on the first part of that definition, while the next chapter will go into the second part.

While the standard does not say so directly, it makes sense for the actual high-speed differential interface to reside in this layer for two reasons. First, this high-speed analog circuitry makes a good candidate for a separate design module. ASIC designers familiar with digital design would be unlikely to have the necessary expertise to develop a robust high-speed circuit of this type, and might prefer to purchase it as a module from another vendor instead. Specifying this interface as a separate layer facilitates this division of labor.

Secondly, the electrical properties of the drivers and receivers are part of what defines the interconnects, so it makes sense to describe the electrical characteristics with the passive components (cables and connectors). As shown in Figure 17-1 on page 412, the Physical Layer is described by clause number 5 of the SAS standard. A block diagram showing the receiver side interface of this layer is shown in Figure 17-2 on page 413.

Figure 17-1: SAS Layers

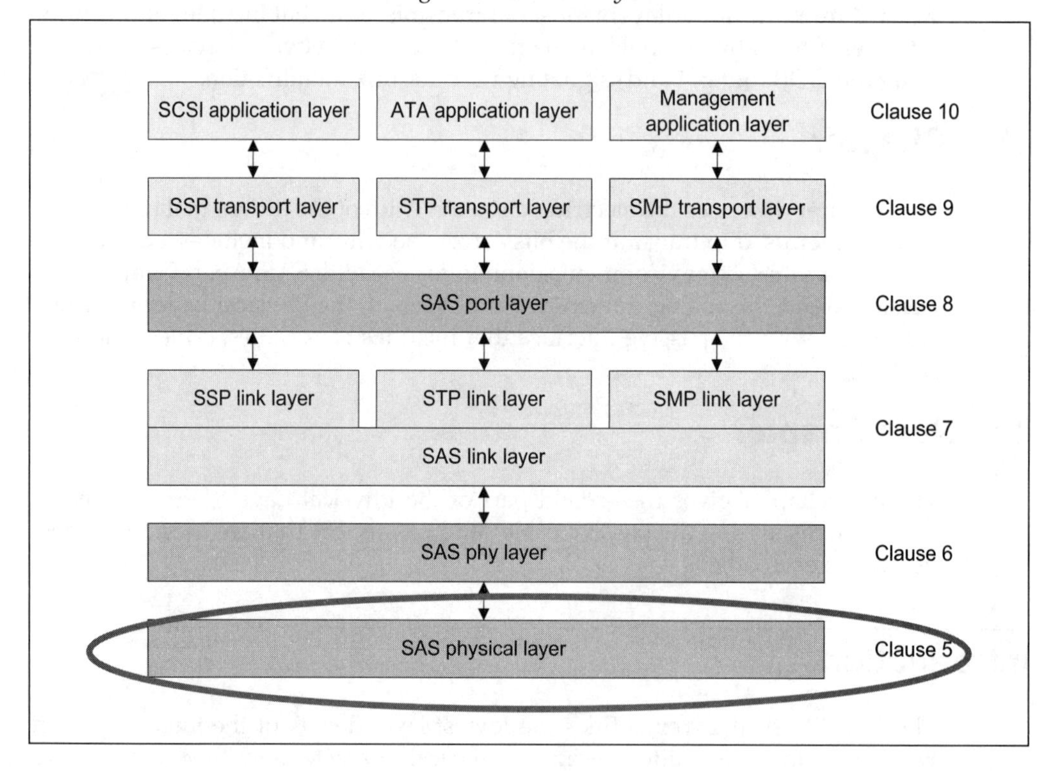

Figure 17-2: Physical Layer Receive Block Diagram

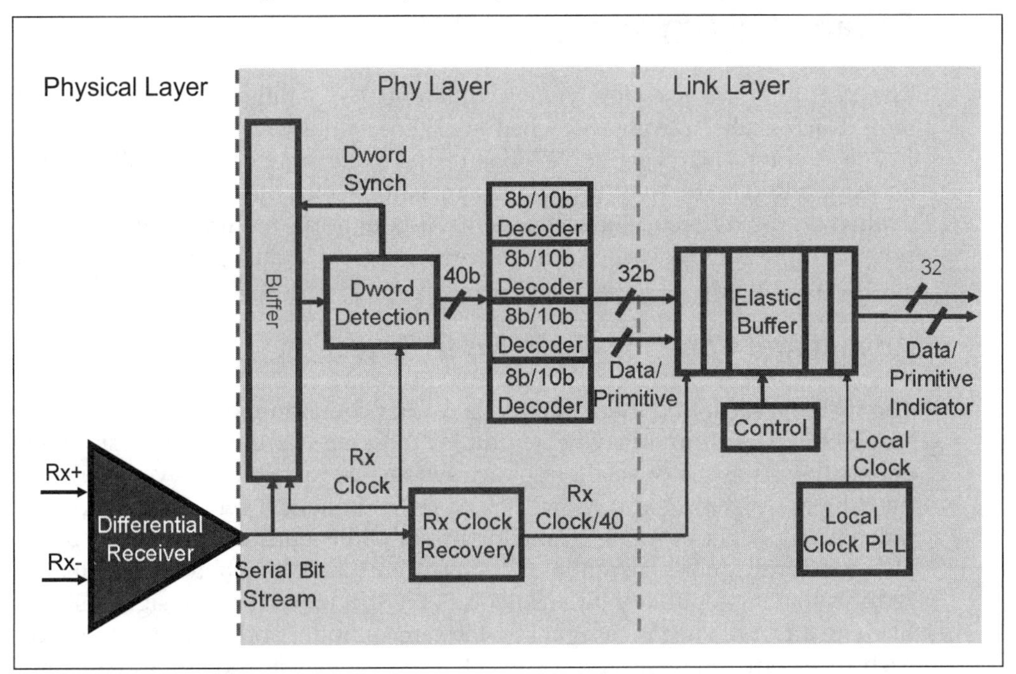

Electrical Interface

The SAS transmitter changes the serialized bits received from the Phy Layer into a differential, NRZ (non-return to zero) encoded signal with a peak-to-peak voltage of between 400 and 600mV for SATA and between 325 and 1600mV for SAS. There are other signal encoding schemes that might have been chosen. For example, PAM-4 (Pulse Amplitude Modulated) encoding uses a multi-level voltage scheme to increase bandwidth by increasing the number of bits visible in each time interval. The problem with such schemes is that they make both transmitter and receiver more complex, and recovering multi-level signals is more difficult and more susceptible to noise. The SAS standard writers evidently chose NRZ because of its relative simplicity and robust operation and because it has been used successfully in many earlier serial architectures. There is room for concern even with NRZ, though, because the working group investigating 6.0 Gb/s implementation for the third generation of SAS speeds has found that NRZ evidently does not work as well at the higher speeds. Another signal encoding scheme may yet be needed for future generations of SAS, but the consensus seems to be that it will be acceptable for 6.0 Gb/s.

Differential Signaling

The SAS interface uses low-voltage differential signaling to transmit the bit stream across the transmission medium. Differential transmitters use mirror-image positive and negative versions of the same signal to transmit the bits across a link. The receiver uses both signals to recover the transmitted bits by evaluating the difference between them. Although this requires twice as many pins to implement as a single-ended signaling environment, differential offers several advantages.

Advantage: Common-Mode Noise Rejection

The first and most important of these is called "common-mode noise rejection" and a little background may be helpful for those new to this term. First, differential allows the use of smaller voltage swings, because the receiver will compare the two signals and thus will see twice the voltage level versus looking at only one signal. Low voltage signaling has other benefits described later, but is also inherently more susceptible to noise. Fortunately, differential signaling reduces that susceptibility because noise that affects the positive signal is very likely to affect the negative signal by the same amount and they tend to cancel each other out. One reason for this is that the signals are routed in pairs and generally in close proximity to each other.

Consider the example shown in Figure 17-3 on page 415, which shows a differential transmission line affected by two types of voltage noise. In one case, ground bounce or some other noise has momentarily changed the reference voltage used for single-ended signals. The differential receiver is unaffected by this because it doesn't compare the signals to the reference, but to each other. In the other case, transient environmental noise causes a voltage spike. Since both signals are affected by such events to approximately the same degree, the receiver is again able to see the intended signal and remains largely unaffected by the noise. Single-ended signals could easily suffer loss of signal integrity in either of these cases, but a differential receiver sees very little change.

Figure 17-3: Differential Signaling Rejects Common-Mode Noise

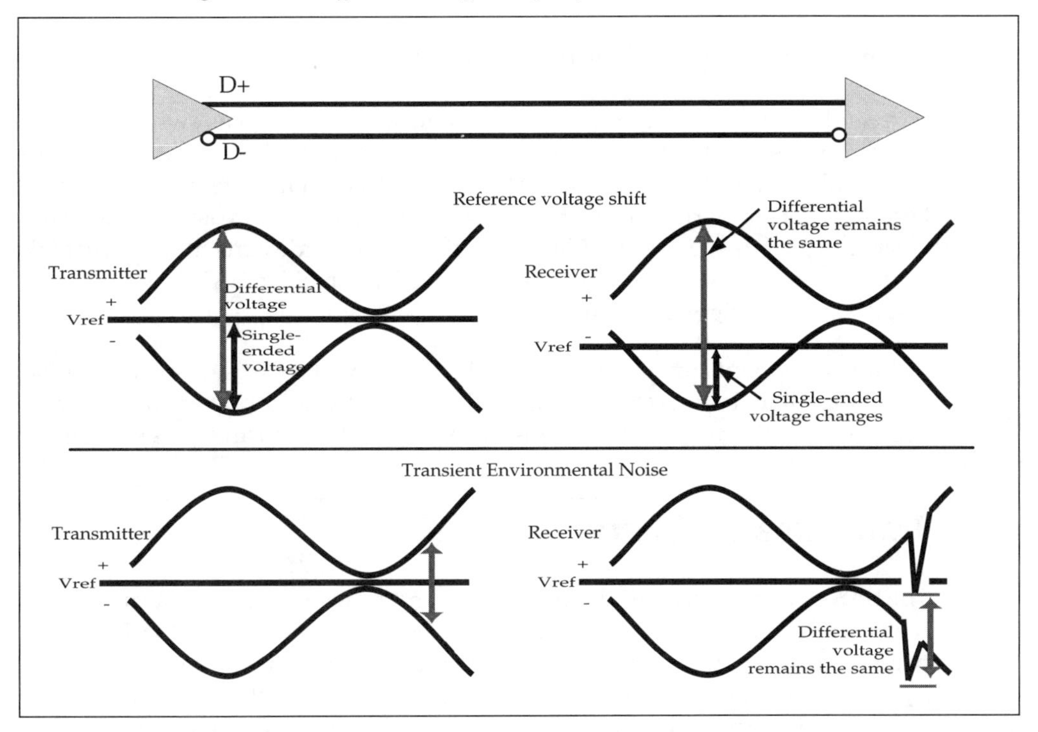

Before leaving this topic, it seems prudent to point out that the minimum amount of common-mode voltage that a SAS receiver is required to tolerate is actually fairly small at 150mv peak-to-peak (see Table 17-5 on page 422). Some devices in use today are sensitive to this, mainly because of the OOB detect circuitry they employ, and won't tolerate much more than the minimum. Clearly, system designers should make the effort to build margin into their systems wherever possible so as to leave more margin available for devices that only tolerate the minimums. One way to do that is to put stricter requirements on the transmission medium and termination used. For example, the differential impedance is listed as 100 ohms nominal but, for a variety of reasons, many board designs vary from that quite a bit. Getting this value as close as possible to exactly 100 ohms will improve the transmission characteristics and thus improve the budget for other parts of the system. Similarly, the receiver common-mode impedance is listed as 20 ohms min and 40 ohms max. Designers should make every effort to get these values balanced between the differential pair as much as possible. Balancing the impedance of the two signals helps ensure that environmental noise affects both signals in the pair by the same amount. If these are not evenly matched, it will increase the perceived noise at the receiver.

Other Advantages of Differential signaling

A second advantage of differential is that, since the two signals switch in opposite directions and the traces must be in close proximity to each other, the signals tend to cancel out each other's EMI and crosstalk effects. This benefit becomes more important as the transmission frequencies increase, adding to the desirability of using differential in serial interface designs that have high switching speeds. This also reduces the need to shield the signals and, as a result, can allow tighter routing densities.

A third important advantage is that the lower voltages used in differential switching allow both faster switching times and reduced power consumption because the voltage change that must be driven by the transmitter is smaller.

Transmission Characteristics

The SAS standard specifies the transmitter and receiver characteristics, some of which are listed in Table 17-1 and illustrated in Figure 17-4 on the following page. In the drawing, an in-line capacitor is shown at each end of the transmission line, but the standard only mandates the use of this capacitor at the receiver. The purpose of these capacitors it to provide A.C. coupling: allowing the A.C. part (high-frequency components) of a signal to pass through, but blocking the D.C. part (low-frequency components). This allows the common-mode voltages at the transmitter and receiver to be different, which would be desirable in cases where they were not in the same physical enclosure. The capacitors are always required on the receiver inputs, but they are only required for transmitters that are designed to support a SATA device.

Figure 17-4: Differential Buffers

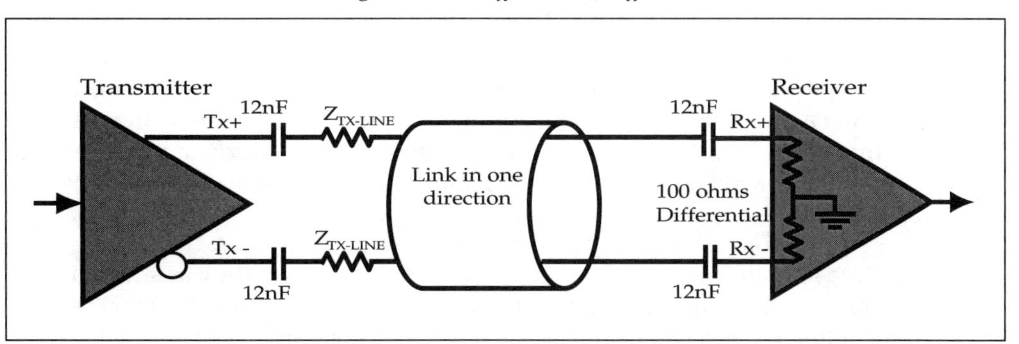

Table 17-1: General Electrical Characteristics

Characteristic	1.5 Gb/s (G1)	3.0 Gb/s (G2)
Physical Link Rate	150 MB/s	300 MB/s
Unit Interval (UI) (Nominal)	666.66 ps	333.33 ps
Differential Impedance (Nominal)	100 ohms	100 ohms
A.C. Coupling capacitor (max)	12 nF	12 nF
Transmitter rate tolerance	+/- 100 ppm	
Receiver rate tolerance, for both internal and external use, if SATA is not supported	+/- 100 ppm	
Receiver rate tolerance, for internal use if SATA is supported	+350/-5350 ppm	

A 100 ohm differential termination is required at the receiver and could be created with external components, but it's expected to be implemented internally for reasons of cost, reduced part count, and improved signal integrity. There is evidently a wide range of opinions on the best way to do this. Some engineers with whom the author has spoken on this topic recommended external resistors tied to ground. One vendor recommended that both Rx+ and Rx- should each be independently connected through a 1K ohm at 100 MHz ferrite bead, then a 0.01 μF capacitor, to V_{DD}. Another vendor states that, "Ferrite beads are not advisable in digital switching circuits because inductive spiking (di/dt noise) is introduced into the power rail." Still another vendor says, "No external resistor terminations are necessary on the high-speed I/O." Clearly, it will be incumbent on a designer to become familiar with the high-speed signaling issues affecting a given implementation. For more on this topic, refer to materials such as the book *High-Speed Signal Propagation: Advanced Black Magic* (Howard Johnson and Martin Graham, 2003 Prentice Hall Professional Technical Reference (PTR)).

The transmission medium itself exhibits its own characteristics, as shown in the diagram by the line impedance. However, while the standard specifies the transmitter and receiver characteristics, the transmission line itself is not strictly defined. Instead, the description basically says that whatever is implemented must not be worse than the behavior defined by the TCTF (transmit compliance transfer function). For more on the TCTF, see the section called "Test Loads" on page 429.

The main reason that the transmission medium is only loosely defined is to allow vendors to create versions of cables and connectors to achieve certain design goals. For example, increasing the thickness of the wires would add cost to a cable but would also allow it to be made longer while still achieving acceptable signal attenuation. Conversely, the wires could be made thinner to produce a lower-cost but shorter cable that still met the transmission requirements.

Numerous characteristics are given in the standard that define the transmitter (see Figure 17-2 on the following page) and receiver (see Figure 17-5 on page 422). Some of these are based on the operating frequency, while others are based on both frequency and compliance point, as shown in Table 17-3 on page 419. There are four compliance points defined, as listed in Table 17-4 on page 420, that define the places where measurements are to be taken when testing transmit and receive parameters.

Table 17-2: Transmitter General Electrical Characteristics

Characteristics	Units	Value
Physical link rate tolerance at IT and CT	ppm	+/- 100
Max Transmitter transients	V	1.2
Differential impedance	ohms	100
Common-mode impedance	ohms	15 min/40 max

Table 17-3: Transmitter Characteristics Measured with Test Loads

Signal Characteristic	Units	1.5 Gb/s	3.0 Gb/s
Max Voltage, if SATA not supported	mV(p-p)	1600	1600
Max Voltage, if SATA is supported	mV(p-p)	see note 1	N/A
Max intra-pair skew	ps	80	75
Max rise/fall time	ps	273	137
Deterministic Jitter	Unit Interval	0.35	
Max Total Jitter	Unit Interval	0.55	
Minimum Eye Opening, if SATA not supported	mV(p-p)	275 CT, 325 IT	275
Minimum Eye Opening, if SATA ia supported	mV(p-p)	see note 1	N/A
Note 1: In the SATA II standard, the Rx voltage range is 240 to 600 mv(p-p), and the Tx voltage range is 500 to 600mv(p-p), but the standard also states that the Tx voltage can be higher as long as the Rx voltage is not exceeded at the far end of the interconnect.			

Table 17-4: Compliance Points

Compliance Point	Type	Description
IT	Internal (Intra-enclosure)	Internal Transmitter - measured at probe points of a test load attached to an internal connector.
IR	Internal (Intra-Enclosure)	Internal Receiver - measured at probe points of a test load attached to an internal connector.
CT	Cabinet (Inter-Enclosure)	External Transmitter - measured at probe points of a test load attached to an external connector.
CR	Cabinet (Inter-Enclosure)	External Receiver - measured at probe points of a test load attached to an external connector.

Most of the units described in these tables are self-explanatory, but for those who are new to some of the concepts, it may be helpful to explain some of them. The term "mV(p-p)" means peak-to-peak millivolts. Peak-to-peak is defined as the difference between the voltage for representing a logical 1 versus that for representing a logical 0. The individual signals are referred to as single-ended and their voltage is measured as a peak value, while differential voltages are measured as the combination of two single-ended signals and are thus twice the value, as shown in Figure 17-5.

Figure 17-5: Single-Ended and Differential Voltages

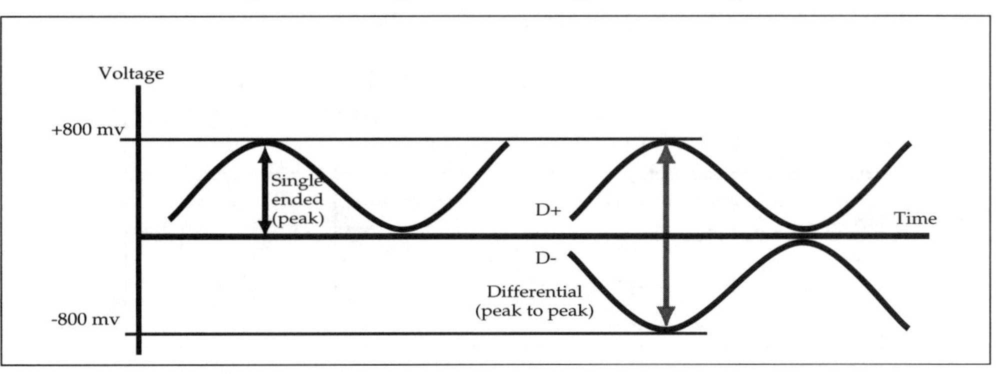

Another view of the peak-to-peak voltage can be illustrated by an overlay picture of the two single-ended signals that make up the differential pair, as shown in Figure 17-6. The measurement and result is still the same, adding the full voltage swing of one signal (800mV in this illustration) to the full voltage swing of the other signal which is also 800mV.

Figure 17-6: Differential Voltages Overlay View

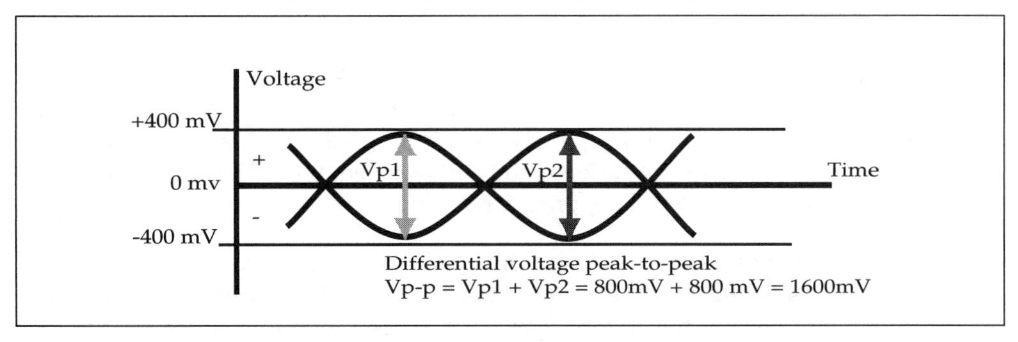

This view, in which the signals overlap, is common when creating eye diagrams by sampling the signals over a long period of time. Judging by the number of questions this generates, though, it can be confusing. That's because it's easy to misinterpret the peak-to-peak voltage as being just Vp1 alone, for example. It helps to think of the peak-to-peak voltage as the sum of the total voltage swing for the positive signal (labeled as Vp1) and the total voltage swing for the negative signal (labeled as Vp2).

Regarding the voltage and jitter values, it is helpful to view eye diagrams for both the transmitter and receiver. However, the standard points out that it's not sufficient to use a sampling scope to verify compliance with the eye diagrams, referring instead to the ANSI/INCITS spec TR-35-2004 titled *Methodologies for Jitter and Signal Quality* (MJSQ) for details on verifying such compliance.

Table 17-5: Receiver General Electrical Characteristics

Characteristic	Units	Value
Link rate tolerance at IR if SATA supported	ppm	+350 / -5350
Link rate tolerance at CR and at IR if SATA not supported	ppm	+/- 100
Receiver A.C. common-mode voltage tolerance, minimum	mV(p-p)	150
Differential impedance	ohms	100 +/- 15
Common-mode impedance	ohms	20min / 40max

Eye Masks

The transmitter eye mask in Figure 17-7 on page 423 shows the max and min voltage values sent by the transmitter as well as the max jitter allowed. The signal, and thus the size of the eye opening, is affected in terms of voltage (vertically) by transmission line attenuation and received noise. The eye is affected in terms of timing (horizontally) primarily by jitter.

An example of what this looks like in a real system is illustrated in Figure 17-8 on page 424 where a trace capture from the transmitter is shown at the top and from the receiver at the bottom. The eye mask is drawn to scale in the pictures, so this transmission line would appear to have acceptable performance. The pattern generated for this test is not a normal data pattern but is a Pseudo-Random Bit Sequence (PRBS-7) standard polynomial generated by test equipment. Because it generates patterns that would be illegal during normal operation (e.g., 10 zeros in a row), it's actually worse than any legal pattern.

Figure 17-7: Transmitter and Receiver Eye Diagram

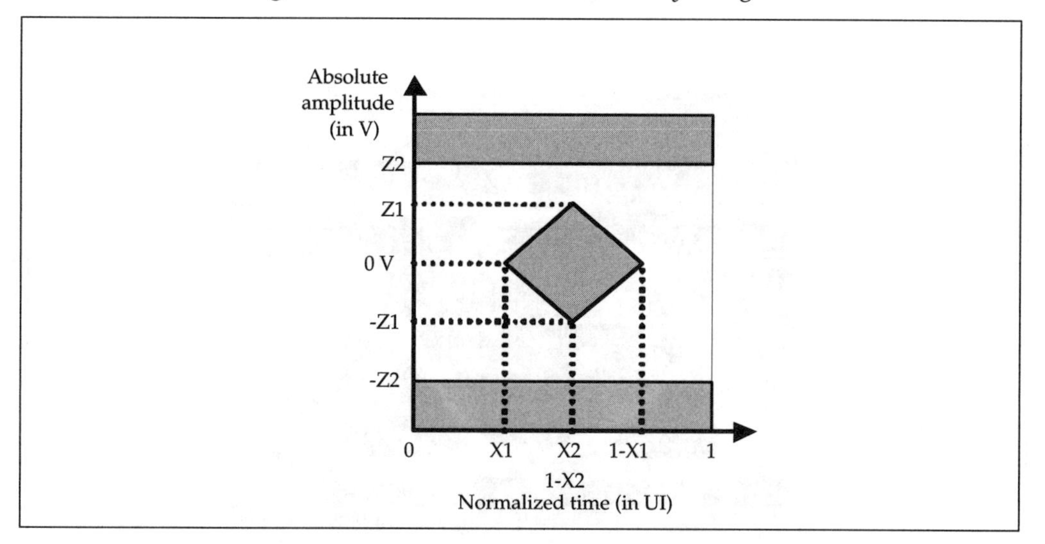

Consequently, a system that passes when using this pattern should work with any legal patterns. As expected, the signals suffer some loss in propagation through the cable, resulting in a reduced eye opening at the receiver. Since this is a relatively short transmission path, the loss is not so great as to encroach on the limits for the eye mask, but it can be seen that the signal experiences reduced voltage and increased jitter. Longer paths make this problem worse because both attenuation and phase shift are proportional to distance. Consequently, chip designers typically must take steps to compensate for this loss and the amount of compensation depends on the expected system environment.

Figure 17-8: Eye Diagram Measured On a Short Cable

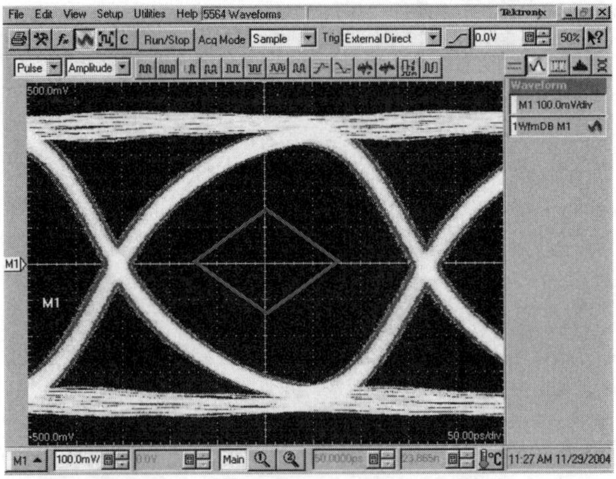

Transmitter

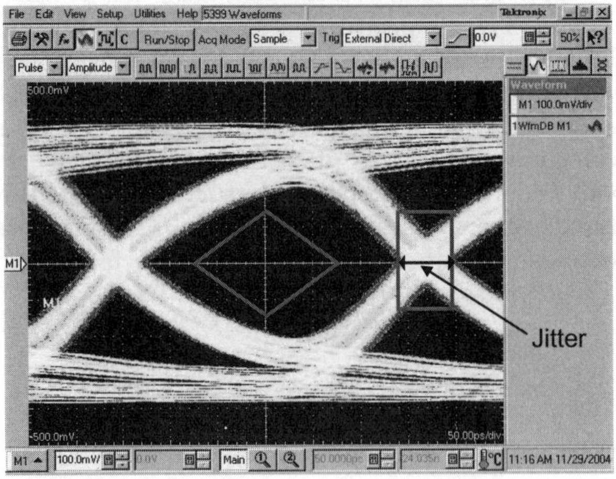

Receiver

Signal Compensation

Compensating for signal loss typically takes one or both of two forms: pre-emphasis at the transmitter, or equalization at the receiver. Neither of these techniques is required by the SAS standard; in fact, pre-emphasis is only mentioned while equalization is not discussed at all. And neither technique is mentioned in the SATA standard, since that environment was designed for short transmission paths of only about one meter and would not expect to encounter much signal distortion.

Pre-emphasis

Pre-emphasis (also sometimes referred to as de-emphasis) is a method by which the transmitter attempts to compensate for the distortion the signal will experience during transmission by pre-distorting it on the way out. The loss of power a signal experiences in transmission reduces the high frequency components more than the others. This approach compensates for that by either boosting the power of the high frequencies (pre-emphasis), or reducing the power of the lower frequencies (de-emphasis). Either approach helps alleviate the problem created by electrical issues such as skin effects and dielectric loss. The loss and jitter in the signal prevent the bits from reaching their full strength in time, causing them to spill over into the next bit time. The magnitude of this problem depends on the bit patterns on the wire. This pattern-dependent jitter is called ISI (inter-symbol interference) because it results when the pattern of the previous symbol's bits interferes with proper reception of the current symbol. As an example of ISI, consider the diagram in Figure 17-9 on page 426. In this picture, the waveform on the left shows the transmitter's output of one of the two differential signals (single-ended), while the picture on the left shows the same signal at the receiver. At the receiver, the transitions have experienced attenuation and jitter, and one effect that can be readily observed is that repeated bits of the same polarity tend to charge up the line, causing it to reach a higher voltage than it otherwise would and making it more difficult to switch to the proper level for a bit transition within the given time.

Figure 17-9: Inter-Symbol Interference

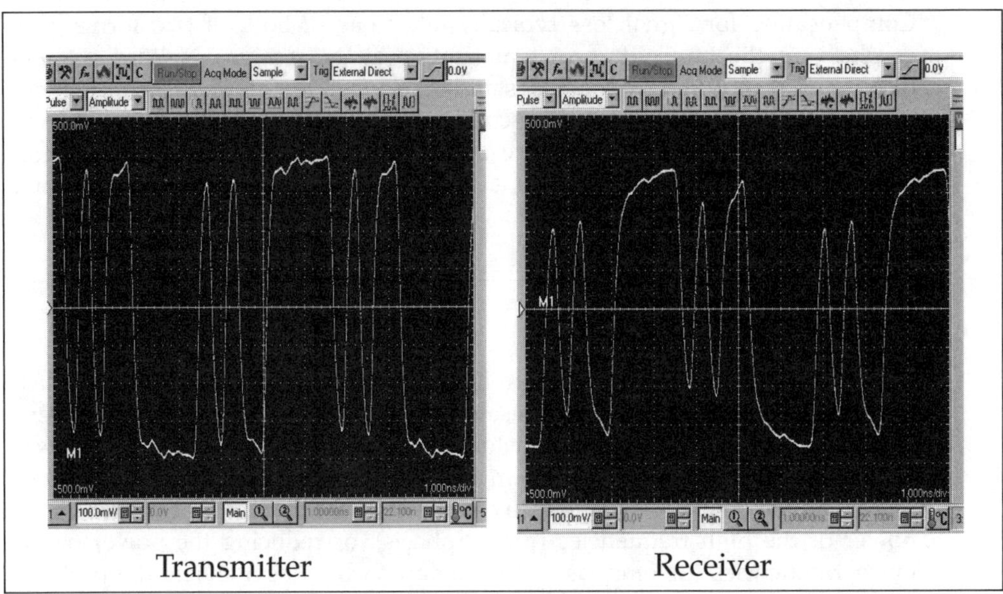

Figure 17-10: ISI Reduced by Use of Pre-emphasis

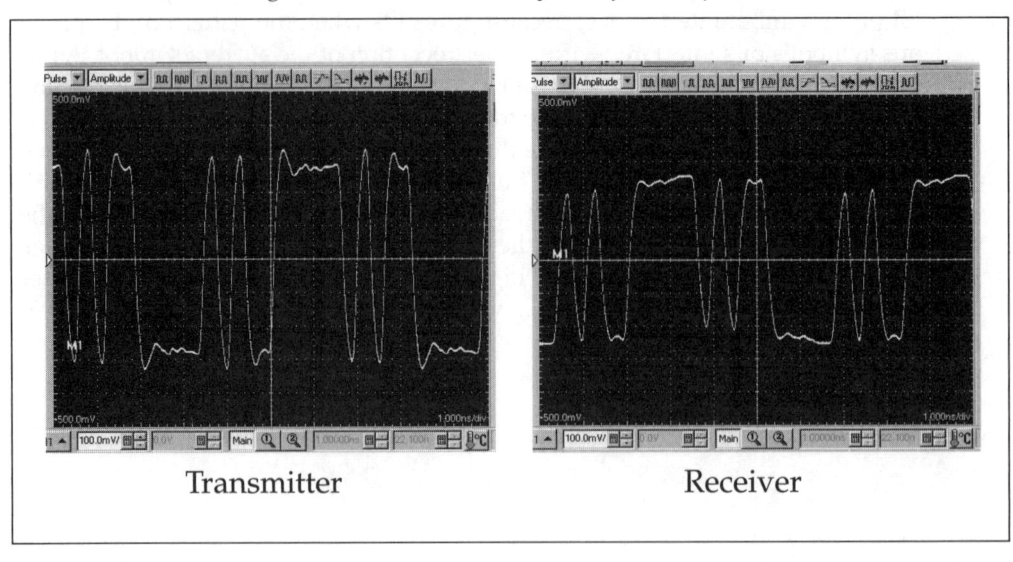

In Figure 17-10 on page 426, this effect is reduced by pre-emphasizing the transmitter waveform to compensate for the expected distortion of the signal during transmission. Note that the transmitter's waveform shows pre-emphasized transitions (the high-frequency components of the signal), or de-emphasized bits when they do not change state to prevent the "charge up" effect on the line. The amount of pre-emphasis or de-emphasis applied to the signal is typically programmable within the transmitter, allowing the system to increase it for longer transmission environments or reduce it for short transmission lengths.

Clearly, programmable compensation is important if the signaling environment is not known ahead of time, since applying pre-emphasis on a short path would actually make it worse. Figure 17-11 shows a trace capture for the short cable with pre-emphasis applied. At the top, it can be seen that the output at the transmitter has been significantly distorted. If the connecting path was short enough, the receiver would also see that distortion. In this case, though, the compensation improves the signal and the eye opening at the receiver compared to the way it looked in Figure 17-8.

Figure 17-11: Eye Diagram Showing Pre-Emphasis

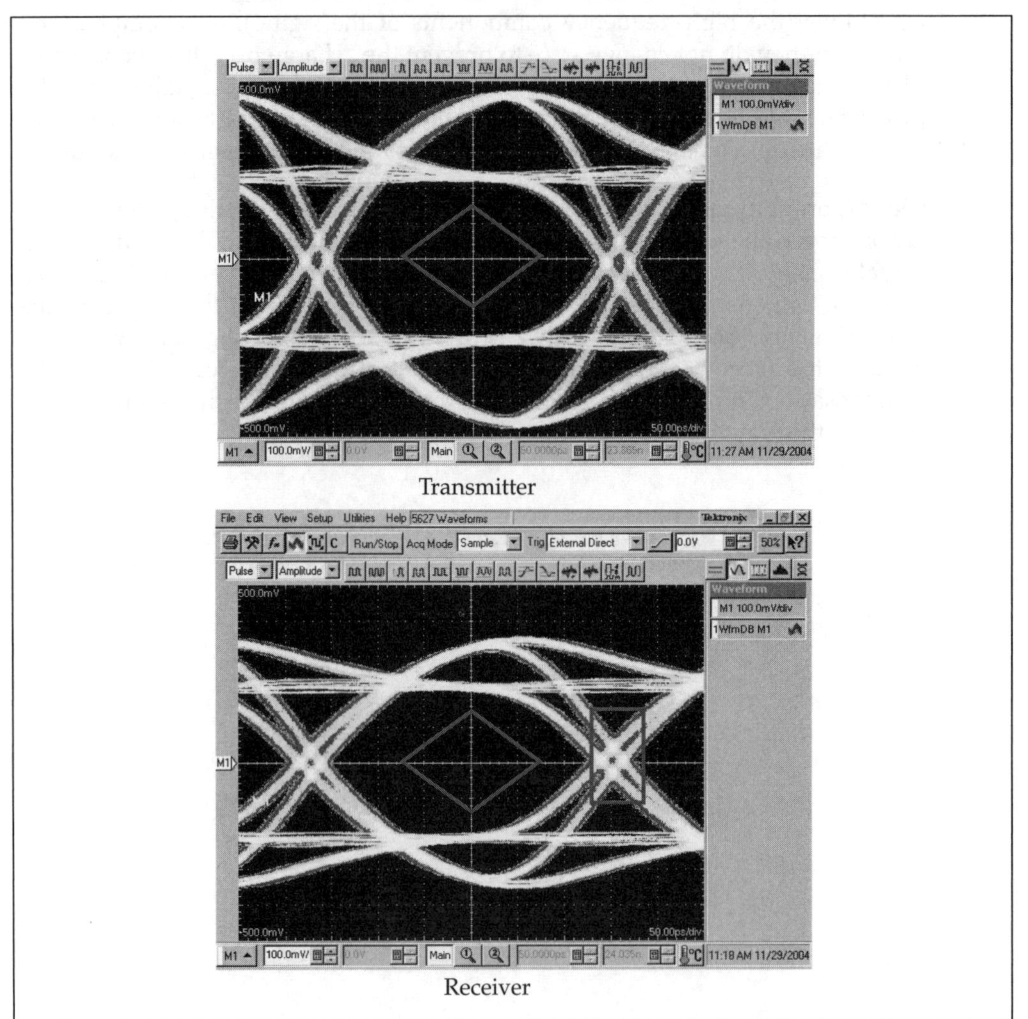

Equalization

The equalization approach involves applying a high-pass filter at the receiver and then amplifying the result to recover the original signal. Since this method is applied inside a device, no waveforms are available to show the results, but

SPICE simulations indicate a similar improvement in the eye opening. The advantage of this approach is that the receiver can detect how well the applied compensation is working and adjust the equalization parameters to improve the results as needed. A disadvantage is that when the signal is amplified, all the noise associated with it is also amplified, and it can also be more complex to implement.

Comparing the Compensation Methods

Comparing the two types of compensation, we can see that each of them has advantages and disadvantages. Pre-emphasis has no feedback mechanism to automatically recognize how well it's working, can cause increased cross-talk by amplifying high frequencies, and uses more power. Equalization does allow for performance feedback but, because it amplifies everything coming in, it also amplifies the noise, which can be an issue if the signal to noise ratio is low. Reliable system operation might well involve using both of these techniques together to minimize transmission line loss effects.

Compliance Points

A separable connector can be identified by a vendor as a compliance point if the signal behavior at that location complies with the signal characteristics defined by the standard. Those points are listed in Table 17-4 on page 420. The signals are measured at physical positions called probe points in a test load. An example of using a zero-length test load to verify a receiver compliance point is shown in Figure 17-12.

Test Loads

Test loads are used to specify and verify transmitter characteristics and receiver inputs. There are three versions defined in the standard:

- **Zero-length test load**, used for testing both transmitter and receiver compliance points. As shown in earlier illustrations, this is simply a connector with very short trace lengths attached to a termination load. Probe points allow for connecting a scope and for the easy measurement of the transmitter or receiver signal characteristics.
- **Transmitter Compliance Transfer Function (TCTF) test load**, for testing transmitter compliance points. This function is made up of a set of S-param-

eters that define a simulation model for use with devices like network analyzers. Such an analyzer uses the simulation model to test the response as it sweeps through a range of frequencies, providing what should be a reasonably accurate map of signal loss at each frequency. As an aside, two types of loss are typically considered: the loss experienced by the signal as it propagates through the transmission line (referred to as insertion loss); and the loss caused by the energy reflected back to the transmitter that should be minimized by accurate termination (referred to as return loss). Only the magnitude of the insertion loss is defined for the SAS standard (defined by TCTF at 1.5 and 3.0 Gb/s). This may change for the 6.0 Gb/s rate.

- **Low-loss TCTF test load**, for testing transmitter compliance points when a SATA device is supported, or the SAS device does not support the signal levels through a full TCTF test load.

Figure 17-12: Zero-Length Test Load for Receiver Compliance Point

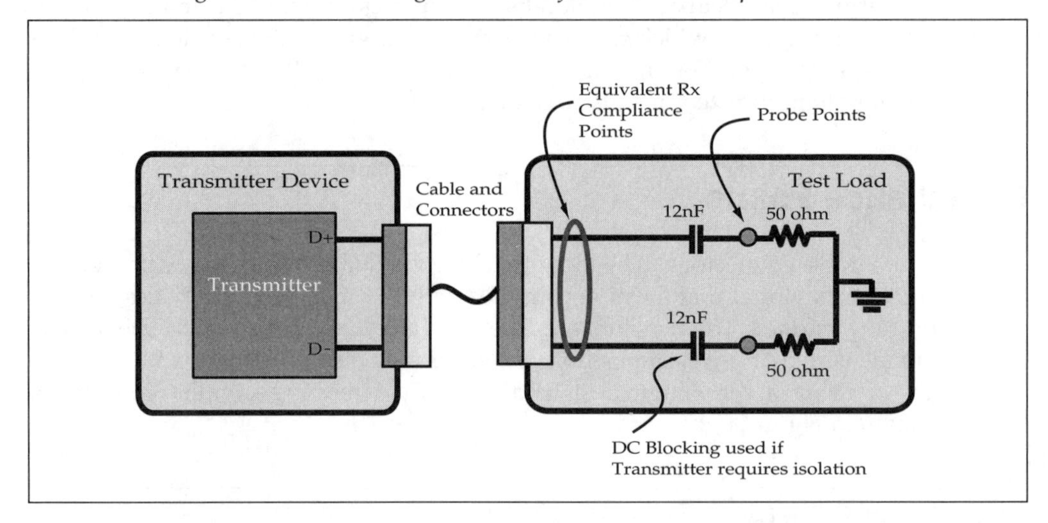

Several diagrams are provided in the standard to help clarify where the compliance points are located. The compliance point for the receiver is on the near side of the connector nearest the receiver, while the compliance point for the transmitter is on the far side of the connector nearest the transmitter. This is readily seen in Figure 17-13 on page 431, in which the signal must cross several connectors in the path between transmitter and receiver. Looking first at the top part of the diagram, the labeled circles on the drawing indicate compliance points where measurements can be made for both transmitter (IT) and receiver (IR). The IT compliance point is shown just on the far side of the connector nearest the transmitter, while the IR compliance point is shown just on the near side of the connector nearest the receiver.

Figure 17-13: Compliance Points

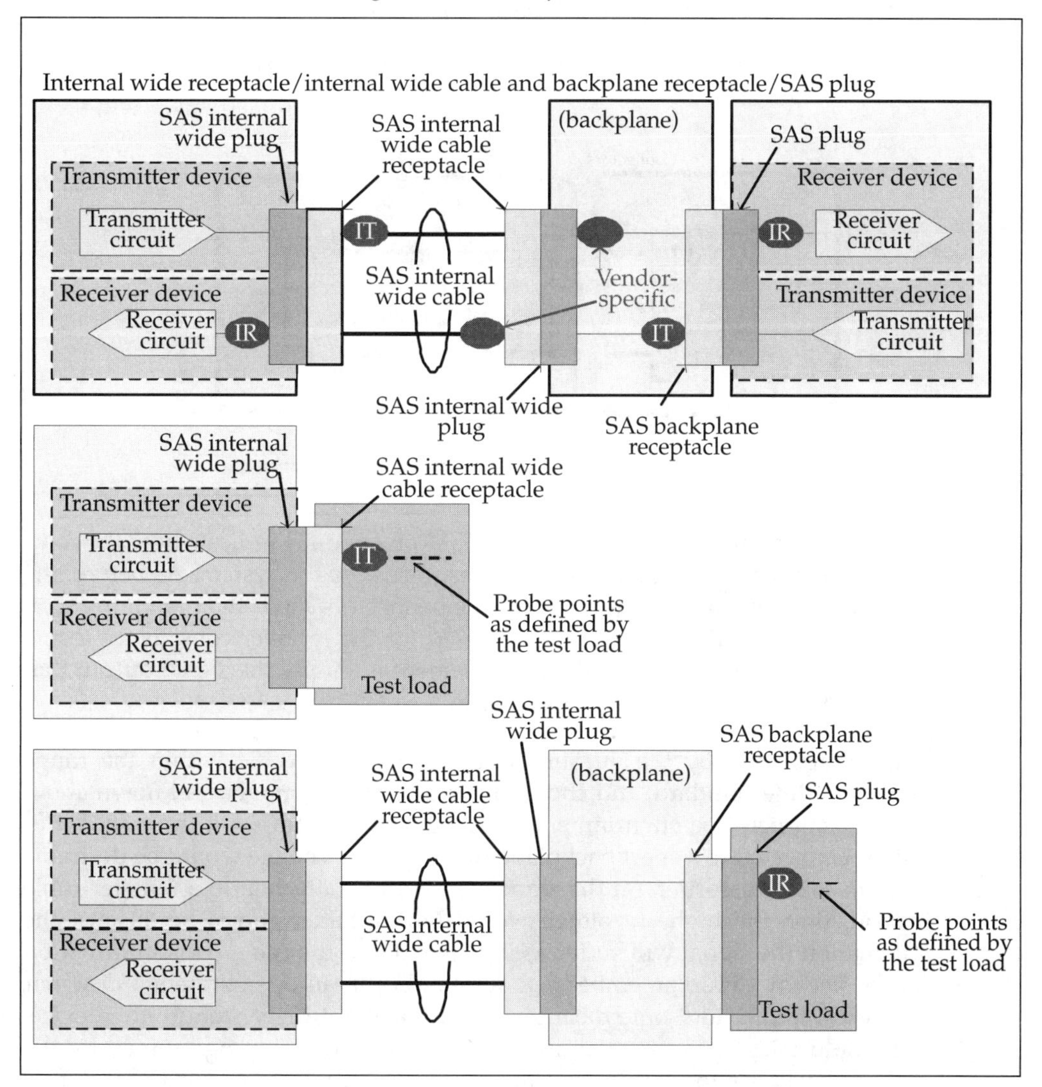

The fact that there are other connectors in the path or even that there is both a cable and a backplane in the path are not important for this definition, although they may present other, vendor-specific testing points. As another example showing compliance point location, Figure 17-14 shows the zero-length test load case for verifying a transmitter's compliance point. Note that the only difference is that there is no cable or other transmission medium in place, so this setup would be for testing the transmitter characteristics.

Figure 17-14: Zero-Length Test Load for Transmitter Compliance Point

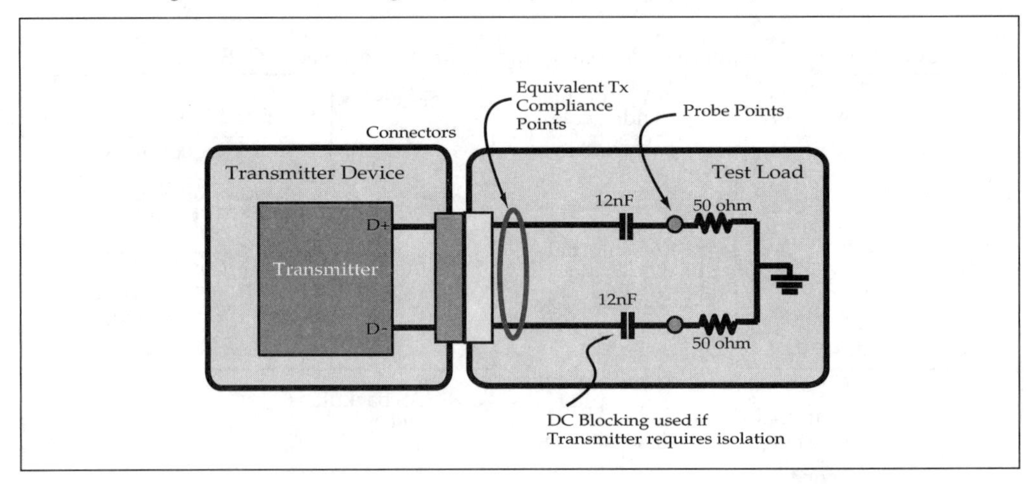

The middle and bottom parts of Figure 17-13 on page 431 indicate how the compliance points are defined when using test loads for the system. As before, the definition is related to the location of the connectors more than anything else. Note that an actual receiver is not required for the receiver compliance test; a test load is sufficient because the measurement is simply the signal output that arrives at the end of the transmission line.

The voltage used by the output driver is vendor specific within the range allowed by the standard, and should be chosen based on what is known about the transmission line environment of this link. For example, if the transmitter will be connected to a short backplane trace, a lower voltage would be desirable so as to avoid distortion on the signal. If it will be attached to a 6 meter cable instead, then the highest voltage would be the better choice because of the attenuation the signal will suffer as it passes down the cable. This information can be known within an embedded system, but in an open system a designer may want to provide some means of feedback about the system to the device. This could take the form of an external EEPROM that is programmed by the system developer to load in system parameters at power up, or the interface might be designed with some form of measurement logic that would actively sense the signaling environment and make adjustments. There has also been some discussion in the working group about specifying connectors that would give an indication about the environment automatically in a standardized way, but the outcome of that discussion was still pending at the time of this writing.

18 Cables and Connectors

The Previous Chapter

The previous chapter described the electrical characteristics of the differential transmitter and receiver used to transmit the bits across the wire, and included a discussion of the four interface environments defined for use with SAS. Apart from the discussion about the analog transmitter and receiver, the Physical Layer is largely concerned with the passive interface that includes backplanes, cables, and connectors.

This Chapter

This chapter describes the second part of the Physical Layer definition, discussing the passive cables and connectors used to connect devices to each other.

The Next Chapter

The next chapter describes the function and responsibilities of the various layers in support of SATA.

Introduction

This second part of the SAS Physical Layer describes the passive interconnect, or the cables and connectors used to physically attach devices. These are designed to be compatible with SATA cabling and interfaces so that a SATA device can plug directly into a SAS interface. They are also designed to support different signaling environments as well.

Interconnect Environments

The SAS standard defines four interconnect environments: Drive backplane, Drive cable, Internal cable, and External cable environments. One significant difference between backplane and cable environments is that backplane connectors are usually designed with characteristics that support hot-plug operations, such as staggered pins and guided connecting mechanisms. Cable plugs, on the other hand, are expected to be hand-attached so cable environments do not always share those characteristics. In addition, for the internal environment the cables are designed to be backward compatible with existing SATA cables that were not intended for hot plug use. A block diagram of the internal cable and connector usage for SATA is shown in Figure 18-1, while the corresponding diagram for SAS is shown in Figure 18-2 on page 435.

Figure 18-1: SATA Cable and Backplane Environments

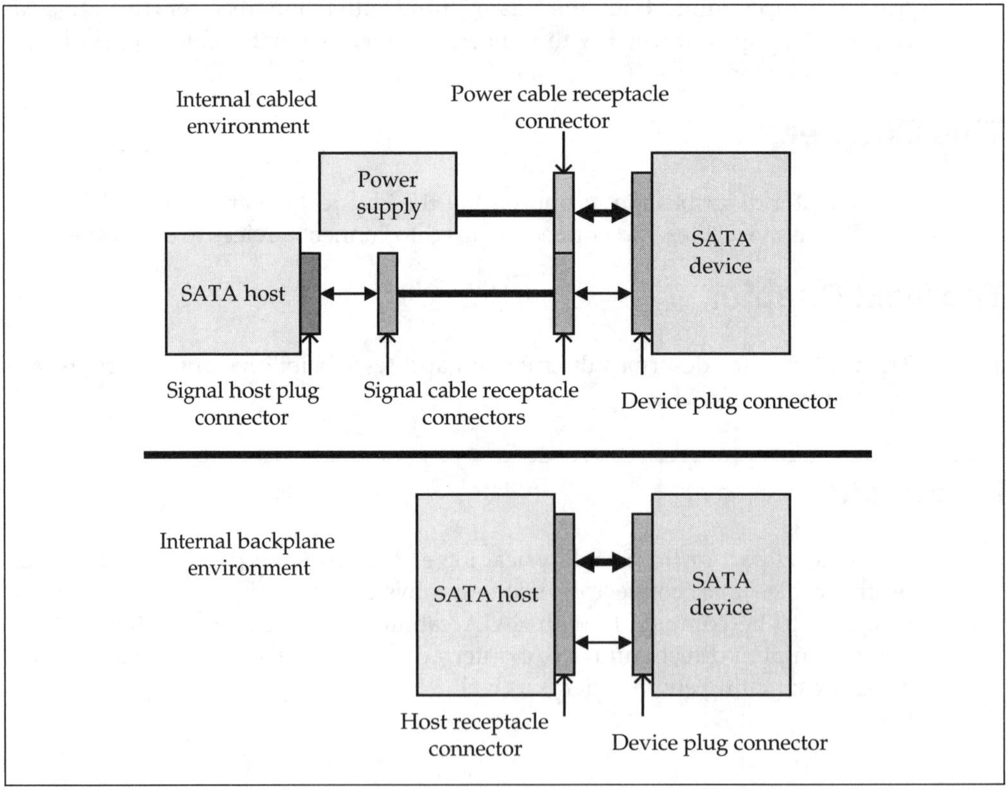

Figure 18-2: SAS Single-Port Cable and Dual-Port Backplane Environments

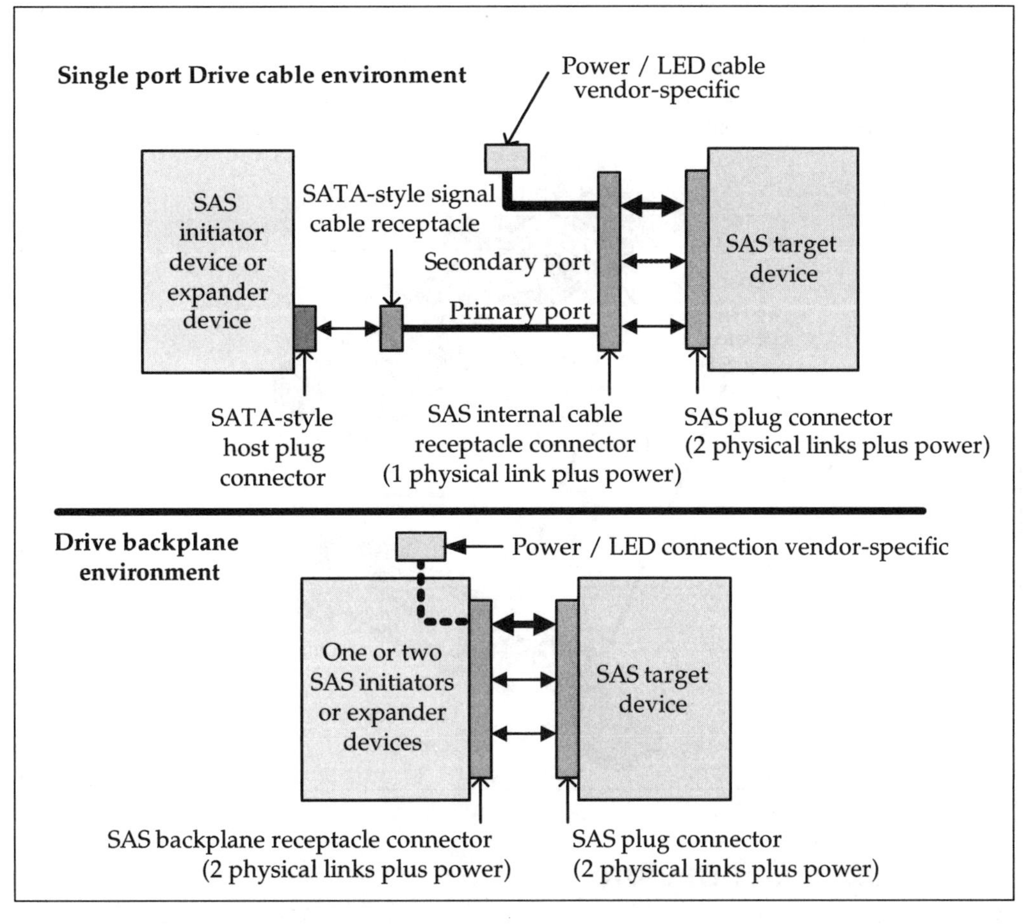

As can be seen from these simple diagrams, the difference between SAS and SATA is the option of a second data port and a dedicated LED indicator. A SATA drive can also use that LED pin (pin 11 of the power connector) for an LED activity indicator, although it's not designed to drive the LED directly and must send it to the host or other logic for help with that function. SATA also uses pin 11 as an input during initialization to determine whether an automatic spinup is permitted. Note that the SAS and SATA connectors are not interchangeable. The SATA connector leaves a gap between the power pins and the signal pins, as shown in Figure 18-3 on page 436, whereas the SAS connector fills in the gap on the connector. This prevents a SAS device from plugging into a SATA backplane but allows a SATA device to plug into a SAS connector. The SAS connector is also designed to support two ports, and the bridge across that gap is used for the signals of the second port, as shown in Figure 18-4 on page 437.

Figure 18-3: SATA Backplane Connector

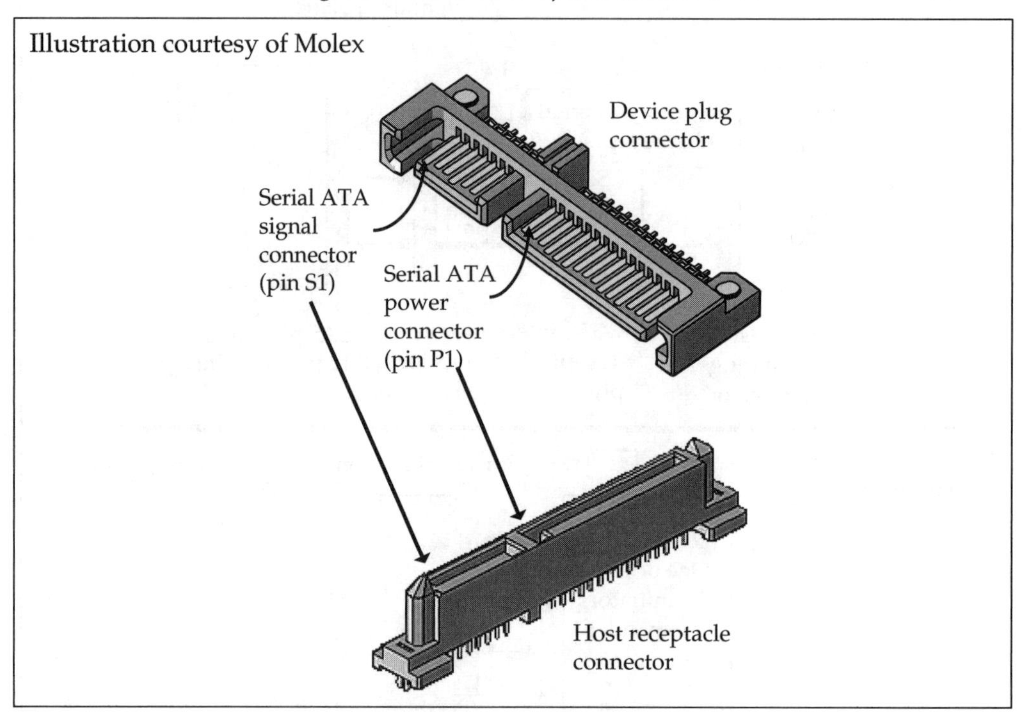

Internal Connectors

In addition to the SATA-style signal plug for which SAS maintains backward compatibility, the SAS standard defines three other drive connectors for internal use. These include the plug attached to the drive itself, shown in Figure 18-4, and two receptacles for the plug. The receptacles into which the plug is mated include a backplane receptacle shown in Figure 18-5, and a single- or dual-ported cable receptacle. The dual-ported cable version is shown in Figure 18-6; the single-ported version simply omits the pins for the secondary port. All the receptacle types can support SAS and SATA drives.

Figure 18-4: SAS Drive Plug Connector

Illustration courtesy of Molex

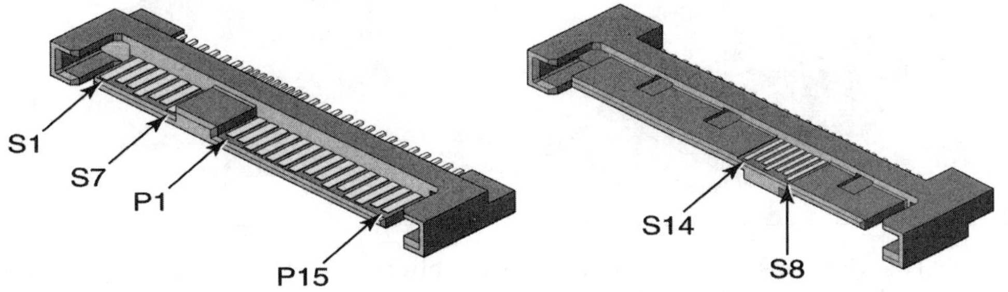

S1
S7
P1
P15
S14
S8

Figure 18-5: SAS Drive Backplane Receptacle

Illustration courtesy of Molex

S8
S14
P15
P1
S7
S1

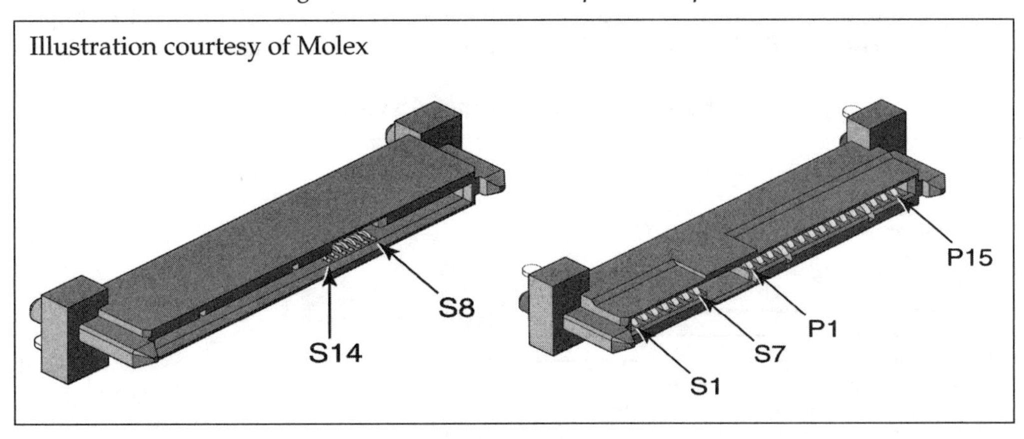

Figure 18-6: Dual-Ported SAS Drive Cable Receptacle

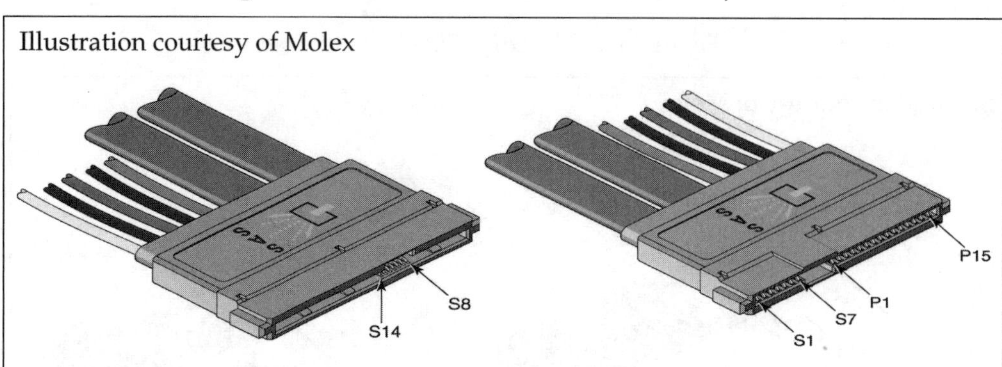

The wiring inside the connectors is straightforward, as can be seen in the drawing in Figure 18-7, which shows the connections inside the dual-ported cable above. The pinout for the connectors is given in Table 18-1, from which it can be seen that the understanding of which pins are transmit and which are received is based on the fact that the plug or cable is expected to be connected to a target device while the backplane connector expects to be connected to an initiator.

Figure 18-7: Dual-Ported SAS Cable

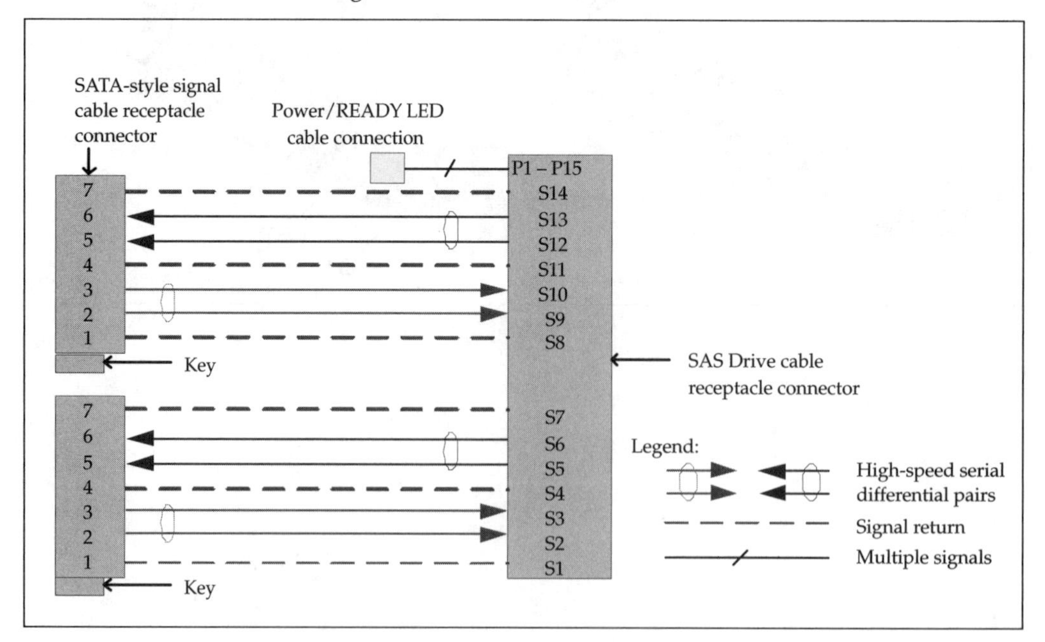

Table 18-1: SAS Drive Connector Pin Assignments

Segment	Pin	Mating Sequence	Backplane Receptacle	SAS Drive plug and SAS Drive cable receptacle
Primary Signal Segment	S1	Second	Signal Ground	
	S2	Third	TP+	RP+
	S3	Third	TP-	RP-
	S4	Second	Signal Ground	
	S5	Third	RP-	TP-
	S6	Third	RP+	TP+
	S7	Second	Signal Ground	
Secondary Signal Segment (This segment not connected on single-port connectors)	S8	Second	Signal Ground	
	S9	Third	TS+	RS+
	S10	Third	TS-	RS-
	S11	Second	Signal Ground	
	S12	Third	RS-	TS-
	S13	Third	RS+	TS+
	S14	Second	Signal Ground	

Table 18-1: SAS Drive Connector Pin Assignments

Segment	Pin	Mating Sequence	Backplane Receptacle	SAS Drive plug and SAS Drive cable receptacle
Power Segment	P1	Third	V_{33}	
	P2	Third	V_{33}	
	P3	Second	V_{33}, precharge	
	P4	First	GROUND	
	P5	Second	GROUND	
	P6	Second	GROUND	
	P7	Second	V_5, precharge	
	P8	Third	V_5	
	P9	Third	V_5	
	P10	Second	GROUND	
	P11	Third	READY LED	
	P12	First	GROUND	
	P13	Second	V_{12}, precharge	
	P14	Third	V_{12}	
	P15	Third	V_{12}	

Some notes regarding Table 18-1:

- V_{33} means 3.3V, V_5 means 5.0V, and V_{12} means 12.0V
- P11, the READY LED pin, is also used for staggered spinup on SATA devices
- The Power Segment and the primary signal segment are both the same as they are for a SATA device connector.
- The secondary signal segment does not exist on a SATA connector.
- Mating sequence: Some connector pins are a little longer than the others, so

pins that have long fingers on both connectors will mate first, a long finger mated to a short one will mate second, and the rest will mate third in sequence when the connector is plugged in.

SAS 4i Connectors

The next type of connector defined in the standard is the 4-wide internal cable, referred to as "SAS 4i" and defined by the SFF-8484 definition. SFF stands for Small Form Factor and designates a definition created by the Small Form Factor Committee, an ad hoc group formed to complement the standards process by quickly developing definitions for small computer environments. The list of specifications defined by the SFF committee may be found at their FTP site: ftp://ftp.seagate.com/sff/.

While not readily visible in Figure 18-8, the cable receptacle supports four SAS links and also has six pins available for sideband signals that can be used for any purpose, such as SGPIO signals in support of enclosure management functions. These signals are shown in the schematic of Figure 18-9, where it can also be seen that the signals are reversed when they reach the connector on the other side, so that pin 31 of one plug is wired to pin 2 of the other and vice versa. This matches the signals normally when connecting a controller to a backplane, but is slightly different when connecting two controllers to each other. For that case, it's important to note that link 0 will connect to link 3 on the other side and vice-versa. This isn't an electrical or protocol problem, since the devices don't know or care about link numbers, but it can still prevent them from communicating. If two controllers are connected with this cable and each is only using links 0 and 1, those will be connected to links 2 and 3 on the other end, and neither will be able to see the other's active links.

Figure 18-8: SAS 4i Symmetric Cable and Receptacle

Illustration courtesy of Molex

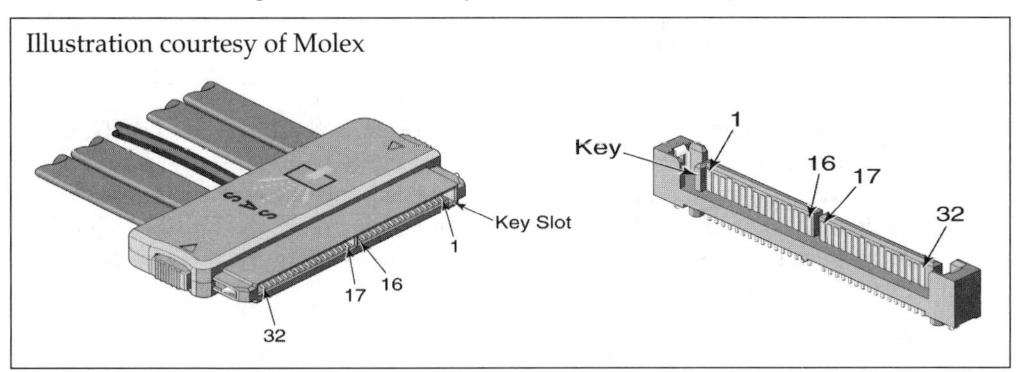

Figure 18-9: SAS 4i Internal Symmetric Cable Assembly

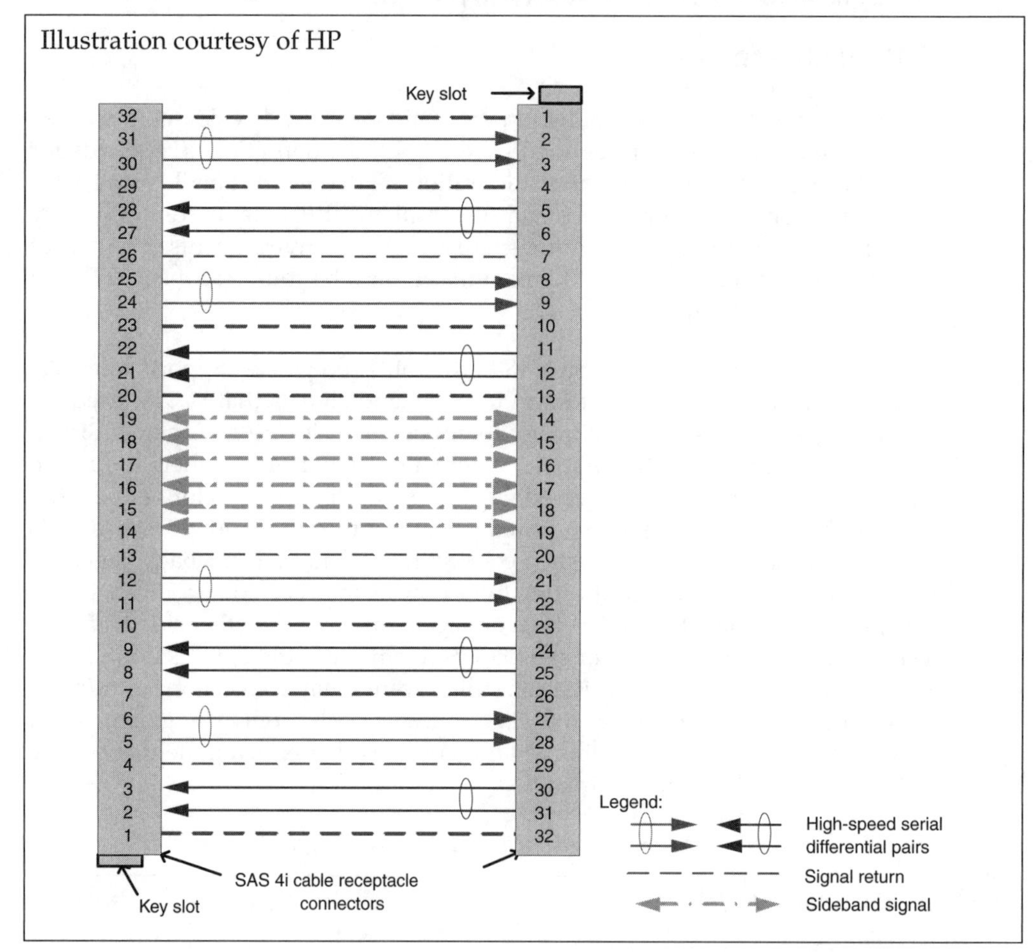

This internal cable has two varieties based on how the links are distributed at the other end of the cable. If all four links are contained in just one connector at both ends, as shown in Figure 18-10 on page 443, then the cable is referred to as an internal *symmetric* cable. If one end of the cable breaks the four links out into four separate cables, as illustrated by the example in Figure 18-11 on page 444, the cable is referred to as an internal *fanout* cable.

While these internal connectors are keyed for proper orientation, they are not keyed to indicate the appropriateness of connecting them into a particular receptacle. For example, it is not a legal topology to attach a fanout port (a port that is not a subtractive port) from one expander to the fanout port of another expander. The expectation is that manufacturers will understand what they're doing when they attach internal cables, so there was no need for keying to reduce the possibility of an incorrect connection. For the external cables that an inexperienced operator may have to connect, guidance about appropriate connections is more important, and that is built into the definitions for the external cables, as will be seen shortly.

Figure 18-10: SAS 4i Internal Symmetric Cable Implementation Example

Illustration courtesy of Molex

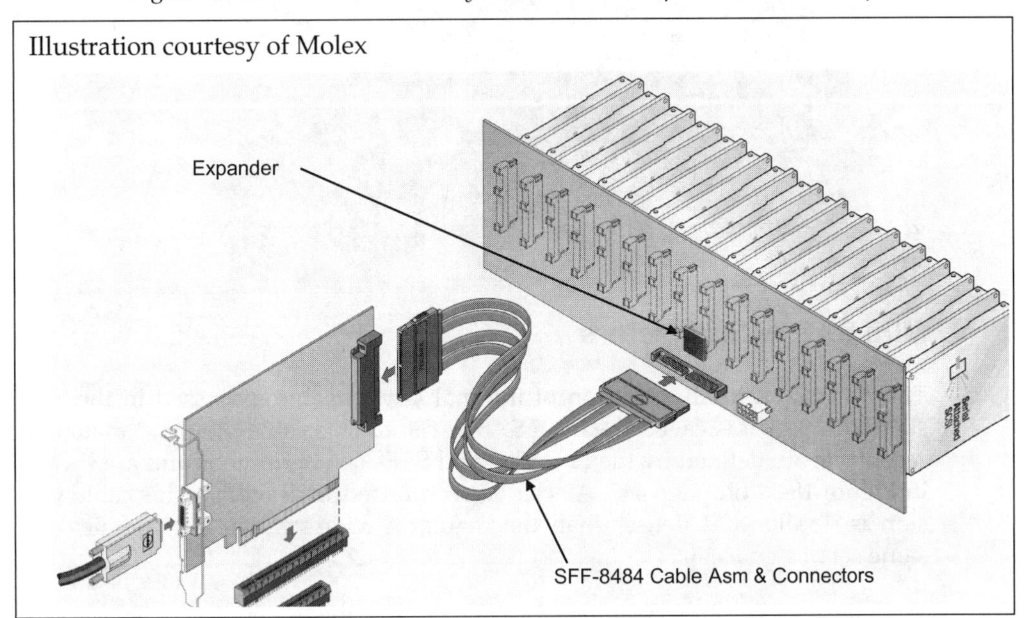

Figure 18-11: SAS 4i Internal Fanout Cable Implementation Example

Illustration courtesy of Molex

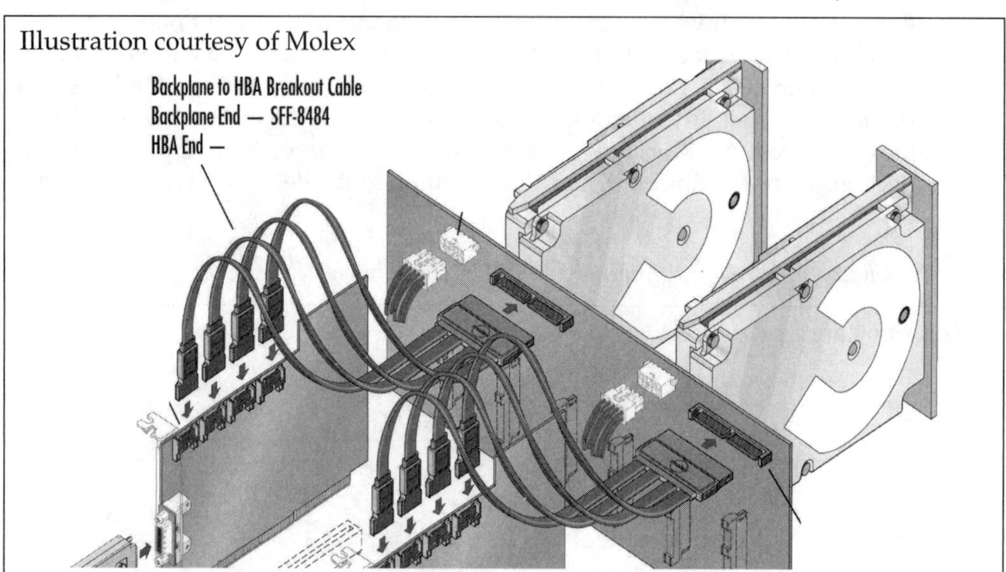

Mini SAS 4i Connectors

There is also a smaller version of internal 4-wide cable discussed in the SAS standard, which is called the Mini SAS 4i cable. This cable plug and matching receptacle are defined by the SFF-8087 and SFF-8086 definitions and are shown in Figure 18-12 on page 445. As can be seen from the drawings, this cable version is smaller and denser than the regular 4-wide version but contains the same set of signals.

The mini SAS 4i cables do not suffer from the pin assignment issue that the regular 4i cables have, so SAS links will connect normally without trouble. However, the sideband signals will have reversal problems if two controllers are connected to each other.

Figure 18-12: Mini SAS 4i Cable Plug and Receptacle

Illustration courtesy of Molex

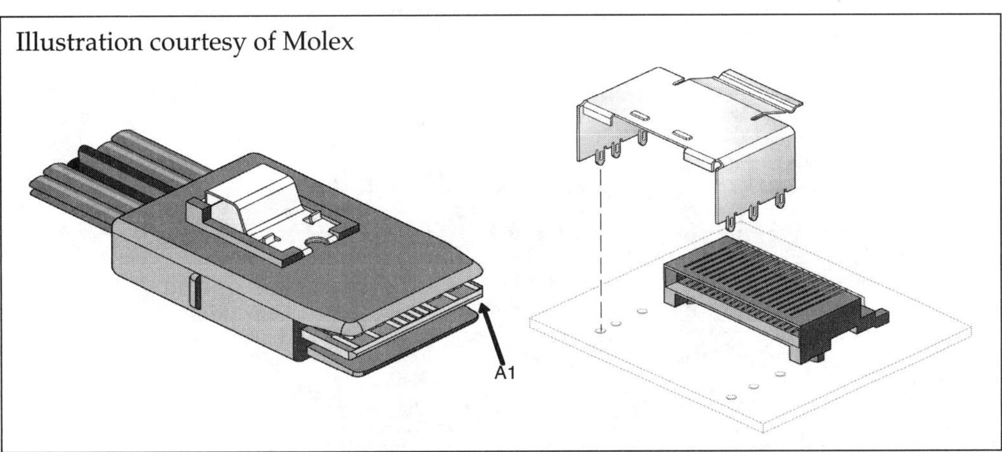

As might be expected, this link-reversing issue does exist for a cable that has a 4i connector on one end and a mini-4i connector on the other end. For that case, it makes a difference which end is connected to what. If both ends are connected to a controller, or if the 4i connector is connected to the controller and the mini-4i to the backplane, the signal pairs match up normally. However, if the mini-4i connector is attached to a controller and the 4i connector is attached to a backplane then the link numbers will be reversed.

Other Internal Cables

While the standard lists the compliant cables and connectors, other cables for internal use also logically suggest themselves as slight variations on these types. As one example, the cable shown in Figure 18-13 uses the same connectors, but bundles the four signal pairs into a single round cable assembly instead of four separate flat cables.

Figure 18-13: HBA to Backplane Cable

Illustration courtesy of Molex

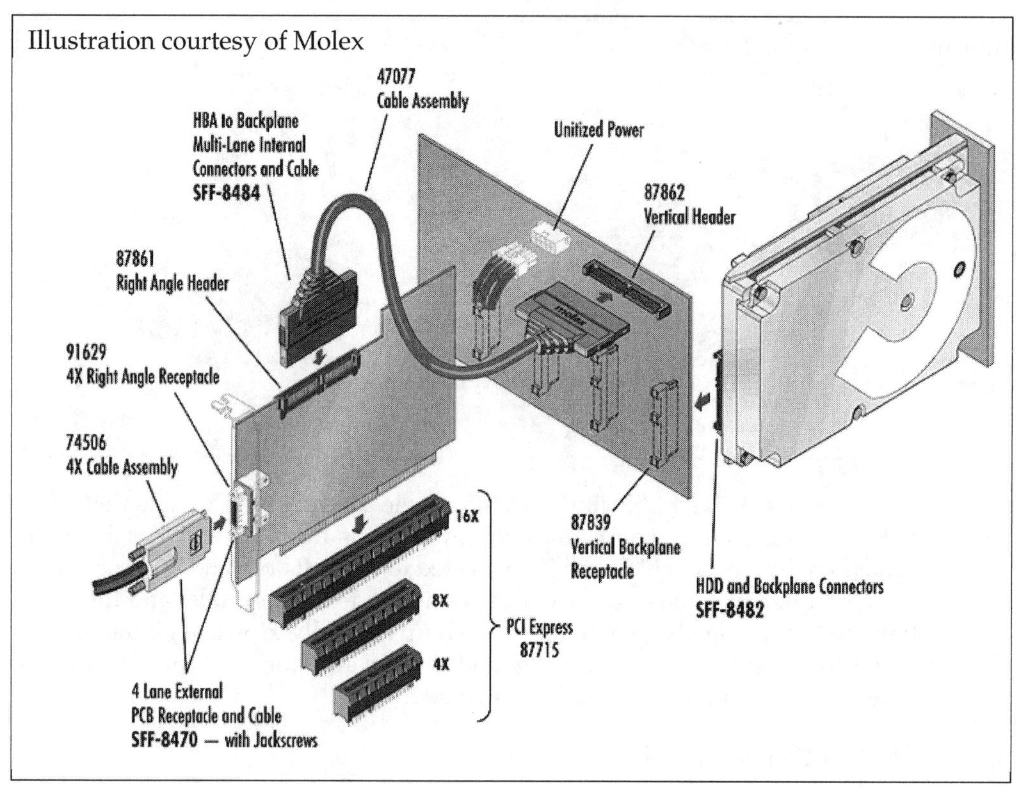

External Connectors

There are two versions of external cables and connectors given in the SAS standard, the SAS 4x cable and the Mini SAS 4x cable.

SAS 4x Connectors

The first external cable given in the standard is actually the same as the InfiniBand 4-wide cable, which is defined by SFF-8470. The cable connector, as shown in Figure 18-14, is not allowed to have keys, but can optionally have vendor-specific key slots. Since it contains four SAS signaling pairs, this cable can support up to four SAS devices but, if used with an expander, only one expander can use it at a time, and all the links must connect to the same expander port. This cable is less popular than one might expect, in spite of the fact that it was already in production before the introduction of SAS, because it is considered bulky and expensive.

Figure 18-14: SAS 4x Cable Plug and Receptacle

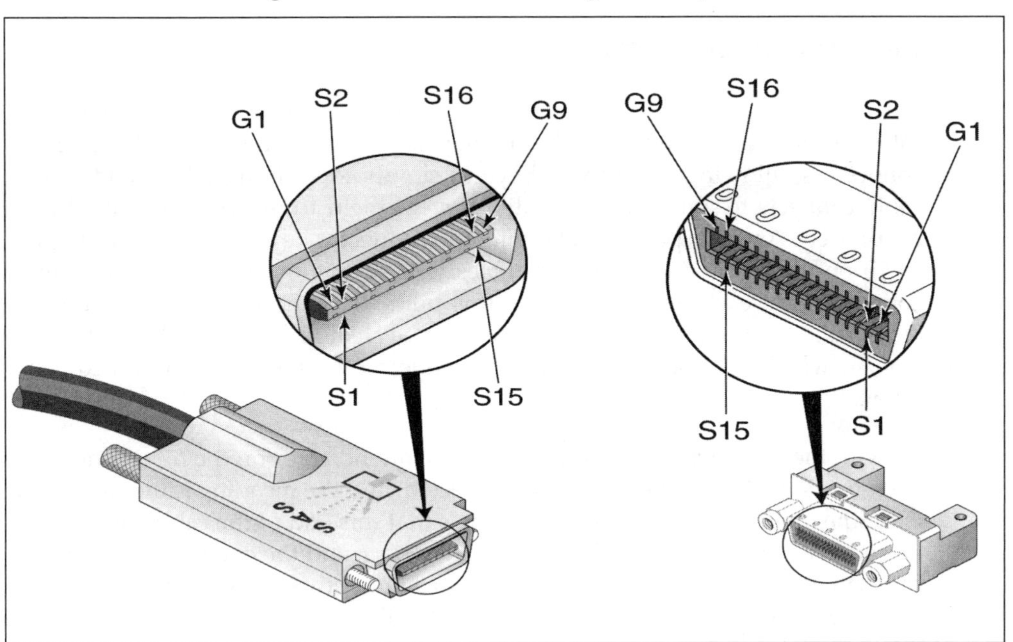

Although Figure 18-14 doesn't show it, there can be an indicator on the connector itself, or possibly on a tag attached to it, that shows into which plugs it can be connected. A diamond symbol will indicate that one end of the cable can be connected to an end device or an enclosure "out" port, and a circle will indicate that it can be connected to an end device or enclosure "in" port. The definition of in and out is intended to guide an end user in constructing legal topologies at the customer site.

Understanding Cable Topologies

To understand what this means, recall from our earlier discussion of attaching expanders together that it is permissible to connect a table-routed expander port only to the subtractive port of another expander, but not to connect two table-routed ports to each other. While it is legal to attach two subtractive ports to each other, doing so is considered to be an unlikely end-user arrangement. With that in mind, the "in" term defines a subtractive port, while the "out" term indicates a table-routed port: they can each be connected to the other type but not ordinarily to the same type. These indicators can be present on the InfiniBand connectors to assist the operator in this regard, but the connectors are not keyed to prevent them from being attached inappropriately. Still, following the guidance provided by the connector markings can help an operator set up legal topologies and stay out of trouble.

SAS Mini 4x Connectors

A smaller version of the external cable was also defined, called the Mini SAS 4x cable. An interesting aspect to the smaller cables is that these do include keyed connectors, allowing them to go beyond simply identifying which end of the cable connects to which and actually prevent them from being attached inappropriately. An example cable showing the connector keying is shown in Figure 18-15 on the following page. The cables will always ordinarily have different connectors on each end to facilitate this purpose. A non-standard cable with "in" connectors on both ends would need to be created for the legal but unlikely case in which an operator wanted to connect two subtractive ports to each other.

As with the previous connector, there is also an indicator on the mini connector itself that shows into what it can be connected, and the meaning is the same as it is for the other cable. A diamond indicates that this end of the cable can be connected to an enclosure "out," or table-routed port, and the circle indicates that it can be connected to an enclosure "in," or subtractive-route port. When both markings are present on the same connector then the plug is intended for an end device. Backplanes simply follow the recommendations of SFF-8460.

The receptacles for the cable plugs are shown in Figure 18-16Figure 18-16 on page 450.

Figure 18-15: Mini SAS 4x Cable with Keyed Connectors

Illustration courtesy of Molex

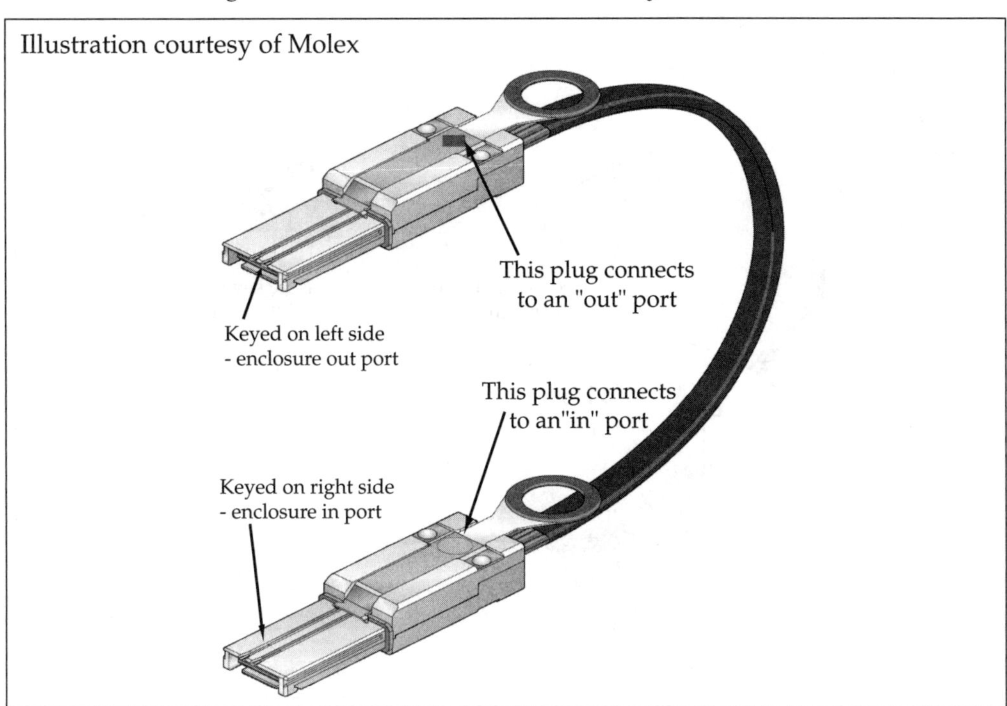

Figure 18-16: Mini SAS 4x Receptacles

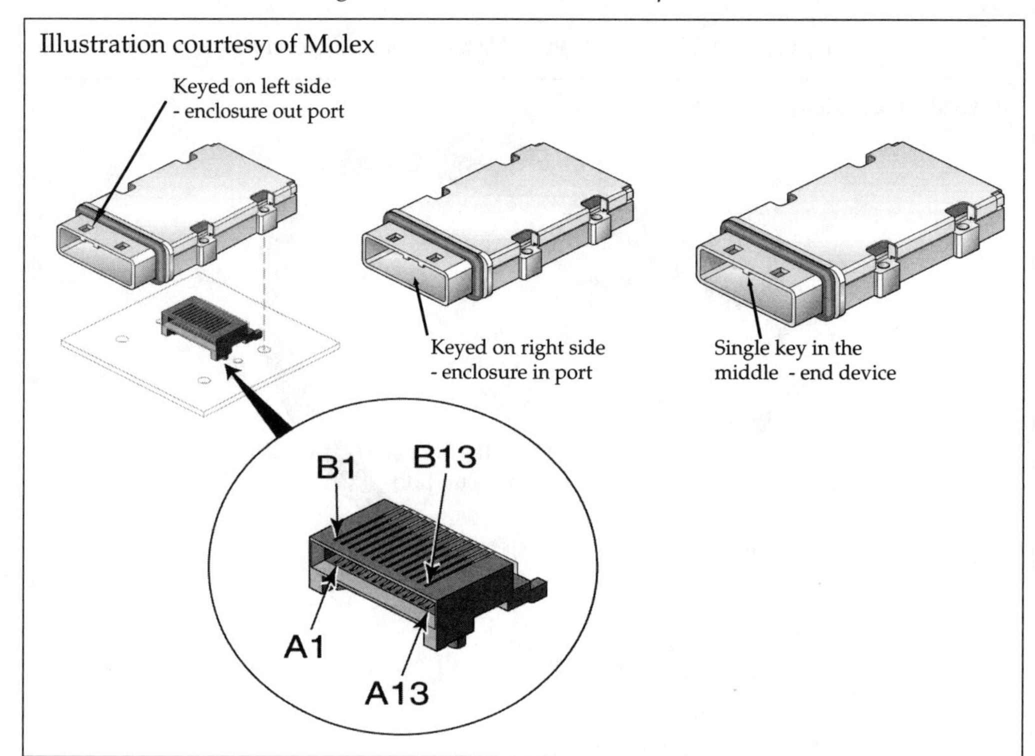

Other Physical Layer Considerations

Non-tracking clock

A SAS target device is not allowed to be tracking, meaning it cannot use the recovered clock derived from the bit stream coming into its receiver to generate the transmit clock. SATA does allow targets to be tracking, though, so a receiver designed to support SATA must tolerate this behavior. However, a target using a tracking clock adds a great deal of jitter to the transmitted data, meaning that the HBA has to tolerate about twice the usual amount of jitter. For SAS, where longer cable lengths mean signal integrity is a more important consideration than it is for SATA, such additional jitter would not work well at all. Consequently, SAS transmitters must never do this, and receivers that do not support SATA are not required to support it.

READY LED characteristics

Since we have been describing the physical connectors, it's important to note that all SAS devices using the SAS drive plug connector shown in Figure 18-4 on page 437 must support the READY LED signal (pin 11 in the power portion of the connector). This pin is designed to be an open-drain or open-collector transmitter used to pull down the cathode of an externally visible LED. It's also important to remember that this same pin is used by SATA target devices as both an activity indicator output and also as a staggered spin-up disable input. For more on the use of this pin during spin-up, refer to "SATA Spin-Up" on page 203.

Part 4: SATA Support

19 SATA Support

The Previous Chapter

The previous chapter described the second part of the Physical Layer definition, and discussed the passive cables and connectors used to connect devices to each other.

This Chapter

This chapter describes the function and responsibilities of the various layers in support of SATA. This support is optional for SAS devices and so, rather than describe how each part of it operates in the context of the earlier SSP chapters, all of the discussion on STP is presented together here.

The Next Chapter

The next chapter describes the hardware initialization process of SATA devices. Much like SAS devices, the neighbors on the link undergo a sequence of steps after reset to recognize that they are attached to a device and begin the process of communicating with it. The overall process is simpler for SATA because one device acts as the host or initiator and the other behaves as the target device.

Introduction

The expectation in this chapter is that the reader has progressed sequentially through the book and is therefore familiar with the functions of the layers as they relate to the SSP and SMP protocol support that are mandatory for a SAS initiator or expander. The material presented here, then, is only that optional part of the SAS protocol that is unique to SATA Tunneled Protocol (STP) connections.

SATA Background

To understand the application of SATA to the SAS environment, it may be helpful to review some background. ATA and SATA are most commonly implemented in single-user environments. Consequently, there was little expectation for more than two drives in a master/slave configuration, and that allowed the protocol to be simple. SATA uses a dedicated point-to-point connection between the target and the host. No provision was made in the HBA link to access any other SATA devices in the system.

Programming Methods

Legacy Method

The application layer in legacy programming initiated an operation by having the CPU write to a set of registers within the target device to inform it of the command. When the command register was updated, the device would begin to take action on it based on the parameters set up in the other registers.

AHCI (Advanced Host Controller Interface)

Newer systems have the application software construct a list of commands and the scatter/gather lists for the data in a memory structure and then just inform the HBA about the location of that structure. In that case, the HBA fetches each frame, referred to as a FIS (Frame Information Structure), already properly formatted and forwards it to the drive. This method is described in a separate spec, referred to as the AHCI, that was intended to give more definition and structure to the SATA standard. By using one of these two programming methods, the command is delivered to the drive which executes it. This process became a little more complicated when Port Multipliers and Port Selectors are used (see "SATA II" on page 484) because they introduce more complex topologies, but the basic process is still the same.

Register Access

In the ATA environment software wrote to a set of registers called Task File registers that were located within the drive. The ATA HBA simply passed writes from the processor directly to these registers within the drive, as shown in Figure 19-1 on page 457. In SATA, a separate copy of these registers, called shadow registers, are included in the HBA and software accesses these shadow registers instead of the registers within the drive. This allows the host to gather the register updates into larger, more efficient packets that are delivered to the drive at high speed.

Figure 19-1: ATA Register Updates

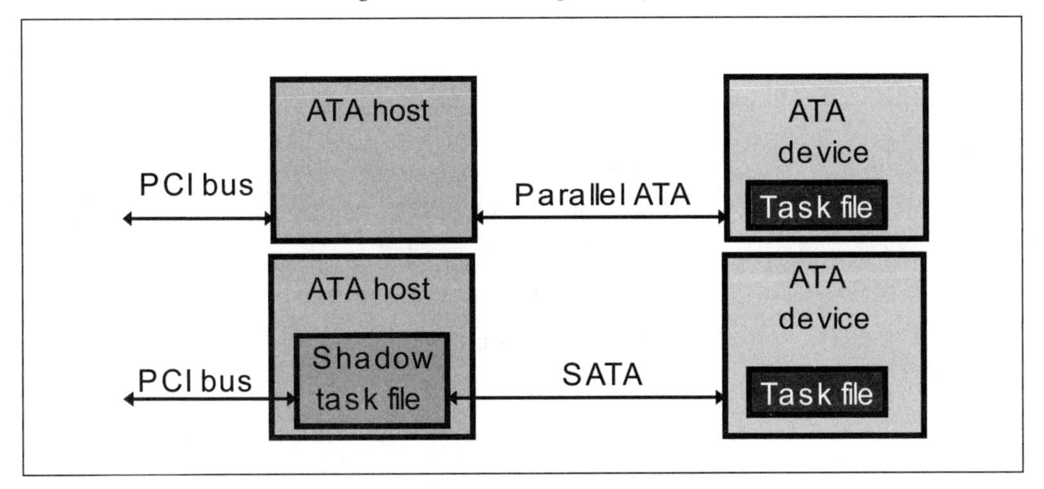

The SATA Interface Layered Definition

The layered architecture defined by the SATA specification is slightly different from that of SAS. Figure 19-2 on page 458 shows the SATA layered hierarchy. The primary responsibilities of each layer are summarized below:

Application Layer — This layer represents the programming interface for the SATA environment. The programming interface is a simple register set intended to provide software compatibility with ATA.

Transport Layer — This layer constructs and delivers the frames, which are called "Frame Information Structures" or FISes by the SATA specification. When receiving a FIS, this layer decodes the FIS and reports any errors to the application layer.

Link Layer — In SATA the link layer manages virtually all of the link protocol. During transmission, this layer generates a CRC for each FIS, scrambles the FIS to reduce EMI, and generates the Primitives used in the SATA protocol. During reception of FISes the inverse operations are performed.

Physical Layer — During FIS transmission and reception this layer simply provides the SerDes and Transceiver functions. This layer is also responsible for link initialization and speed detection.

The functionality of these layers is incorporated into the SAS layered structure to support SATA.

Figure 19-2: SATA Layers

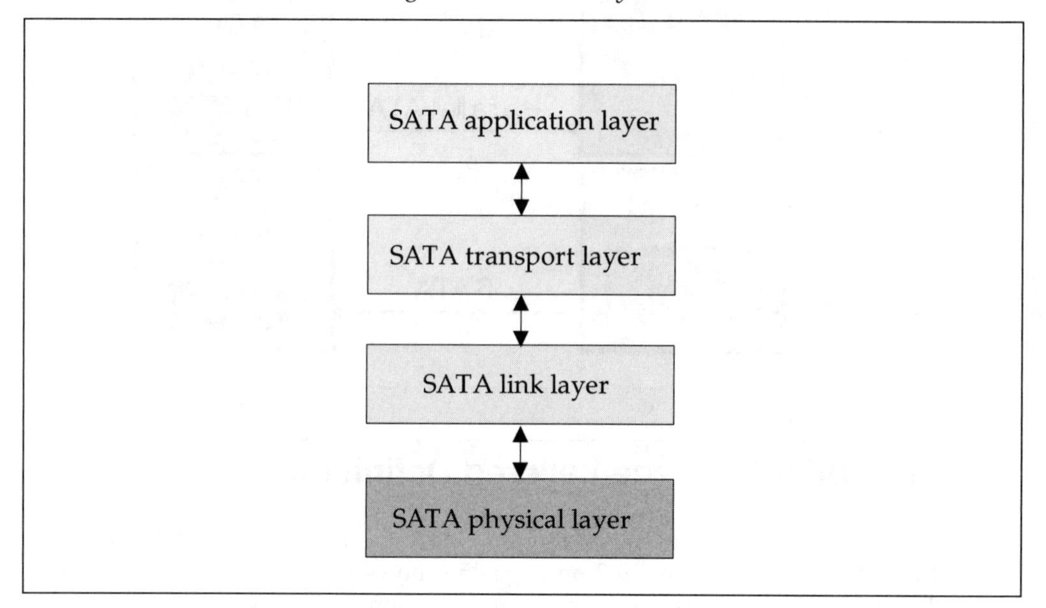

STP Supports SATA

The focus of the SATA Tunneled Protocol is to support the attachment of SATA drives directly into a SAS network. This requires that SATA-compatible frames and protocols be observed. Therefore, the primary focus is on the SAS Host Bus Adapter (originator of SATA traffic) and on any expanders that are in the path between the HBA and SATA drive (see Figure 19-3 on page 459).

Figure 19-3: SAS Topology with SATA Drives Present

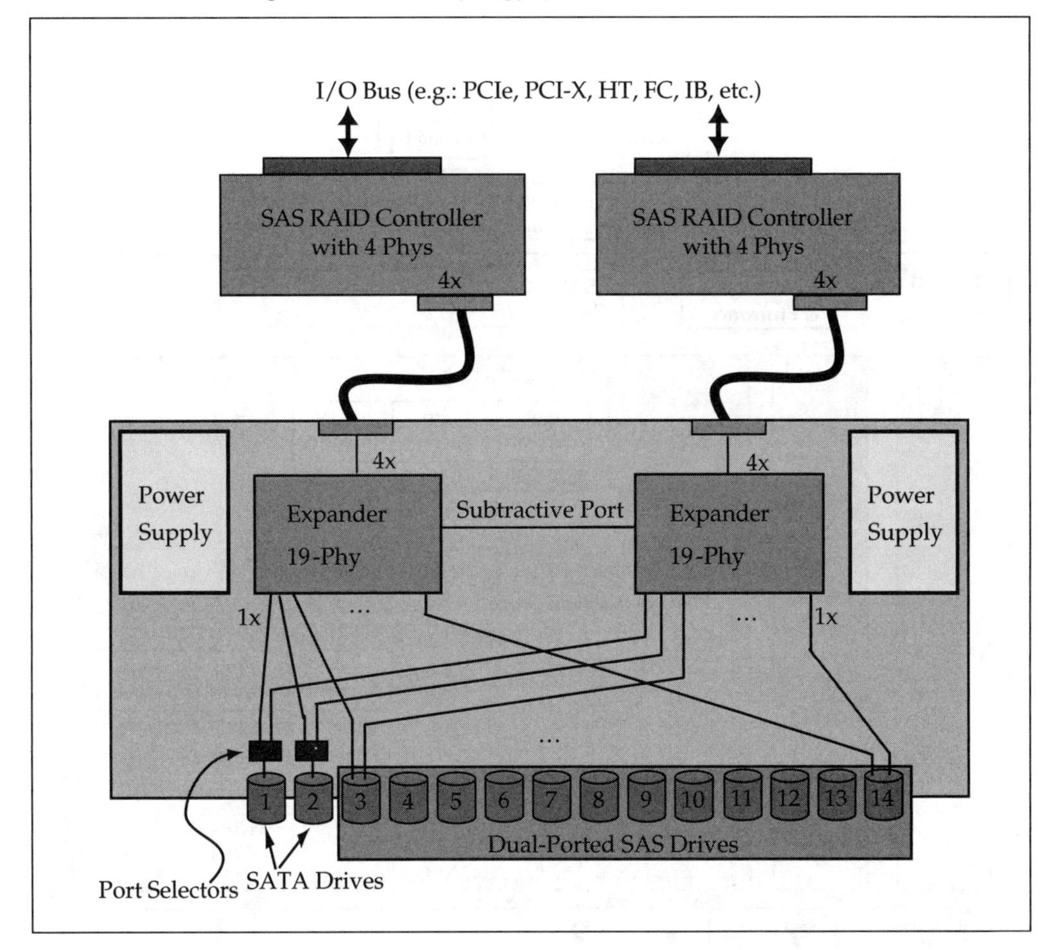

As seen in Figure 19-4 on page 460, the SAS Application Layer, Transport Layer, Link Layer, and Phy Layer optionally include a separate functional block for SATA support. This is because of the different way SATA frames are requested and constructed, and the way SATA (STP) connections are managed.

Figure 19-4: Functional Block Diagram of Layers

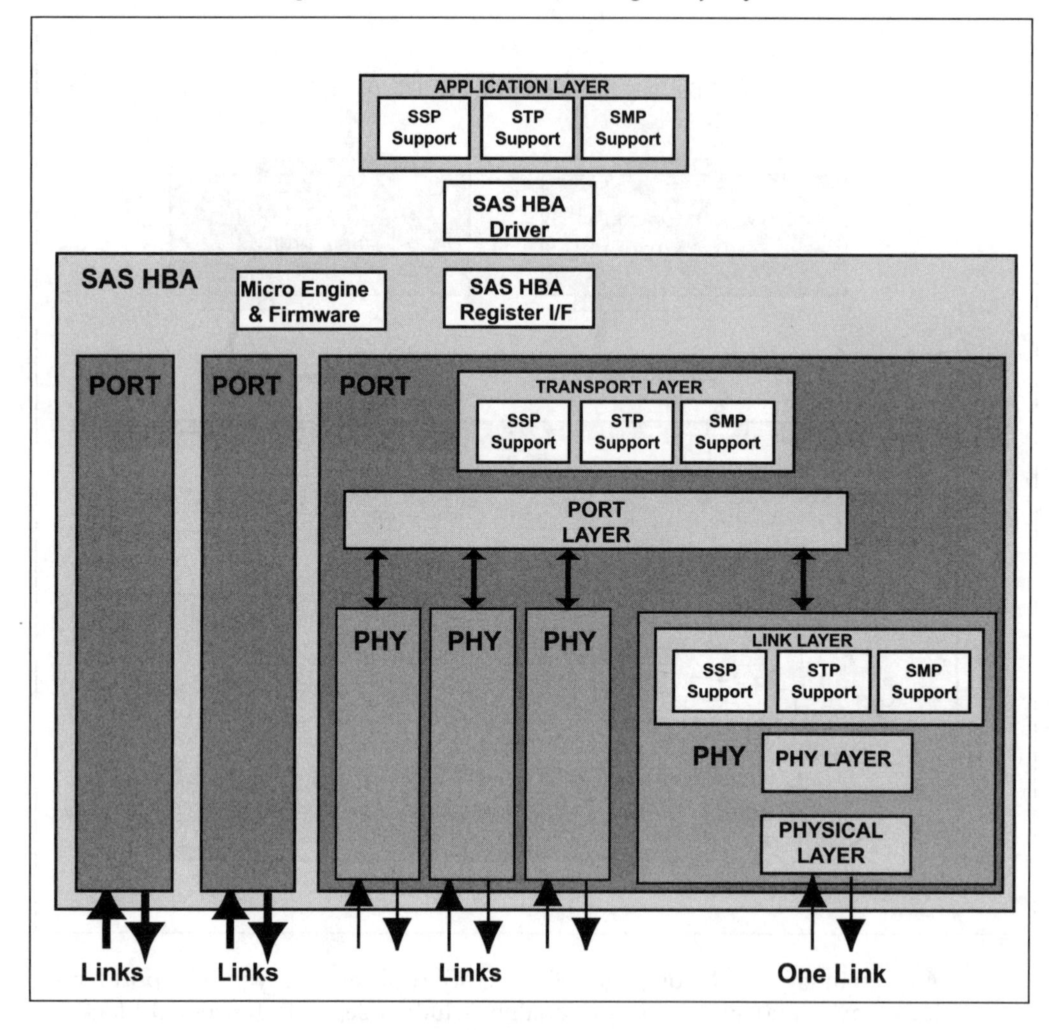

A SATA FIS is passed through the Application and Transport Layers much like an SSP or SMP frame. However, STP does not use the Port Layer at all because the main function of the Port Layer is to distribute outgoing frames between phys in a wide port and SATA does not implement wide ports. Another difference is that the SATA Link Layer performs many of the functions provided by the SAS Phy Layer. As a result, STP essentially combines the SAS Link and Phy Layers into the STP Link Layer.

As with any layered model the functions defined for each layer exist solely for the purpose of specifying the required functionality. The actual implementation often results in a single-chip solution with no particular interface defined between the layers.

The STP (SATA Tunneled Protocol) Concept

To support SATA transfers across a SAS network, STP must simulate the SATA directly-connected host-to-drive topology. If a SATA drive is directly connected to a SAS initiator that supports STP, as shown in Figure 19-5, the initiator will detect this condition during the OOB sequence. For that case, the link simply operates using SATA protocol and there is no need for a connection or the use of STP to support it.

Figure 19-5: SATA Drive Connected Directly to a SAS HBA

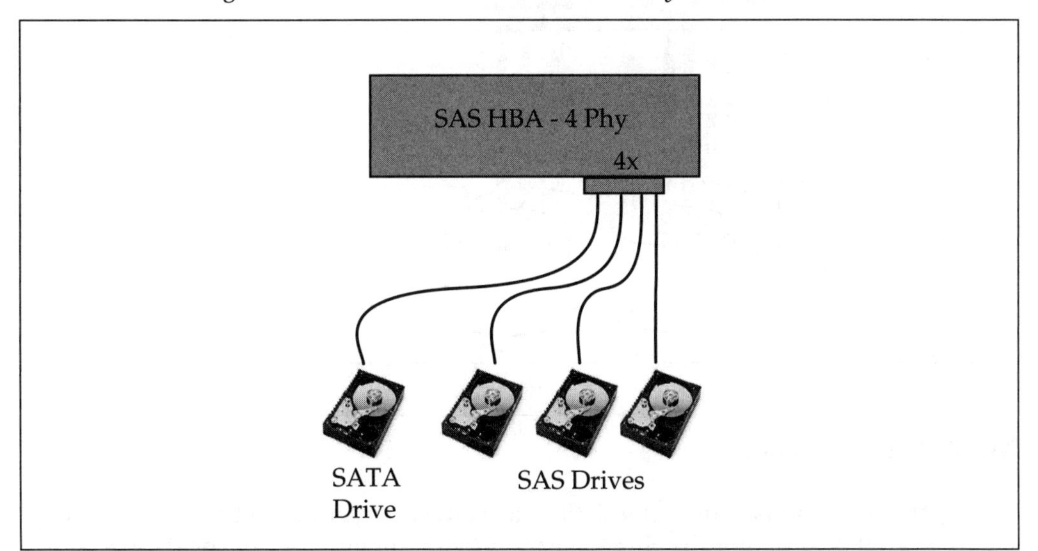

If the SATA drive is attached to an expander instead, as illustrated in Figure 19-6 on page 462, then SAS devices in the path must first establish a connection that will use the STP protocol. When an STP connection is accepted, a virtual wire is established between the HBA and SATA drive that operates according to the SATA protocol, allowing the SATA target to communicate with the initiator as it normally would. This is referred to as a "tunneled protocol" because it represents a communication mechanism between two parties using one protocol while operating within the context of a different protocol. In this case, SATA protocol is embedded within the SAS infrastructure when the connection goes through one or more expanders.

Figure 19-6: SATA Tunneled Protocol

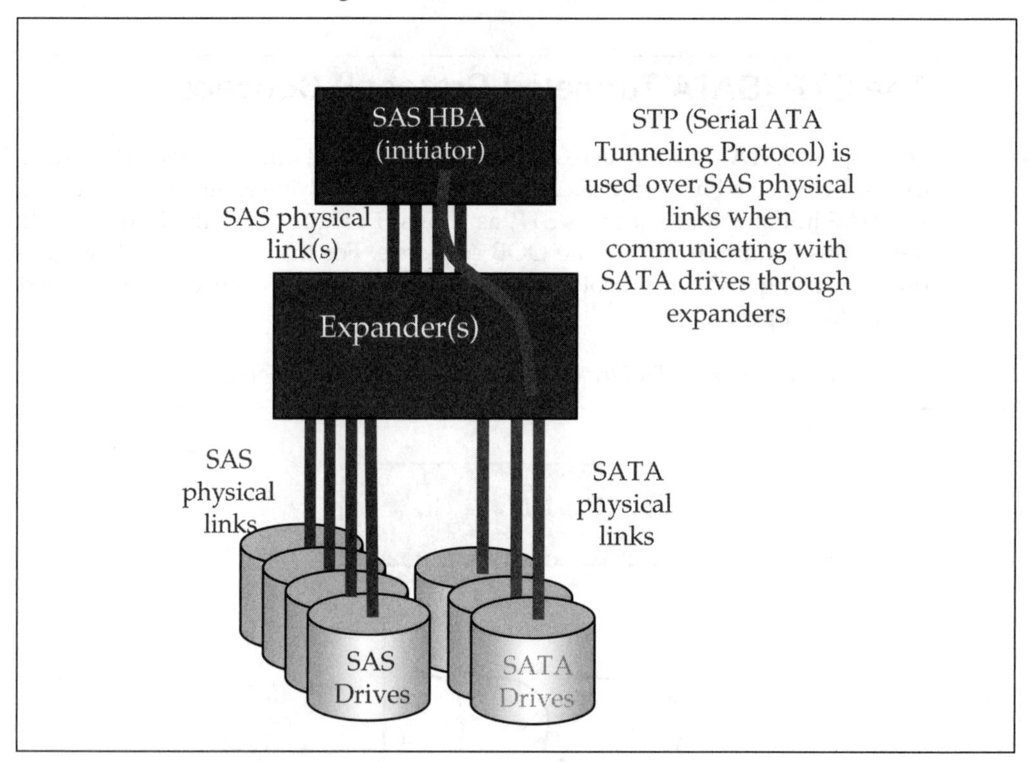

Application Layer

The SAS standard does not define the software interface to the HBA. Whether the HBA supports the SATA legacy programming interface or defines some other programming interface that triggers the execution of a SATA command is implementation specific. Depending on the interface provided, application software should need minimal changes, if any.

For SATA Application Layer information, refer to the ATA/ATAPI–7 standard available at http://www.ansi.org or http://www.incits.org. Working drafts and proposals of updates to this standard can also be viewed at the T13 working group site: http://www.t13.org.

Transport Layer

Similar to SSP and SMP, the STP transport layer receives commands from the application layer and creates the proper FIS for transmission. It also parses incoming FISes so as to put the information into the proper format for the application layer. As mentioned earlier, the older style of sending commands involved the software updating the task file registers. When the command register was updated, the FIS was automatically generated in response. Using AHCI would mean the entire FIS is fetched from memory and forwarded to the drive.

Frame (FIS) Construction

One of the main responsibilities of this layer is to construct outgoing frames and parse incoming frames. A SATA FIS looks similar to an SSP frame on the link, as shown in Figure 19-7. One important difference between a SATA FIS and an SSP frame is that a FIS can carry up to 8KB of data, as compared to only 1 KB for SSP. The FIS header fields vary according to the type of transaction, but follow the general form shown in Table 19-1

Figure 19-7: STP FIS Construct

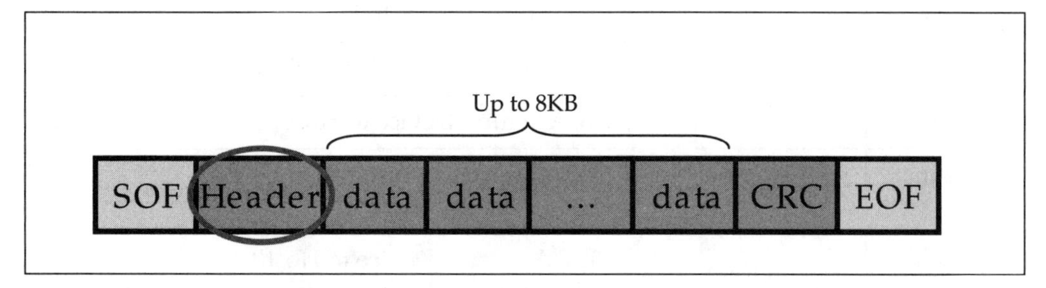

Table 19-1: SATA Frame Header Format

Byte	Field(s)	
0	FIS Type	
1	FIS-specific	PM Port

Table 19-1: SATA Frame Header Format

Byte	Field(s) (Continued)
1 to (n-4)	FIS-Specific
(n-3) to n	CRC

- **FIS Type:** Indicates the type of frame being sent, from the options listed in Table 19-2.
- **PM Port:** Indicates which of several devices behind a port multiplier is being selected for access.
- **CRC:** Cyclic Redundancy Code - protects the entire frame.

Table 19-2: SATA Frame Types

FIS Type	Size (Bytes including CRC)	FIS name
27th	24	Register - Host to Device
34h	24	Register - Device to Host
A1h	12	Set Device Bits - Device to Host
5Fh	20	PIO Setup - Device to Host
39h	8	DMA Activate - Device to Host
41h	32	DMA Setup - Device to Host
46h	8 to 8196	Data - Device to Host Data - Host to Device
58h	16	BIST Activate - Device to Host BIST Activate - Host to Device
60h	16	First Party DMA Read
61h	16	First Party DMA Write

By way of comparison, several SATA FIS's are analogous to SAS frames as described below:

- **Register host-to-device FIS**: Communicates new values to the Task File registers in the SATA drive. This is similar to a SAS command frame because a change to the Command or Control registers indicates that the drive will need to take some action, such as executing a command.

- **Register device-to-host FIS**: Like a response frame, this is sent with the result of a command.
- **Data FIS**: Corresponds to SAS Data frame.
- **DMA Setup and PIO Setup FIS**: These are similar to XFER_RDY, in that they indicate readiness to send or receive data. ATA sends one to request write data and another before sending read data. The DMA Setup FIS is very similar to XFER_RDY in that it contains a tag, data offset, and transfer length and is used to program the DMA engine. Interestingly, DMA Setup is only used in conjunction with Native Command Queuing, which will be discussed later.

Link Layer (STP)

As was the case for the transport layer, the STP version of the link layer is similar in many respects to that for SSP and SMP. It still generates the necessary primitives and manages the link protocol, but those aspects are somewhat different for SATA support.

Link Layer Serial Support

Primitives Within STP Connections

To distinguish the primitives used by STP connections from the other SAS primitives, the SAS standard adds the prefix "SATA_" when referring to all SATA primitives except ALIGN. The following is a list of those primitives and a brief description of the function of each one:

- SATA_X_RDY - Requests permission to begin sending a FIS.
- SATA_R_RDY - Grants permission to send one FIS. Like the other primitives, this one may be sent numerous times, but it always only indicates readiness to receive one frame. SATA does not have a mechanism for giving permission for more than one frame so these primitives are not counted or accumulated at the receiver.
- SATA_SOF, SATA_EOF - Start of Frame and End of Frame mark the framing context for the FIS.
- SATA_HOLD — Initiates the flow control sequence. For a receiver, this indicates a buffer-full condition and requests a temporary pause in transmission. For a transmitter, this indicates a buffer-dry condition and is used

to pause the outgoing dwords.

- SATA_HOLDA — "Hold Acknowledge" is the response to the SATA_HOLD flow control indication. This indicates that the device has recognized the flow control condition and has ceased transmission of the data. SATA_HOLDA must be returned quickly in response to the SATA_HOLD to avoid buffer over-run conditions, so the transmitter cannot send more than 20 additional dwords of data before returning SATA_HOLDA.
- SATA_WTRM — Wait for Termination indicates that the sender is waiting for an indication of the status of the FIS reception after the transmission has been completely sent.
- SATA_R_IP — Frame Receipt in Progress.
- SATA_R_OK — Received OK is returned in response to SATA_WTRM if the frame was received with a good status. This is analogous to the ACK primitive in SSP.
- SATA_R_ERR — Received with Error is returned in response to SATA_WTRM if the frame was received with a bad status. This is analogous to the NAK primitive in SSP.
- SATA_PMREQ_P — Power Management Request Partial indicates the desire of the sending device to transition the link to the "partial" power management state. The purpose is to achieve some power savings while still permitting a quick recovery back to the full-power state.
- SATA_PMREQ_S — Power Management Request Slumber indicates the desire of the sending device to transition the link to the "slumber" power management state. The purpose is to achieve deeper power savings than the partial state would provide.
- SATA_PMACK — Power Management Acknowledge is the response from a device that receives a power management request for a partial or slumber state. This response indicates that this device has agreed to make the transition and so the link can proceed to the lower power state that was indicated. Power management is not supported by STP, so a device will not respond with PMACK to requests from a SATA device.
- SATA_PMNAK — Power Management Negative Acknowledge is the response from a device that receives a power management request if the device does not agree to make the transition. As a result, the link will not be permitted to go to the requested lower power state. STP does not support power management and will respond with PNMAK to SATA power management requests.
- SATA_ERROR — Used only by STP to forward invalid dwords, this is not defined by the SATA standard. This is not actually a primitive, strictly speaking, because it starts with the K28.6 character which is not legal for STP. Instead it's an intentionally invalid dword that is forwarded by an expander to a SATA link in response to invalid incoming dwords. When an

invalid dword arrives on the incoming Phy, an expander can send the error primitive on the outgoing Phy to make sure the STP device sees an invalid dword.

- SATA_SYNC — The SATA logical primitive Idle dword.
- SATA_DMAT — Primitive that terminates a DMA operation in progress.
- SATA_CONT — Indicates the beginning of a string of data that will be scrambled but will be understood by the target as a continuation of the primitive that was being sent. This is used to avoid EMI problems that could otherwise be caused by sending a long string of primitives, which are not scrambled.

CRC Generation and Checking

Outgoing Frames

STP handles CRC generation and checking differently from SSP and SMP, by skipping two steps:

- Bit transposing
- Inversion of the CRC result

SAS devices operate on dwords in big-endian order, while SATA devices deliver information using little-endian ordering. Consequently, SAS devices using STP protocol must transpose the CRC byte order so it appears the way the SATA devices expect to see it (See Figure 19-8). This is only needed because the frame is coming from a SAS transmitter; a pure SATA transmitter would not need to transpose the bytes because it would use little-endian ordering internally, too.

Figure 19-8: STP Transmitter CRC Generation

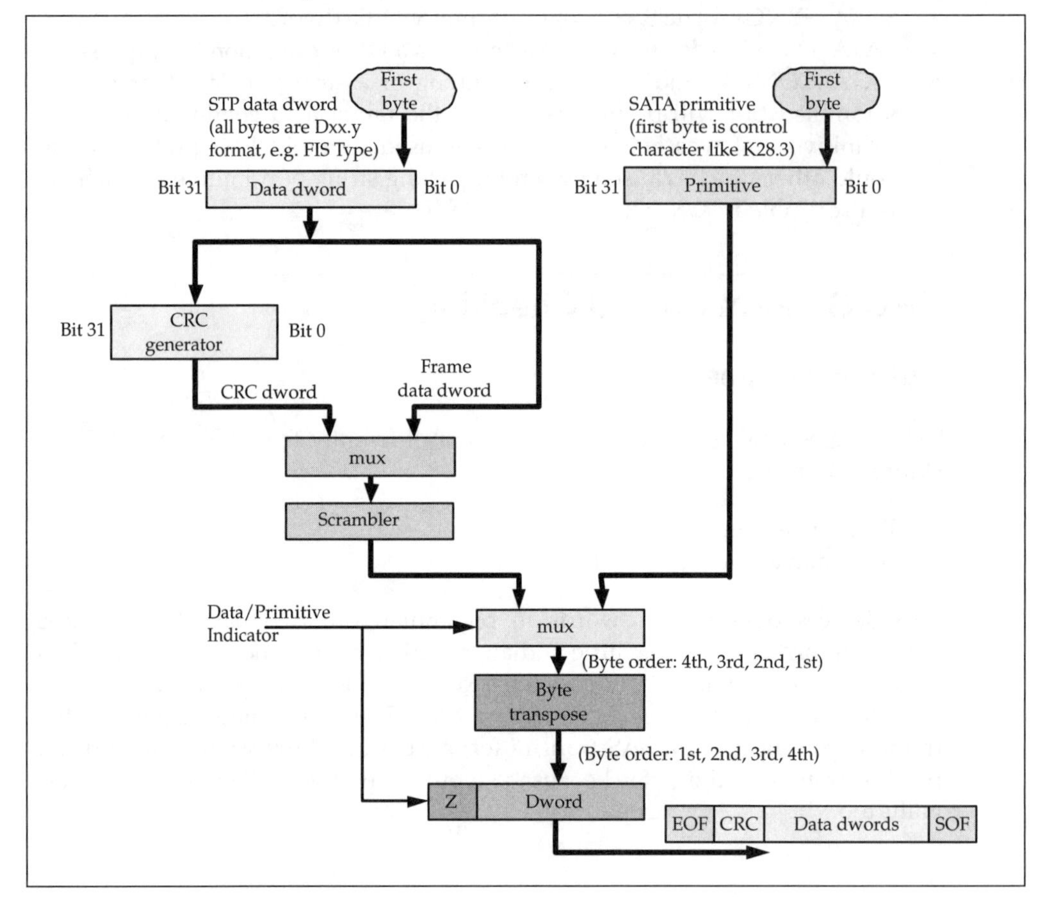

Incoming Frames

The process of checking the CRC at the receiver is also vendor specific, but provides an opportunity for discussing the differences between the way it is handled for different devices. For example, SSP frames cannot be larger than 1KB, and SAS hard drives will typically choose to buffer up the entire frame so as to be able to verify the CRC before taking action on it such as committing the data to the media. This requires a large input buffer space and adds cost to the design, but for higher-end drives the gain in reliability makes it a good trade-off. SATA FISes, on the other hand, can be up to 8KB in size and the drives are too cost sensitive to afford large buffers, so a different trade-off was made.

Rather than buffering the entire FIS, the drives may evaluate the FIS type and take action on it, such as writing data to the storage media, and then validating the CRC only at the end. This creates a risk that data will be written to a drive that will later turn out to have an error. That problem will have to be handled by software and will incur some overhead, but the trade-off for lower cost is considered acceptable.

Scrambling

As described earlier (refer to "Scrambling" on page 310), SAS transmitters scramble outgoing data to avoid excessing EMI during periods when the same data is repeatedly driven on the wire. This is a common approach for serial architectures and SATA uses the same technique.

STP Needs Two Scramblers

STP puts an interesting twist on this scheme, though. For SSP and SMP frames, only one scrambler is needed, but STP requires two separate scramblers:

1. FIS Scrambler — used to reduce EMI noise associated with the transmission of each FIS. This provides EMI protection on the packets themselves.
2. Primitive Suppression Scrambler — used to reduce EMI due to repeated primitives. This comes into play for Continued Primitives as described below.
   An SSP or SMP connection may also need to send back-to-back primitives for an extended period of time, but those protocols chose to handle that problem by implementing different versions of the ALIGN primitive that mean the same thing but are encoded differently. Mixing those different primitives avoids the problem of a repeated pattern.

To see how this works, let's consider the different types of repeated primitives that an STP connection might experience.

Repeated primitives

These may be sent more than once but only need to be detected once to be valid, allowing for the loss of a primitive without loss of information. Only SATA_PMACK and SATA_PMNAK are listed as Repeated primitives in the standard.

Continued primitives

The other primitives can also be repeated and often are, but they don't have to be. In cases where they are repeated, the sequence can potentially last for a long time. For example, when the link is idle the SATA_SYNC primitive is sent repeatedly until there is something else to send. Recall that normal data dwords are scrambled to reduce system EMI but primitives are not. This presents a potential problem: primitives that continue for a long time will also cause EMI problems for the system. The solution to this problem in SATA is different from that chosen by SAS (for a description of SSP continued primitives, see the section titled "Scrambling" on page 310). For SATA, a transmitter handles repeated primitives as follows:

1. Send at least two instances of the same primitive that is to be repeated (receiver only needs to detect one, allowing for the loss of a primitive without loss of information).
2. Follow that with the "continue" primitive, listed in the SAS standard as SATA_CONT, which indicates to the receiver that this primitive pattern shall be understood as continuing until another primitive is sent.
3. Use the Primitive Suppression scrambler to send scrambled data dwords. The dwords that follow the SATA_CONT will be ignored by the receiver until it sees another primitive so, from that point onward, scrambled data dwords can be sent instead. The scrambled data is simply discarded at the receiver, where the previous primitive is understood as being repeated, so the problem of a long primitive string is avoided (see Figure 19-9).

Figure 19-9: Continue Primitives Example

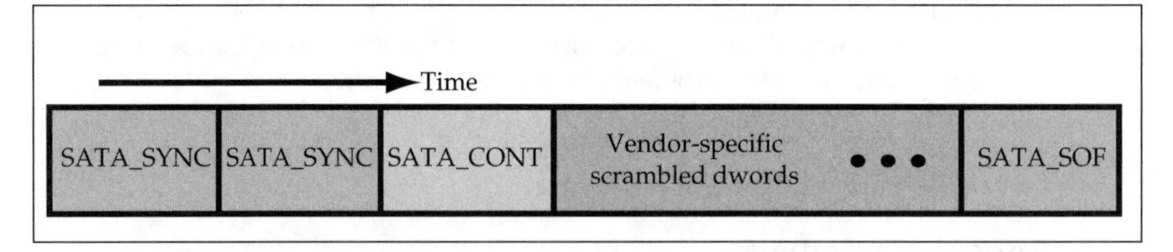

Why Two Scramblers Are Needed

An obvious question arises in the course of this discussion as to why a separate scrambler is needed. Couldn't the devices simply use the regular data scrambler for this purpose? It turns out that a separate scrambler is needed because the dwords following a SATA_CONT will be discarded. In a system with intermediate devices like an expander between the host and target, the intermediate device could discard those dwords internally rather than passing them on to the destination device. In that case, the number of scrambled dwords that arrived at the receiver would be different from the number that were sent, causing the receiver's scrambler to be out of sequence and rendering the remainder of the FIS unrecognizable. To solve this problem, a separate scrambler is implemented for the throw-away characters in a repeated primitive, allowing the main transmitter scrambler and receiver descrambler to maintain their states until the data transmission resumes.

In a similar case, an expander is also allowed to recognize that a string of repeated primitives has been received and then choose to send the SATA_CONT primitive instead when it forwards the information to the destination phy. This would result in the same potential problem of keeping the scrambler and descrambler in step with each other unless a separate scrambler was used for this purpose.

Link Layer Connection Management

Recall that SAS networks must establish connections that temporarily take control of a path through the network in order to exchange frames. The frames themselves are requested and constructed at higher levels, but the actual protocol on the link used to send and receive them is a Link Layer responsibility. The Link Layer tasks involved in meeting these responsibilities include the following that are specific for STP:

- STP OK/ERR Protocol
- STP Flow Control
- STP Affiliations

STP Connections

The function of STP is basically to encapsulate the SATA protocol inside the connection management needed to use it in a SAS domain. Oddly, given that the other protocols are specified in such detail, the standard gives no state machines or detailed behavioral descriptions for STP. However, the issues of flow control and confirmation of frame receipt are addressed in the SATA standard.

STP allows access to SATA devices attached to the SAS network. STP connections differ from SSP connections in that they are always only half-duplex, use little-endian dwords instead of the big-endian style for SSP and SMP, and they use a different form of flow control. The half-duplex interface only allows frames to go one way at a time, but the other direction on the link (sometimes called the back channel) carries feedback about the progress of the frame.

Opening a Connection

The process of opening a connection was described earlier in Chapter 13, entitled "Link Layer - Connection Management," on page 313, and that process is largely the same for an initiator that wants to communicate with a SATA device in the system, but there are some differences. A SATA target device is unaware of connection protocol, because it expects to be the only resident on a dedicated connection and doesn't need to deal with network addresses or connections. Consequently, there must be a bridge device somewhere to handle the connection protocol on its behalf. Intuitively, that bridge would reside in an expander, since that would allow the expander to work with whatever type of drive it discovered, but the bridge could instead reside on the drive module itself, making a SATA target appear physically as a SAS device to the system.

Regarding this connection protocol, consider the example shown in Figure 19-10 on page 473. The OPEN address frame from the initiator specifies that the protocol is to be STP, and is routed through the system as before, based on the destination address. If the expander has a bridge using that address that supports STP, it will return an OPEN_ACCEPT and establish the connection to the SATA device. At that point, the next thing the initiator will see is whatever is currently being sent by the target SATA device because the link from the initiator to the target has become a dedicated path. In this example, the target is simply exchanging idle dwords with the host port (SATA_SYNC primitives). The SATA primitives and frames are sent from the target device in little-endian format, but the initiator knows that will be the case for an STP connection and handles the change from the big-endian format used to open the connection.

Once the connection has been established, the bridge is no longer concerned about the flow of packets and just passes them through as is, with two exceptions.

1. The bridge has to recognize the SATA flow control primitives so it can participate as needed.
2. The bridge will also need to recognize the CLOSE primitive from the initiator to know when to close down the connection.

Beyond that, the flow of packets looks exactly as it would between a SATA host and target device. The tunneled protocol creates a path that carries packets unchanged from the SATA protocol over the SAS topology.

Figure 19-10: STP Open Connection Example

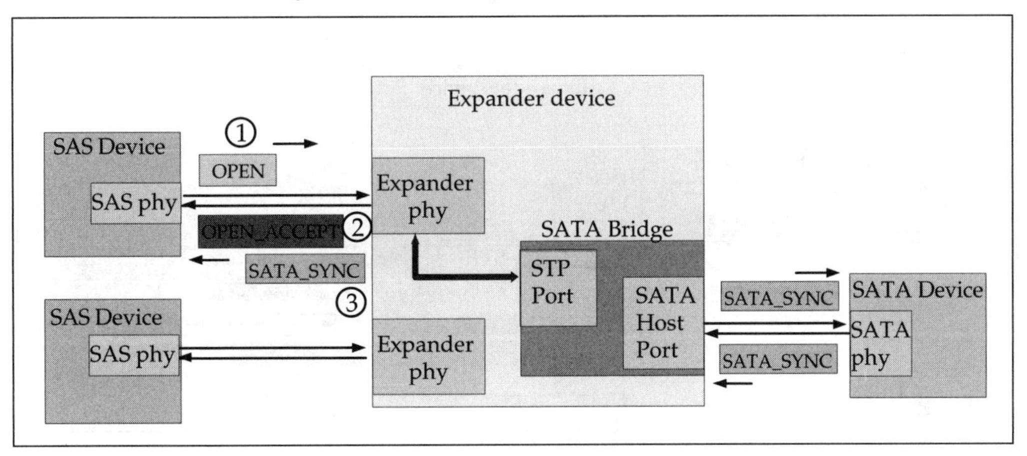

Sending a FIS

Once the connection is established the initiator takes on the role of the SATA host. In this example, it indicates the desire to transmit a FIS by sending SATA_X_RDY repeatedly while waiting on a response from the target. The target indicates that it's ready by switching from SATA_SYNC to sending SATA_R_RDY repeatedly. That indicating its readiness to accept one FIS, as shown in Figure 19-11 on page 474. The SATA_R_RDY primitives arrive many times but, unlike the way SSP handles this process, they are not counted at the receiver. STP protocol does not allow for the possibility of indicating a different target buffer space or the readiness to accept more than one frame at a time.

Figure 19-11: SATA Request to Send FIS

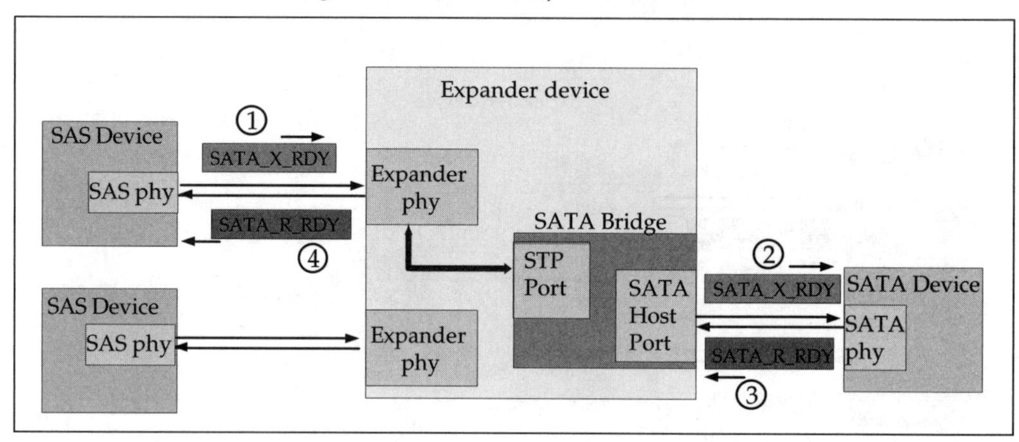

Once the SATA_R_RDY has been received by the initiator, it sends the FIS, which the bridge simply forwards to the target. When the target detects the arrival of the FIS, it begins to respond with SATA_R_IP to indicate that it is currently receiving it. The target will send SATA_R_IP at least once, as shown in Figure 19-12, even if the FIS is very short.

Figure 19-12: SATA FIS Transmission

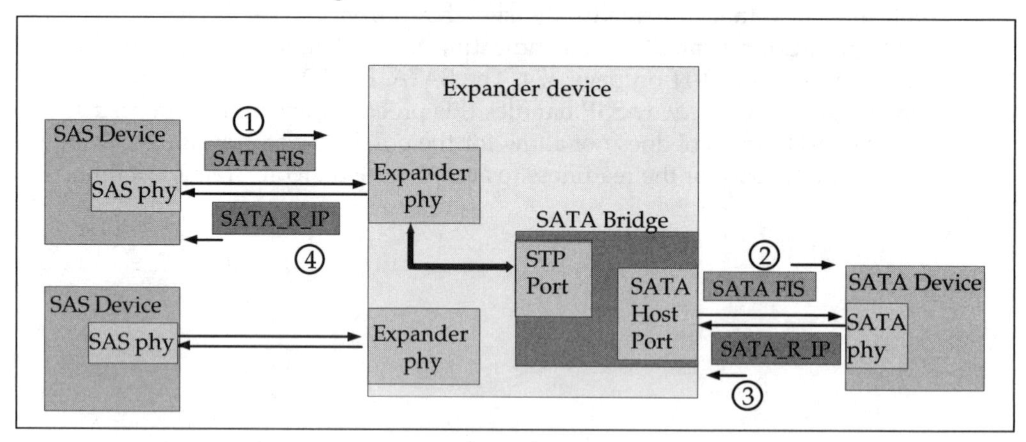

Acknowledging the FIS

For our example, assume the FIS conveys a read command to the target. The initiator indicates that the FIS is complete by sending SATA_WTRM (wait for termination) repeatedly, as shown in Figure 19-13. These primitives are forwarded by the bridge to the target, which responds by sending SATA_R_OK (Received OK) to indicate that the FIS arrived in good shape. This is roughly equivalent to the SSP ACK response. If the target had detected an error it would have sent SATA_R_ERR instead, which is similar to the SSP NAK. Notice that, unlike SSP, there can be no "non-interlocked" transfers in STP (for more on this, refer to the section titled "Non-Interlocked Frames" on page 350).

Figure 19-13: SATA Ending Transaction

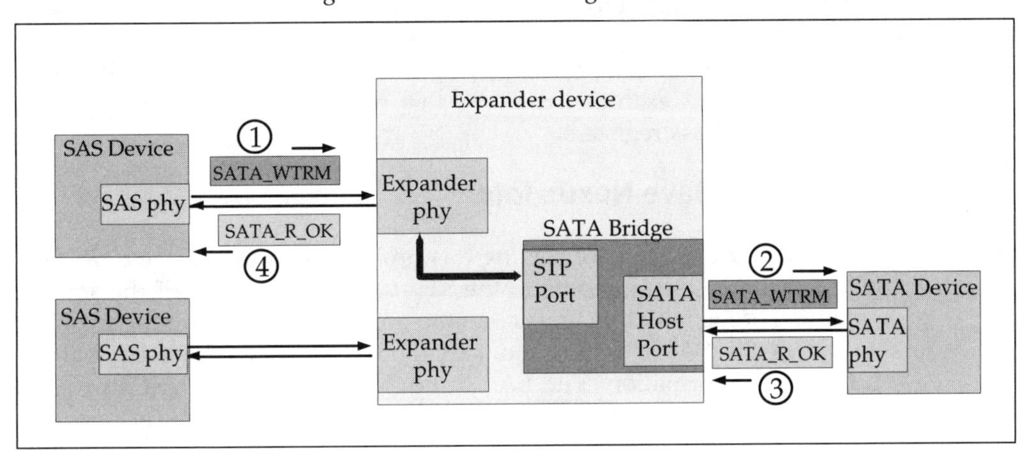

Closing the Connection

When the initiator sees that the frame was received without error, it sends SATA_SYNC to indicate a return to the idle state and waits for the SATA_SYNC primitives to be returned by the target. The device always waits to see that both sides are sending idle before taking the next step, which will be to close the connection. In the example, the time needed for the target to fetch the data is such that it makes sense to close the connection and let the target indicate later when it is ready to return the data. The initiator indicates a readiness to close by sending the CLOSE (NORMAL) primitive sequence and waiting for the matching response from the target. The SATA device is unaware of this part of the process because the bridge device intercepts it and responds by returning CLOSE (NORMAL) to the initiator. When the CLOSE is returned the expander finishes breaking down the connection and the resources are available for use by other devices.

Affiliations

The Problem with SATA in a SAS Environment

SATA devices are designed for use in an environment where a host is directly connected to a target device like a disk drive. There is no need to track which of several hosts may have issued the command or to lock out other hosts until a transaction with the current host is completed. Consequently, no mechanism exists in SATA to handle those conditions. In a SAS topology, though, there might be many initiators trying to access the same SATA target, resulting in the possibility of data integrity problems. It falls to the STP target, which is the bridge in the current example, to avoid this problem and provide coherent access to the SATA task registers.

One Solution - Save Nexus Info

There are actually two ways of solving this problem, and the bridge must use one or the other. In the first option, the STP target keeps track of the source address for all of the initiators that access the port. It may allow multiple initiators to access the SATA device and keep some memory of the equivalent I_T_L_Q nexus information. The SAS standard does not describe how this would be implemented.

Another Solution - Affiliations

The second solution is to implement affiliations, and if a device supports this it is reported in the response given to the SMP REPORT PHY SATA function. Affiliations work by having the STP target automatically store the source address of the initiator whenever it accepts a connection request and then only allowing access by that initiator until the affiliation is cleared. While active, the STP target will reject connection requests from initiators other than the affiliated one. Affiliations are cleared by one of several options:

- If only one initiator will access the device, then the affiliation remains active until the power is cycled off.
- If several initiators will share access, they can clear it by sending an SMP request with either Clear Affiliation or Hard Reset whenever they need to use it.
- It would be simpler for the shared case, though, if each initiator closed the connection using the CLOSE (CLEAR AFFILIATION) primitive.

Until the affiliation is cleared, connection requests from any other initiator will be rejected with the OPEN_REJECT (STP RESOURCES BUSY) primitive, as shown in Figure 19-14, indicating that a previous initiator has not yet finished using the target port. If more than one initiator will use the same target it is important that software be aware of this situation and take care to clear affiliations in a timely manner to avoid locking out initiators unnecessarily or for long periods.

Figure 19-14: STP - Affiliation Rejects Connection Requests from Other Initiators

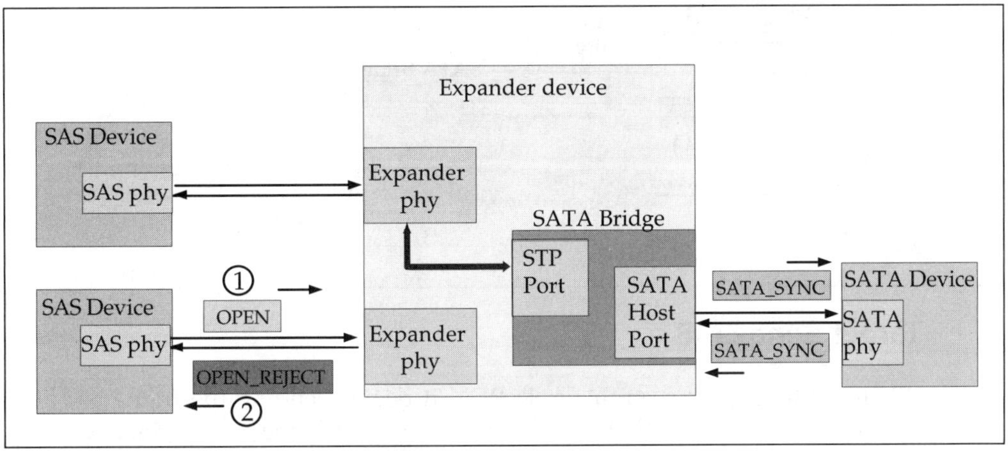

Using Affiliations: Target Reconnects to Host

Continuing our example and looking now at Figure 19-15, assume the target device is now ready to return the data that was requested earlier. First, it indicates the desire to send a FIS by sending SATA_X_RDY repeatedly and waiting for the host to respond. Since the host in this case is the bridge within the expander, the bridge continues to return SATA_SYNC while it generates a connection request to the initiator associated with this transaction. As described earlier, the bridge must have a way of determining the destination for this transaction, because the SATA request contains no address or connection information. If affiliations are being used the process is simple because there is only one source address stored. In this case, then, the bridge sends a connection request to the appropriate address and waits for the response. When an OPEN_ACCEPT is returned, the connection is established and the primitives from the SATA device flow through to the initiator. Eventually, the initiator responds to the SATA_X_RDY from the target by repeatedly sending SATA_R_RDY to indicate its readiness to receive one FIS. As before, the SATA_R_RDY may be received several times, but it only means that one frame may be sent.

Figure 19-15: SATA Target Indicates Readiness to Send Data

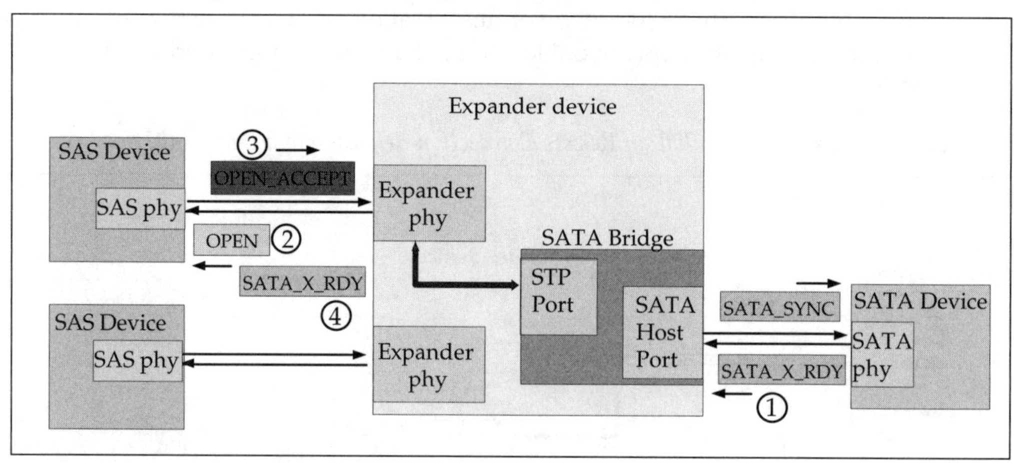

Target Sends FIS

When the target has seen SATA_R_RDY, it begins sending the frame and the initiator begins to send SATA_RIP when it sees the frame coming in, as shown in Figure 19-16 on page 479. As before, the target finishes the frame and begins sending SATA_WTRM. When the initiator has received the frame and verified that everything is correct, it returns SATA_R_OK. Next, both finish the transaction and indicate the idle condition by resuming the transmission of SATA_SYNC to each other. Finally, the connection needs to be closed, and either device can begin that process, although it's logical for the bridge to do so in this case, acting as the liaison for the SATA device. If the initiator initiates the close, it can use CLOSE (NORMAL) or CLOSE (CLEAR AFFILIATION). If the bridge STP target port begins the close, it just uses CLOSE (NORMAL).

Figure 19-16: SATA FIS Returned to Initiator

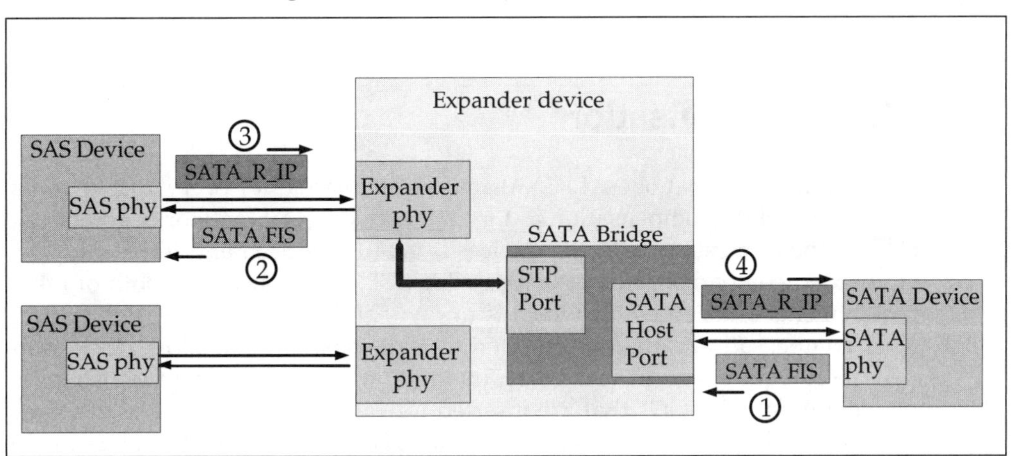

XRDY/XRDY Collision

An interesting point regarding SATA protocol comes up here, and that is the possibility of what is referred to as an XRDY/XRDY collision. What should be the result if both the host and the device send SATA_X_RDY at the same time? The solution chosen for SATA was that the device should always win that contest because it might have limited resources and need to get information delivered to the host in a timely manner. There is a drawback to this approach, however, because it's possible for a failed device to starve out the host and prevent the host from even resetting it. There is a recovery mechanism defined for this case when a device needs to interrupt the traffic flow, and that is to send a SATA_SYNC primitive at a time when it is not expected. Referred to as a "SYNC Escape", this should terminate the FIS in progress when it is received but is not counted as an error status the way receipt of SATA_R_ERR would be.

Throttling and SSC (Spread-Spectrum Clocking)

During an STP connection, there are two aspects affecting the flow of data in STP: initiator throttling of data and flow control by both devices. The initiator must throttle the outgoing data somewhat because it is required to insert two ALIGN primitives into the stream for every 256 dwords to compensate for the frequency difference between a SATA transmitter and receiver caused by the use of SSC (Spread Spectrum Clocking). Note that attached SATA devices do not have this requirement because only host devices must add the extra ALIGNs and SAS does not permit a SATA host device to be attached to a SAS network.

Clock Compensation

SAS also requires that one ALIGN primitive be injected for every 2048 dwords to allow for clock compensation in the SAS network. SAS networks do not use SSC, so the clock skew between devices is greatly reduced and fewer ALIGNs are needed compared to the case for SATA. STP hosts must meet both of these requirements independently, which is to say that the ALIGNs inserted for SAS clock compensation cannot be counted toward satisfying the SATA clock compensation requirement or vice versa. In addition, this requirement is also independent of any ALIGNs that are inserted for rate matching. Each of the three rules for adding ALIGNs must be met in an STP connection without relation to the ALIGNs added to meet the other two. For more information on clock management, refer to the section called "Clock Compensation" on page 300.

Flow Control

Both initiator and target implement a form of flow control in STP, and it is different than that used by SSP. In SSP flow control, a device indicates its available buffer space with XFER_RDY and RRDY, but in STP no indication of buffer space is communicated other than the fact that the receiver can accept one FIS, which could legally be as large as 8KB.

Toward a Bufferless Architecture

STP flow control gives both devices a way to pause the flow of data in the middle of a frame if their buffers approach an overflow or underflow condition. The motivation for this is that it permits the devices to be designed with buffers that are much smaller than the allowable FIS size. In fact, the buffers are only required to be 20 dwords in size to accommodate the protocol signaling latency. This small buffer can even be combined into the elasticity buffer to further reduce the device buffering requirements, making it trivial compared to implementing a full 8KB buffer to hold an entire data FIS. For the STP target port, the requirements are slightly different to account for the delay of sending the flow control signals across a cable (that might be as long as 10 meters) to the initiator after receiving the first indication from the target. This flight time makes the required storage frequency-dependent, as shown in Table 19-3.

Table 19-3: STP HOLD Latency

Frequency	Buffer Size
1.5 Gb/s	24 dwords
3.0 Gb/s	28 dwords

Flow Control Handshake

STP flow control operation is very simple. For example, if the receiving device approaches a buffer full condition and wants to pause the flow, it stops sending SATA_RIP and begins to send SATA_HOLD. In response, the transmitter can only send 20 more dwords before it must stop sending data and start sending SATA_HOLDA. Similarly, a transmitter might reach a buffer dry condition and need to pause its output. In that case, it stops sending data and begins to send SATA_HOLD instead. The receiver will respond with SATA_HOLDA, but the timing is not very important, since the data flow has already stopped. Since there can be expanders in the path between the STP initiator and target, they will need to participate in this process as well.

In our example, assume the target is sending data and the initiator has reached a temporary buffer-full condition. It indicates this by changing what it is sending from SATA_RIP to SATA_HOLD, as shown in Figure 19-17 on page 482. It could take some time for the neighboring device to act on that notification, so the initiator buffer must be able to accept 24 more dwords if the link is operating at 1.5Gb/s. In the meantime, the bridge receives the hold and replies with SATA_HOLDA while it forwards the SATA_HOLD on to the next level. The bridge also must have buffer space to accept up to 24 more dwords while it waits for SATA_HOLDA to be returned from the target device. Finally, the SATA target sees the SATA_HOLD and sends no more than 20 dwords of data before it begins to send SATA_HOLDA in reply.

When the initiator has emptied its buffer and is ready to take more data, it stops sending SATA_HOLD and begins to sends SATA_RIP again. The bridge responds to this by starting to send whatever data it has stored in its own buffer. When that buffer has been drained, it then stops sending SATA_HOLD to the target device and begins sending SATA_RIP again. When the target sees that change, it stops sending SATA_HOLDA and resumes sending the data again. This process can be repeated for a given frame as many times as necessary.

Figure 19-17: STP Flow Control - Pause

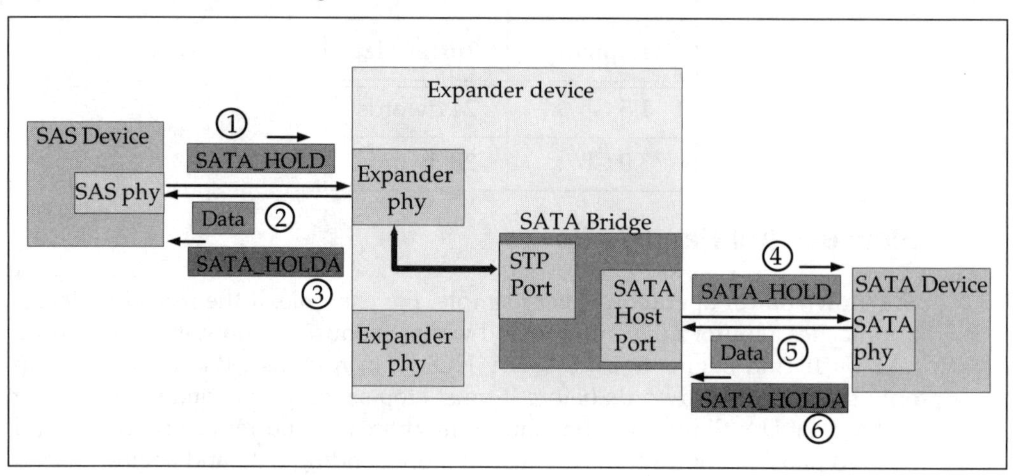

Phy Layer

Clock Management

The number of ALIGNs required for an STP connection to a SATA target is higher than it is for an SSP connection, due to the much higher frequency differences caused by the use of SSC. The number of ALIGNs that must be sent to a SATA target is 2 within every 256 dwords, but there is no particular requirement regarding the number of them sent the other way, from the STP/SATA bridge back to the SAS initiator phy. The standard points out that it may be easier for the STP/SATA bridge to simply delete all the incoming ALIGNs and NOTIFYs from the incoming dword stream and then simply inject them as needed into the outgoing dword stream to the target. This approach would seem to be the simpler solution to maintaining this timing between two links.

8b/10b Encoding and Decoding

This topic is covered in detail in "8b/10b Encoding and Decoding" on page 370, but there are a few notes to make here with regard to SATA. Only three of the available control (K) characters are used in the SAS standard, as shown in Table

19-4, and all three can appear in SATA. The K28.5 character, which contains the comma pattern used for achieving dword synchronization, is only used in the ALIGN primitive. This is the same encoding used by SAS for the ALIGN(0) primitive, so those two are indistinguishable on the link. The K28.3 character is used for all the other STP primitives, while K28.6 is only used by bridge devices to force a SATA device to see an error. In fact, K28.6 is only sent by expanders that receive a frame during an STP connection that has an invalid dword or other error. That gives the expander an easy method of reporting an error on the SATA link when an error was seen on the SAS side of the bridge.

Table 19-4: Control Character Usage in SAS

First Character of a dword	Use in SAS physical links	Use in SATA physical links
K28.3	Primitives that are only used inside STP connections	All primitives except ALIGN
K28.5	ALIGN and most primitives defined within the standard	ALIGN
K28.6	Not used	SATA_ERROR

Endianess

All the other serial transports with which the author is familiar (PCIe, SAS, IB, etc.), use the same scheme in this regard: big-endian bytes and little-endian bits. SATA is atypical but more logical because its ordering is little endian for both bytes and bits. As a result, SATA dwords appear to have the bytes in reverse ordering compared to SAS and most other serial transports, as shown in Figure 19-18 on page 484. This does not ordinarily present any difficulties, but devices like expanders that will support SATA will clearly need to comprehend both variants. Fortunately, the primitives for SAS and SATA are both big endian, as illustrated by Figure 19-19 on page 484, so there is less likelihood of confusing them.

Figure 19-18: Endianess in SAS and SATA

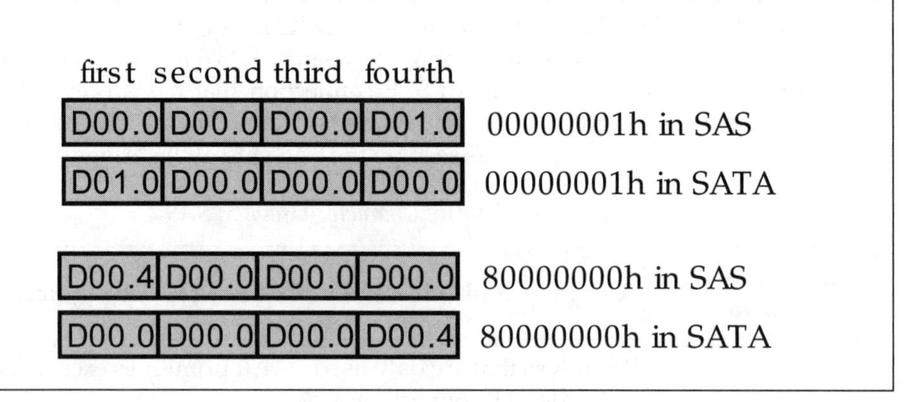

Figure 19-19: Primitives Used by Phy Layer

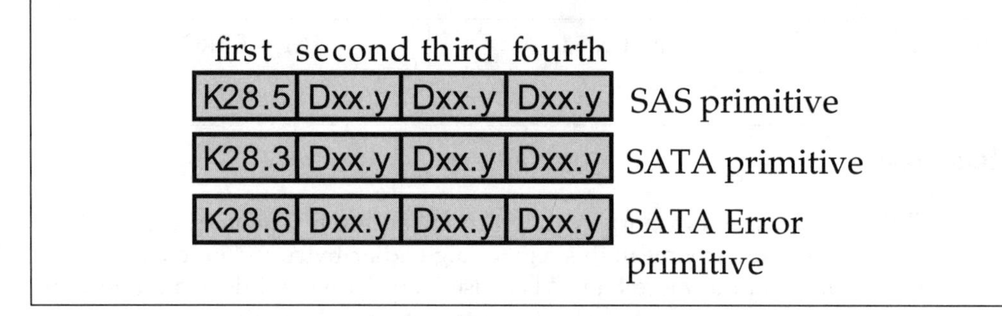

SATA II

The next generation of SATA, called SATA II, includes several extensions to migrate SATA toward the higher end. The new features include:

- **Port Multipliers:** These allow more devices per host as shown in Figure 19-20 on page 485. The host can access up to 15 targets while each of them perceives itself as residing on the usual dedicated bus. FISes arrive from the host using a previously reserved field in the FIS header that informs the Port Multiplier about which device is being selected. The port multiplier zeros out that field when passing the FIS on to the device. For FISes coming back to the host from the target, the port multiplier reverses this operation, adding the appropriate value into the PM Port field of the header so the host can tell which target is responding. While similar in some respects to a SAS expander, these are much simpler devices and cannot be cascaded to form more complex topologies.

Figure 19-20: Port Multiplier

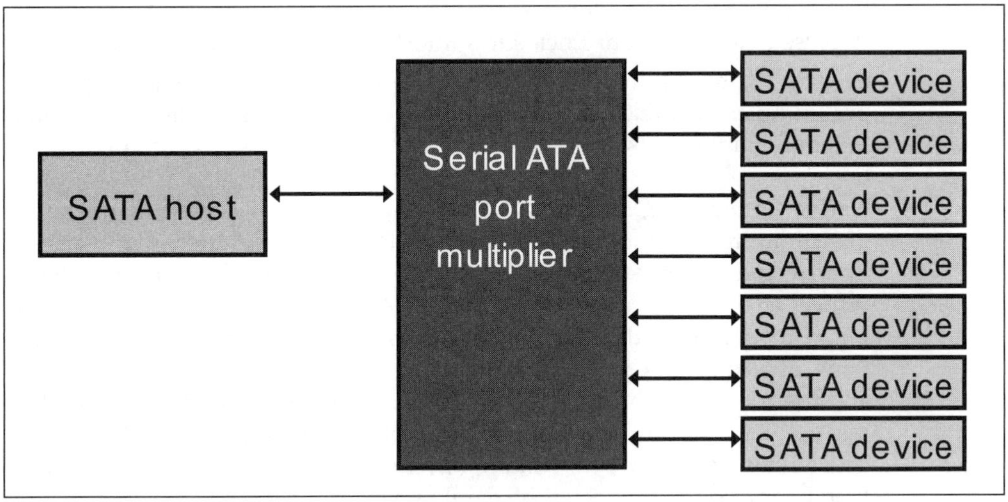

- **Port Selector:** These allow a SATA device to operate somewhat like a dual-ported device by providing more than one access path to the same device, as shown in Figure 19-21.

Figure 19-21: Port Selector

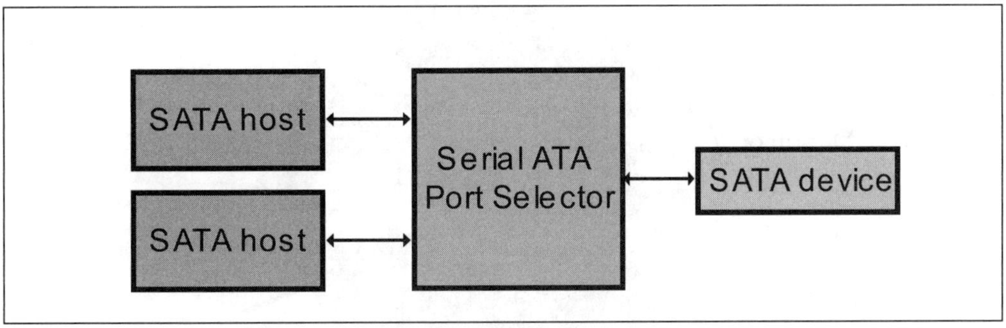

This does meet a primary goal for SATA II, which is the fail-over capability needed in enterprise-class storage environments, but does not create a true dual-ported device because both ports cannot be active at the same time. Instead, whichever host performs OOB first becomes the active port, and the latecomer is inactive. Should it become necessary to switch and make the second port active, this can be done by sending a particular sequence of COMINIT OOB signals from the device wishing to become the new master.

- **Enclosure Management:** SATA II defines a SATA Enclosure Management Bridge (SEMB) which can be a standalone SATA device or embedded in a port multiplier as a virtual device. The bridge accepts new ATA commands that carry SES (SCSI Enclosure Services) or the older SAF-TE (SCSI Accessed Fault-Tolerant Enclosures interface) payloads and forwards them over an I^2C bus to the Storage Enclosure Processor (SEP). The purpose of providing enclosure management access over SATA is to allow a machine that only implements a SATA infrastructure to handle such enterprise functions.
- **Native Command Queuing (NCQ):** Command queuing permits the target device to re-order queued commands to achieve better performance. Improvements come from analyzing the position of requested data with respect to the physical position of the storage media. In the illustration of Figure 19-22, a disk drive platter is shown with data stored in various locations labeled A, B, C, and D. If the data pieces are requested in that order and the motion of the drive is clockwise, the media would be required to make several revolutions to fetch them all. On the other hand, if the drive could evaluate the situation and re-order the commands to fetch D first and then C, and so on, the seek time would be greatly reduced.

Figure 19-22: Command Queuing

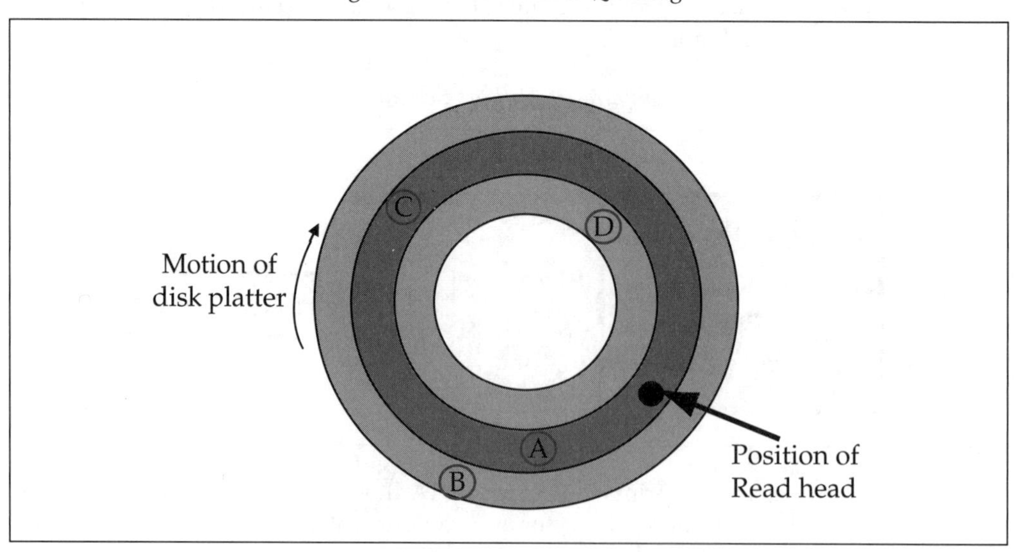

This situation is much more common in multi-threaded systems that generate highly random accesses, both of which are more common in servers than in the consumer market for which SATA was originally developed. For this reason, SCSI implemented queued commands years ago to improve server drive performance, but ATA did not need it because single-user desktop accesses are not as random. However, the advent of Hyper-threaded processors and multi-core processors has changed this situation, since now even a desktop can have accesses from several threads in progress at once that may appear random with respect to each other.

NCQ allows up to 32 commands for each HBA port to be queued and then executed in whatever order the target device chooses. However, there are some issues regarding the use of NCQ. First, it can only be used if the drive has an HBA that supports it, so both the hardware and software support must be in place. Secondly, the use of a Port Multiplier limits the usefulness of NCQ because the drives on the other side will all be sharing the command queue, which means that none of them will be able to queue up as many commands as they otherwise might. Since queuing more requests allows better optimization, this would be a limiting factor.

By comparison, SCSI and SAS implement three levels of TCQ (Tagged Command Queuing). The first level is Ordered, in which commands are executed in the order they arrive. The second level is Head of Queue, which allows a command with this attribute to be placed immediately at the front of the queue. The third level is called Simple and allows the target device itself to control the sequence of all commands in the queue. This typically gives the best performance because the device is aware of its own characteristics such as the physical position of a sector. The queue available to SAS is larger than the 32 that NCQ can use, but real-life servers don't normally queue more commands than that anyway.

20 SATA Initialization

The Previous Chapter

The previous chapter described the function and responsibilities of the various layers in support of SATA. This support is optional for SAS devices and so, rather than describe what it needs in the context of the earlier layer discussions, it was aggregated there for convenience.

This Chapter

This chapter describes the hardware initialization process of SATA devices. Much like SAS devices, the neighbors on the link undergo a sequence of steps after reset to recognize that they are attached to a device and begin the process of communicating with it. The overall process is simpler for SATA because one device acts as the host or initiator and the other behaves as the target device.

Introduction

As with SAS devices, there are two parts to initializing a SATA device, and they are very similar to those for SAS. The first is hardware based and happens after a reset. Devices on either end of a link automatically begin the process of detecting whether another device is present and at what speeds the interface may be run. There are some steps that have to take place before a receiver can recognize dwords as information from the transmitter, and those are accomplished by the hardware initialization process. The second part is software initialization, and this optional step is under the control of the application software. It consists of reading configuration information from the device and writing values into that space to setup the desired parameters for the device. Since SATA programming is defined by the SATA standard and no changes to it are required by a SAS system in support of a SATA device, it is not covered in this book. For more on that topic, refer to MindShare's upcoming book titled, *SATA System Architecture.*

Hardware Initialization

General

The goal of hardware initialization is to accomplish the following steps:

1. Detect the presence of an attached device.
2. Negotiate the highest common transmission rate supported by both devices.

SATA host and target devices have a fixed role as they participate in this process because each will only expect to be attached to the other type. Consequently, each device understands what their role will be.

The first step is accomplished using OOB signaling, as described in "OOB Signaling" on page 129. The next step is to negotiate the transfer speed on the link. As part of this process, since a steady stream of data is received by both devices, dword synchronization is achieved and receivers can begin to detect valid symbols and meaningful dwords in the data stream.

Both of these steps are taken whenever the Phy is reset. There are levels of reset for a device, but all of them involve this part, referred to as the Phy reset sequence, and will result in the hardware initialization steps.

Reset Sequence

As can be seen in Figure 20-1, the SATA version of the Link Reset is similar to the SAS Phy reset and involves sending OOB and performing speed negotiation. The difference is that the Link reset is the same as the Phy reset because SATA devices don't have an Identification Sequence.

Figure 20-1: SATA Link Reset Sequence

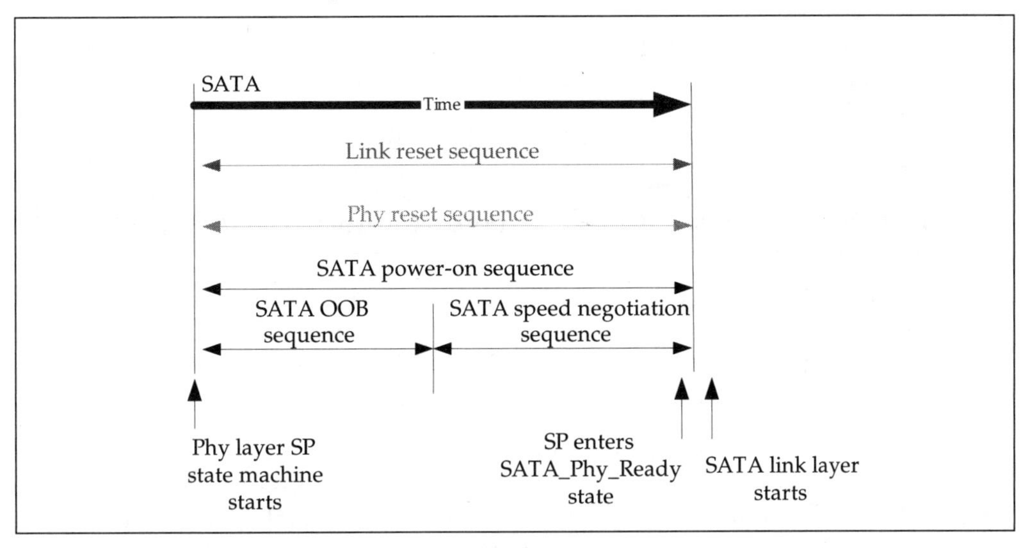

OOB (Out of Band) Signaling

OOB communication is described in detail in the section called "OOB Signaling" on page 129, so here we just want to discuss the ways that OOB for a SATA device differs from that for a SAS device.

For example, the peak-to-peak OOB signal voltages are different for SAS (1600mV) and SATA (700mV). Consequently, for devices designed to support SATA, it's preferable to start the initialization process with the lower voltage to avoid any risk of damage to a SATA device. If the initialization doesn't work or shows the neighbor to be a SAS device, then the higher voltage can safely be used.

OOB — Transmission

SATA OOB doesn't include the COMSAS pattern, so there are really only two patterns used, COMWAKE and COMINT/COMRESET. The timing for these patterns is listed in Table 20-1 on page 492.

Table 20-1: SATA OOB Timing

OOB Signal	Burst Time	Idle Time	Negation Time
COMWAKE	160 OOBI (106.66 - 106.68ns)	160 OOBI (106.66 - 106.68ns)	280 OOBI (186.65- 186.69 ns)
COMINIT/ COMRESET	160 OOBI (106.66 - 106.68ns)	480 OOBI (319.0 - 320.0 ns)	800 OOBI (533.28 - 533.39 ns)

OOB — Reception

The timing for the reception of the SATA OOB patterns is summarized in Table 20-2 and Table 20-3 below.

Table 20-2: SATA Receiver OOB Idle Detection Timing

OOB Signal	May Detect	Shall Detect	Shall Not Detect
COMWAKE	55 to 175 ns	101.3 to 112 ns	outside the range 55 to 175 ns
COMINIT/ COMRESET	175 to 525 ns	304 to 336 ns	outside the range 175 to 525 ns

Table 20-3: SATA Receiver OOB Negation Detection Timing

OOB Signal	Shall Detect
COMWAKE	> 175 ns
COMINIT/ COMRESET	> 525 ns

SATA OOB Protocol

For SATA, the link and Phy reset are the same, as is the power-on sequence: SATA OOB followed by SATA speed negotiation. The OOB sequence for SATA is shown in Figure 20-2, where it can be seen that the host and target device exchange the COMRESET/COMINIT pattern to start. These are both the same pattern, the difference is in the direction and meaning: when sent from the host it's called COMRESET and resets the target; when sent from the target it's called COMINIT and simply indicates readiness for the next step. If the target sends COMINIT before the host is ready, the host won't see it, but when the host sends COMRESET, the target will reset and then send COMINIT again, so the order of events will be end up being the same.

Figure 20-2: Initial SATA OOB Sequence

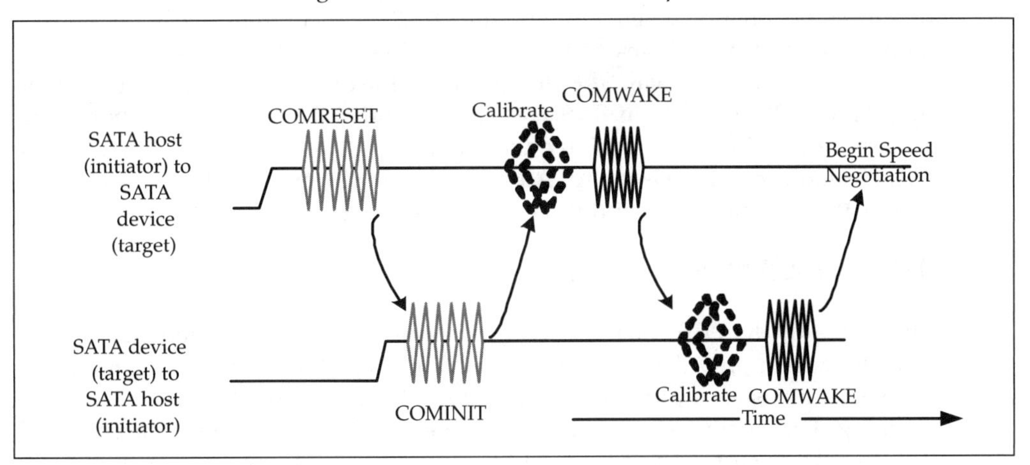

If the host succeeds in sending and receiving this pattern, it next waits a period of time designed to allow transceivers to calibrate the transmission line and make adjustments. This process, which might be done with a TDR (time-domain reflectometer) test or some other means, would let the transmitter adjust the output voltage or signal compensation parameters like de-emphasis to better match the transmission line characteristics. SATA allows the opportunity for this but does not require devices to do anything with it, and it's the author's understanding that it is not commonly used.

Once the host sends COMWAKE, it becomes the target device's turn to run the optional calibration routine. When the device is ready, it responds with COMWAKE and both devices recognize that OOB is completed and the next step will be speed negotiation.

SATA Speed Negotiation

After the initial OOB patterns are sent and the device recognizes the attached device type, the next step is to negotiate the operational speed of the link. This is accomplished by sending a pattern at the desired rate to the neighbor and listening for the response.

Roles During Speed Negotiation

For SATA, the target controls this process and the host acts as the responder. Once the target has sent COMWAKE, it begins speed negotiation by sending ALIGN primitives at the fastest rate it can support. The host, when it is ready for speed negotiation, begins to send the D10.2 character repeatedly until it recognizes ALIGN primitives at its receiver. SATA doesn't have more than one version of ALIGN the way SAS does; it sends the one it does have. Fortunately, the ALIGN(0) primitive in SAS was chosen with exactly the same characters, and since primitives do not have the endianess issue to worry about, a SATA ALIGN looks the same as a SAS ALIGN(0). When incoming ALIGNs are recognized, the host begins to send them back to the target.

D10.2 Used as a "Dial Tone"

Interestingly, the D10.2 symbol was chosen for host transmission during this time because it provides an alternating 1s and 0s pattern on the wire and therefore appears as an input clock to the target device during this part of the link training. The reason behind this is that when SATA was first introduced it had to compete on cost with parallel ATA. However, serial transports need an accurate clock (+/- 350 ppm for SATA), requiring a precision crystal oscillator, while parallel transports do not. The parallel drives used a cheaper but less accurate ceramic clock. The cost difference was considered significant enough that it was decided that SATA targets could also implement the ceramic oscillators and use the D10.2 "clock" from the host to establish a more accurate version during the link reset sequence. This incoming clock only runs at the slowest rate supported by the host and may not be the negotiated link rate, so the target can't simply use it to generate its transmit clock directly. Still, it provides a more accurate reference until the data stream is established. For a modern design today it seems unlikely this would be an issue, as clock sources have become less expensive since the first SATA standard was written, but it's interesting to understand some of the background.

Speed Negotiation Example

In the example shown in Figure 20-3 on page 495, the SATA target tries a rate that the host does not support. In response, the host continues to send D10.2 as an indication that it is still working but has not yet seen a recognizable pattern from the target. Each rate window takes 54.6µs, and the target sends the number of ALIGNs that can be sent during that time, meaning there will be more ALIGNs at higher rates and fewer at slower rates. For example, 1.5 Gb/s for

54.6 µs equals 81,900 bits or 8,190 symbols, and dividing that by 4 gives 2048 dwords. At a higher rate like 3.0 Gb/s, the number of ALIGNs that could be sent would therefore be 4096.

Figure 20-3: SATA Speed Negotiation Example

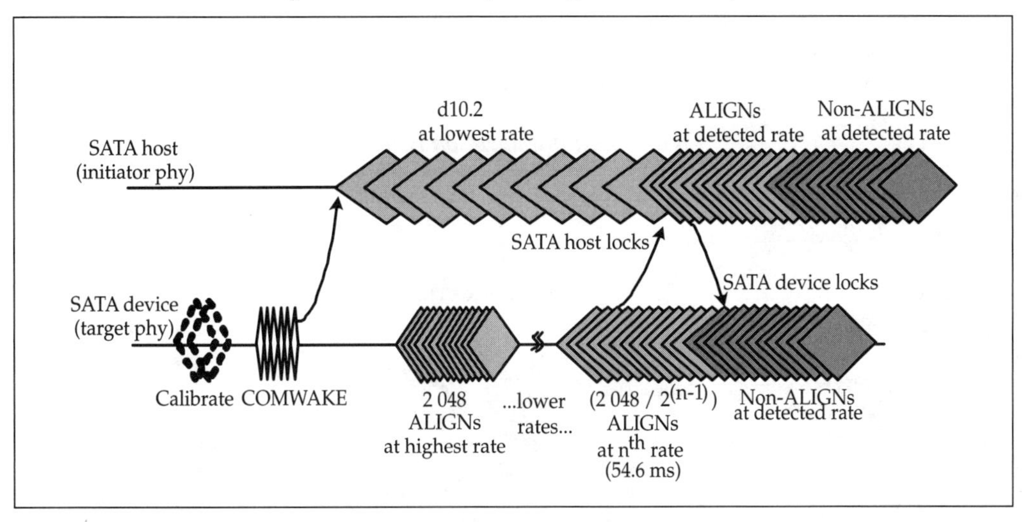

If the correct response from the host was not seen, the target switches to the next lower speed it supports and repeats the process. Eventually a compatible speed is attempted and the host does recognize ALIGNs, which it indicates by sending ALIGNs back to the target. In response, the target then begins to send SATA_SYNC, which the host also begins to send, and that completes the negotiation. One advantage of always starting at the highest rate and working down is that future devices will not have to maintain support for the slower speeds, since the slower speeds will not have to operate in order to complete the negotiation.

SATA Link Initialization Example

Consider the example shown in Figure 20-4, which has an expander attached to a SAS initiator, a SAS target device, and a SATA target. The SAS interface part of this example has already been described in the section called "SAS Link Initialization Example" on page 136; now we want to look at how the SATA link interacts with the expander in this process.

Assume at this point that other parts of the system have initialized but that the SATA device has not. When the other devices complete initialization, that will cause the expander to detect a change on its Phys and report that change by sending a BROADCAST (CHANGE) primitive on all of its Phys except the one that had the change. These primitives will not be sent on a link that has not yet been initialized, nor will they be sent to a port that the expander knows is a SATA port. SATA does not include the concept of changes to the topology, so of course there would be no notification to a SATA device. At this point, device Z has still not initialized, so the expander will continue to retry that link at the hot-plug timeout rate of every 500ms.

Figure 20-4: Initialization Example

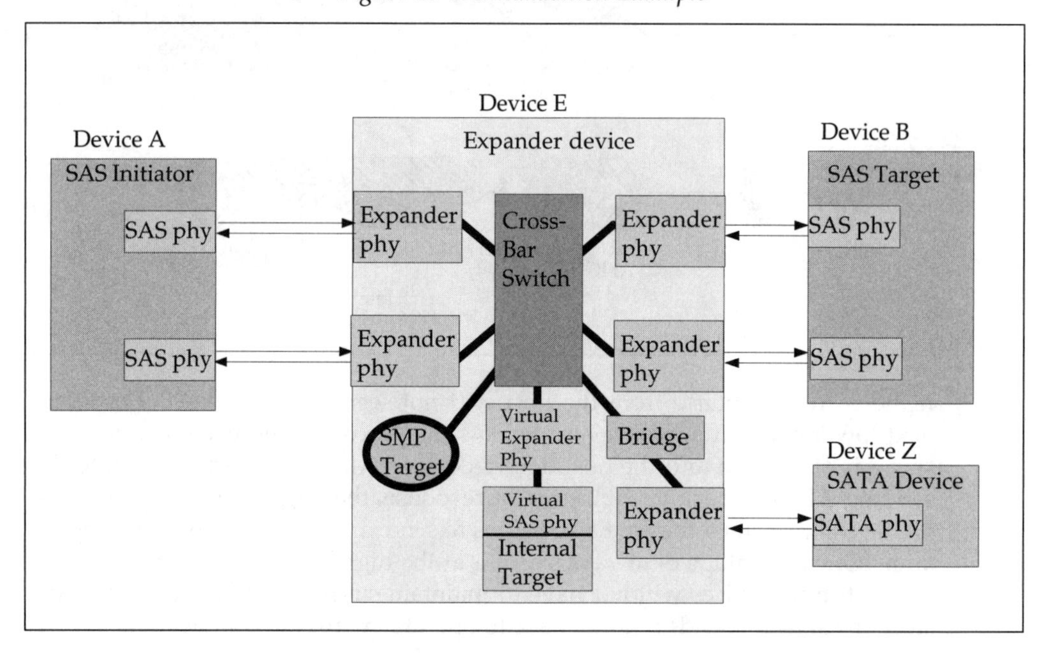

Next, assume the SATA drive (device Z) powers up and sends the OOB pattern for COMINIT to the expander Phy. As shown in Figure 20-5, after seeing COMINIT, the expander will send COMSAS. Assume that Z misinterprets this as a COMRESET, since it doesn't understand COMSAS, and sends COMINIT again. The expander detects that there was no COMSAS within the timeout period and concludes that Z must be a SATA device (or a broken SAS device). It then changes the Phy Layer to SATA host emulation mode and send COM-WAKE, making it appear as a SATA host. The target responds with COM-WAKE and then SATA speed negotiation can begin.

Figure 20-5: SATA OOB Sequence with SAS Expander

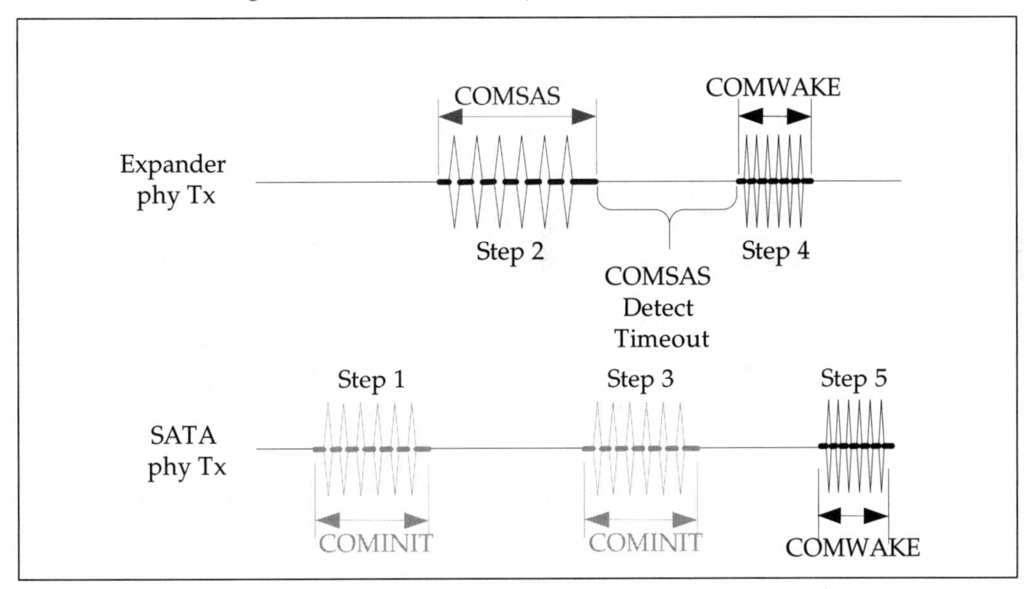

Once that negotiation is complete, the expander informs the rest of the system that a new device has come online by sending a BROADCAST (CHANGE) primitive on all the ports except the one to which Z is attached (see Figure 20-6 on the following page). Recall that this broadcast only informs the system that some change has occurred and contains no information about what that change was (in keeping with the design goal of keeping expanders simple and inexpensive). It's up to the initiators in the system to respond to this notification by repeating as much of the discovery process as needed to learn what has changed.

Figure 20-6: Broadcast (Change) Primitives Result from SATA Device Initialization

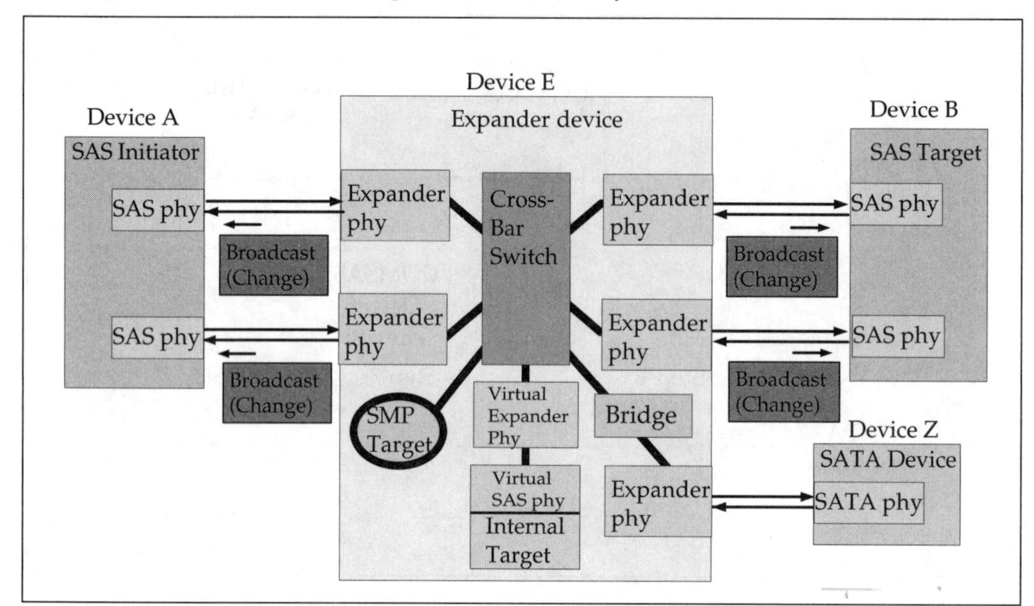

Software Initialization

After hardware initialization has completed, the next step is software initialization. The first step in this process occurs after the Phy reset sequence, when the target device runs diagnostic tests and reports the results to the host with a Device-to-Host Register FIS (FIS is the SATA name for a frame and stands for Frame Information Structure). Application software can then read the contents of the shadow registers in the host, and this information is referred to as the device's power-on signature. One thing the signature indicates is the type of the device. Possible device types indicate whether they support the basic ATA protocol or the ATAPI protocol (ATA Packetized Interface — used to encode SCSI commands into the data portion of a SATA FIS), as well as whether the device is a System Enclosure Management Bridge (SEMB), Port Multiplier or Port Selector.

Changes for SATA II

The second generation of SATA introduced two new device types to facilitate the use of SATA in the server market. In that space, expendability and reliability are important, so two devices were devised that act as intermediaries between the host and target device to achieve those goals: Port Multipliers and Port Selectors. These new devices introduce a few variations in the initialization process.

Port Multiplier

A Port Multiplier (PM) is illustrated in Figure 20-7. Its purpose is to allow one host port to access up to 15 target devices (ports 0 through 14), which requires the use of a previously reserved 4-bit field in the FIS header to indicate which port is being selected for service by the host.

Figure 20-7: Port Multiplier Example

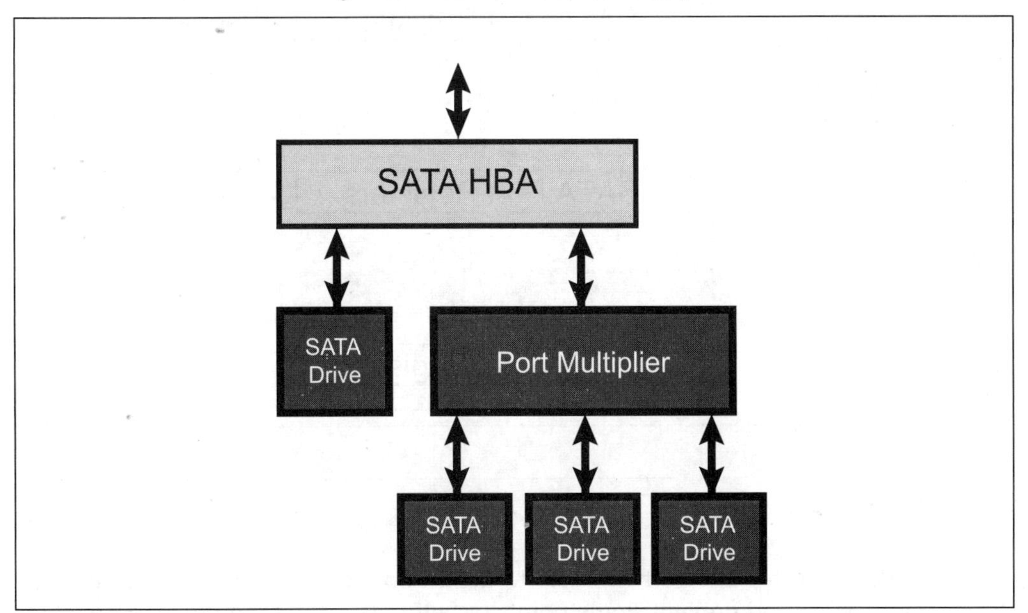

During hardware initialization, though, the host cannot detect the presence of a PM. Instead, when the Phy reset sequence takes place the host is communicating by default with the device that is attached to port 0. As a result, the Device-to-Host register FIS that occurs once the link is working will return the power-on signature from the set of registers for the device attached to port 0. To find out whether a PM exists, application software sets the port value to 15, which is the internal target of the PM as illustrated in Figure 20-8, and sends that device a software reset. The result of the reset will be that the internal target of the PM will perform diagnostics and return a register FIS to the host with the power-on signature of the Port Multiplier. The software can then read the registers to look for this signature. If a Port Multiplier is present, the software simply reads the capability registers and learns the number of ports. Then it can check the registers associated with each port to get the information about the devices attached to each port.

Figure 20-8: Port Multiplier Registers

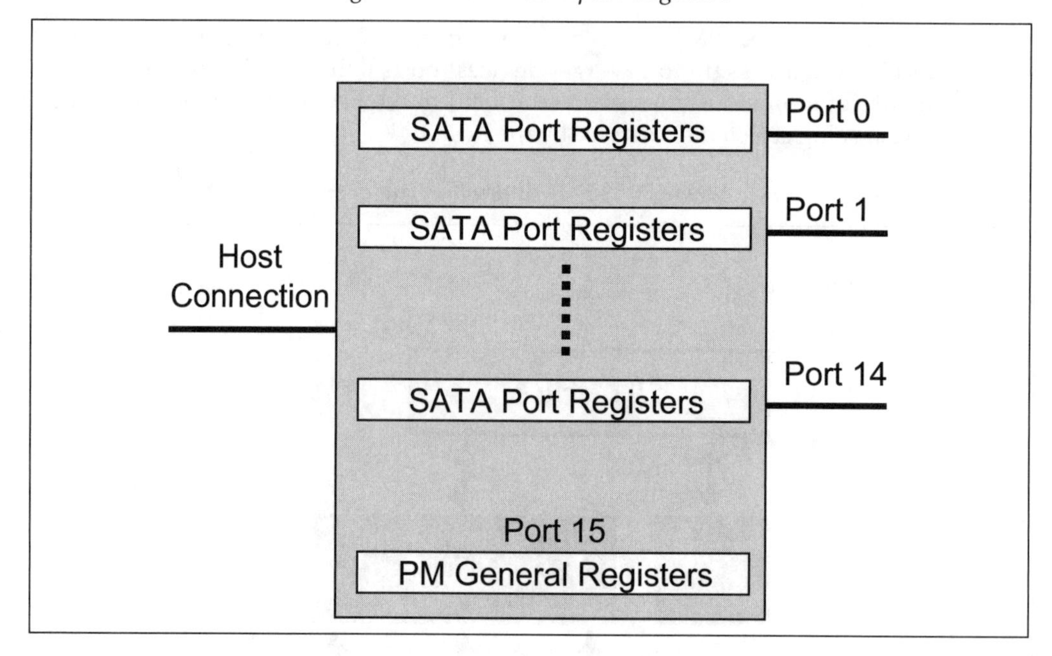

Port Selector

A Port Selector allows two hosts to access one device to provide a fail-over mechanism and prevent single points of failure (see the example in Figure 20-9 on page 501). Since two hosts may attempt to access the Port Selector at the same time, the process is simply for the Port Selector to correspond with the host that is the first to start the process and ignore the latecomer. Later, when some higher-level software detects the need to switch from one host to the other, it can accomplish that by using either a side-band signal to control the Port Selector, or an in-band method that involves having the new master execute a sequence of COMINIT OOB signals.

A Port Selector is detected by the host during OOB when the response to the COMRESET signal from the host is first COMWAKE prior to the expected COMINIT. The hardware only needs to know that this is not an error condition. For software, a Port Selector is easily recognized by means of a bit in the Diagnostics register called the Port Selector Presence Detected bit (see Figure 20-10).

Figure 20-9: Port Selector Example

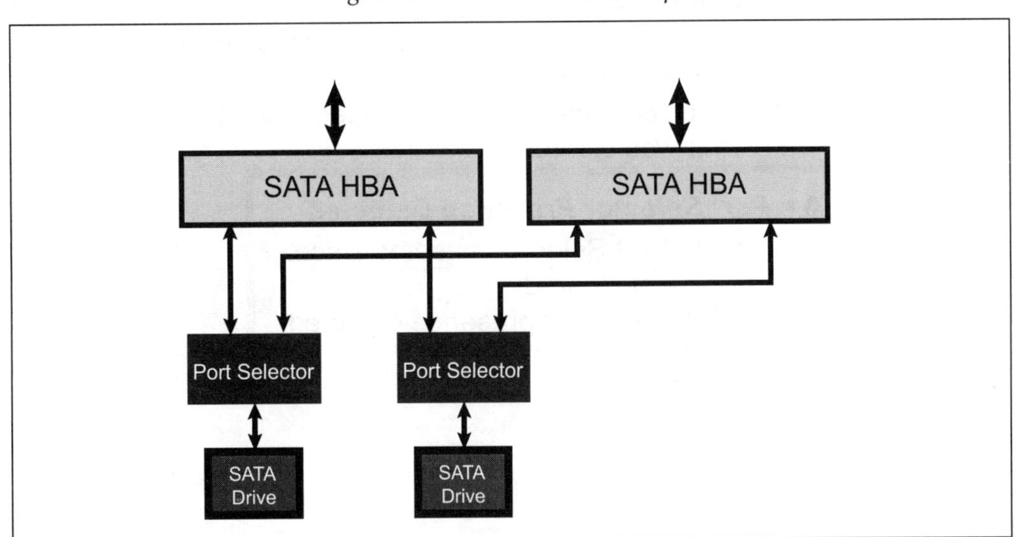

Figure 20-10: SATA Diagnostic Registers

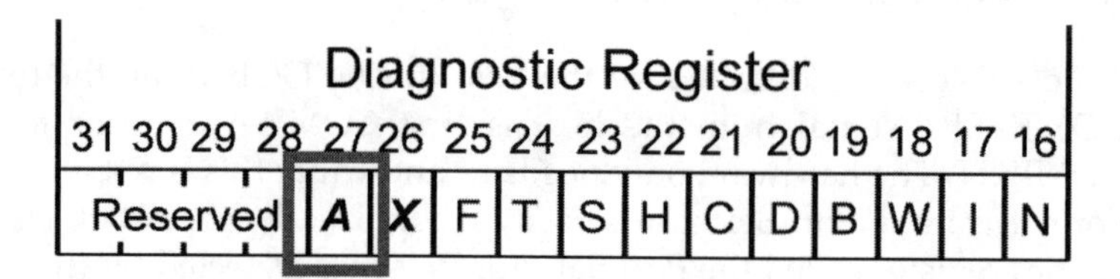

X = Exchanged

0 = No Device presence change detected since bit last cleared

1 = Device presence has changed since this bit was cleared

A = Port Selector Presence Detected

0 = No Port Selector detected since bit last cleared

1 = Port Selector presence detected

Appendices

Appendix A
Expander Devices

Scope

This appendix describes SAS expander devices, their role in the system, and the way they handle connection requests. Expanders are responsible for sorting out competing connection requests and must ensure fairness in the arbitration process. They also check to see that requests don't accidently block each other's progress and create a deadlock scenario. If such an event does happen, they reject some requests until the situation is resolved. The logical blocks that define the expander behavior are covered and some operational examples are explored.

Role of Expanders

The purpose of expanders in SAS is to provide scalability and increase the number of connections available to a device. Fanning out an HBA port is a logical example of this expansion, since expander ports are expected to be inexpensive compared to HBA ports. This example also makes sense in terms of bandwidth. An average data rate for today's enterprise drives is about 75 to 80 MB/s, so one HBA port with a bandwidth of 300 MB/s could support 3 or 4 drives without much risk of throttling their data flow. Regarding the number of connections available, SCSI permitted 16 or 32 devices to share the parallel bus, and an initiator could connect with any one of them at a time. A SAS Phy can only use one connection at a time, but expanders permit that connection to be to any of the over 16,000 possible target devices in the system.

Expanders provide the equivalent of simple network switches in a storage topology. They are limited to 128 accessible addresses for reasons of cost and simplicity, but a group of them can provide access to many more addresses and establish connections through a SAS network topology based on the target address. A target's SAS address is built into the device (disk or tape or some other device) and permanently fixed in that device when it is manufactured. The address is derived from the manufacturer's ID (assigned by the IEEE) and a serial number assigned to the device, which is then fixed into the firmware within the device itself.

Expander Definition

An expander device is shown in a high-level view in Figure A-1. Expanders are defined as devices that contain the features listed below the figure.

Figure A-1: High-level View of Expander Device

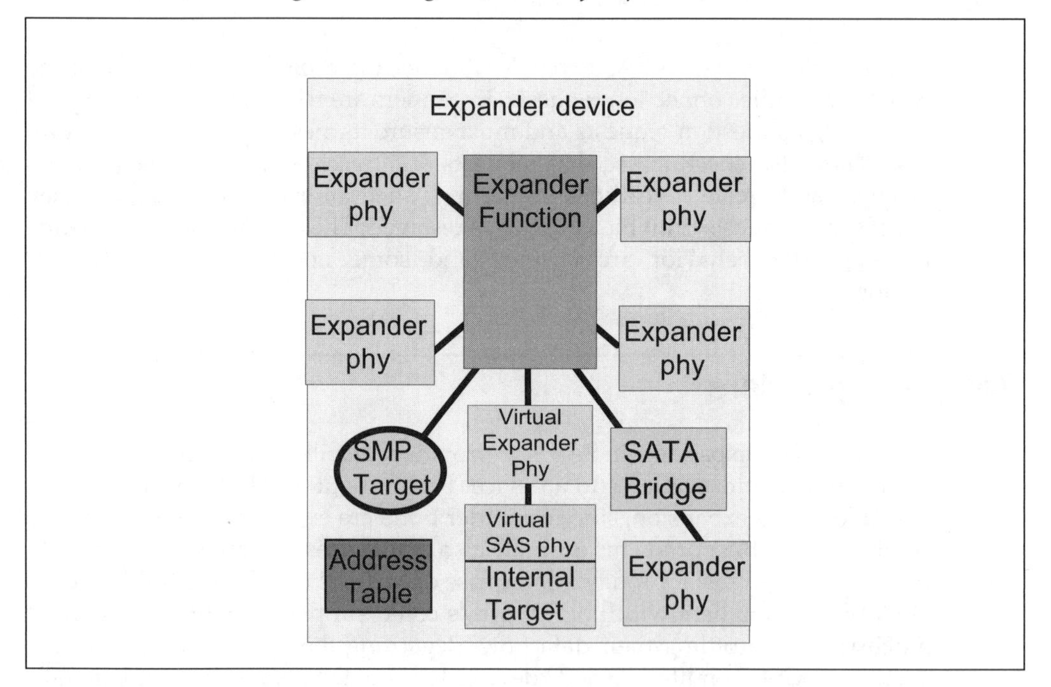

- An expander function comprised of three logical blocks: the ECM (Expander Connection Manager), ECR (Expander Connection Router), and BPP (Broadcast Primitive Processor). It also includes the logic to perform the actions required of an expander to establish connections between its phys.
- At least two external Phys (to provide a connection path).

- Expander ports available to support the phys. The actual number of ports will depend on the topology in which the expander has been installed, but an expander may be designed to have a specified mix of wide and narrow ports.
- An internal SMP target port to provide a means of discovering the addresses to which the expander has access and then storing them as needed into a routing table. An SMP initiator port can also optionally be included for an expander which is designed to be self-configuring. It is expected that, in future versions, many vendors will choose this option to simplify the discovery process.
- An optional address table. For some topologies a table will be required, so whether a vendor implements it will depend on the expected application of the device.
- Optional bridges for SATA drive compatibility. Some vendors will choose to implement this capability on every Phy so as to maximize the possible applications for their devices by enabling every Phy to support SATA devices. Others may choose to do this only on selected phys or none at all as a cost-saving measure.

Internal Details

Figure A-2 on page 508 shows a more detailed view of the workings of an expander, including the various logical blocks and state machines that define its behavior. Interestingly, expanders do not follow the normal SAS hierarchy of layers. For example, an expander port without SATA support has no Port Layer, Transport Layer, or Application Layer. The Expander Function takes the place of these end device upper layers, but is considered hierarchically *lower* than the phys. A connection request is forwarded down to the expander function, where the Expander Connection Manager (ECM) resolves the port to which it should be routed and sends that notification to the Expander Connection Router (ECR). The expander function does not, however, carry out the actual upper layer operations such as creating a pool of frames for transmission or tracking the protocol of the traffic within the connection. Once a connection has been established, the expander simply passes traffic in both directions as it arrives.

Figure A-2: Detailed View of Expander Device

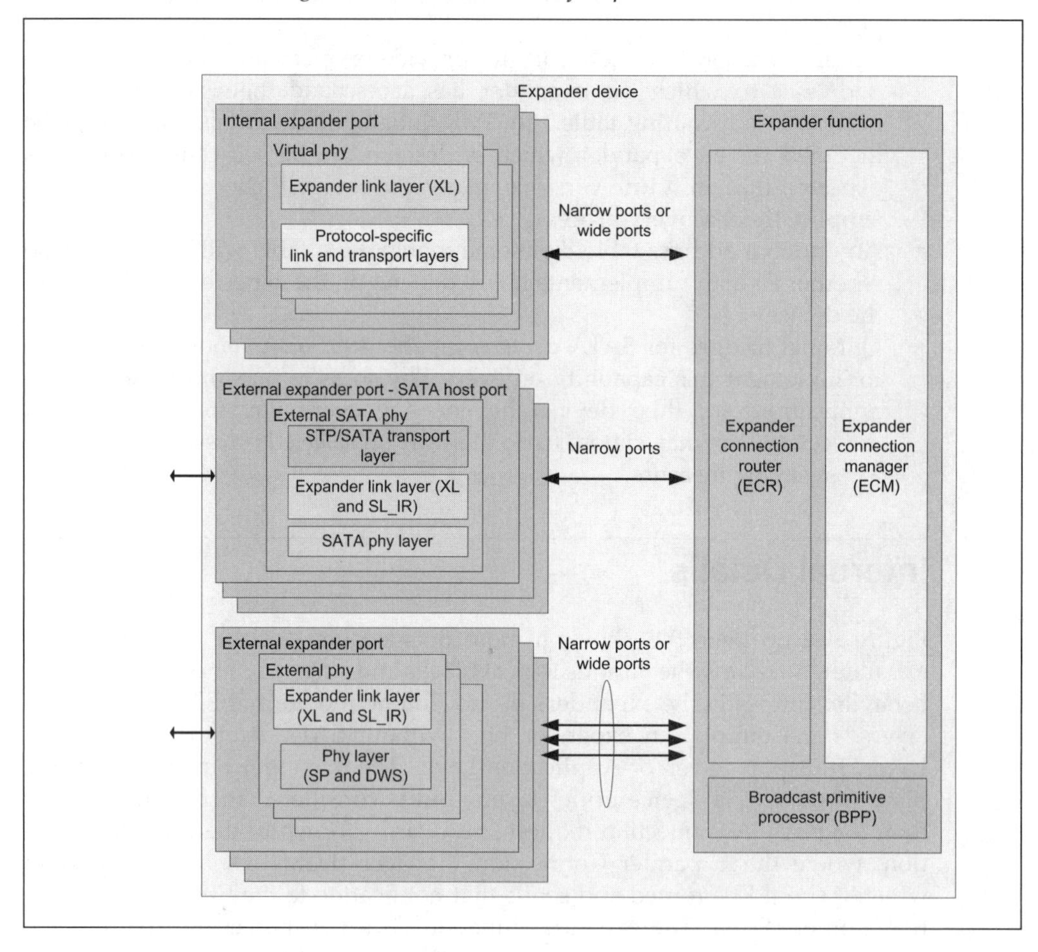

This is an interesting point to clarify, as well. Expanders are similar to switches in some regards but significantly different. For example, an expander does not evaluate every frame that passes through it, or do much in the way of "store and forward" operation. Instead, it evaluates a connection request for validity, commits the internal resources to create the connection, and then becomes more like a passive component in the frame transmission process. Frames are forwarded between the two connected devices at speed and the expander ignores the traffic flow unless it sees primitives that affect the connection itself, such as DONE, or CLOSE, or BREAK.

State Machine Interaction

When establishing and managing connections, the interaction between the state machines and phys is as shown in Figure A-3. The Phy that receives the incoming request acts as the source and forwards a request to the ECM for a connection. The request includes relevant arguments (e.g., the destination address) that the ECM will use to determine the destination Phy and arbitrate among competing requests.

Figure A-3: Expander Function

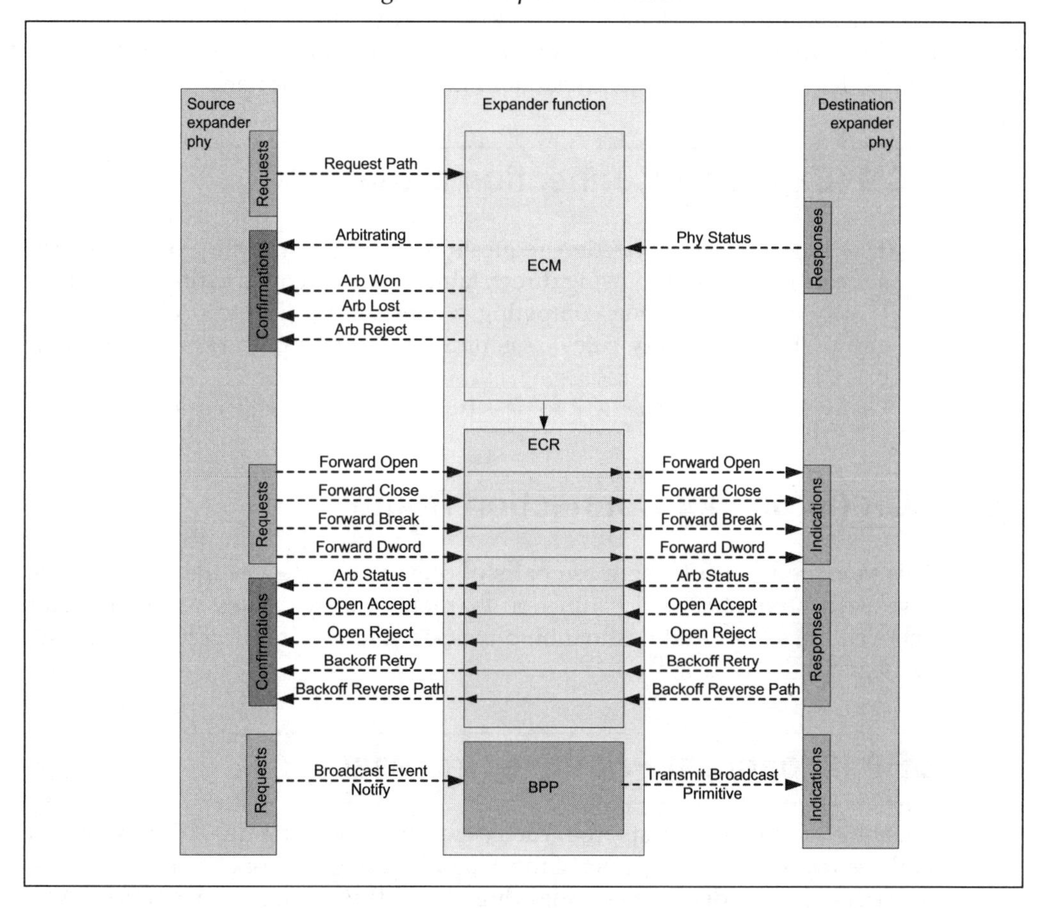

The process by which this is accomplished is described in "Example 1 - OPEN Arrives from the Link" on page 525. At this point it's enough to show that the source Phy sends a connection request to the ECM, which arbitrates for access to a destination phy, programs the ECR, and returns the status of the arbitration process. Once the path is established, the ECR just forwards the frame.

Expander Function

The several logic blocks that make up an expander are grouped into those that make up the expander function and those in the ports. Each of them sends and receives messages with neighboring blocks and it is this messaging that defines much of their behavior. As can be seen in Figure A-2 on page 508, the highest level within the phys is the expander Link Layer, represented by the XL state machine, and it is this logic with which the expander function interacts. Let's consider what the expander function is doing by looking at each of the sub-blocks. The three parts of the Expander Function are listed here:

ECM (Expander Connection Manager)

- This block maps connection requests to a destination Phy based on the address in the request, using direct, table, or subtractive routing methods.
- It also arbitrates among competing requests according to SAS arbitration and pathway recovery rules, assigning or denying path resources on that basis.
- Lastly, it configures the ECR to pass traffic between the selected phys.

ECR (Expander Connection Router)

This block routes traffic between pairs of phys as directed by the ECM. This is essentially a crossbar switch function that temporarily creates a virtual circuit between the source and destination phys (see "Expander's Crossbar Function" on page 82).

BPP (Broadcast Primitive Processor)

This block receives requests from each expander Phy and requests transmission of those requests on every port of the expander except the one the request came in on. If the expander is self-configuring, the BPP also requests a BROADCAST (CHANGE) message when the configuration is complete.

While some logic blocks in the standard have a state machine representation to condense their behavioral characteristics, the expander function does not. Instead, its behavior is wholly described by the messages it sends and receives. Figure A-3 on page 509 illustrates the messages sent between the expander function and the phys to initiate and manage a connection.

ECM - Requests

Consider first the message from the Phy to the ECM to request a connection, shown in Figure A-3 on page 509 as "Request Path". Table A-1 on page 511 lists the arguments that are presented with the request that the ECM will use to decide which port to select as the outgoing port and, if there are competing requests, which should have priority.

Table A-1: Expander Phy to ECM Request Path Arguments

	Description
Message: Request Path	Request for a connection.
Arguments used for port selection	**Destination SAS Address** - selects destination port **Initiator port bit** - indicates whether an initiator or target device has requested the connection **Protocol** - SAS, STP, or SMP **Connection Rate** - 1.5 Gb/s or 3.0 Gb/s **Initiator Connection Tag** - sent with the request by initiator and then used later in the request from the target to return the data or response for that transaction
Arguments used for arbitration fairness	**Arbitration Wait Time (AWT)** - how long the request has been waiting to be accepted or rejected **Source SAS Address** - address of initiating device **Connection Rate** - 1.5 Gb/s or 3.0 Gb/s **Retry Priority Status** - set to Ignore AWT when AWT should not be considered for arbitration **Partial Pathway Timeout Status** - maintained by the expander phy, this tracks how long the request has been waiting because all expander phys at the destination port are blocked waiting on partial pathways **Pathway Blocked Count** - number of times this connection has been retried by the originating device due to being rejected with a pathway blocked status

The decisions the ECM has to make based on these arguments fall into three categories: port selection, arbitration fairness, and deadlock resolution.

Port Selection

The destination port is selected based on the destination address and the suitability of this request for the intended target. A look at the relevant arguments will help explain how this works.

Destination Address: For port selection this is the determining factor, and the other arguments are used to verify that the matching port will actually support the request.

Initiator Port Bit: An initiator would not normally expect to receive a connection request from another initiator, so if that were the case the request could be readily observed as incorrect for a destination port.

Protocol: Similarly, a SAS device might expect to get requests for SSP connections, but not for STP connections. The expander Phy would be aware of target protocol requirements, because they are included, along with the destination address, in the Identification Sequence that the attached Phy sends after reset.

Connection Rate: This must match a rate supported by the destination.

Initiator Connection Tag: This optional value is assigned to a request from an initiator to facilitate quickly looking up the context when a reply is returned from the target at some later time. The reply would begin with an OPEN request from the target that would contain the same arguments, including this tag field. The initiator can use the tag to take any steps needed to prepare for the response from the target. Of course, this context could have been derived from the source address of the request, which is also contained in the OPEN address frame, but that 64-bit value would take more logic and time to look up than a 16-bit tag. Initiators are supposed to use the same Initiator Connection Tag for all connection requests to the same target and only change it when there are no longer any outstanding requests to that target. However, targets are not required to check for consistency on this.

Arbitration Fairness

Once a port has been selected, it may be necessary to arbitrate between competing requests to that port. Some important attributes of the decision process are fairness, bounded latency, good bus utilization and scalability. Strategies for granting access can intentionally be designed to be unfair, such as a fixed priority scheme, or fair, such as a round-robin arbitration scheme. The purpose of fairness is simply to guarantee that every process eventually gets access and makes forward progress rather than starving for access. SAS employs a least-recently-used algorithm for arbitration fairness based on several values as described below. If it should happen that more than one request has the same values, then the expander can choose any of them because they'd be the same in terms of priority.

Arbitration Wait Time (AWT) timer: Every SAS port and expander port implements an Arbitration Wait Time (AWT) timer to track how long a request has been waiting to receive an accept or reject response. This value has two parts, one that counts microseconds from 0 to 32,768, and another that counts milliseconds from 0 to 32,768.

The counter is started by the initiating device when a request is sent and is normally initialized to zero, but can be set to a non-zero value as high as 32,768 µs by setting the AWT field in the OPEN address frame to as high as 8000h. This makes the arbitration unfair, of course, but gives system administrators a means of assigning relative priorities among various devices. The counter continues to run until an accept or reject response arrives or until it reaches its maximum value, at which point it holds that value rather than wrapping around to zero.

When the request is received by an expander phy, the counter for that Phy is initialized to the value given in the OPEN address frame and the timer is started. When the OPEN address frame is transmitted by the expander, the AWT value is assigned based on the current value of the internal timer. As a result, the AWT is constantly updated as the OPEN address frame makes it way through the fabric. This is important because AWT is the most significant consideration in determining which requests have priority in an expander: requests that have been waiting longer are deemed to have higher priority. This is illustrated by Table A-2 that shows the relative bit position for this information during arbitration.

Source SAS Address: The second-highest priority term for arbitration is the SAS address of the originating device. Like AWT, this is conveyed in the OPEN address frame, and is readily compared between competing requests. For requests that are passing each other on the same link (one outgoing and one incoming), only the AWT and source address are compared to see which will win access to that link.

Table A-2: Arbitration Priority for Passing Requests

Bits 79-64 (79 is MSB)	Bits 63-0 (0 is LSB)
Arbitration Wait Time	Source SAS Address

Connection Rate: For requests that are competing for access to the same outgoing port there is a third-level term to evaluate, and that is the connection rate, as shown in Table A-3.

Table A-3: Arbitration Priority for Competing Requests, Retry Status: Normal

Bits 83-68 (83 is MSB)	Bits 67-4 (67 is MSB)	Bits 3-0 (0 is LSB)
Arbitration Wait Time	Source SAS Address	Connection Rate

Retry Priority Status: There is an interesting twist to the use of AWT, though, in that requests also include a field that can be used to override the AWT value and indicate that it should be ignored. This happens when a port sends an outgoing request and instead of receiving an accept or reject, it receives a higher-priority request from an address other than the destination. That means the outgoing request lost the arbitration, so the Retry Priority Status bit will be set when it is sent the next time. If more than one request competes for the same resource and one of them has the Retry Priority Status bit set, it has the effect of setting AWT to its maximum value for that request, eliminating this field as a consideration in the arbitration process (see Table A-4). This should result in the request that was backed off being treated with much higher priority the next time. The goal for this feature was to help complex environments resolve arbitration more quickly.

Table A-4: Arbitration Priority for Competing Requests, Retry Status: Ignore AWT

Bits 67-4 (67 is MSB)	Bits 3-0 (0 is LSB)
Source SAS Address	Connection Rate

Deadlock Detection and Resolution

In the process of arbitration, it's possible that a deadlock condition could arise, so expanders must be able to detect and resolve this case. More discussion on this topic can be found in the section on "Deadlock and Livelock" on page 338. For now, we will just look at the mechanism used by expanders for this purpose, which uses two fields in the request arguments.

Partial Pathway Timeout timer: Each expander Phy maintains a counter to identify potential deadlock conditions and request resolution by the ECM. The counter is initialized with the partial pathway value that is reported in the SMP DISCOVER response of this device, and is started by a Phy when it's acting as the source of a request and all the phys in the destination port it's trying to reach are returning Phy Status (Blocked Partial Pathway). The timer is programmable, and the time selected for this timeout should relate to the topology: larger topologies need correspondingly larger times for detecting potential deadlocks to avoid reduced performance. If the timer expires, the ECM determines whether to continue with the connection request from this Phy by comparing the Pathway Recovery Priority fields of this request, shown in Table A-5, against the other competing requests. If this request loses, the expander will send an OPEN_REJECT (PATHWAY BLOCKED) to it and the initiator will have to try again later. However, this request will have a higher priority when it is retried later because its Pathway Blocked Count will get incremented.

Pathway Blocked Count: This value is included in the OPEN address frame and indicates the number of times this request has been forced to retry because it received an OPEN_REJECT (PATHWAY BLOCKED) response. The goal is to ensure that a request which has previously been retried will have a higher priority the next time and thus be less likely to be retried again.

Table A-5: Pathway Recovery Priority

Bits 71-64 (71 is MSB)	Bits 63-0 (0 is LSB)
Pathway Blocked Count	Source SAS Address

ECM - Confirmations

Confirmations are sent back to the source Phy from the ECM in response to the Request Path. When the request is received, the ECM confirms that it has received the request and that arbitration is in progress by sending an Arbitrating confirmation to the phy, as shown in Table A-6.

Table A-6: ECM Confirmations to Source Expander Phy

Message	Description
Arbitrating (Normal)	ECM has accepted a Request Path
Arbitrating (Waiting on Partial)	All the phys within the destination port are returning a Phy Status (Partial Pathway) or Phy Status (Blocked Partial Pathway) response, and at least one of them is returning a Phy Status (Partial Pathway) response.
Arbitrating (Blocked on Partial)	ECM has determined that each of the phys within the destination port is returning a Phy Status (Blocked Partial Pathway) response. When the source Phy sees this special case, it starts the Partial Pathway Timeout timer and waits that long before requesting that ECM resolve the blockage. If the timer expires, the ECM compares the destination phys that are sending Phy Status (Blocked Partial Pathway) to see whether they are higher or equal to the source phys Pathway Recovery Priority. If they all are, the ECM sends Open Reject (Pathway Blocked) to the source phy, terminating its request.
Arbitrating (Waiting on Connection)	The connection request is blocked for one of two reasons: a) no phys in the port are available but one has a active connection currently in progress, or a) there are insufficient routing resources within the expander to complete the connection request.
Arb Won	The ECM succeeded in mapping this request to the destination phy.
Arb Lost	Everything else is OK, but there was a higher priority request for the destination expander phy.
Arb Reject (No Destination)	No operational Phy was found on which to route this request, or the request maps back to the Phy from which it came.
Arb Reject (Bad Destination)	The requested destination address maps back to the source Phy and the ECM has chosen not to send Arb Reject (No Destination).

Table A-6: ECM Confirmations to Source Expander Phy

Message	Description (Continued)
Arb Reject (Bad Connection Rate)	A destination port was found, but it has no phys that will support the requested rate.
Arb Reject (Pathway Blocked)	The requesting expander Phy has been backed off according to SAS pathway recovery rules.

These confirmations inform the XL state machine in the source Phy of the status of the request. The ECM can generate some confirmations from information it can find on its own, such as recognizing that the destination address would have to be routed back to the same port that the request arrived on. For other confirmations it is necessary to see the response from the destination Phy to know whether the request can proceed, and these responses are listed in Table A-7 on page 517. For the destination Phy to respond it needs to see the arguments of the request, so the ECM instructs the ECR to forward the OPEN address frame to it. If everything is legal and the destination Phy does not return one of the problem responses listed below, then the connection succeeds.

Table A-7: Problem Responses from Expander Destination Phy to ECM

Message	Description
Phy Status (Partial Pathway)	The destination Phy is being used for an unblocked partial pathway, or has itself sent a Request Path to the ECM and is receiving an Arbitrating (Waiting On Partial) confirmation.
Phy Status (Blocked Partial Pathway)	The destination Phy is being used for a blocked partial pathway, or has sent its own Request Path request to the ECM and is receiving Arbitrating (Blocked On Partial) from the ECM.
Phy Status (Connection)	The destination Phy has a connection already in progress, or has sent its own Request Path to the ECM and is receiving Arbitrating (Waiting On Connection).

ECR - Requests and Indications

The ECR receives requests from the source Phy and forwards them to the destination Phy selected by the ECM. Recall that the standard defines a *request* as information passed from a higher-layer state machine to a lower-layer state machine, usually to initiate some action. When the request is forwarded, it is called an *indication*, defined as information passed from a lower state machine to a higher state machine, usually relaying a request. In describing the direction of these messages, it's helpful to know that the ECM and ECR of the expander are considered to be at a lower level with reference to the expander Phy XL state machine, as illustrated in Figure A-4. The requests and indications summarized in Table A-8 show that these are simply relaying the activity seen on the source phy.

Figure A-4: Expander State Machine Relationships

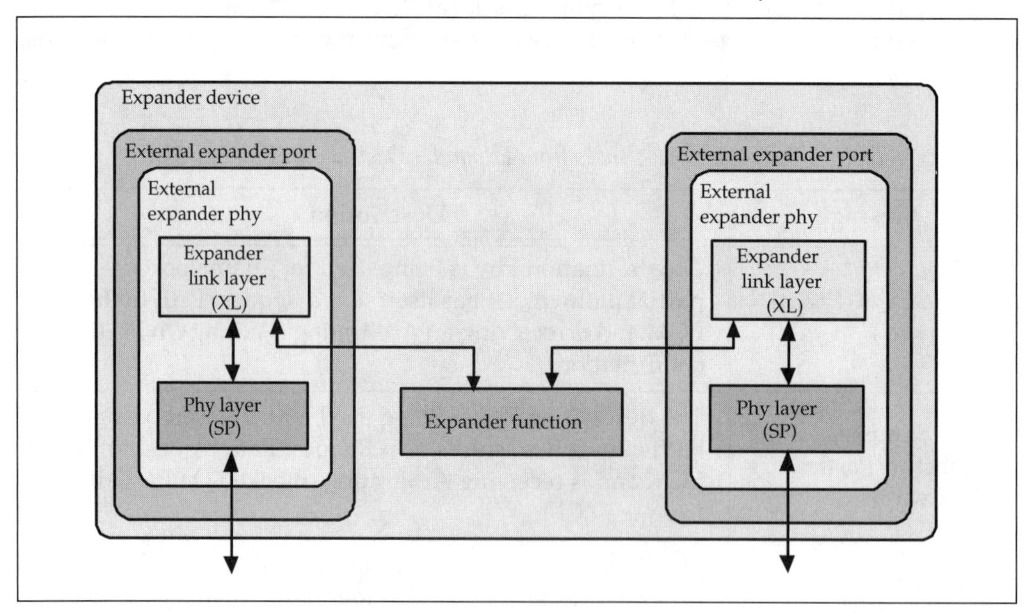

Table A-8: ECR Requests/Indications

Message	Description
Forward Open (arguments)	Request/Indication to forward an OPEN address frame
Forward Close	Request/Indication to forward a CLOSE
Forward Break	Request/Indication to forward a BREAK
Forward Dword	Request/Indication to forward a dword

The arguments given with the Forward Open are the same as those described for the Request Path request to the ECM, except that three more fields from the OPEN address frame are included. These fields are: Features, Compatible Features, and More Compatible Features. Since the standard states that they all must be set to zero in the OPEN address frame, these fields are evidently for future reference and therefore not of much interest at this time.

Information returned by the destination Phy as a *response* is forwarded back to the source Phy as a *confirmation*, and these are summarized in Table A-9. Most of these are simply relaying to the source Phy what the destination Phy received. The last two, however, confirm that another request has come in while this one was going out, and the incoming request has higher priority.

Table A-9: ECR Responses/Confirmations

Message	Description
Arb Status (Normal)	AIP (NORMAL) was received
Arb Status (Waiting on Partial)	AIP (WAITING ON PARTIAL) was received
Arb Status (Waiting on Connection)	AIP (WAITING ON CONNECTION) was received
Arb Status (Waiting on Device)	AIP (WAITING ON DEVICE) was received, or the open request was sent and the Phy is waiting on a response from the device
Open Accept	OPEN_ACCEPT was received
Open Reject	OPEN_REJECT was received

Table A-9: ECR Responses/Confirmations

Message	Description (Continued)
Backoff Retry	A higher priority OPEN address frame has been received, but it was not from the destination address for this request. The connection did not succeed and will have to try again later.
Backoff Reverse Path	A higher priority OPEN address frame has been received from the destination address for this request. In this case, a connection will still be established with the destination.

Broadcast Primitive Processor Interface

The BPP receives notification from expander phys about various events they have detected, and generates a primitive that is sent on every Phy except the one that sent the notification. The reason for doing this is to inform the devices attached to an expander that there has been a change in the fabric. As can be seen from Table A-10, the response in most cases is to request that a BROADCAST (CHANGE) primitive be sent out. This primitive is a very simple response, containing very little information, which helps to keep expander devices simple and cheap by keeping its interaction with external devices very simple. When change events occur, expanders simply inform the system that something has changed and then it's up to the initiators to sort out what has happened and what they need to do. The trade-off for this simplicity is some overhead traffic on the fabric as initiators poll devices to learn what has changed.

Table A-10: BPP Notification Events and Responses

Event	Description	Response
Phy Not Ready	An expander Phy was ready and now it is not, or an internal Phy has been disabled.	Request a BROAD-CAST (CHANGE) on all ports except the one that notified about the event
SATA Spinup Hold	The SATA spinup hold state has been reached.	
Identification Sequence Complete	An expander Phy has completed the sequence, or an internal Phy has been enabled.	
CHANGE received	A BROADCAST (CHANGE) was received.	
SATA Port Selector Change	SATA port selector has appeared or disappeared.	
RESERVED CHANGE 0 or 1 received	Processed the same as BROAD-CAST (CHANGE) by SAS ports	Request a BROAD-CAST (RESERVED-CHANGE 0 or 1) on all other ports
SES received	An asynchronous event has occurred in an enclosure; initiators should poll the SES logical units to learn what happened	Request a BROAD-CAST (SES) on all other ports
RESERVED 1 received	Reserved	Request a BROAD-CAST (RESERVED 1) on all other ports

Expander Port State Machines

The behavior of expanders is defined in the standard with several state machines. Some of these, such as the Link Layer state machines, are common to all SAS phys.

Link Layer State Machines -

- **SL_CC (SAS Link Layer connection control)** - Controls connections, handling OPENs, CLOSEs, and BREAKs.
- **SL_RA (Receive OPEN Address frame)** -
- **SL_IR (Identification and hard Reset)** - Controls the flow of dwords on the link that are associated with transmitting or receiving identification and hard reset.
- **XL (expander Phy Link Layer)** - Controls the flow of traffic on the link and works with the ECM to establish and maintain connections with another Phy as needed. This machine is only found in expanders.

Phy Layer State Machines

SP (SAS Phy Layer) - This machine basically controls the Phy reset sequence on the link.

DWS (Phy Layer dword synchronization) - Synchronizes dword boundaries at the receiver with those at the attached transmitter by searching for control characters in the received stream of characters.

The XL State Machine

Unlike those state machines common to all SAS ports, the XL state machine is unique to expander phys and is defined by a massive state machine that requires three pages to display in the standard. In an effort to make them more readable, those state machines are redrawn here, but it remains difficult to make it fit into a concise drawing. In the standard it was broken into three parts, and those parts are carried forward here in Figure A-5, Figure A-6, and Figure A-7 on the following three pages.

Figure A-5: XL State Machine, Part 1

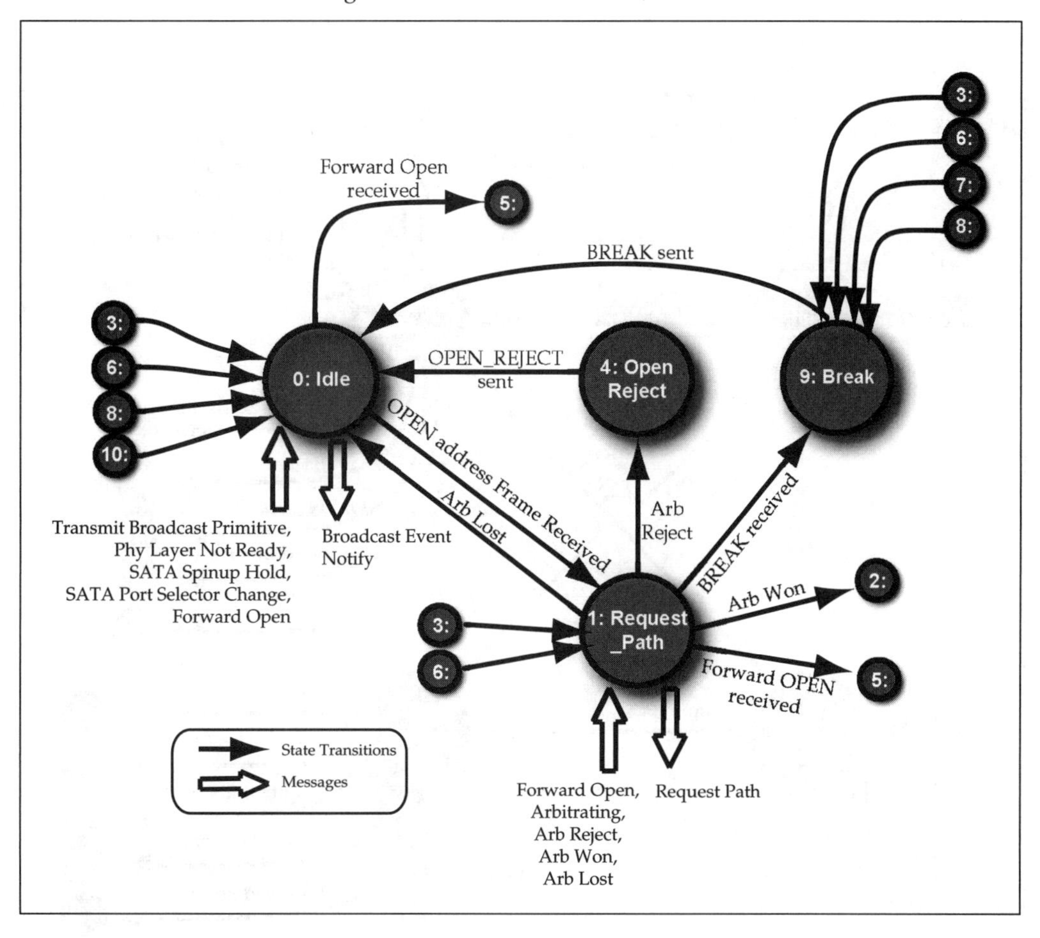

Figure A-6: XL State Machine, Part 2

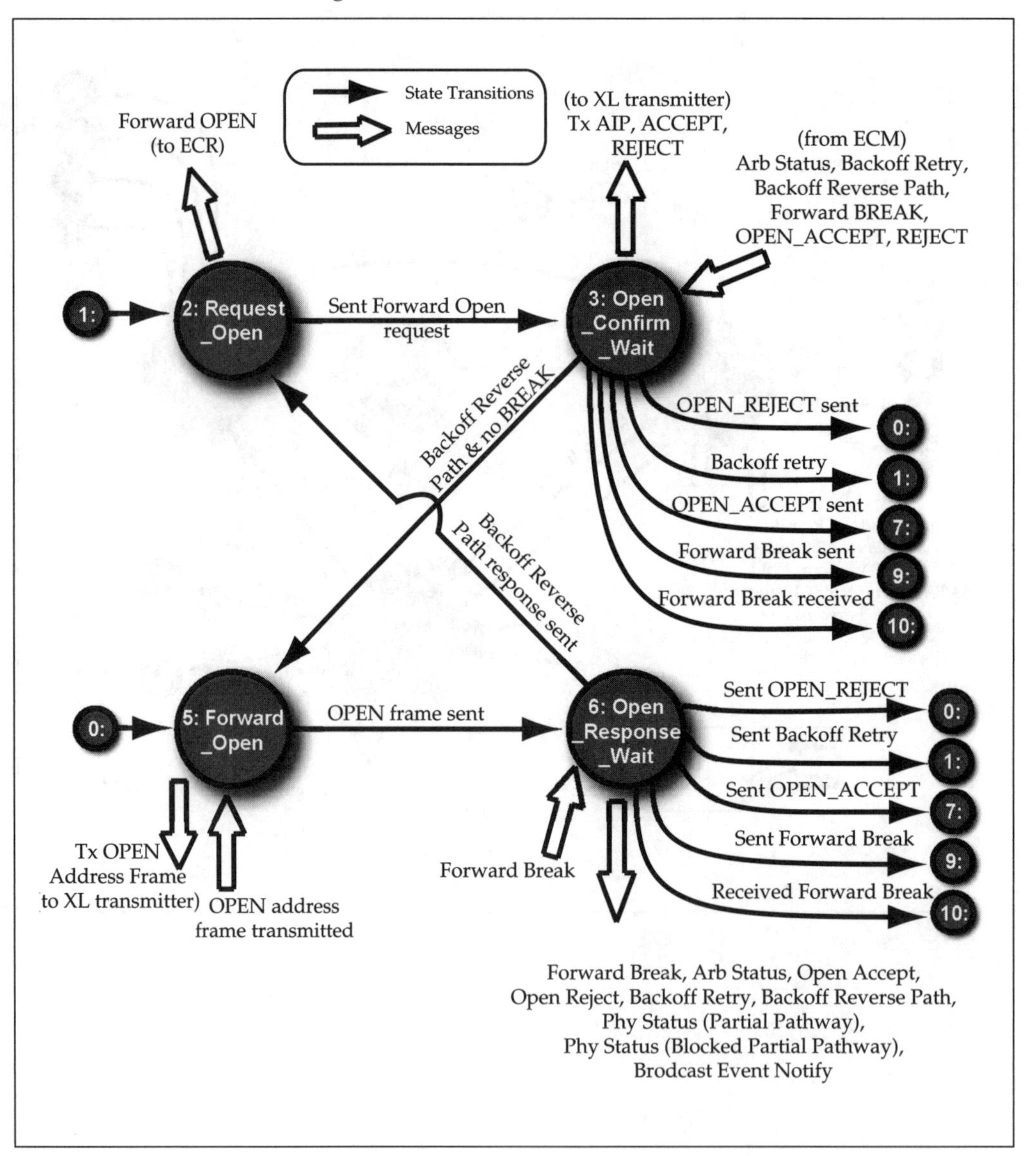

Figure A-7: XL State Machine, Part 3

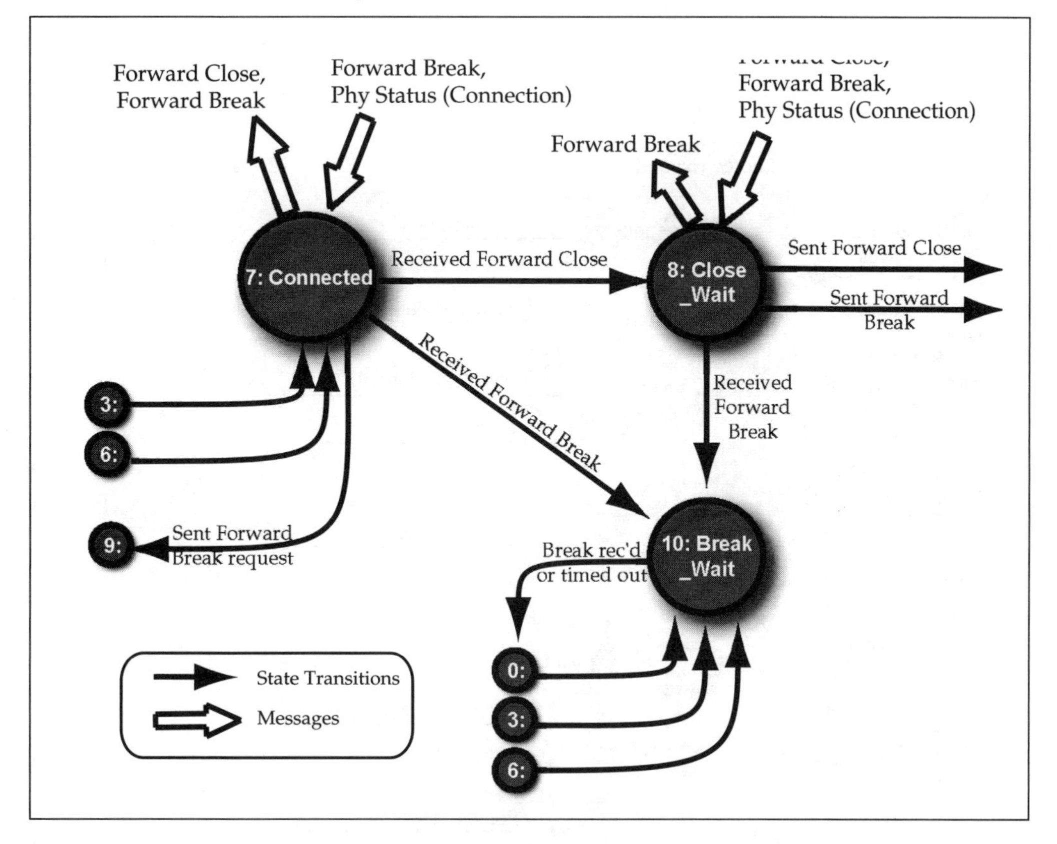

Rather than attempt to go through all the possible cases, it would seem more instructive to describe a few example behaviors. The state machine approach is well suited for the purpose of providing answers to specific questions about behavior, so let's examine two example situations and step through the behavior that results. The accompanying diagrams will help to visualize the process and keep track of which part of the expander is involved.

Example 1 - OPEN Arrives from the Link

For the first example, refer to Figure A-8 on the following page. The events and the steps to be taken by the XL state machine for the source Phy in this simple case are described in the text that follows the diagram.

Figure A-8: XL State Machine Example 1

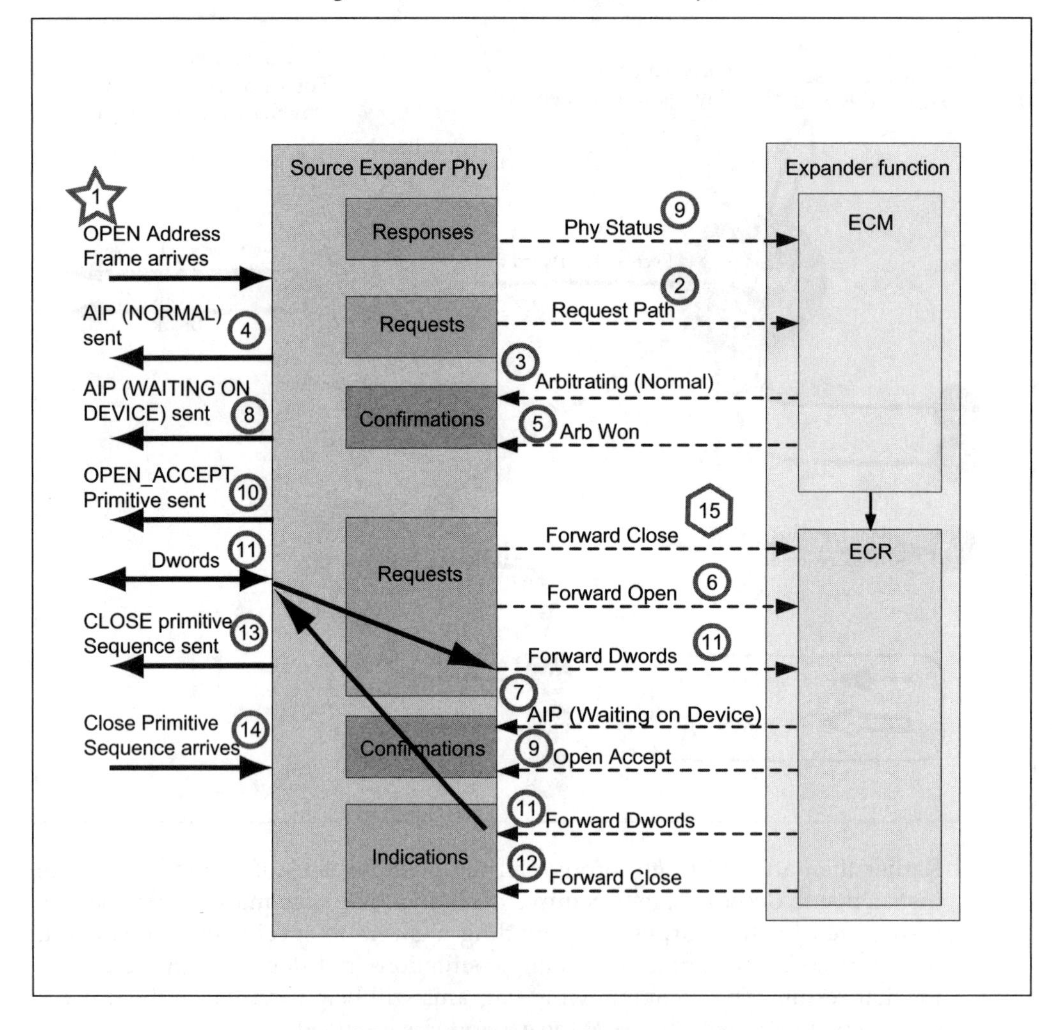

1. Let the arrival of the OPEN address frame start the process.
2. The XL state machine transitions from XL0:Idle to XL1:Request_Path and sends a Request Path request to the ECM with the appropriate arguments from the OPEN address frame (protocol, connection rate, destination address, etc.).
3. The ECM sends an Arbitrating (Normal) confirmation while it sorts out the request to let the Phy know that it is in progress.

4. In response, the expander Phy periodically sends AIP (NORMAL) followed by idle dwords onto the link until there is a change in arbitration status, to inform the originating device that the request is making headway. The list of possible arbitration primitives that an expander may send while arbitrating is shown in Table A-11. All of these are sent repeatedly except the last one; AIP (WAITING ON DEVICE) is only sent once to indicate that the connection succeeded through this expander and further responses will thus come from the next device in the path.

Table A-11: Results of ECM Arbitration Confirmations

Message	Resulting from ECM Confirmation
AIP (NORMAL)	Arb Status (Normal)
AIP (WAITING ON PARTIAL)	Arb Status (Waiting on Partial)
AIP (WAITING ON CONNECTION)	Arb Status (Waiting on Connection)
AIP (WAITING ON DEVICE)	Arb Status (Waiting on Device)

5. Assume the ECM succeeds in finding an available destination Phy for this request and sends back an Arb Won response. Based on this outcome, the ECR is instructed to connect this Phy to the destination Phy pending further developments, and the path is now partially complete.
6. The state machine transitions to XL2:Request_Open and sends a Forward Open request to the ECR with all the fields of the OPEN address frame as arguments. The ECR passes this through to the destination Phy that was assigned by the ECM.
7. The XL state machine now transitions to XL3:Open_Confirm_Wait, where it waits for a response to the open request. Once the frame has been sent out on the destination Phy of the expander, that Phy returns AIP (WAITING ON DEVICE) to the ECR.
8. That AIP response is then forwarded to the originating phy. Unlike the other AIP responses, this is only sent one time, because the connection is now tentatively established through this expander and all the remaining responses will come from the next device in the path.
9. Whatever confirmations come back from the ECR are now forwarded to the link. Assume next that an Open Accept confirmation is now received.
10. Based on that, the Phy will send an OPEN_ACCEPT primitive on the link.

11. The state machine transitions to XL7:Connected and periodically sends a Phy Status (Connection) to the ECM for as long as the connection is in progress. At this point a full-duplex circuit has been established between the phys, so all dwords that arrive from the link, except the primitives BREAK and CLOSE that indicate the connection will need to be torn down, are passed to the ECR as Forward Dword requests. The same thing will be happening on the destination phy, so any dwords from the ECR that arrive as Forward Dword indications are sent out on the link. The state machine remains in this state until a CLOSE or BREAK arrives from the link or a Forward Close or Forward Break indication arrives from the ECR.
12. Assume now that a Forward Close indication arrives from the ECR with an argument based on the CLOSE primitive that generated it. There are 4 variations of CLOSE, as listed in Table A-12 below, and from here it can be seen that, at present, the argument for the Forward Close can only be NORMAL or CLEAR AFFILIATION.

Table A-12: CLOSE Arguments

Primitive	Description
CLOSE (CLEAR AFFILIATION)	Close an open STP connection and clear the affiliation
CLOSE (NORMAL)	Close a connection
CLOSE (RESERVED 0)	Reserved. Processed the same as CLOSE (NORMAL)
CLOSE (RESERVED 1)	Reserved. Processed the same as CLOSE (NORMAL)

13. Based on this close indication, the state machine transitions to XL8:Close_Wait, and sends a CLOSE with the appropriate argument onto the link to pass along the indication, following that with repeated idle dwords. Incoming dwords from the link are still forwarded to the ECR while the Phy waits for the response from the attached device.
14. Assume now that a CLOSE (NORMAL) is received from the link.
15. A Forward Close request with the argument Close Received is sent to the ECR, the path resources are released, and the state machine goes back to XL0:Idle. If a BREAK had been seen instead of the CLOSE, a Forward Break request would have been sent to the ECR, the path resources released, and a BREAK primitive sent back on the link to the attached device before the state machine returns to Idle.

Example 2 - Incoming and Outgoing OPENs at Same Time

Using another example, as shown in Figure A-9, an address frame arrives at the same time as a Forward Open indication from the ECR. The steps to be taken by the XL state machine for the source Phy in this case will involve arbitration between competing requests in both directions. This is the responsibility of the XL state machine rather than the ECM because the ECM did not know about the incoming request and has already forwarded an open request to this Phy from another phy.

Figure A-9: XL State Machine Example 2

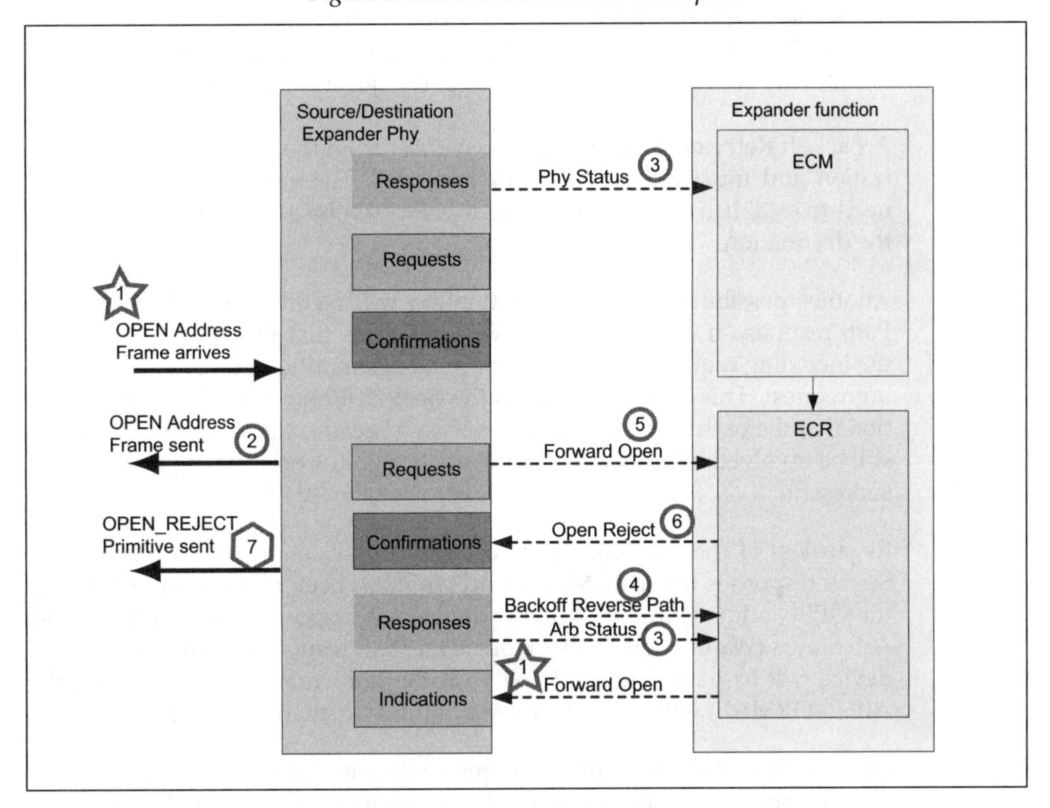

The following are the steps illustrated in the diagram of Figure A-9:

1. From XL0:Idle, if open requests appear simultaneously on both incoming and outgoing sides, the state machine transitions to XL5:Forward_Open.
2. For this case, the ECM has already arbitrated and assigned the outgoing

connection to this phy, so the outgoing request is automatically given first priority and the Phy will send the OPEN address frame on the link using the arguments passed with the request, followed by idle dwords.

3. Next the state machine transitions to XL6:Open_Response_Wait and sends Arb Status (Waiting on Device) and Phy Status (Partial Pathway) to the ECM. Here it compares the incoming OPEN address frame with the outgoing request. Based on the outcome, it will send a Backoff Retry response through the ECR back to the source Phy if the incoming request is not from the destination of the outgoing request, and either of two conditions is true:
    • the incoming OPEN address frame arrives *before* an AIP message is received, and the incoming request has a higher priority based on the arbitration fairness rules discussed earlier.
    • the incoming OPEN address frame arrives *after* an AIP message is received, this indicates that the expander that earlier sent the AIP has already concluded that this new open request is a higher priority.

A Backoff Retry response means the request from the ECR has lost the arbitration and must release the path resources. The expander function will need to establish a new path using this Phy as the source now rather than the destination.

Another possibility is that the evaluation will result in a Backoff Reverse Path response if either of the above cases finds that the source address of the incoming request actually matches the destination address of the outgoing request. This case is similar to the Backoff Retry with the main exception that the path resources are not released because the same two phys will still be involved in the connection, even though the original request was not successful.

Regardless of the outcome of the arbitration, this state will also send Arb Status responses to the ECM to report what has been received after sending the OPEN address frame. While waiting for a response, the state will send Arb Status (Waiting On Device), but after that, responses from the external device will be passed to the ECM with the same arguments. For example, AIP (NORMAL) will generate an Arb Status (Normal) response.

4. Assume now that the incoming request evaluates to a higher priority, and that the source address matches the destination address of the outgoing request. The result is a Backoff Reverse Path response to the ECR.
5. The state machine next enters XL2:Request_Open and sends a Forward Open request to the ECR with the contents of the OPEN address frame as arguments.
6. The state machine then transitions to XL3:Open_Confirm_Wait, where it

forwards whatever confirmations it receives from the ECR regarding the connection status. Just to make things interesting, assume that the destination phy, for some reason, does not accept the connection request from this phy. There's really no reason why it should do that, since the connection would still have been made with the destination it was trying to reach, but let's say that it does anyway. The result would be an Open Reject confirmation received by this phy.

7. The state machine sends an OPEN_REJECT primitive out on the link. If no BREAK was received, the rejection will cause the state machine to transition back to XL0:Idle and cause the path resources to be released.

Types of Expanders

Two types of expanders are listed in the standard: *fanout expanders* and *edge expanders*, and both are illustrated in the simple topology shown in Figure A-10.

Figure A-10: Expander Example

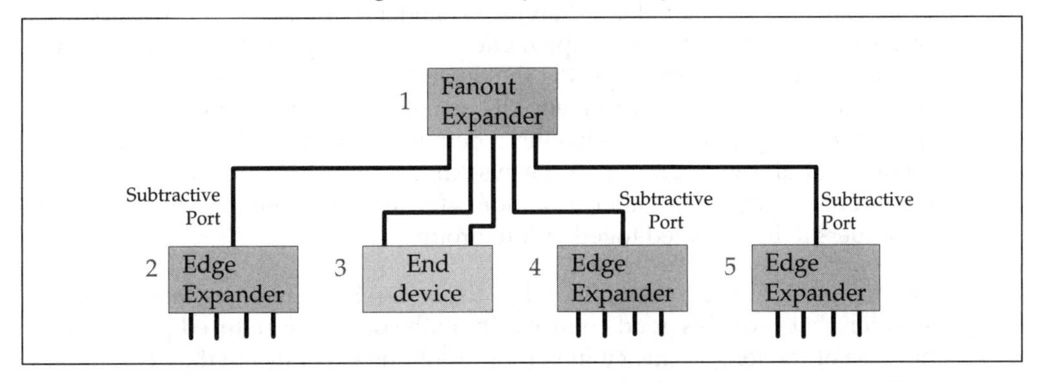

Fanout expanders act as a routing path between all the subsets of a network, and so must be aware of all the possible addresses in the network. Fanout expanders have two methods for routing connection requests, and every Phy will be assigned one of these methods. One way this might be done would be to have an external EEPROM from which the device reads after reset to learn what these assignments are.

- Direct Attach: A device that is directly attached to the expander, with no other intervening expanders.
- Routing Table: An address not directly attached should be found in the address table, which keeps track of the addresses that are visible to this expander indirectly through other expanders. Fanout expanders need to be

aware of all the addresses in the network because they have no default port to which unknown addresses may be routed. The size of the memory in the device needed for this table is vendor-specific, but the maximum number of addresses the standard allows is 16,384. This number is derived from the fact that a fanout expander can have as many as 128 addresses. If each of those is associated with an external Phy connected to an edge expander set which can also have up to 128 addresses, the total becomes 128 times 128, or 16,384.

As an aside, this fanout limit of 128 is currently based on the Phy identifier field that is reported with the results for the Report General request or Discover request. The field is only one byte long, although another byte was left available above it for future expansion. The 16K address limitation is not expected to be constraining – even Fibre Channel only implements drive groupings of a hundred or so. The bigger constraint for expanders will be implementing the memory required for a routing table in the device, since each entry contains a 64-bit SAS address and one enable/disable bit.

Edge expanders are similar to fanout expanders, but differ in one important respect: they may optionally implement a third routing method which is a subtractive port. A subtractive port is the default to which addresses are routed if they cannot otherwise be resolved. This makes edge expander designs simpler than fanout expanders, since having a default means they do not need a complete list of all the addresses in the system. A subtractive port can attach to a table-routed Phy of another expander, for the purpose of allowing edge expanders to be cascaded together into groups.

Grouping several together into Edge Expander Sets creates a less-expensive solution that provides good connectivity with somewhat reduced performance because of the longer latency in getting from one expander to the next. From a performance standpoint, it is preferable to use a fanout expander only, since that puts every address just one hop away (up to 128 phys). Having a central fanout design improves failover, too, since in a cascaded setup any failure could cause all the downstream devices to go offline. Consequently, fanout expanders should become a more popular solution in the future, but earlier implementations will probably use the cascaded topology so they can use smaller, lower-cost chips and simple designs.

Like fanout expanders, edge expander devices route connection requests between their phys based on address, and can access up to 128 addresses at most, including external phys and internal (virtual) phys. Edge expanders may be constructed as a set like the one shown in Figure A-11, where the set as a whole is considered to have the properties of a larger edge expander. In the figure, four addresses are consumed internally, one for each of the three downstream expander devices and one for the wide-port embedded end device, leaving 124 addresses available for other phys.

Figure A-11: Edge Expander Set

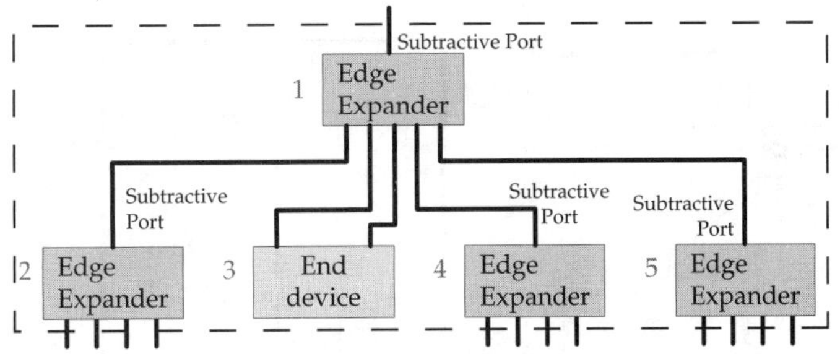

A more sophisticated topology example is shown in Figure A-12, where several edge expander sets have been assembled into a larger topology. Using edge expander sets provides a couple of advantages. First, it improves the manufacturability of the devices, since smaller chips are inexpensive and easier to make compared to building one large chip with as many as 128 interfaces. Secondly, it improves flexibility, since the smaller parts can be arranged in ways that are more suitable for different applications than a single large part could be. The trade-offs for these advantages are longer latencies and potentially reduced performance, as downstream devices compete for access to upstream ports.

Figure A-12: Fanout Expander with Edge Expander Set

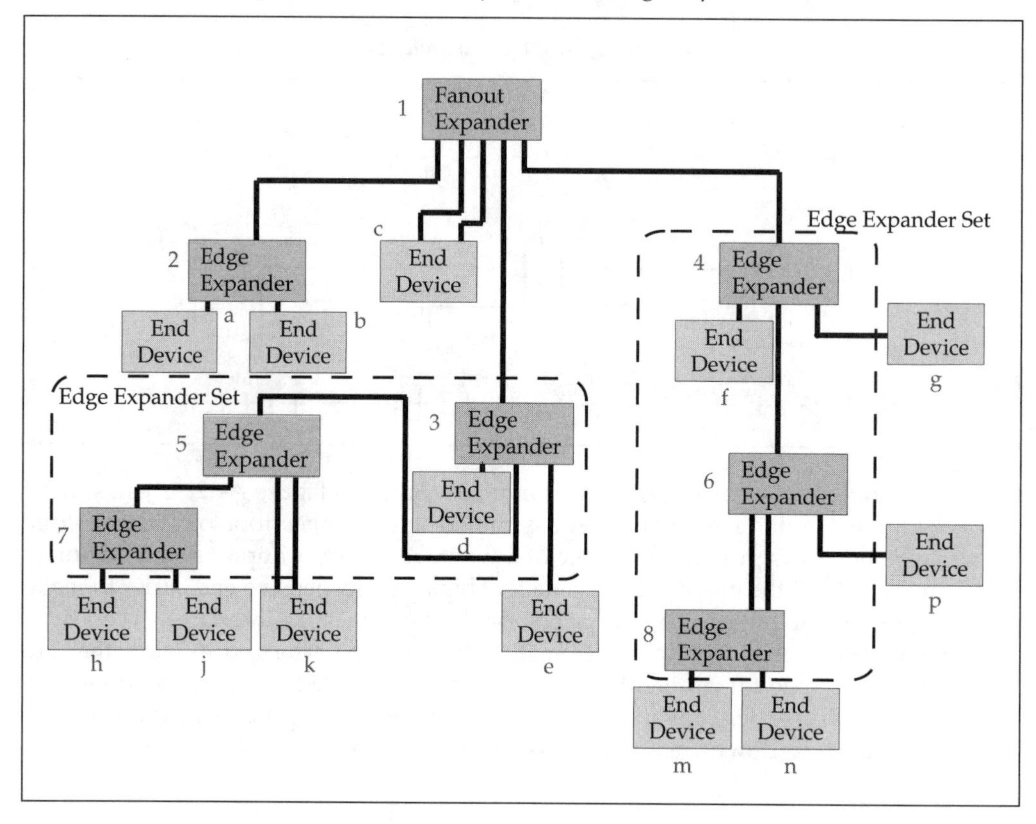

The standard does not describe how edge expander sets may be constructed, giving designers considerable implementation freedom by providing only general guidelines. For example, the sets are bounded by expander phys that are attached to end devices, or not attached to any device, or by an expander Phy that has the subtractive attribute and is attached to another expander.

As mentioned earlier, edge expanders have three ways of routing system addresses:

- Direct-attached addresses
- Routing Table list of indirect addresses
- Subtractive Routing

The devices that can be attached to a subtractive port are an end device, a fanout expander, or another edge expander. However, if two expanders are connected internally within a set, one must use its subtractive port for that purpose. In keeping with the notion of upstream and downstream, the expander that aggregates the others beneath it uses table-routed ports, and the lower devices use their subtractive port to connect to it. Interestingly, this restriction on the possible hierarchy of SAS topologies was largely a marketing decision to keep SAS simple and inexpensive. If this limitation were not in place and the table-routed Phy from one expander could connect to the table-routed Phy of another expander, the number of addresses to be tracked could increase dramatically, as would the potential for accidentally creating loops. Devices can have wide ports connecting between them but it is illegal to create any loop structures. Also, given that there can only be one level of edge expander sets, the largest number of edge expander sets that can be installed in a network without a fanout expander is just two. Their subtractive ports would need to be attached to each other, as shown in Figure A-13.

Figure A-13: Peer Edge Expander Sets

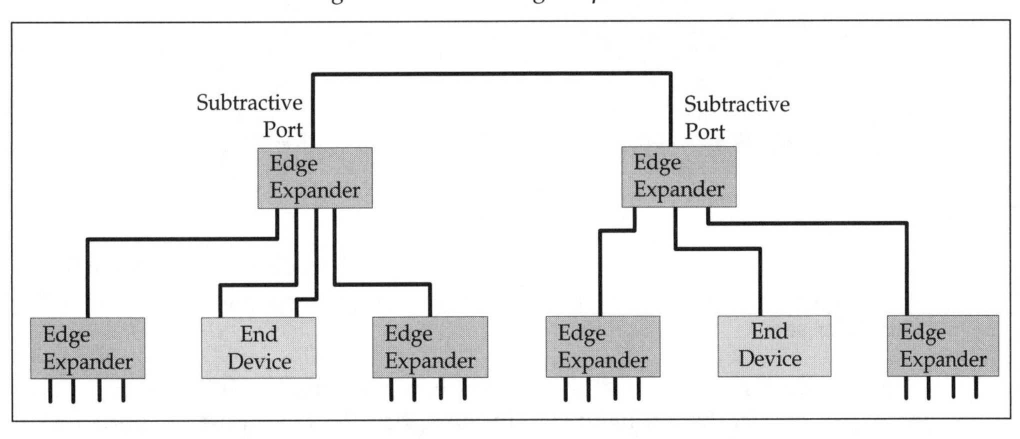

A practical example of the way this might be used is shown in Figure A-14, in which a rack of dual-ported drives has been connected to leave the subtractive port available to attach another edge expander set into the network as needed.

Figure A-14: Practical Edge Expander Example

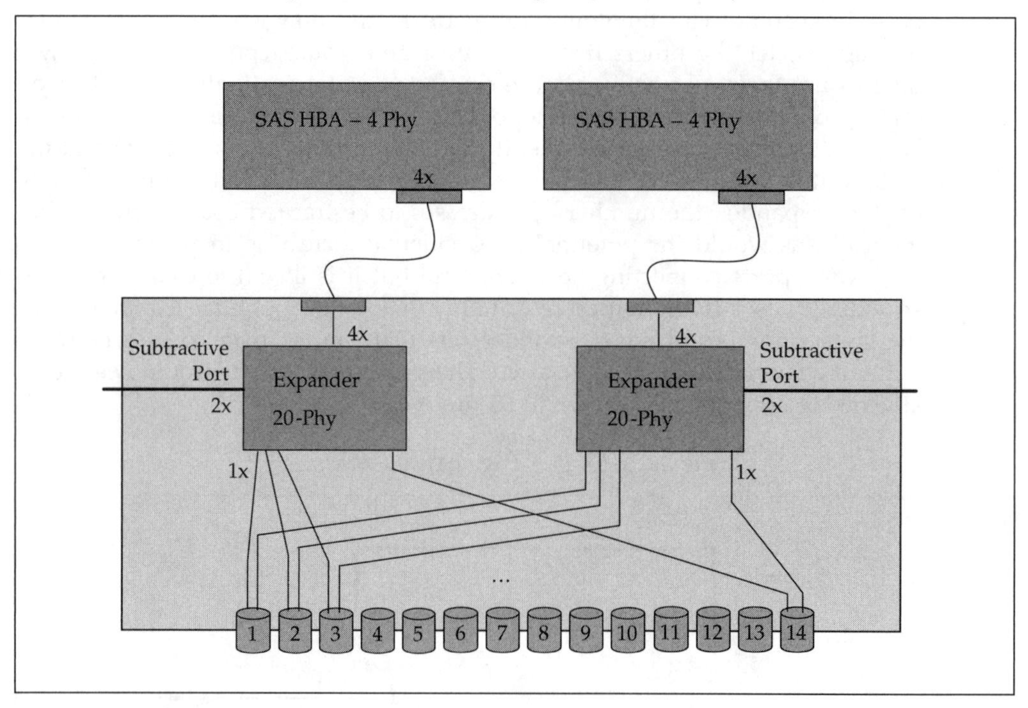

Toward the goal of keeping the system simple and inexpensive, a SAS network is only allowed to have one fanout expander and does not allow cascading edge expander sets.

For ease of reference, Figure A-15 repeats here the diagram showing the parts of an expander. On the left-hand side in the figure, the three possible ports for an expander are shown: External SAS expander port, Internal SAS port, and external SATA host port.

Figure A-15: Expander Details

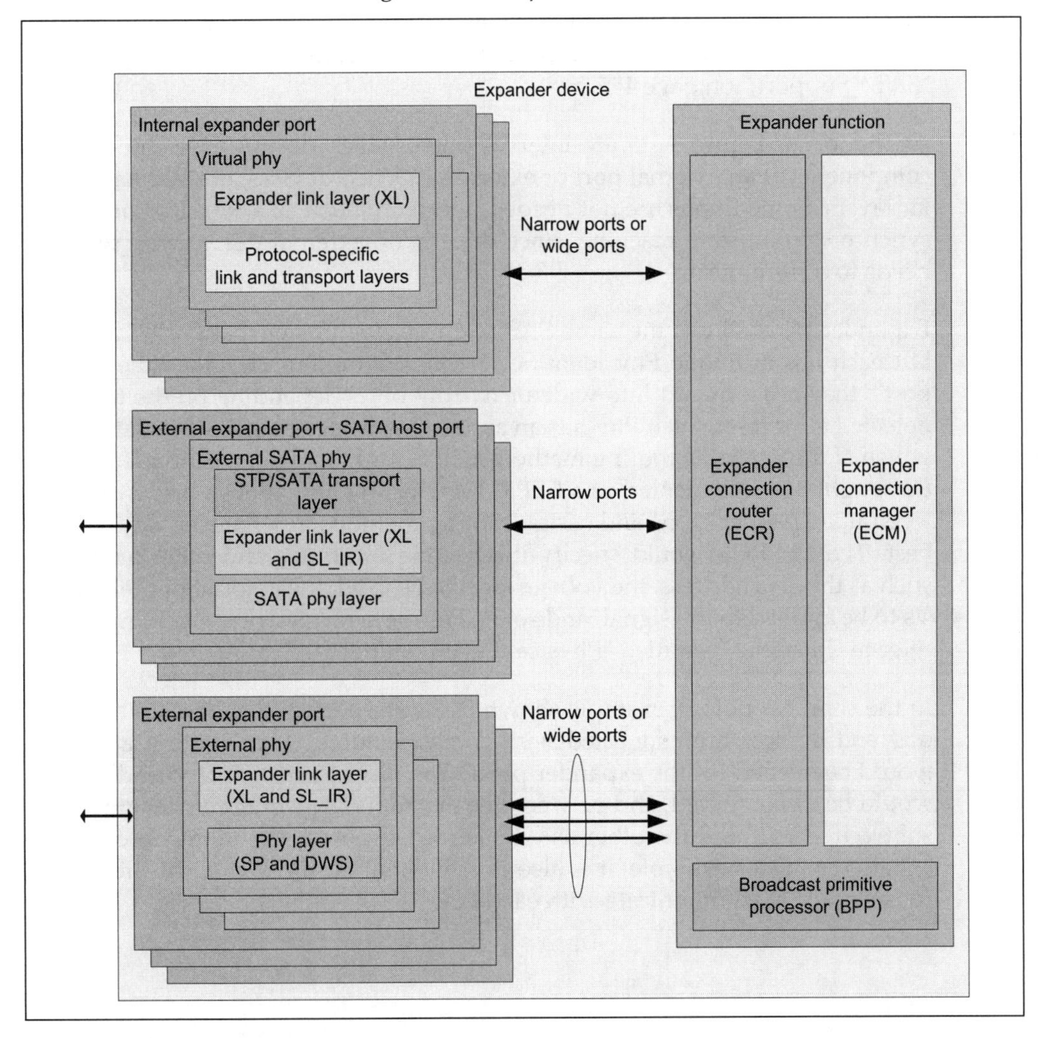

A SAS port may have several phys and be a wide port. The Link Layer includes an Expander Link Layer state machine (XL), and a SAS Link Identification and Reset state machine (SL_IR). The Phy Layer contains SAS Phy (SP) and DWord Synchronization (DWS) state machines. Those state machines and the protocol details are covered in "State Machines" on page 354.

Ports that are capable of acting as SATA ports must contain a bridge function to translate the STP protocol used internally by the expander into the SATA protocol used externally. This bridge function is represented in the diagram by the STP/SATA Transport Layer block. An expander Link Layer is also included, as is a SATA Phy Layer. The protocol details are covered in Chapter 19, entitled "SATA Support," on page 455.

At the top of Figure A-15 are internal ports, which do not have the physical components of an external port or external attached devices, but still have similar layers. Some things are not needed internally, such as a SAS Phy or Dword synchronization state machine, since there is no external device with which it needs to communicate.

Expander phys all use the same SAS address, even for virtual ports internally, but each has a unique Phy identifier for internal reference. Like other device ports, they are grouped into wide or narrow ports depending on the topology detected after reset. Each Phy has an assigned routing attribute that determines which of the available routing methods will be used for it. As mentioned earlier, this might be implemented as a EEPROM which would allow a board designer to group expander chips and assign routing methods in whatever way seemed best. The EEPROM could specify the routing attributes and other attributes, such as the SAS address, the voltage level to be used, the amount of pre-emphasis to be applied to the signal, and so on. For more on electrical signaling topics, refer to Chapter 17, entitled "Physical Layer," on page 411.

In the simple topology example shown in Figure A-16 on page 539, where several end devices are connected with two expanders, what routing attributes would be needed for the expander phys? The phys that connect to end devices would be direct routed, and between the expanders one might be assigned as a subtractive port and the other as a table-routed port. Since there are only two expanders in this example, it is also possible that both could use a subtractive routing port to communicate with each other.

Figure A-16: Simple Expander Topology

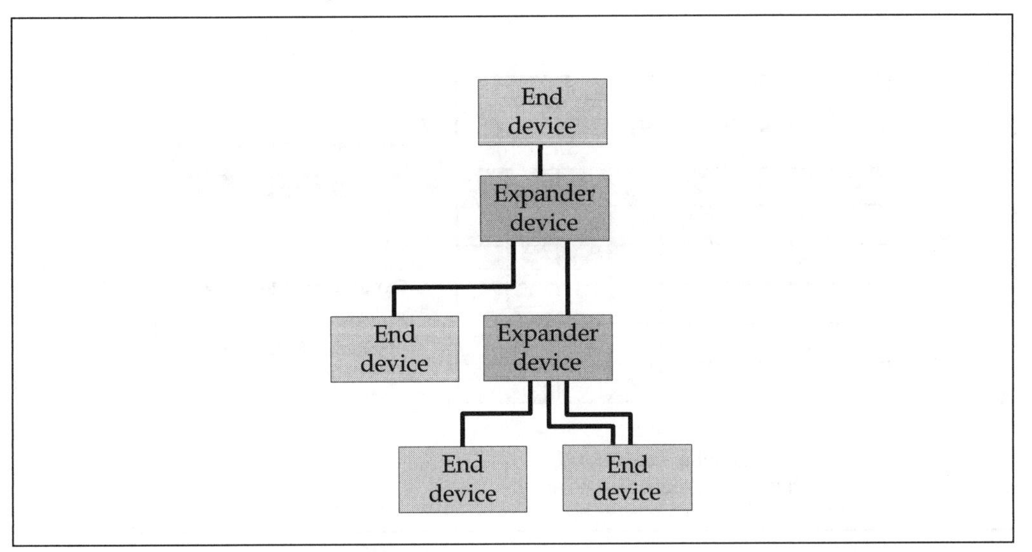

Phys that use the table-routed scheme must implement memory for storing this information. Designers have the freedom to do this in whatever way seems best, but the information must be visible to the system as a two-dimensional array with the format shown in Figure A-17 on page 540, where the columns are the Phy identifier in the device and the rows, or route indexes, represent the number of addresses visible to that phy. For each table entry, the SAS address is stored, as is a bit to indicate whether this entry is enabled or disabled. Possible implementations include a fixed two-dimensional array, which is simplest, but possibly inefficient since some phys may not need table entries. Another option would be a one-dimensional array that stores address and phy/index information, which would be more complex, but probably more efficient and flexible. Similarly, if the table were implemented as an "address-to-port" lookup, that would potentially give better performance if the table was large.

Figure A-17: Routing Table

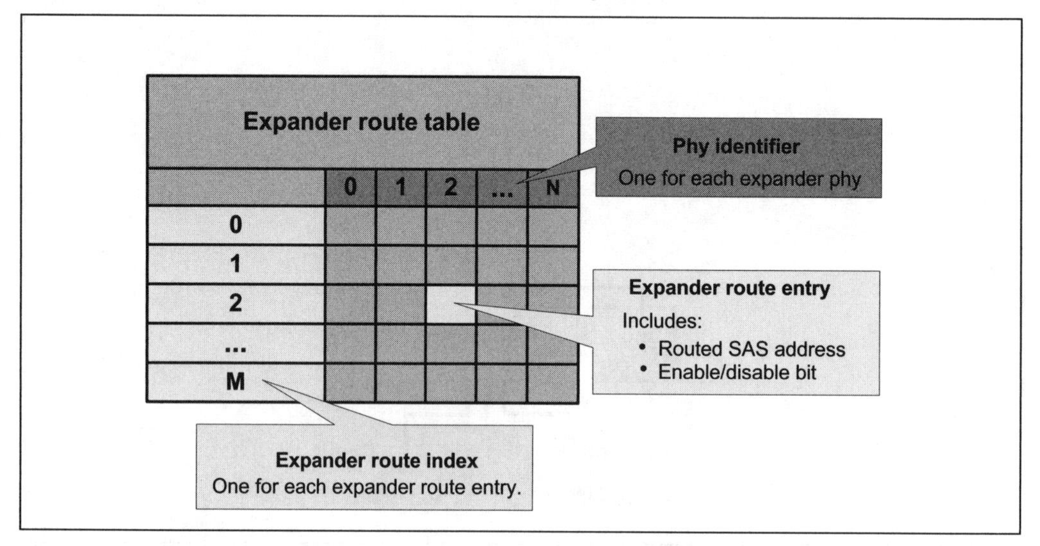

Consider the simple topology shown in Figure A-18. The several steps involved in finding all the addresses in the system and filling in the routing table are collectively referred to as the Discovery process, and details about it can be found in Chapter 7, entitled "Discovery Process," on page 159. As an introduction, the process is briefly summarized here.

As a starting point, as part of the link reset sequence, every SAS device communicates its SAS address, device type, protocols supported, and Phy identifier to its attached neighbors. This is done by sending an IDENTIFY address frame from each Phy and gives expanders all the information they need about the attached devices, but not about devices that are connected through another expander. Those addresses will need to be discovered and stored in the routing table, and this can be done by the expander on its own if it is self-configuring. Otherwise, the initiators in the system will have to program the table for it. For this very simple topology the expanders could simply be connected to each other with subtractive ports and then there would be no need for table routing at all but, for discussion, assume device "V" will use table routing.

Since there are three phys in the device, and we will arbitrarily limit the number of indexes to three as well, the resulting table will have a software-visible format as shown in Table A-13 on page 541.

Figure A-18: Discovery Process Example

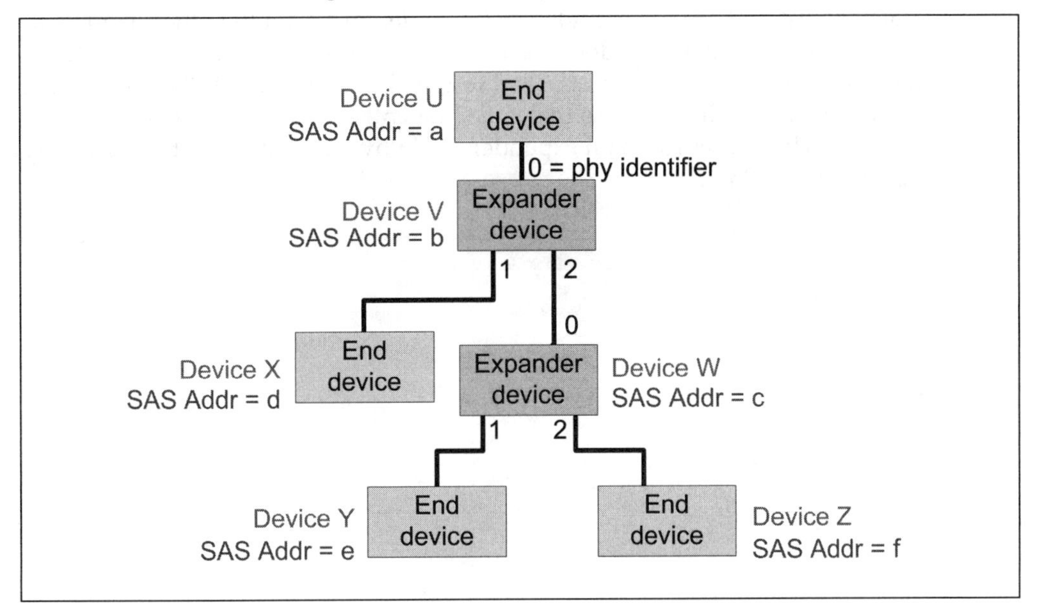

Table A-13: Expander Device "V" Routing Table

Index	Phy 0	Phy 1	Phy 2
0			b
1			e
2			f

At least one of the end devices in the system will be an initiator, so let's assume device "U" will take that role and will begin the discovery process by doing an SMP read of the attached addresses in expander "V". The results will show that there are 3 phys, and that Phy 2 has an expander device that uses address "c" attached to it, so the next step will be to do the SMP reads of the expander at address "c". Again reading each Phy of that expander, the initiator can see that they are attached to address "b" on Phy 0, "e" on Phy 1, and "f" on Phy 2. The table for expander "V" will be programmed with this information in the order in which it was discovered. As shown in Table A-13 on page 541, there are no address table entries for phys 0 and 1, and the reason is that those phys have directly attached devices. Those addresses are stored in a separate "direct attached" list and are not included in the table. Phy 2, on the other hand, connects to an expander and does have indirect addresses that will need to be tracked. Reading the address attached to Phy 0 of expander "W" indicates that it is attached to address "b", so that's the first entry in the table of expander "V" for Phy 2. The address seen on expander "W" Phy 1 would be next, followed by the address on Phy 2.

Appendix B

SAS Test, Debug & Verification

Challenges, Issues and Hints

by Chuck Trefts, Sr. Marketing Manager at Catalyst Enterprises

Scope

After more than two decades as the predominant server storage interface, legacy Small Computer System Interface (SCSI) standards are reaching the limits of their capabilities. While SCSI Ultra320 achieves an impressive burst transfer rate of 320MB/s, making performance improvements to this parallel bus technology for future demands presents such massive technical and economical barriers that it has become impractical to pursue. Consequently, SCSI is instead making the same transition that many other parallel designs have made, moving from a relatively slow parallel design to a faster serial architecture. Serial Attached SCSI (SAS) is well-positioned to more than meet the modern demands for SCSI in terms of compatibility with other storage technologies, substantially increased performance, clear and achievable roadmaps to future generation speeds, and greatly increased drive addressability features.

There are several areas where SAS development, test, and validation differ radically from those of its parallel predecessor. These differences create new and unique challenges that developers need to consider carefully when entering into this new technology, and these issues are covered in this section.

Serial Bus Topology

When working with parallel buses, designers had to consider the usual inherent pitfalls such as bus termination, crosstalk across wide ribbon cables, signal skew, clock skew and distribution, and the unpleasant reality of trying to route large parallel cables in dense physical environments. A serial environment inherently solves many of these problems, but presents new challenges of its own. The designer is now faced with a much higher speed serial bus using point-to-point interfaces, fabric-like topologies, increased addressability, one or more full duplex links (wide port), multi-ported drives, and complex multi-layer protocol requirements.

Unlike parallel buses, the information content of serial buses cannot easily be recognized by simply monitoring the individual control signals. A more complex process is required for the following reasons:

1. Data is transferred one bit at a time in a differential pair format, sometimes over multiple links. Information on a serial bus, including the clock, addressing, individual bytes, words, packets, commands, etc., are embedded in a serialized sequence rather than on individual, dedicated lines.

2. The bus idle state on a serial bus, generally speaking, cannot simply be quiet, since serial buses require transmission activity on the wire in order to keep the receiver's clock recovery circuit active and enabled. In order to support the transitions necessary to maintain a receiver's lock on an incoming bit stream, encoding and scrambling techniques are employed, which are used to prevent long-running sequences of ones or zeroes.

3. On a parallel bus, commands and other events are typically presented in their entirety during a single clock cycle. On a serial bus, information must be collected bit by bit, and assembled into information structures on the fly.

4. Serial protocols are highly structured into various architectural layers, as opposed to their more monolithic parallel predecessors. Such multi-layer information structures require specific interpretation and present new and complex challenges to the developer.

Figure B-1 illustrates a scope capture of one side of a differential 3Gb/s serial data bus. While the various signal-specific lines of a parallel bus can be monitored on a logic analyzer or scope to easily determine information content such as commands or responses, this is nearly impossible and highly impractical on a high-speed serial bus.

Figure B-1: High-Speed View of a 3Gb/s Serial Stream

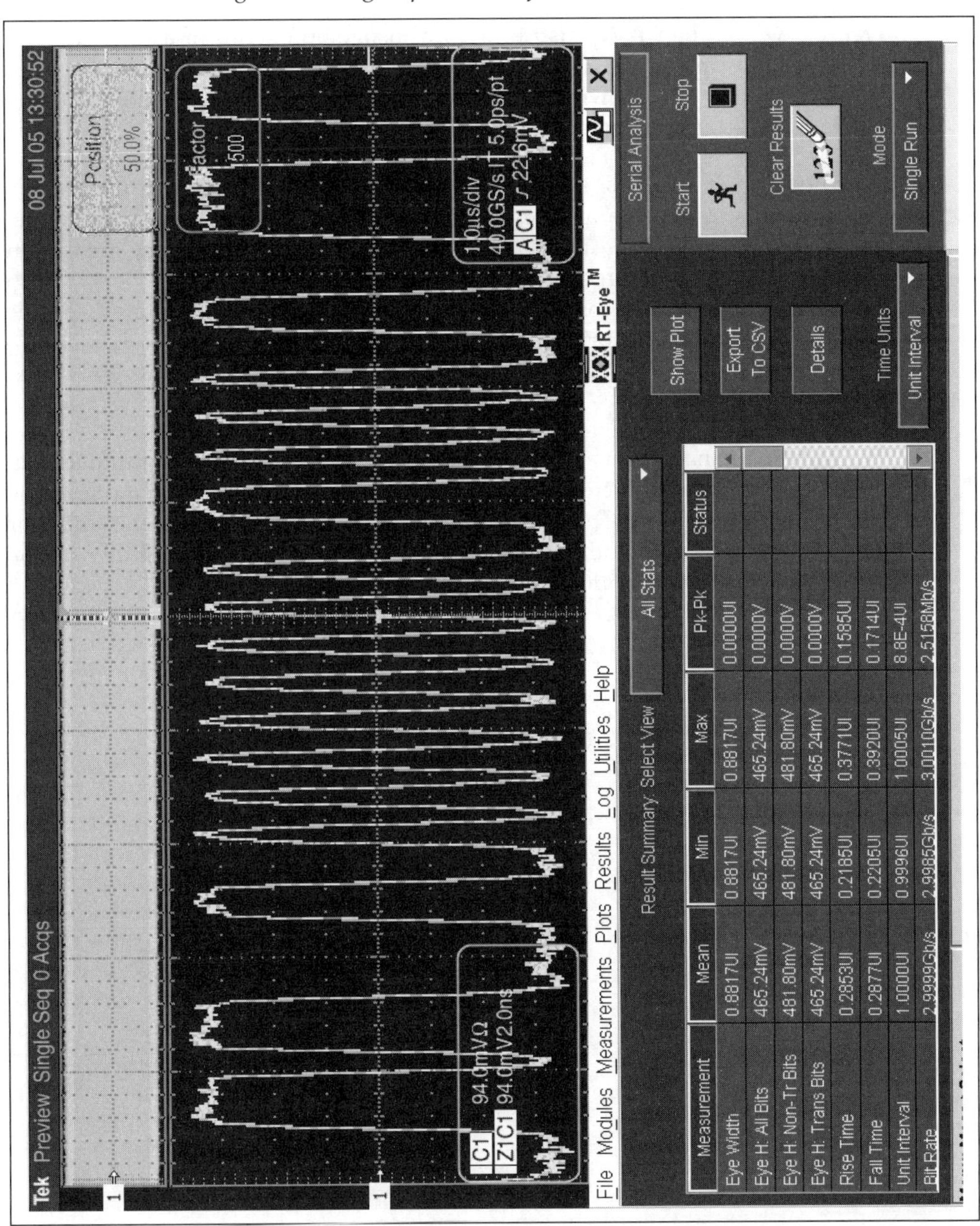

Using a Protocol Analyzer/Exerciser

Figures A-2 through A-6 illustrate typical usage and setup of a protocol analyzer in capturing traffic on a SAS link. To review complete menus, features, and sample captures, download Catalyst's SAS Analyzer application software from www.getcatalyst.com.

A protocol analyzer is a specialized tool used by developers to capture and display data bus traffic for purposes of validating, characterizing, and debugging hardware and software. An associated protocol exerciser function, such as an initiator emulator or a target emulator, may also be used in conjunction with an analyzer to force certain conditions on the bus, such as high data rates, specific commands, frames, and primitives, or error conditions in order to characterize the behavior of a device, such as an expander, initiator, target, or its associated software.

Typically, an analyzer is passively inserted between two communicating devices, whereas a protocol exerciser (emulator) assumes the role of one of the communicating devices. The analyzer function remains in place as the emulator communicates with the other device, thus providing the user visibility on the activities of the device under test as well as the emulator.

Figure B-2: PCI Express serial bit stream

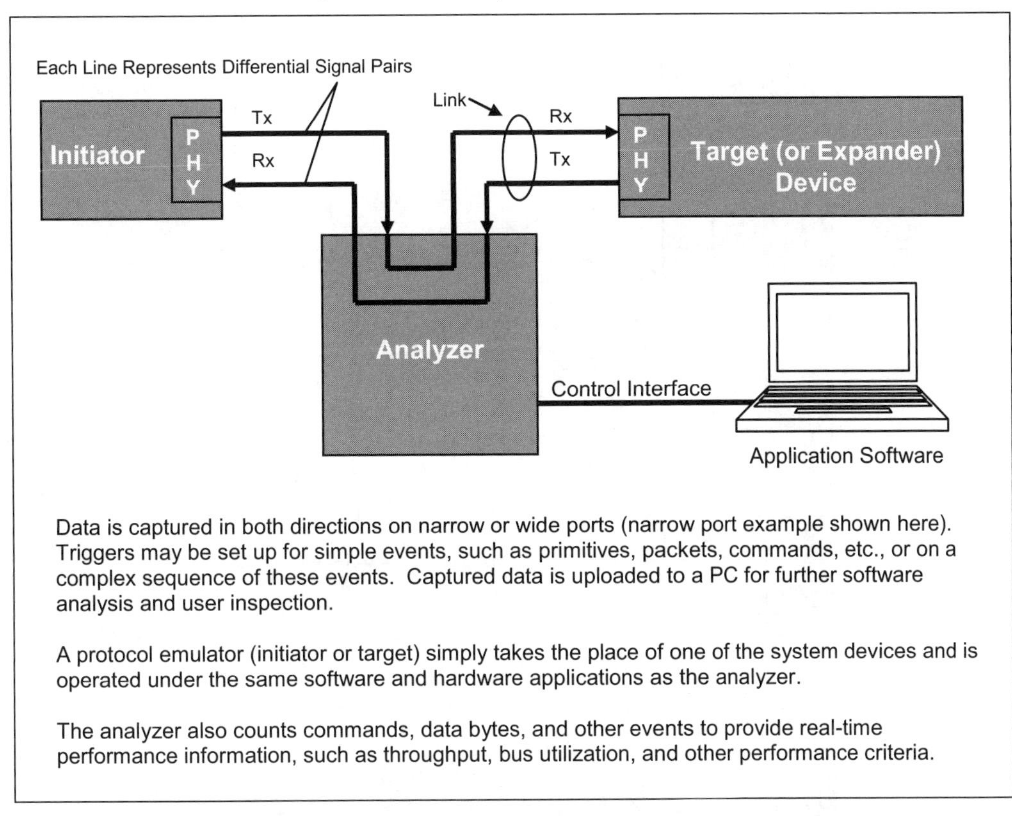

Figure B-3 on the following page provides an example of the capture (pre-filter) portion of a protocol analyzer capture/trigger project. The user may select specified items for inclusion or exclusion to/from the capture. Often, certain primitives that are highly prevalent in normal bus traffic are excluded from the capture. In some cases, a user may elect to specify a "Pattern" condition, whereby only selected bus events — SCSI commands, for example — are captured.

Figure B-3: Basic Setup to Define Capture Conditions

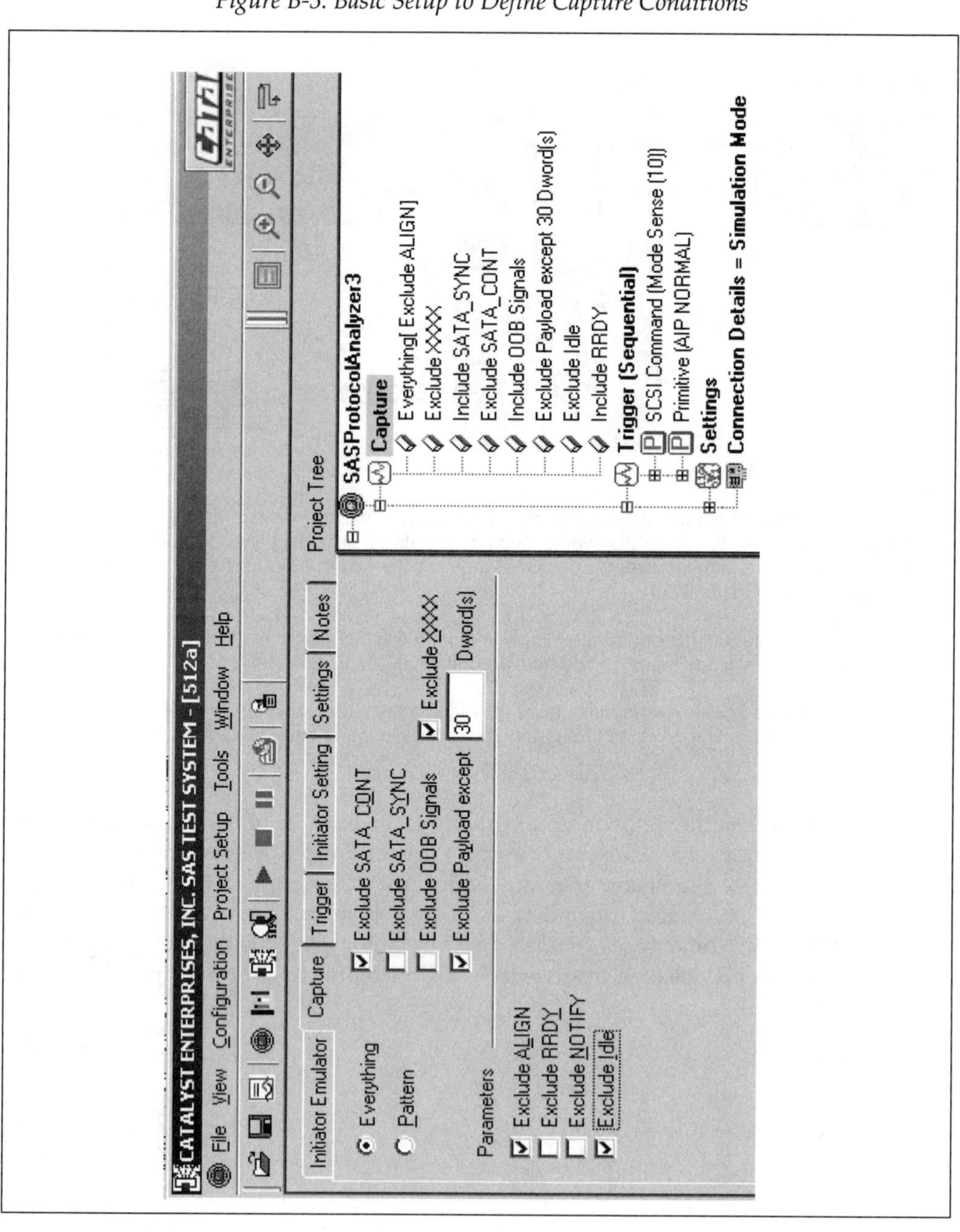

Typically, engineers working at application or device driver levels prefer to capture only command-layer traffic and exclude everything else. Engineers working at the hardware level tend to prefer captures that show all activity, especially physical and Link Layer events.

In Figure B-4, the user is provided with various terms to use for triggering. A trigger event essentially stops the continual capture process, allowing the user to "trap" desired conditions, errors, events, or commands. Available trigger terms consist of bus conditions, such as OOB events, protocol error conditions, STP/SSP/SMP frames, SCSI commands, SATA commands, K/D characters, data patterns, and address frames. The user may select one or more of these terms to be installed as trigger points, either in an OR fashion (any one of the selected terms will cause a trigger) or in a sequential fashion (each select term must occur, in order, for the trigger to occur).

Figure B-4: Basic Setup to Define Trigger Conditions

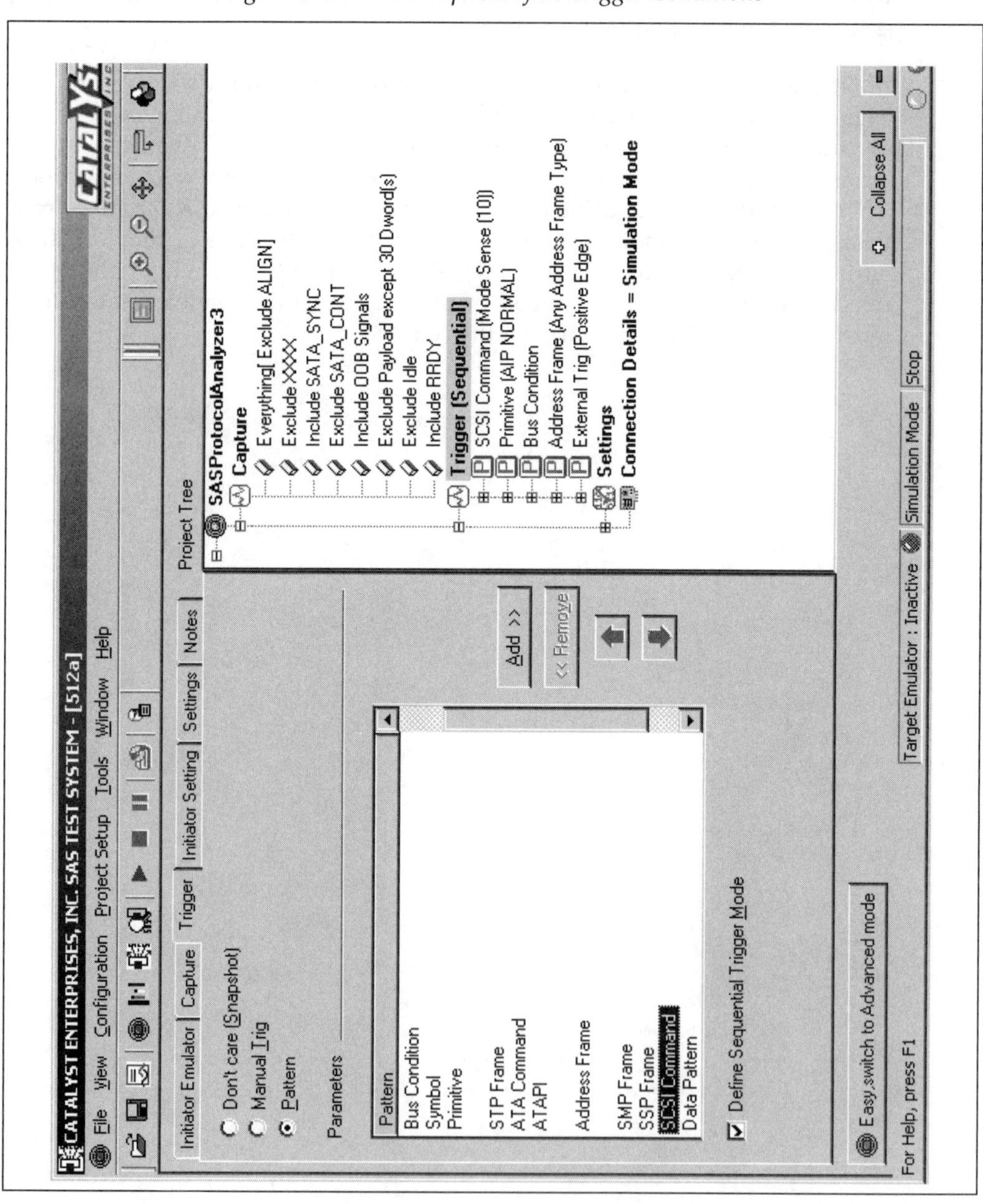

In certain cases, a simple sequential trigger or multi-term OR-type trigger is not sufficient to trigger on complex bus events, timeout conditions, sequences, or error conditions. An advanced trigger/capture mode (see Figure B-5 below) can be used to create complex logical structures (states) that provide for conditional triggering and filtering. This mode, which employs counters, timers, jump paths, and state-by-state filtering, is especially useful when trying to trigger on time relationships between specified events, or when trying to isolate complex bus conditions that may be conditionally based on other events.

Figure B-5: Using an Advanced Mode Capture/Trigger Sequencer

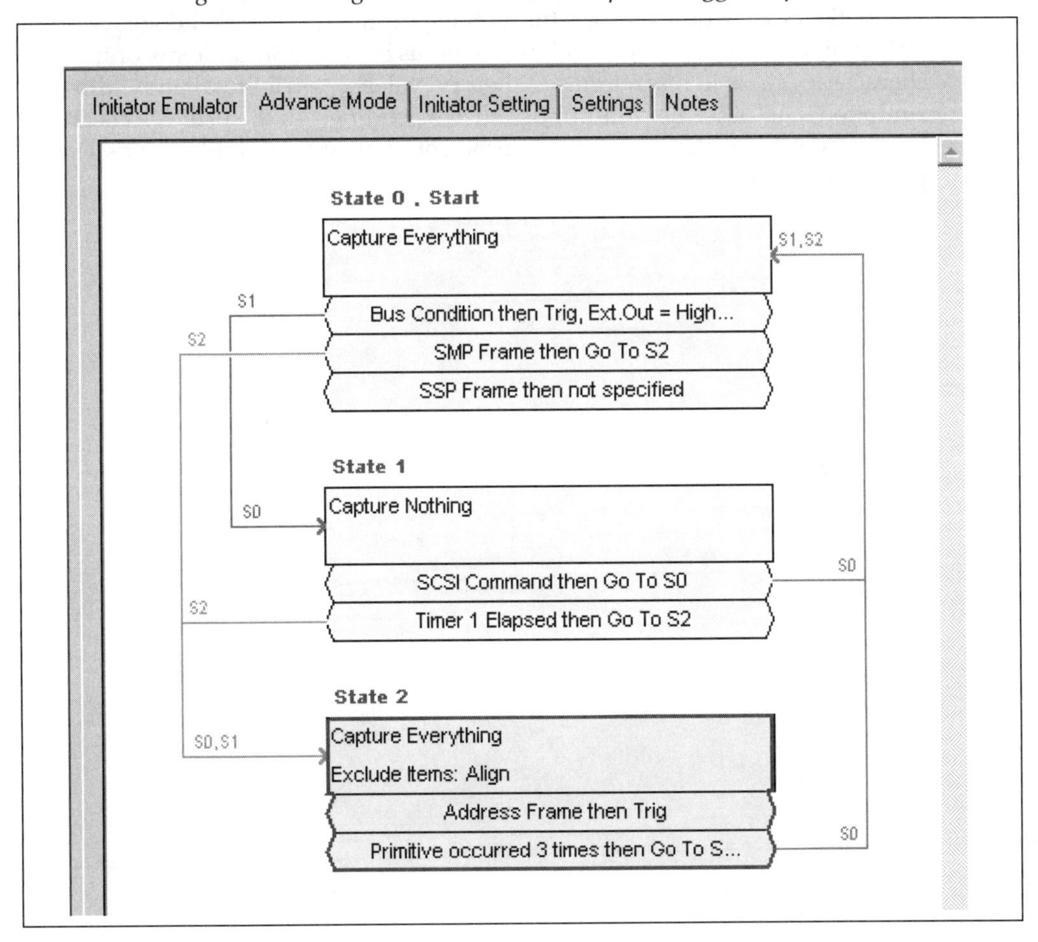

Once bus traffic is captured and displayed to the user, the next challenge is to sort through the mass of information presented. Typical SAS captures include various types of traffic, including 10b and word-level displays, OOB sequences, and progressing up the protocol stack to primitives, Link Layer activities, multi-protocol Transport Layer frame types, SCSI commands, SATA commands, management commands, and more. Note that the capture display in Figure B-6 reflects a post-capture filter selection that excludes all but SCSI command-level activity.

The user is provided various post-capture tools in an effort to find or view only what is of interest, such as search and filter mechanisms, but a statistics reports, such as shown in Figure B-6, can go a long way in reducing the time an engineer spends sifting and searching through the multitudes of captured information. The statistics view quickly sorts through the captured traffic and displays a logical breakdown of this traffic, allowing the user to zero in on items of interest, characterize these items in terms of their prevalence, attributes, bandwidth consumption, and other helpful utilities such as sorting. As the user selects any of the items in the statistics view, the protocol view automatically jumps to that point in the capture.

Figure B-6: Statistics Report on Captured Traffic

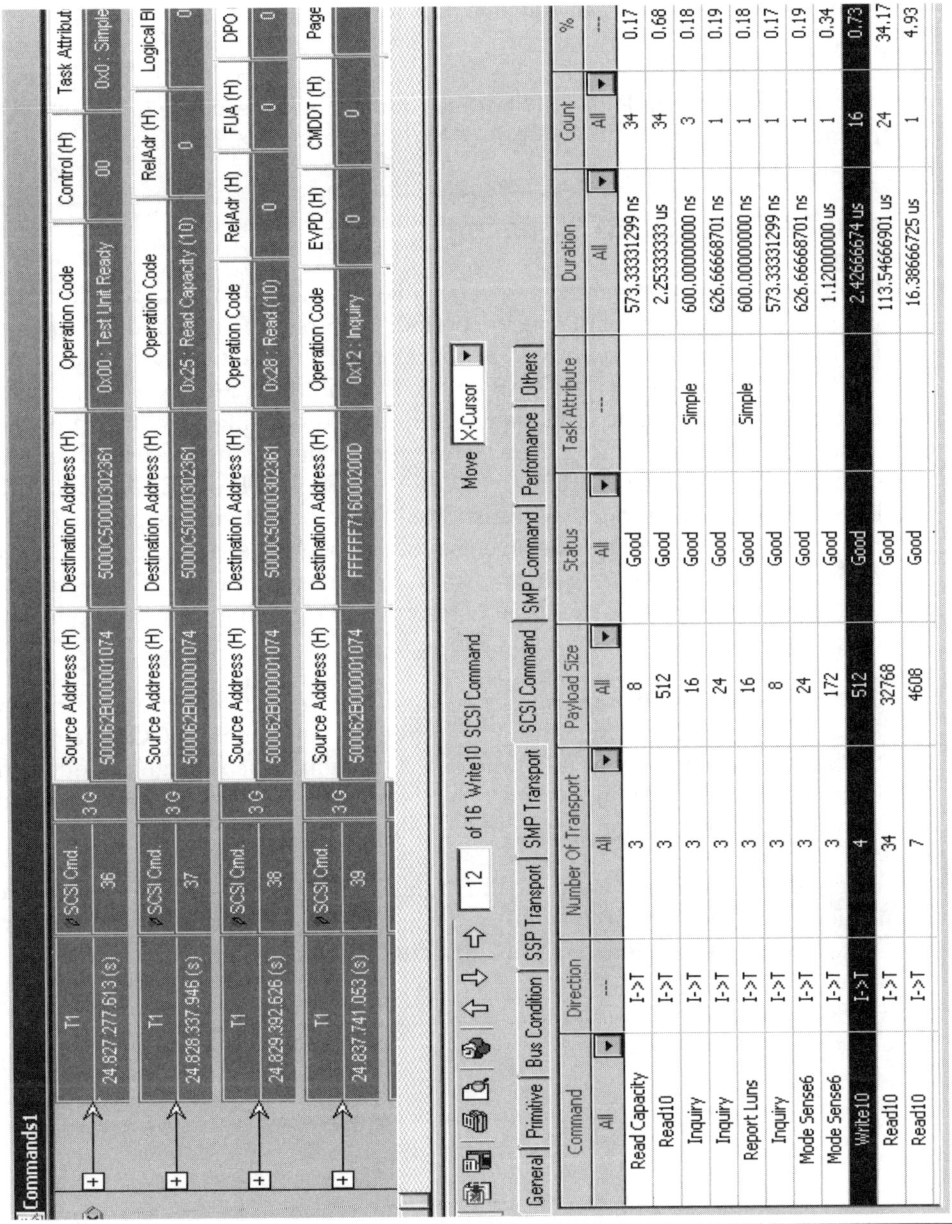

Commands1

T1	SCSI Cmd.		Source Address (H)	Destination Address (H)	Operation Code
24.827.277.613 (s)	36	3 G	500062B000001074	5000C50000302361	0x00 : Test Unit Ready
24.828.337.946 (s)	37	3 G	500062B000001074	5000C50000302361	0x25 : Read Capacity (10)
24.829.392.626 (s)	38	3 G	500062B000001074	5000C50000302361	0x28 : Read (10)
24.837.741.053 (s)	39	3 G	500062B000001074	FFFFFF716000200D	0x12 : Inquiry

12 of 16 Write10 SCSI Command — Move X-Cursor

General | Primitive | Bus Condition | SSP Transport | SMP Transport | SCSI Command | SMP Command | Performance | Others

Command	Direction	Number Of Transport	Payload Size	Status	Task Attribute	Duration	Count	%
All	---	All	All	All	---	All	All	---
Read Capacity	I->T	3	8	Good		573.33331299 ns	34	0.17
Read10	I->T	3	512	Good		2.25333333 us	34	0.68
Inquiry	I->T	3	16	Good	Simple	600.00000000 ns	3	0.18
Inquiry	I->T	3	24	Good		626.66668701 ns	1	0.19
Report Luns	I->T	3	16	Good	Simple	600.00000000 ns	1	0.18
Inquiry	I->T	3	8	Good		573.33331299 ns	1	0.17
Mode Sense6	I->T	3	24	Good		626.66668701 ns	1	0.19
Mode Sense6	I->T	3	172	Good		1.12000000 us	1	0.34
Write10	I->T	4	512	Good		2.42666674 us	16	0.73
Read10	I->T	34	32768	Good		113.54666901 us	24	34.17
Read10	I->T	7	4608	Good		16.38666725 us	1	4.93

The SAS PHY, Connections, and Identification

When two SAS devices are first connected, various initialization processes must take place before they can reliably transmit and receive information. A reset sequence occurs after initial power-on, loss of Dword synchronization, after a drive is inserted into an active system, on receipt of a HARD_RESET primitive sequence prior to an IDENTIFY address frame, and in response to various other events. This sequence involves out-of-band signaling (OOB) and a speed negotiation process.

Out-Of-Band (OOB) Signaling

OOB signals are relatively low-speed patterns which do not appear in normal data streams and consist of specific periods of burst time (on) and DC idle time (off). These signals are used by a SAS PHY to determine whether the device on the other side of the link is a SAS device (it could be a SATA device), whether that device is trying to establish a link, and other internal PHY processes, including an internal amplitude and frequency calibration. SAS uses three OOB signals: COMINIT/COMRESET, COMSAS, and COMWAKE. An individual burst consists of continuously transmitted Align primitives. A single OOB signal consists of six burst/idle events, followed by a signal-specific negation period, where DC idle is again transmitted. The length of the DC idle between each burst distinguishes the three types of OOB signaling from each other (the burst duration is the same for all OOB signals).

Testing challenges here are numerous, and may include verification or debug tasks relating to correct signal timing, a receiver's handling of OOB recognition timeouts, receiver burst or idle time detection requirements, signal sequencing, improper handling of supported or non-supported OOB burst rate transmissions, PHY state machine errors, and amplitude marginalities.

Figure B-7 on the following page illustrates successive COMRESET signals (collections of 6 bursts each) as well as the associated COMRESET negation time. Note the pass/fail criteria assigned to a cursor-set measurement of the negation time.

Figure B-7: Scope Capture Showing COMRESET and Negation Time Measurement

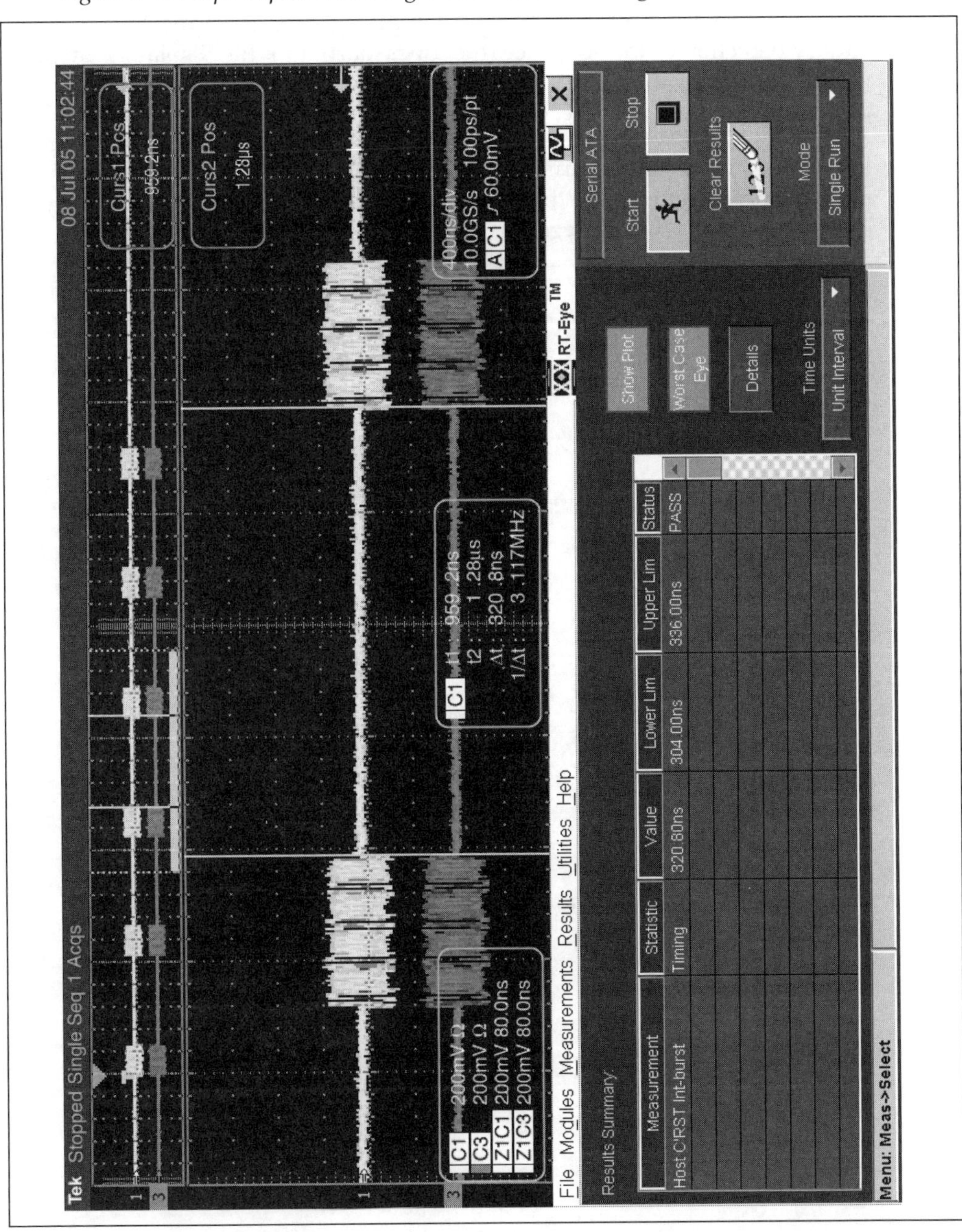

In Figure B-8, a protocol analyzer detects and displays an OOB sequence, showing the duration of bursts, DC idles, and negation times, and displaying these in unit intervals (OOBI). An initiator transmits the COMINIT signal, followed by an exchange of COMSAS signals between the initiator and a disk drive. A secondary depiction of the sequence (the lower portion of the display) provides a graphical view of the timing relationships between the different OOB signals, negation times, and within each individual signal.

Difficulties encountered during the OOB sequence, such as failure to complete the sequence or out-of-spec timing criteria, are easily understood and analyzed by setting the protocol analyzer to trigger upon detection of this sequence.

Figure B-8: Signal Exchange between an Initiator and a Disk Drive

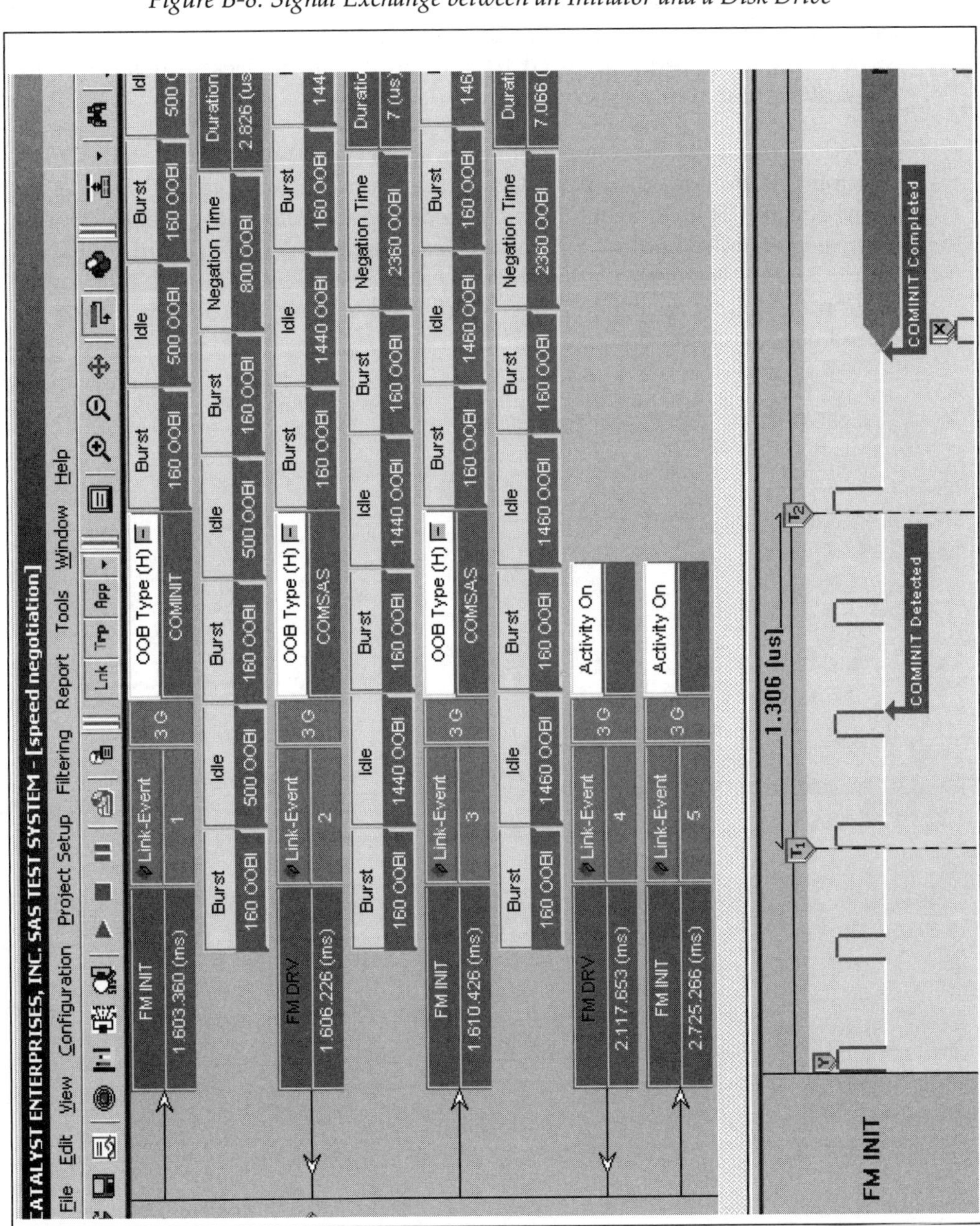

Speed Negotiation

SAS devices may support more than one link speed. The speed negotiation process, beginning at the end of the OOB sequence, uses speed negotiation windows for each speed supported by the individual devices to determine the highest supported rate common to both devices.

Speed negotiation is purely peer-to-peer and assumes no initiator/target roles. During this process, SAS devices progress from attempts to negotiate at the Gen1 speed (1.5Gb/s) to any higher speeds supported by either device. During each negotiation window, a successful exchange of ALIGN(0) and ALIGN(1) primitives between negotiating devices establishes a common link rate. Figure B-9 on the following page depicts a primitive exchange sequence during the speed negotiation sequence.

Figure B-9: Primitive Exchange During Speed Negotiation

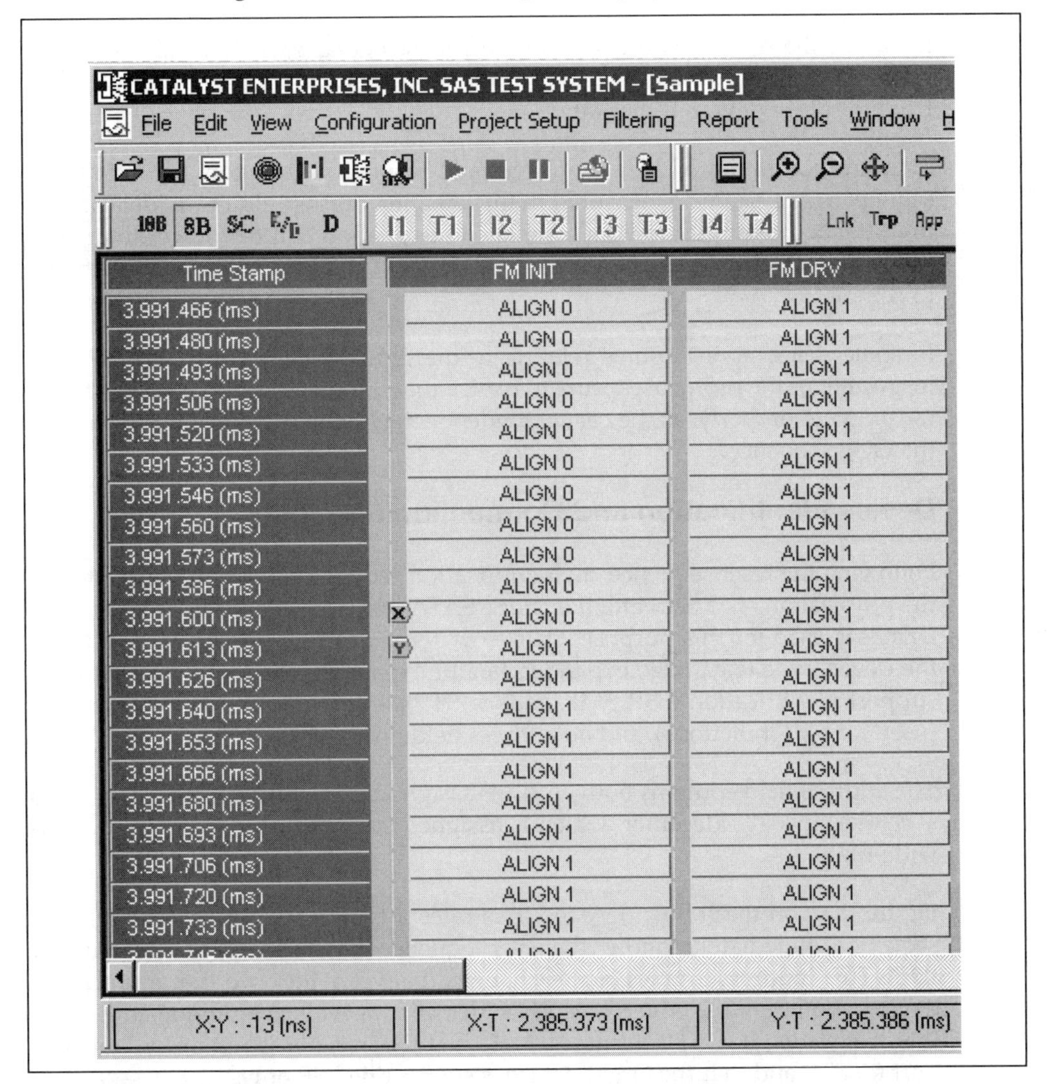

In the primitive exchange shown in Figure B-9, ALIGN(1) primitives from a SAS disk drive are being sent to an Initiator. This represents a small portion of one speed negotiation window. The line rate is 3Gb/s, as evidenced by the Dword transmission rate time-stamping on the left. Note the X-Y cursor placements and associated X-Y Delta time information.

The Initiator, which had been sending ALIGN(0) primitives to the disk drive, begins to send a stream of ALIGN(1) primitives to indicate it has achieved synchronization with the primitives being sent from the disk drive.

If one of these devices did not support a particular rate, it would not send ALIGN primitives at that rate and would not respond to ALIGN primitives sent from the other device at that rate.

The duration of the ALIGN sequences and response (detection) times to these sequences can easily be measured in this manner. This would be an ideal area to investigate if two SAS devices completed negotiation at a rate lower than their highest commonly supported rate, or in the event that speed negotiation failed to complete.

In some cases, upon failures relating to the reset sequence, it may take close inspection of the protocol capture to realize that the speed negotiation has failed to complete properly, as the casual tendency may be to assume a problem with the OOB sequence.

Device Identification and Connection Requests

Following the reset sequence, an identification sequence is typically executed, if the physical link is a SAS link (i.e., not a SATA link). An exchange of IDENTIFY frames is used for this purpose. Data exchanged during this sequence includes the device type (e.g., edge expander, fanout expander, or end device), protocol support identification (SSP, SMP, and/or STP), a device-unique PHY identifier (used for SMP functions), and an address field.

The address field contains both an IEEE-assigned Company ID value as well as a Vendor Specific Identifier, which is assigned such that the address is world-wide-unique.

Figure B-10 on the following page illustrates a typical identify sequence. This sequence immediately follows the reset sequence (OOB and speed negotiation). IDENTIFY address frames are exchanged between the two communicating devices. Both devices advertise a PHY identifier as well as a unique address in their respective IDENTIFY frames. Note that the initiator is not providing support for STP and that the target device is supporting SSP only.

Issues with conflicts in protocol support, addressing, and other related issues are easily understood by using a protocol analyzer to trigger on an IDENTIFY frame.

Figure B-10: Identify Address Sequence

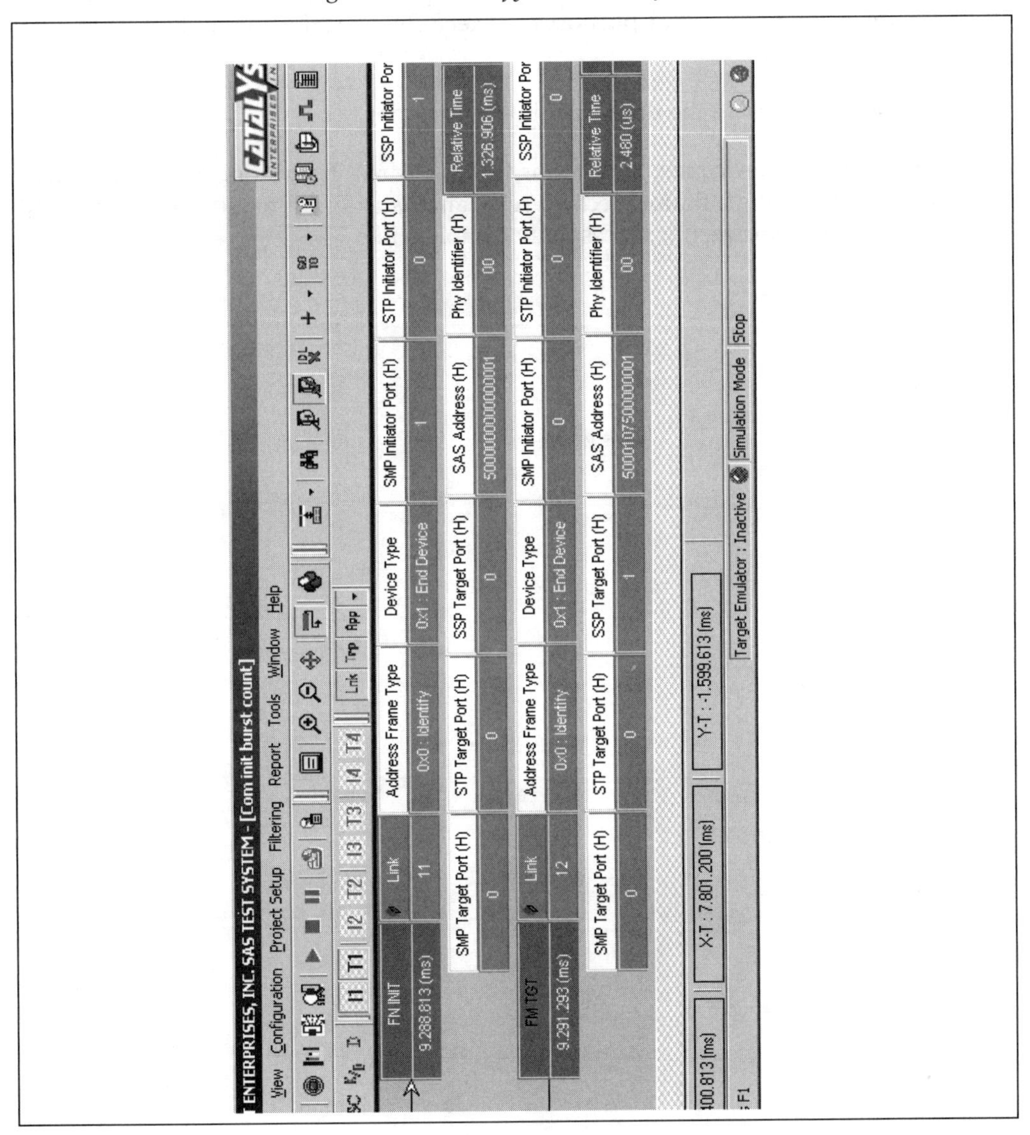

The sequence of frames and commands illustrated in Figure B-11 on page 563 represents a critical point, in that the devices have exchanged addressing information, port identification, and protocol capabilities, and an attempt was made to open a connection for purposes of executing a SCSI command (an INQUIRY in this case).

Areas of interest to the developer in this include:

- How the device responds to the OPEN address frame, or command request;
- Whether the initiator elects to retry an unsuccessful request or command if the device does not successfully complete it.

Figure B-11: Identification Sequence followed by OPEN Address Frame and SCSI Command

ATALYST ENTERPRISES, INC. SAS TEST SYSTEM - [Com init burst count]

ile Edit View Configuration Project Setup Filtering Report Tools Window Help

I1 T1 I2 T2 I3 T3 I4 T4 Lnk Trp App 10B 8B SC

FM TGT	Link	Address Frame Type	Device Type	SMP Initiator Port (H)	STP Initiator Port (H)	SSP Init
9.291 293 (ms)	12	0x0 : Identify	0x1 : End Device	0	0	

SMP Target Port (H)	STP Target Port (H)	SSP Target Port (H)	SAS Address (H)	Phy Identifier (H)	Link Data
0	0	1	5000107500000001	00	

Duration
133 (ns)

FM INIT	Link	Address Frame Type	Protocol	Initiator Port (H)	Connection Rate	Features (H)	Initiat
9.400 813 (ms)	13	0x1 : Open	0x1 : SSP	1	0x9 : 3.0 Gbps	0	

Destination SAS Address (H)	Source SAS Address (H)	Compatible Features (H)	Pathway Blocked Count (H)	Arbi
5000107500000001	5000000000000001	00	00	

More Compatible Features (H)	Link Data (H) +	Relative Time	Duration
00000000		109.520 (us)	133 (ns)

FM TGT	Link		Link Data (H) -	Relative Time	Duration
9.401 160 (ms)	14	3 G		346 (ns)	53 (ns)

Target	RD
OPEN ACCEPT	-+-+
R_RDY NORMAL (x3)	-+++

FM INIT	SCSI Cmd.		Source Address (H)	Destination Address (H)	Operation Code	EVPD (H)	CMDDT (H)
9.422 253 (ms)	1	3 G	5000000000000001	5000107500000001	0x12 : Inquiry	0	0

Allocation Length (D)	Control (H)	Task Attribute	Tag (H)	Status	Duration
0	00	0x0 : Simple	0000	0x00 : Good	413 (ns)

Notice that an OPEN_ACCEPT primitive is sent from the receiving device to the initiator, indicating that the request has been accepted. Instead of an OPEN_ACCEPT, it is quite possible that the initiator might receive various other responses or even no response at all. For example, if the receiving device is an expander, an arbitration-in-progress primitive (AIP) may be sent back to the initiator, to indicate that the expander is attempting to internally arbitrate for port access. In this event, the initiator must reset an internal timeout mechanism to provide the expander enough time to complete its arbitration. The ability of the initiator to properly execute its attempt to achieve a connection as well as the ability of the expander (or target device) to properly handle the connection request can be influenced by a variety of hardware or software issues and is a particularly complex and rules-driven area of the SAS protocol requirements.

A connection attempt might also be rejected by the destination port due to an unsupported rate, which might indicate issues with the earlier speed negotiation sequence (reset sequence) or the characteristics of the OPEN frame itself. A connection request might be aborted for a number of reasons, some legal, some not, including the failure of the receiving Phy to provide a connection response within a specific timeout period. Using a protocol analyzer to zero in on such problematic areas can quickly identify root causes.

SAS Initiator and Target Emulation: In-Depth Verification

An important component to characterization of SAS hardware and software design is the ability to fully emulate a system device for purposes of testing and characterizing the link partner device. A major challenge for developers is to validate that their design will operate properly under various adverse conditions that are either difficult or impossible to replicate with standard SAS devices.

For example, to fully test the behavior of an initiator or expander device, it is critical to the developer to be able to employ an emulated (and highly-controllable) target device. Conversely, an emulated initiator device can be used to test and characterize the behavior of a target or expander device. See Figure B-12 on the following page for a simplified view of an initiator emulator setup.

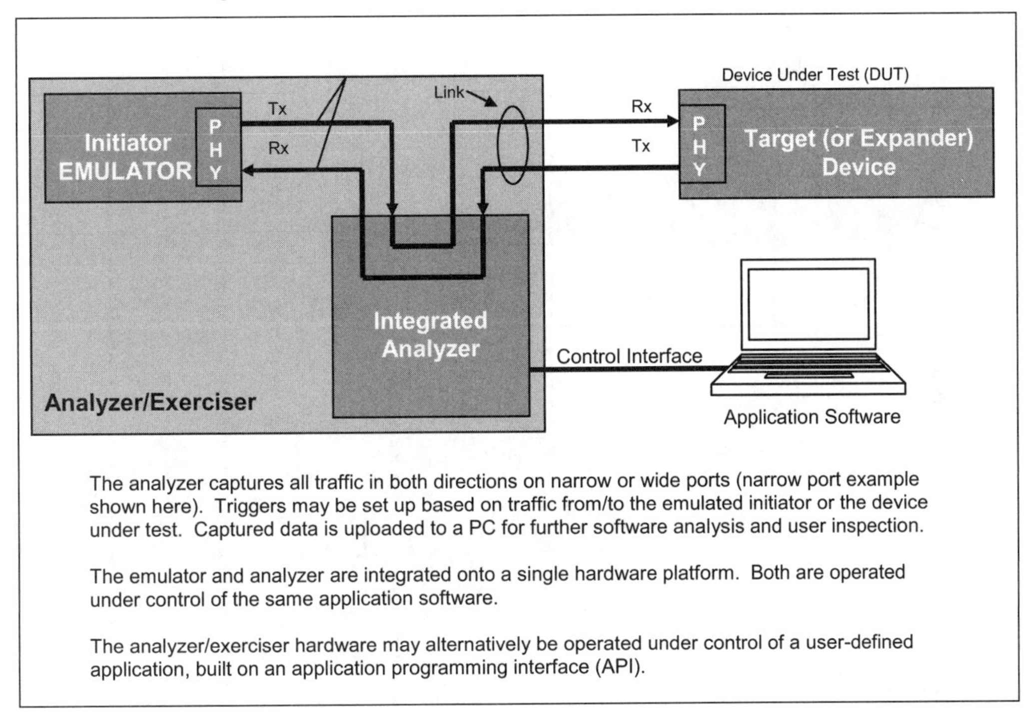

Figure B-12: Simplified Drawing of Initiator Emulator Setup

Routing the connections between the device under test (DUT) and the emulated device through an analyzer provides the user full visibility on bus traffic exchanged between the two devices. The ability to provide both compliant and non-compliant multi-layer stimuli and responses from the emulated device allows the developer to fully test the DUT's compliance to a wide spectrum of standard requirements.

While analyzer and emulator features can be operated through a GUI, many developers choose to access these features programmatically, by way of an application programming interface (API). An API approach allows the user to automate various testing under the control of a custom application built using the API. These applications are often used in production environments to confirm devices are operable and ready for shipping, but are also used often for regression testing and in compliance or interoperability validation labs. Figure B-13 on the following page illustrates various selections for disk drive emulation.

Figure B-13: Emulation Configured to Provide Error on Data Frame for Selected Commands

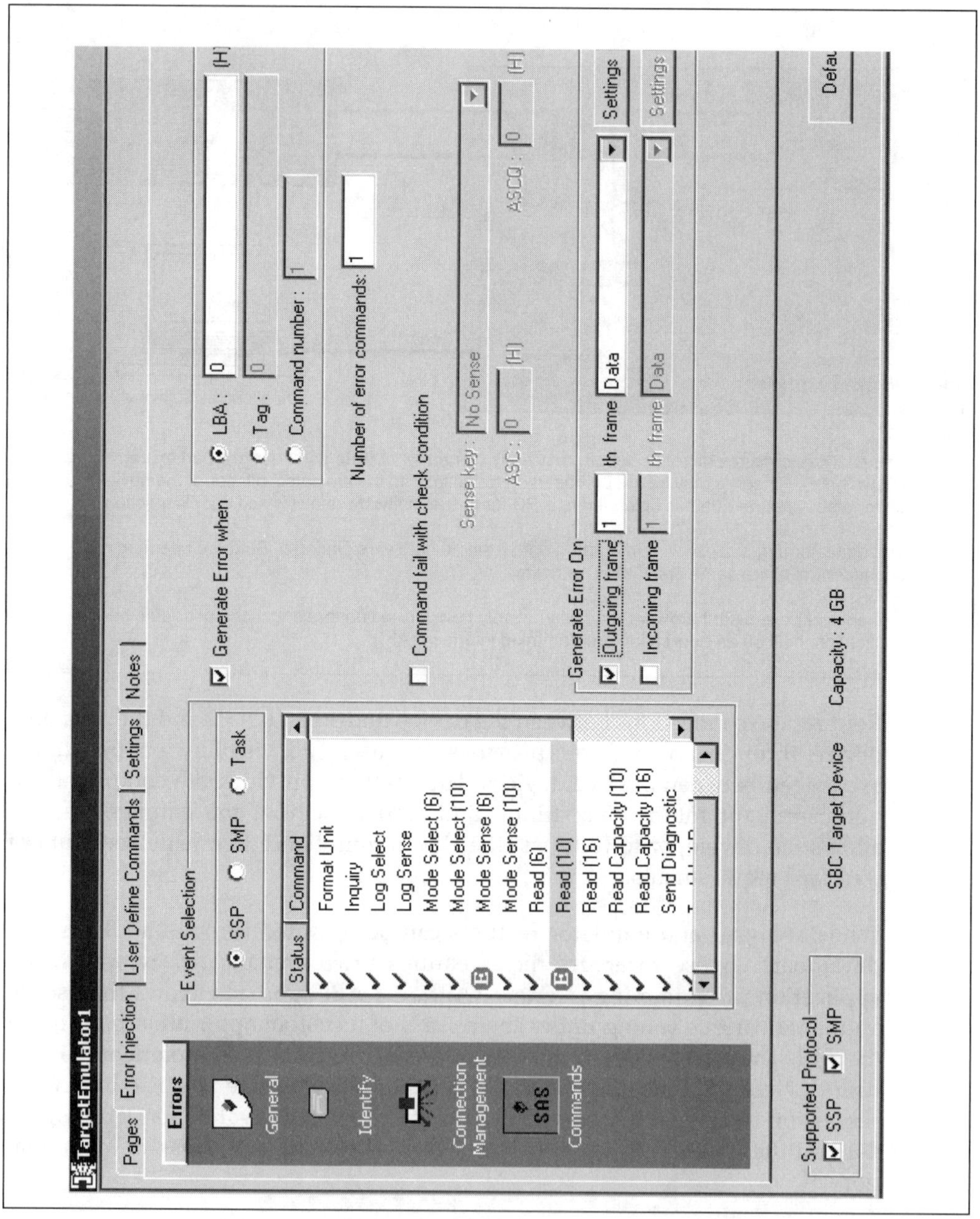

Appendix B: SAS Test, Debug & Verification

Signal Integrity, Design, and Measurement

Without proper hardware design and measurement practices, developers will have difficulty meeting compliance and interoperability requirements. At the frequencies used by SAS, various physical losses and anomalies impact the quality of the signal that passes through the physical media, which may include internal and external cables and connectors, printed circuit boards, and backplanes.

The developer needs to be aware of many hardware design requirements and test practices. Particular attention should be paid to signal routing, signal pair trace symmetry, bend control, PCB hole diameter, ground placement, jitter control, receiver sensitivity, and a host of other requirements. Consideration to extensive research on high-speed design guidelines and simulation by system modeling are strongly recommended.

Jitter Control

One of the more common signal integrity challenges is controlling jitter. Jitter involves the displacement of a signal event from its ideal arrival time and can be described as either deterministic or random. Deterministic jitter is considered a predictable component of total jitter, is bounded in amplitude, and typically comes from systemic sources such as duty cycle distortion, inter-symbol interference (data dependent), and crosstalk. All other jitter is considered random. Random jitter is theoretically unbounded in amplitude, and typically comes from sources such as thermal noise and shot noise.

The two jitter types are not considered to be correlated. Each jitter type typically has different causes and can be separated and characterized using proper test equipment. Excessive jitter can cause data recovery errors at the receiver and will degrade system performance by causing higher than acceptable bit error rates (BER).

As shown in Figure B-14 on page 568, an advanced high-speed scope captures and displays critical physical information, based on a sample from a SAS serial link. Various graphical analyses are displayed, including an eye diagram and a bathtub curve, which provides bit error rate information based on jitter computations. A time interval error (TIE) is determined for each of the recovered clock edges. The TIE represents the jitter in the acquired edges and can be used to determine the spectrum of the jitter in the sample, including a breakdown of various jitter components.

Figure B-14: Scope Measurements Showing, Eye Pattern, Jitter, and BER Information

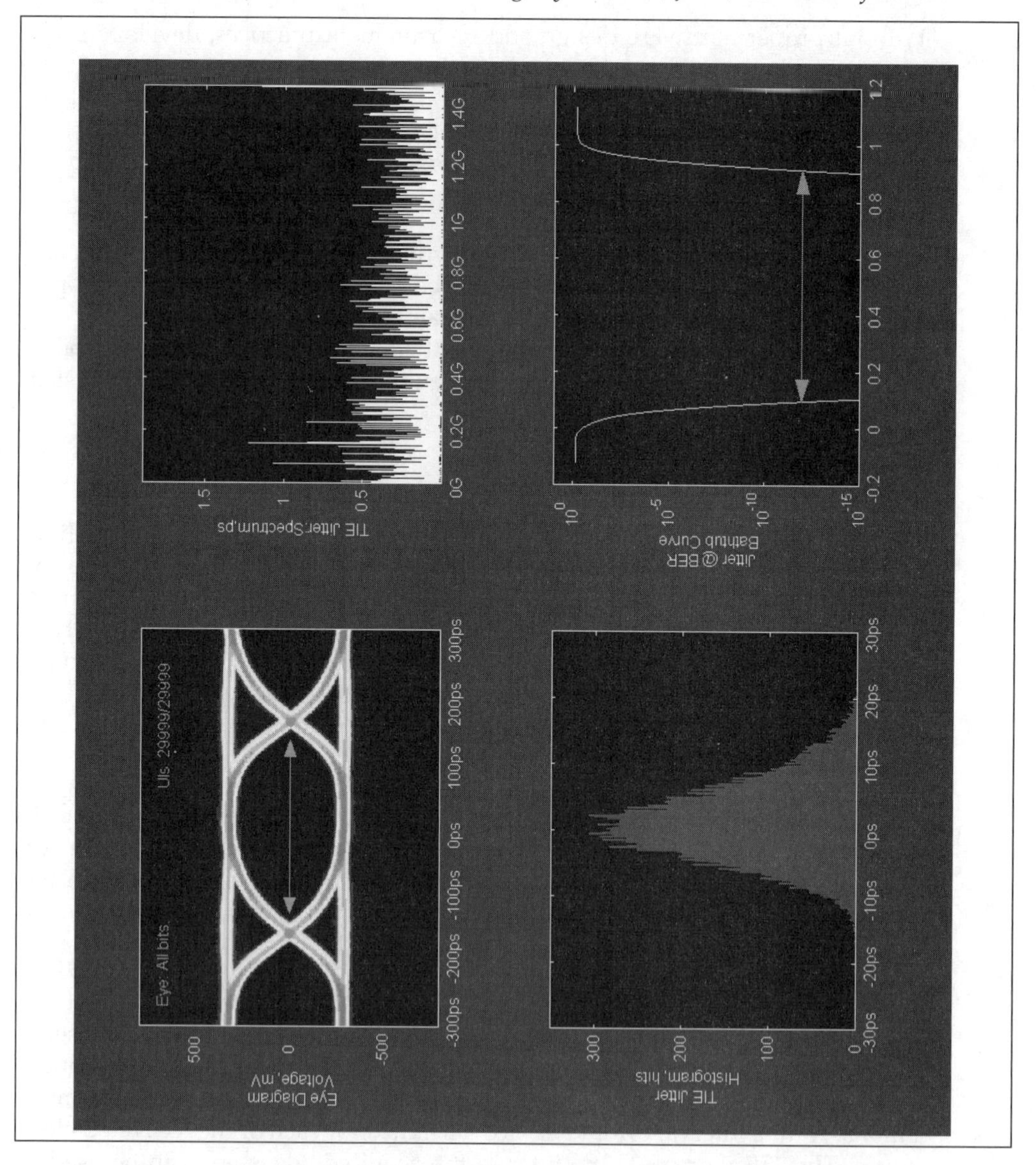

Figure B-15 on page 570 depicts a typical eye diagram. An eye diagram represents a cumulative sampling of a repetitive signal, which will vary over time, depending on the amount of jitter. For validation and compliance, a standard eye mask is inserted in the diagram to represent the minimum allowed opening in terms of time and amplitude.

Looking at the rising and falling edges, notice the wide appearance of the signal edges. This is the result of multiple samples that arrive at different times. Devices will handle some bit patterns better than others, and certain patterns cause some degree of distortion. This distortion, or variance, is not random but is considered repeatable (deterministic). The distortion along the edges is random jitter.

A receiving device ideally attempts to sample the incoming bit stream in the center of the eye, diminishing the susceptibility of the receiver to misinterpretations of the binary data stream. As jitter increases, the eye closes down because the signal uncertainty increases either horizontally or vertically, increasing the likelihood of data stream misinterpretations (bit errors).

Proper filtering and telecopying around clock oscillators and power supplies as well as selection of clock source components that exhibit high stability and low jitter characteristics are critical to winning the battle against jitter and the resulting degradation of system performance.

Figure B-15: Eye Diagram

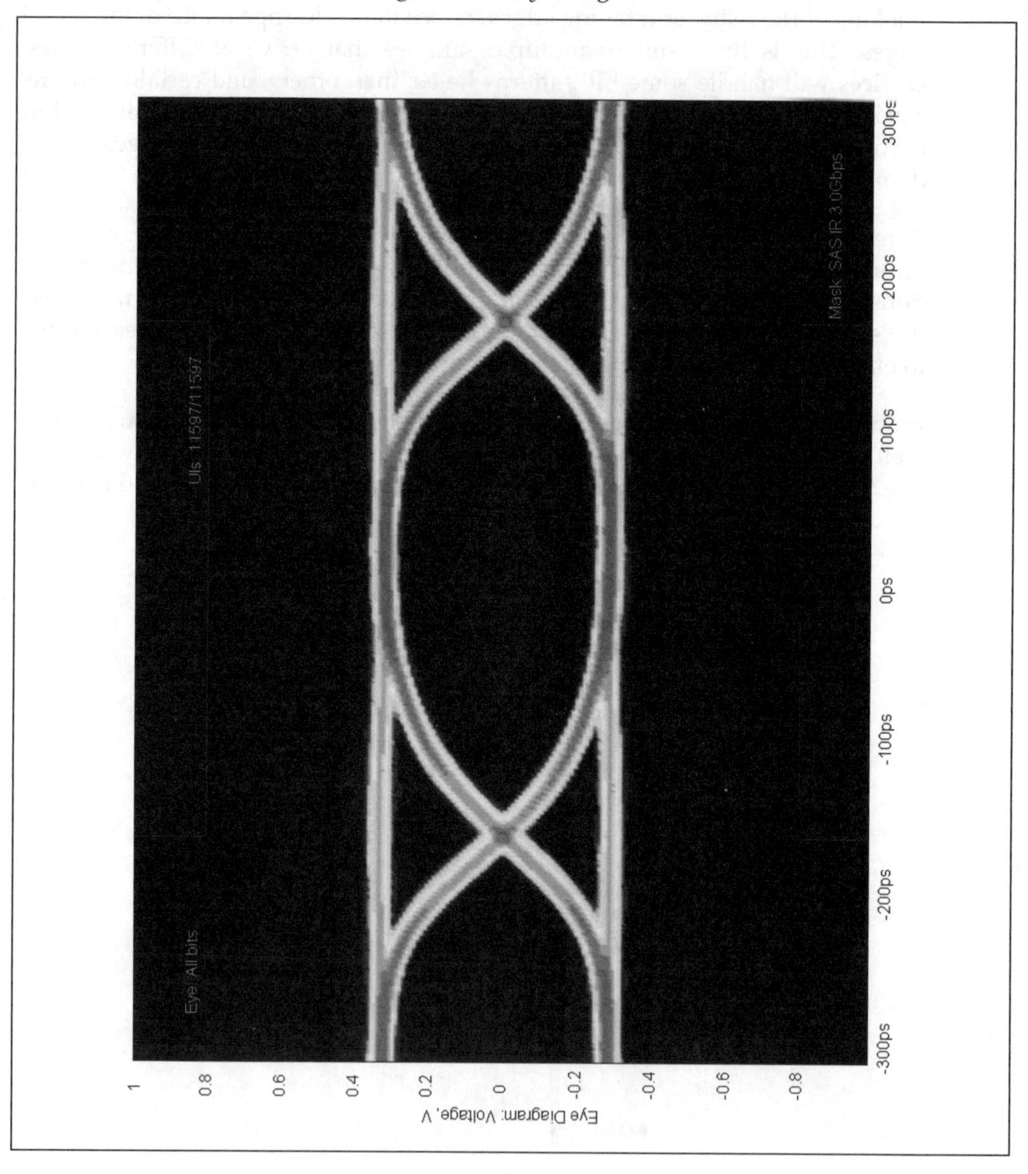

The Bathtub curve shown in Figure B-16 displays jitter distribution over a unit interval (UI), and carries that name because the graph resembles the cross-section of a bathtub.

Figure B-16: Bathtub Diagram Used in Characterizing BER

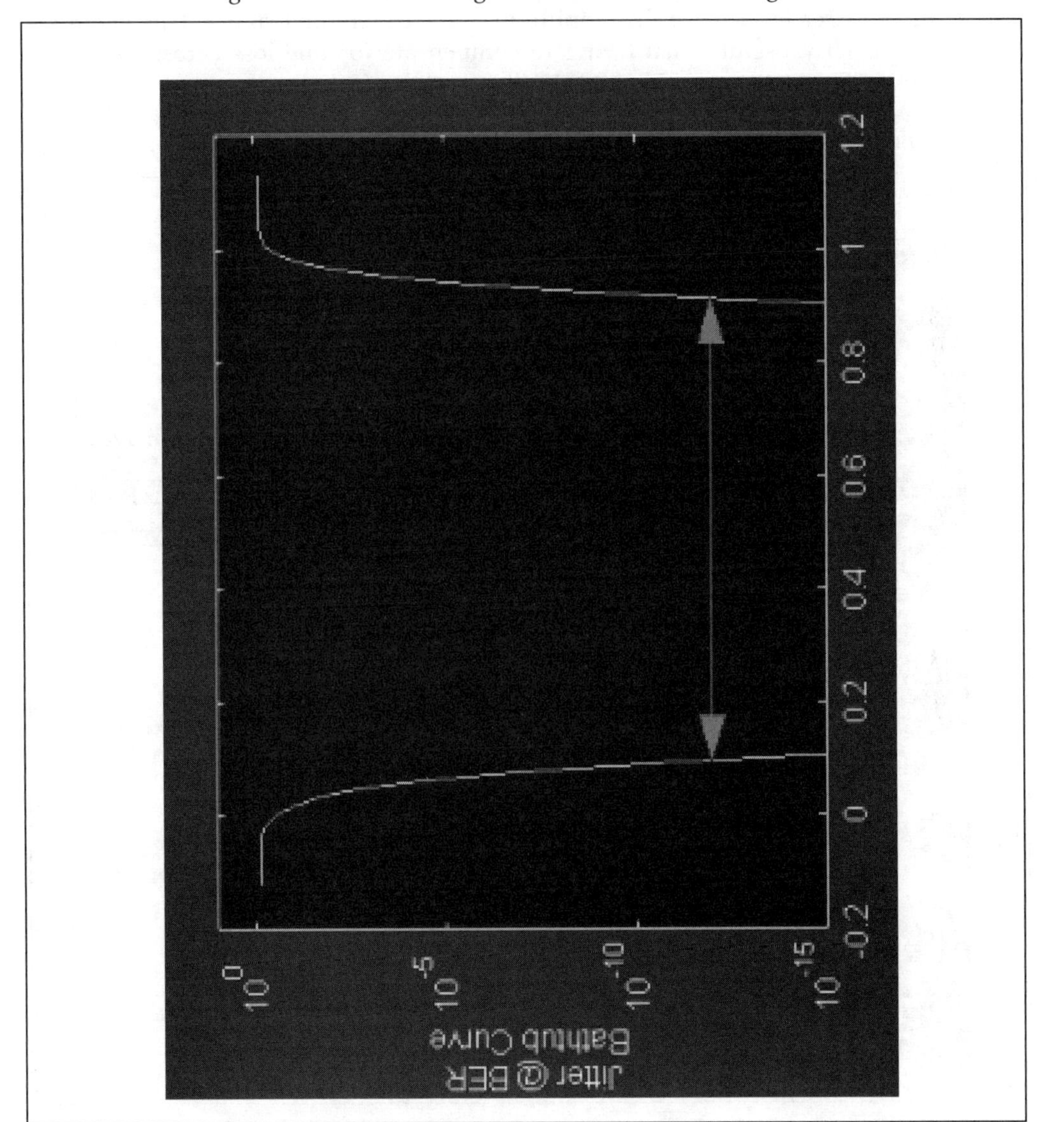

This diagram represents a bit error rate (BER) as a function of the sampling position within a UI. Notice that the curve swings upward drastically as the measurement approaches the outer bounds of the UI, representing the signal threshold crossings. This curve can be used to estimate the eye opening for a given bit error rate.

In some cases, it is helpful to configure the transmitter on the protocol analyzer or exerciser to increase the amplitude of the differential signal. This feature is particularly useful when trying to compensate for line loss across very long cables. Figure B-16 and Figure B-17 illustrate this feature.

Figure B-17: Waveform and Eye Diagram with Tx Vout at Standard Value

Oscilloscope photos courtesy of Tektronix, Inc.

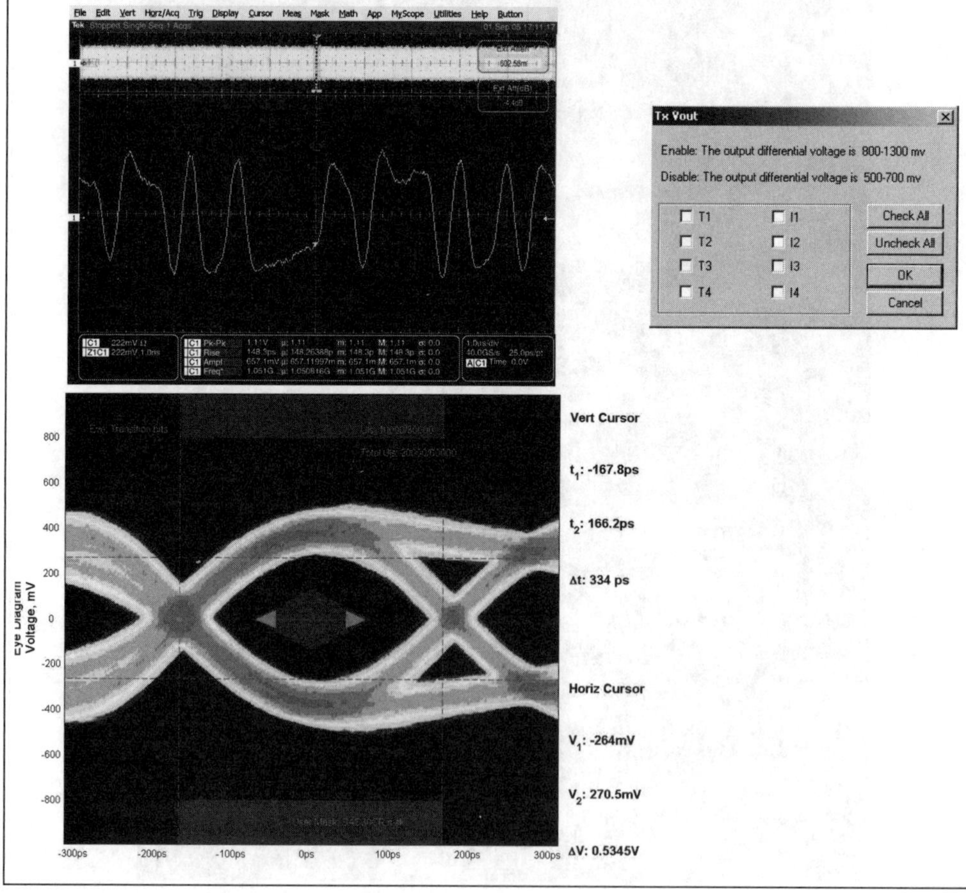

Figure B-18: Waveform and Eye Diagram with Tx Vout at Non-Standard (Increased) Value

Oscilloscope photos courtesy of Tektronix, Inc.

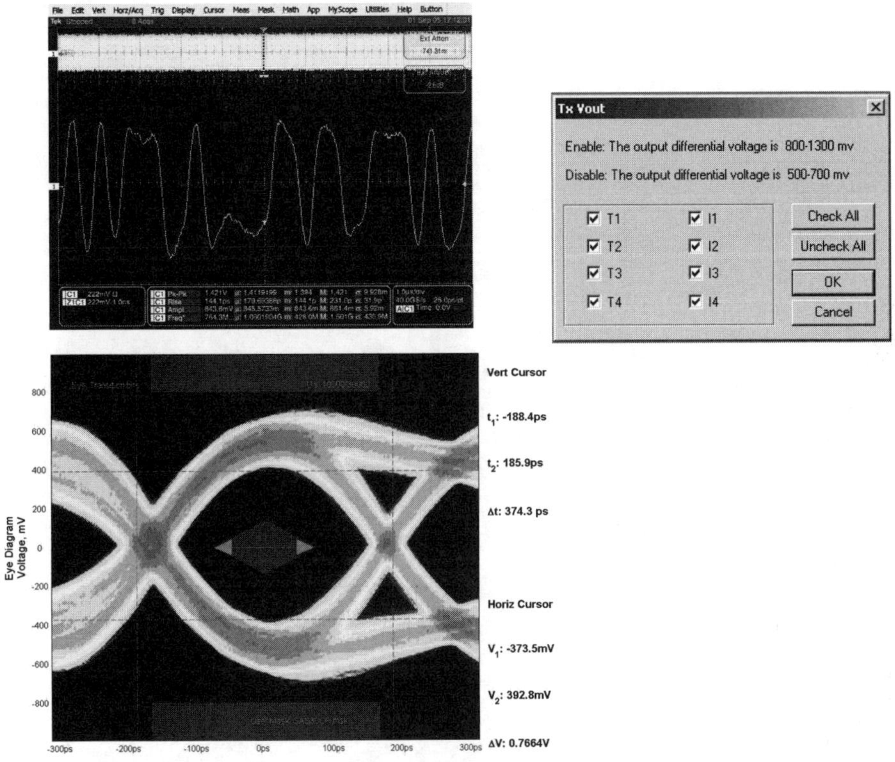

Summary

The transition from SCSI to SAS brings with it entirely new approaches to testing, validation, compliance, and debug. While command sets will look familiar to developers experienced with parallel SCSI protocols, the introduction of this multi-layered, high-speed serial architecture presents new technical challenges. A good understanding of these challenges, as well as a variety of tools to help meet them head on, are essential to every developer.

Appendix C
SAS and SATA Compatibility

Benefits to Data Center Storage

- Submitted by the SCSI Trade Association

Introduction

Networked storage is about to undergo a transformation driven by a powerful new technology based on a long-time industry standard. Blending the best of economics and performance, Serial Attached SCSI (SAS) redefines traditional methods of adding Direct-attached Storage (DAS) to a single computer and also impacts newer, networked storage configurations including Network-attached Storage (NAS) and Storage Area Networks (SAN).

Data storage needs continue to grow at exponential rates. Spurred by lowering prices and increasing capacities, it is becoming commonplace to save data rather than delete it. Recent legislation is also driving the prolonged archiving of electronic data in healthcare (HIPAA), finance (Gramm-Leach-Bliley) and corporate governance (Sarbanes-Oxley).

As the length of time required for storage increases, and the length of time to access data decreases, disk drive technology has stepped up to fill the gap between instantaneous access and archive. Typically, optical and tape media are used for longer-term archival storage, while at the opposite end of the spectrum, high performance Fibre Channel drives and infrastructure make mission-critical data available in an instant (see Figure C-1). The SAS protocol will soon allow a broader array of data storage, with correspondence between the value of the data and the value of the media.

Figure C-1: Enterprise Storage Continuum

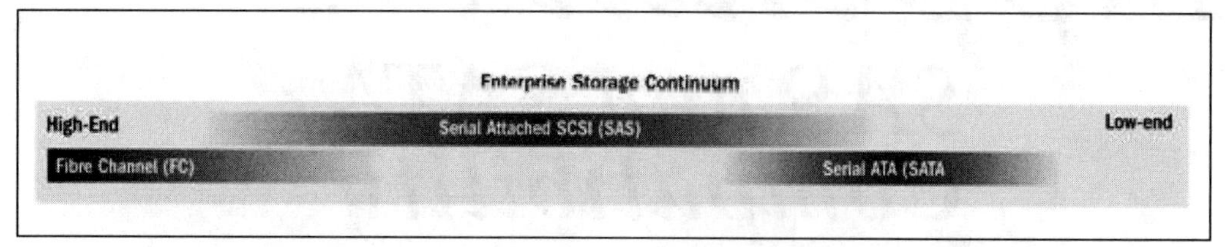

Disk drive reliability metrics have been a challenge at the low end of the price range, with IDA and ATA drives acceptable for desktop applications and consumer price points, but not for enterprise datacenters. SCSI and Fibre Channel provide the high performance and reliability required at the higher end, while increases in reliability have helped SATA bring down price points on the lower end.

Complex and incompatible interface cables and connectors have also increased the difficulty of building storage networks that address reliability and performance needs. The demand for higher availability disk storage with solid reliability and low cost has created an opportunity for a new, unified drive and enclosure interface that supports high-reliability, higher cost primary storage, at the same time as low-cost secondary storage-in one single architecture.

SAS and SATA will serve a Broader Market

The combination of SAS and SATA drives in the SAS architecture offers unprecedented flexibility in designing, building and maintaining storage networks. A broader market can be served at a lower cost, and high availability devices can now be offered to smaller markets that have been traditionally neglected or unable to purchase at historic price points. Information can be managed over its lifetime, from creation to long-term archive, using simpler devices that cost less and provide longer-term value than ever before. In addition, cabling and connectors are standardized for vendor compatibility and interoperability (See Figure C-2).

Figure C-2: SAS Impact on Disk Storage Costs

Sample Disk-to-Disk-to-Tape Solution
SAS Impacts Disk Storage Cost Significantly

	Fibre Channel	Serial Attached SCSI	Serial ATA
Tape Library	~$20,000	~$20,000	~$20,000
Drives	2	2	2
Media	SDLT 320	SDLT 320	SDLT 320
1U Server	~$4000	~$4000	~$4000
Cabling & Controller	~$500	~$500	~$500
Backup Software	~$1000	~$1000	~$1000
Accessory Cost:	~$25,500	~$25,500	~$25,500
Disk Array			
RAID Controller	Dual Redundant	Dual Redundant	Dual Redundant
Disk Drives (3TB)	10x300GB	10x300GB	12x250GB
Enclosure/Drive	FC/FC	FC/SAS or SATA	FC/SATA
Disk Storage Cost:	~$40,000	~$20,000	~$18,000

Sample configuration pricing based on March '05 pricing from several major catalog reseller websites.

The debut of affordable high-capacity SATA drives brought higher performance and greater flexibility to nearline storage applications. SATA delivers the requisite high capacity at low cost, and does so without the connectivity constraints of its parallel ancestor. The authors of the SAS standard well understood the significance of SATA's new role in the enterprise, and the synergies (both fiscal and physical) that would result if SAS and SATA drives would be able to share a single storage subsystem. To ensure full interoperability with SATA, SAS needed to address a variety of issues:

Protocols

Serial Attached SCSI employs three different protocols to transport information over its serial interface: Serial SCSI Protocol (SSP), SCSI Management Protocol (SMP) and Serial ATA Tunneled Protocol (STP). SSP communicates with SAS devices and existing SCSI software, while SMP manages the SAS point-to-point topology. The third protocol, STP, enables SAS controllers to identify and communicate with SATA devices. When data is directed to a SATA drive that is connected to a SAS backplane with an edge expander, an STP connection is immediately opened to enable SATA frames to pass through the connection to the drive. STP operates transparently in the background, with virtually no impact on system throughput (See Figure C-3).

Figure C-3: The Three SAS Protocols: SSP, SMP AND STP

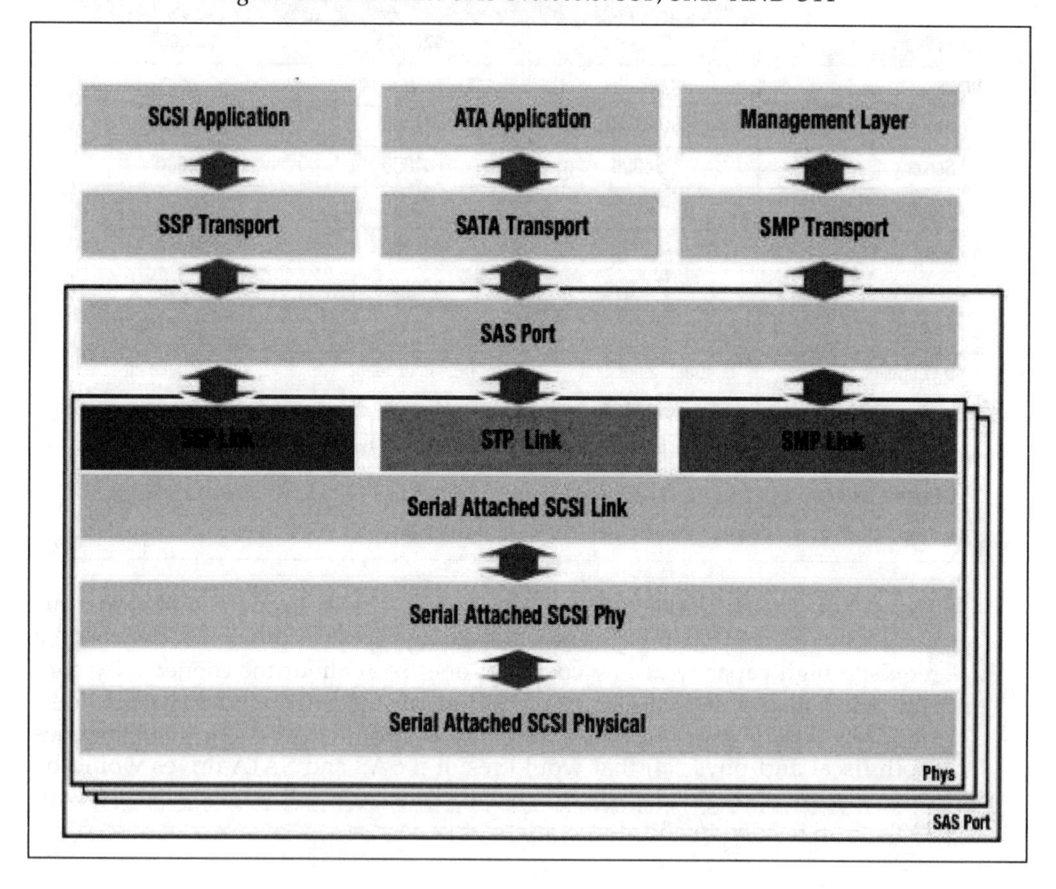

Cables and Connectors

SAS cables/connectors are fully compatible with SATA devices. Note that while SAS and SATA connectors share the same form factor, they are not identical. Unlike SATA's single-port connector that utilizes seven pins (four signal and three ground), the SAS connector fills in the keyway on the SATA connector and adds seven more pins on the opposite side to carry the additional signals in SAS's dual-port interface. The modified keyway thus enables SAS-to-SATA compatibility while ensuring a SAS device cannot be plugged into a SATA port. As is the case with SATA connectors, SAS connectors are designed for hot plugging and blind mating.

Backplanes and Host Bus Adapters

SAS backplanes and HBAs offer full compatibility with SATA (single port) devices, while still incorporating the second data port that gives SAS its fail-over capability. In the event one SAS host controller fails, the additional data port ensures uninterrupted communication with a second controller. In addition, these two ports can be combined into a single "wide port" for higher throughput.

Reflecting its enterprise-class roots, SAS employs higher transmit (Tx) and receive (Rx) differential voltages in order to drive signals over backplanes and long (up to ten meters) cables. As a desktop solution, SATA need only drive short (one meter) cables and thus can use lower differential voltages. To prevent damage to SATA drives when connected to a SAS port, device identification as noted in the STP protocol, is used to ensure the proper voltage is delivered to each device.

Expanders

Key to SAS scalability, expanders are high-speed switches that enable a single SAS domain to contain over 16,000 drives (SAS and/or SATA). There are two types of expanders: edge expanders, capable of connecting up to 128 drives; and fan-out expanders, one of which can aggregate up to 128 edge expanders in a single SAS domain. Not only do expanders feature SAS/SATA compatibility, they also boost SATA scalability far beyond the limits imposed by SATA-based infrastructures. Deploying hundreds, even thousands of SATA drives in a single SAS domain is a straightforward affair, requiring only standard SAS HBAs and expanders.

Form Factors

SAS gives IT users the freedom to choose the right drive for their applications.

For denser computing environments in which raw capacity takes a back seat to higher throughput (IOPS/U), 2.5-inch SAS drives will play an increasingly prominent role. Choosing 2.5-inch SAS drives for transactional applications such as database storage for ERP and CRM software does not prevent IT users from achieving compatibility with 3.5-inch SATA drives that perform periodic back-up and restore functions. For example, servers and storage subsystems of varying sizes (e.g. 1U, 2U, 4U, etc.), stacked on top of one another in a cabinet, can transfer data interchangeably between SAS and SATA drives. Depending on the cabinet's configuration, STP could be implemented in an HBA or expander, thereby eliminating the need for SAS and SATA drives to share the same backplane.

It goes without saying that SAS drives are available in the industry-standard 3.5-inch form factor for storage systems utilizing a common backplane. A single storage subsystem can thus house a low-cost 7200 rpm SATA drive in the same enclosure as the preferred online enterprise solution, the industry-standard 15K rpm SCSI drive.

SAS and SATA were designed to be Compatible

SATA employs modern serial technology to deliver a host of improvements (faster throughput, improved scalability, no master/slave and termination issues, compact cabling and connectors) over its parallel ATA predecessor. Leveraging SATA's established serial, point-to-point architecture, SAS encompasses all of SATA's virtues and then complements them with a comprehensive range of enterprise-class capabilities far beyond those of its desktop-centric sibling. SAS was specifically designed to be synergistically interpreted with SATA, significantly enhancing the value of both technologies.

The SAS Physical Layer borrows from10Gb Ethernet's Attachment Unit Interface specification (XAUI), defined by the Institute of Electrical and Electronics Engineers (IEEE). While XAUI consists of four 3.125Gb/s serial channels running in parallel to yield a 10Gb connection, SAS adapts this time-tested technology in a single-channel, 3.0Gb/s architecture to connect disk drives and HBAs. SATA preceded SAS in the use of such a single-channel architecture, though running at half the speed (1.5Gb/s).

Despite their similarities, there are fundamental differences between these two serial storage solutions. SAS was designed and engineered for high availability, enterprise-class data storage where random-read performance, reliability and data integrity are paramount. SATA is a desktop-class solution that offers high capacity at low cost, and impressive throughput on sequential reads (e.g.

backup and restore operations). The key is to remember that SAS and SATA are complementary technologies, and that compatibility in no way suggests interchangeability.

SAS also borrows features from another trusted serial technology, Fibre Channel (FC). At the encoding layer, SAS uses the same encoding method (8b10b) as Fibre Channel and Gigabit Ethernet to create transmission characters and primitives from bits. Additionally, FC and SAS disk drives both employ rugged, field-tested mechanical platforms engineered for enterprise duty, with every component (drive motor, spindle, actuator, magnetic recording heads, control and servo processors, firmware, etc.) specifically designed and manufactured for such rigorous use.

SAS Plugfests

To ensure seamless interoperability with other SAS components, dependable protocol compatibility with existing SATA products plus the ability to run legacy SCSI software, the SCSI Trade Association (STA) held a series of three "plugfests" in 2004. All were held at the University of New Hampshire InterOperability Lab, where components and test tools alike were tested for performance and interoperability. Regularly attended by key storage industry leaders (both STA members and non-members), these plugfests enabled a broad variety of SAS vendors to rigorously test their components with many other vendors' components. The plugfests were scheduled at the most appropriate points during the SAS development cycle to take advantage of the test results in determining if changes in the design were warranted before proceeding further. Combined with SAS's reliance on proven technologies, these plugfests have helped SAS avoid the lengthy, frustrating growing pains that have hampered development of other storage interfaces, some even after they were available on the market and installed in a user's data center.

The first 2005 plugfest was held the last week of April in which large system "builds," totaling more than 100 drives, were seen to operate smoothly. One additional 2005 plugfest is planned for late September. With SAS products entering the market in increasing numbers, plus the introduction of systems and subsystems in the second half of the year, vendors and end-users alike can be assured that SAS storage solutions will interoperate seamlessly as promised by the plugfest results.

Benefits of SAS and SATA Compatibility

As IT budgets continue to undergo intense scrutiny, the pressure to maximize storage efficiency has never been greater. But in truth, the ultimate goal of any enterprise IT manager has always been to employ the optimal storage solution for the application at hand. The greater the flexibility in choosing and deploying those solutions, the more likely maximum performance and cost-effectiveness will be achieved.

The advent of SAS heralds a new era in enterprise storage flexibility, yielding more targeted solutions that deliver both higher performance and greater efficiency. SAS compatibility with SATA enables seamless deployment of SATA drives and enterprise-class SAS drives in the same SAS domain. As a result, IT managers can now have unprecedented freedom to specify the most appropriate, cost-effective drive for any application.

Because SAS and SATA drives can share a common backplane and be housed in a single enclosure, one SAS-based subsystem is capable of handling the full gamut of enterprise storage duties, from online (transactional, high availability) to nearline (archival, low availability) applications. Should application priorities change, adapting the drive mix is simply a matter of plugging additional SAS or SATA drives into the SAS backplane In the illustration of Figure C-4 below, SAS drives are deployed in place of parallel SCSI in a common cabinet with SATA drives. The left side shows a SCSI/ RAID and JBOD/SATA configuration and the right side shows a SAS/JBOD/SATA configuration.

Figure C-4: SAS Drives Deployed in Place of Parallel SCSI

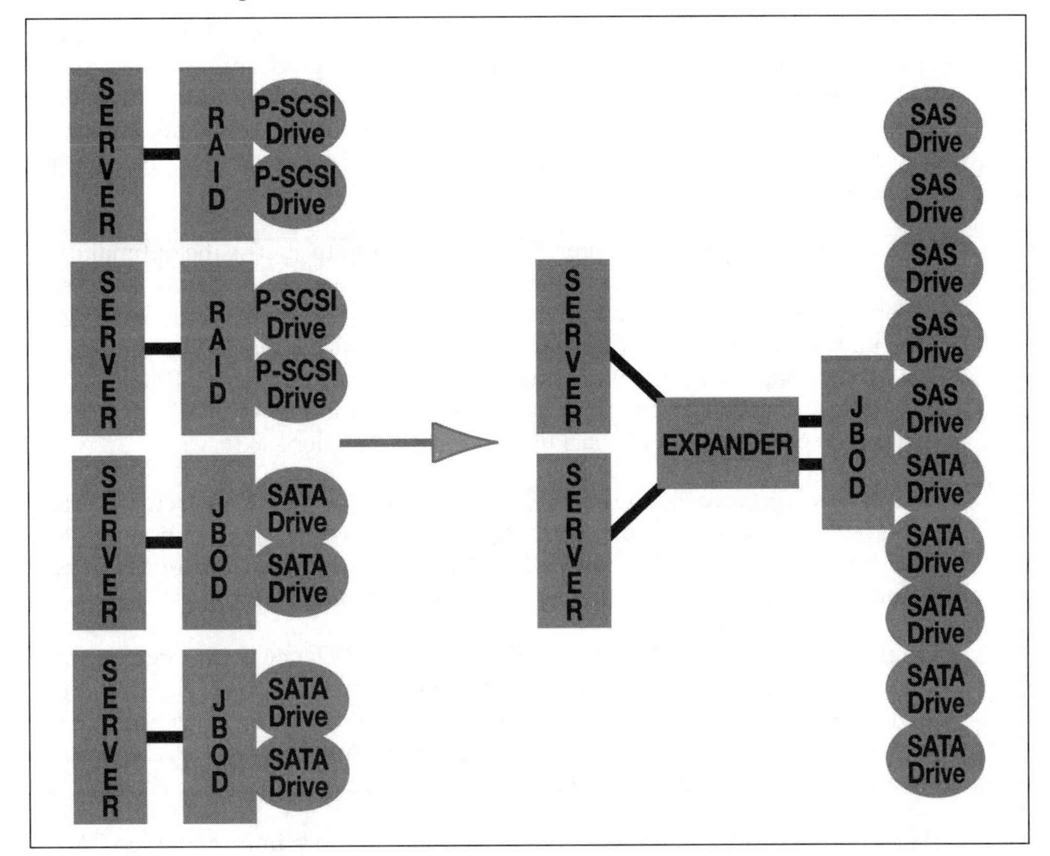

And there is another, less obvious benefit to SAS/SATA compatibility; it boosts SATA scalability far beyond the limits imposed by SATA-based infrastructures. Deploying hundreds, even thousands of SATA drives in a single SAS domain is a straightforward affair, requiring only standard SAS HBAs and expanders.

Simply put, SAS provides the path through which deployment of SATA in the enterprise offers the greatest strategic benefit-the freedom to select the most appropriate disk drive for a given task. SAS was designed and engineered for high availability, enterprise-class data storage where random-read performance, reliability and data integrity are absolutely paramount. SATA is a desktop-class solution that offers high capacity at low cost and impressive throughput on sequential reads (e.g. backup and restore operations).

Choose the Optimal Disk Drive

Beyond the obvious efficiency of specifying the optimal disk drive for a given application, standardizing on the SAS platform will significantly reduce storage TCO by minimizing the number of individual components that must be qualified, purchased, inventoried and maintained. Such component rationalization also results in a smaller data center footprint, and places fewer demands on management resources and support staff.

SAS also ensures that IT managers have the freedom to choose the optimal form factor for their applications. For denser computing environments in which raw capacity takes a back seat to higher throughput (IOPS/U), 2.5-inch SAS drives will play an increasingly prominent role. Choosing 2.5-inch SAS drives for transactional applications such as database storage for ERP and CRM, software does not prevent IT users from achieving compatibility with 3.5-inch SATA drives that perform periodic backup and restore functions.

SAS drives are available in the industry-standard 3.5-inch form factor for storage systems utilizing a common backplane. A single storage subsystem can thus house a low-cost 7200 rpm SATA drive in the same enclosure as the preferred online enterprise solution; the industry-standard 15K rpm SCSI drive.

Enterprise storage is making dramatic strides in efficiency, with targeted solutions available to address a broad variety of needs, from the most rigorous high-availability applications to cost-sensitive bulk storage. Serial Attached SCSI is spearheading this movement, its seamless compatibility with SATA further enhancing SAS's appeal as a powerful, cost-effective enterprise storage solution.

Please visit the SCSI Trade Association web site for more information on SAS at http://www.scsita.org.

Appendix D
SEP Appendix

SES (SCSI Enclosure Services)

The SES (SCSI Enclosure Services) command set is used to communicate with a separate enclosure service processor that may be included in some high-end enclosures for sensing and managing things that are relevant to an enclosure, such as fans, sensors, and LEDs. The SES command set defines a series of Diagnostic Pages to allow devices to communicate with this enclosure processor over SCSI. The SCSI commands for this purpose are SEND DIAGNOSTIC and RECEIVE DIAGNOSTIC RESULTS. The predecessor to SES was SAF-TE (SCSI Attached Fault-Tolerant Enclosure), which was intended to be an inexpensive SCSI target providing enclosure control and visibility. The target for such an interface was called an SEP (SCSI Enclosure Processor) and only acted in a target role. It did not include asynchronous notification of events and required periodic polling instead to detect changes. It allowed for access to enclosure information such as number and status of fans, power supplies, sensors, etc.

The trouble with SAF-TE was that it was not owned by any existing standards body and so was not extensible. Consequently, around 1995 the SAF-TE working group agreed to merge the architecture with the SCSI ESI (Enclosure Services Interface) definition to create one standard called SES.

An simple example system is shown in Figure D-1, where an SES logical unit is embedded in an expander device and used to control the enclosure. As is commonly done, it uses an I^2C or SGPIO bus (the standard does not define a particular interface that must be used) to monitor and control fans, sensors and LEDs for the drives. SES defines a series of diagnostic pages to communicate with the SES processor over SCSI. The commandS SEND DIAGNOSTIC and RECEIVE DIAGNOSTIC are used to transmit the pages with the SES logical unit.

Figure D-1: SES Example

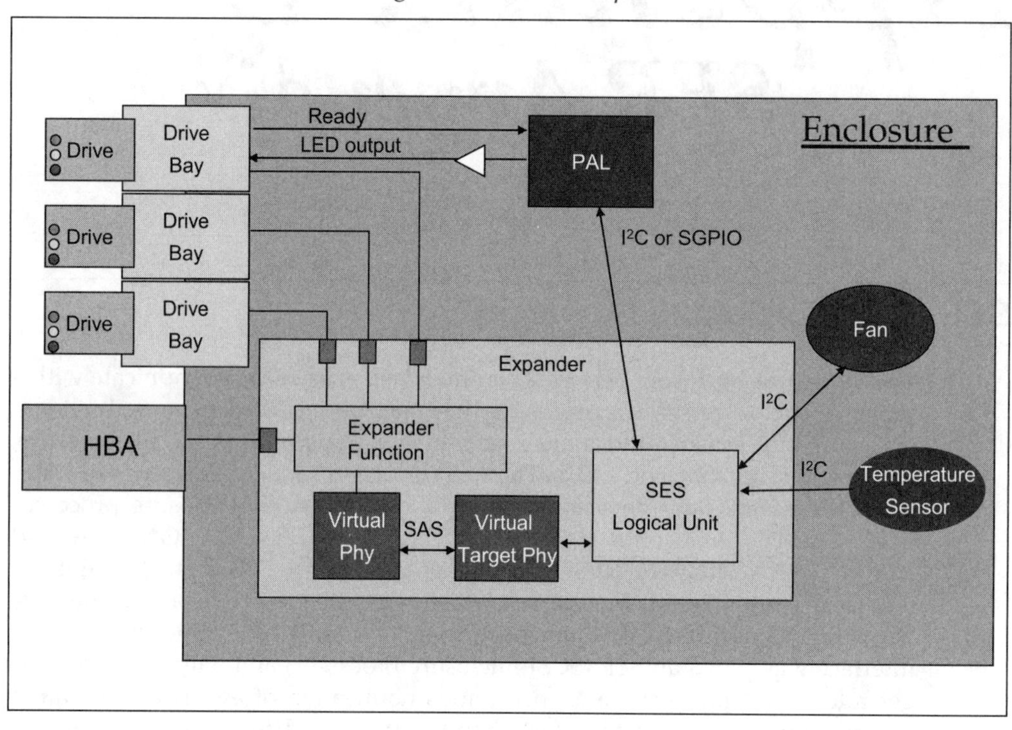

Glossary

Table 1-14: Glossary

Term	Description
8b/10b	Shorthand that describes the encoding scheme used by SAS and many other serial transports. Encoding each 8-bit byte into a 10-bit character for transmission introduces some overhead but provides a number of benefits.
ACA	Auto-Contingent Allegiance - used to tell a SCSI drive not to respond to further commands if an error is encountered on a previous command, this prevents the error status from being overwritten by a subsequent command result before the earlier one can be read. Not needed for SAS because a Response frame is already being sent for each command.
Address Frame	The frame that is sent to request a connection with a destination device. It contains the destination address and other attributes such as the protocol that will be used and the link rate. The routing of the connection through expanders in the system is based on that information.
CDB	Command Descriptor Block
Connection	A temporary virtual path between devices that is requested with an OPEN address frame from the initiating device and confirmed with an OPEN_ACCEPT primitive from the target device. When this handshake is completed, the path is dedicated for transmissions between the two devices and will remain open for traffic until explicitly closed, either actively by the initiator, or as a timeout event by the target device.
EMI	Electro-Magnetic Interference.
HBA	Host Bus Adapter. The device that acts as a bridge between the system bus (host) and the storage bus.

Table 1-14: Glossary

Term	Description
ISI	Inter-symbol interference - results when the pattern of the previous symbol's bits interferes with proper reception of the current symbol.
JBOD	Just a Bunch Of Disks — a very simple collection of disk drives without a specific organization. See also RAID.
NAS	Network Attached Storage — a server dedicated to file sharing. It allows storage to be added to an existing server network without the need to shut down the network.
Near-line storage	Defined as data storage on removable media, the purpose of near-line storage is to provide inexpensive, reliable, and unlimited backup. The access time for recovery depends on where the needed media resides — it can be slow because the media could be off-line when the data is needed. The combination of near-line and off-line storage accounts for 90% of a typical system's storage allocation. (See also *On-line* storage and *Off-line* storage.)
Nexus	A relationship between two devices. When an initiator makes a read request, for example, the connection may be closed while the target fetches the data. The target stores the nexus information (the address for the initiator) so it knows the address to which it should open a connection when it has the data ready to return.
Off-line storage	Storage of data that must be retained but will rarely be accessed. It is typically stored on slow but reliable tape. (See also *On-line* storage and *Off-line* storage.)
OOB	Out Of Band — defined as communication that is considered outside the normal flow of information because it takes place over the link during initialization. The process for SAS is very similar to that for SATA, but different enough that there are separate chapters for each.
On-line storage	Storage that is always available at high speed, providing fast recovery at a relatively high price. A typical system might allocate 10% of its archive space for on-line storage. (See also *On-line* storage and *Off-line* storage.)

Table 1-14: Glossary

Term	Description
PCI	Peripheral Component Interface. This was developed by several vendors associated with personal computer manufacturing as a new IO bus standard for PC architectures to replace the obsoleted ISA bus (Industry Standard Architecture) developed by IBM. (For more information, see the MindShare book on this topic at www.mindshare.com.)
PCIe	PCI Express. This is essentially a serial version of PCI-X, designed to provide higher bandwidth while retaining software compatibility with PCI. (For more information, see the MindShare book on this topic at www.mindshare.com.)
PCI-X	Extended PCI. This interface improved on the original PCI design by registering the bus and adding a split-transaction model to permit higher bandwidth and better efficiency on the bus. (For more information, see the MindShare book on this topic at www.mindshare.com.)
Primitives	Single-dword information blocks transmitted across a connection for Link Layer communication in support of activities like flow control and ACK/NAK. Primitives are easily recognizable because they are the only legal dwords that contain a control (K) character, which must be the first character in the dword.
RAID	Redundant Array of Inexpensive Disks. This is a more sophisticated collection of disks that has been designed to achieve certain properties of robust operation. See also JBOD.
Rx	Receiver
SAM-3	SCSI Architecture Model, version 3. This is one of several standards that define SCSI, and describes the overall model.
SAN	Storage Area Network - a high speed storage network designed to be attached to server network.

Table 1-14: Glossary

Term	Description
SAS Address	A 64-bit, globally-unique number assigned to each SAS device that defines its address for accesses within a SAS topology. These addresses are assigned at the factory and are not normally user-defined or programmable.
SSC	Spread-Spectrum Clocking. This is a method of varying the clock speed slightly but regularly over time to reduce peaks in the EMI generated by a system for any given frequency.
Tx	Transmitter

Index

Numerics

A

B

C

D

Index

xray
ECG
ECHO
Summary
Lab Reports
REimbursement forms

9940086068
76144

11 days →
Ventilator package

= 55,000

CΦ 2,500

ICU w/o ventilat 3days 7500

Duplex/doubl 710.00

9100 @ 700

~~700~~

Oxygen,
ecg
x ray
mont.
pn
Infusion
CV procedure

pharma 67,411.00

Medicare: 98406-95112